A PLUME BOOK

# THE BUNGALOW

SARAH JIO is a journalist who has written for *Glamour*; *O, The Oprah Magazine*; *Real Simple*; *SELF*; *Cooking Light*; *Redbook*; *Parents*; *Woman's Day*; and many other publications. She is the health and fitness blogger for Glamour.com and lives in Seattle with her husband, their three young children, and a golden retriever named Paisley, who steals socks. Learn more about Sarah at www.sarahjio.com.

## Praise for *The Bungalow*

"Sarah Jio whips romance, history, and a page-turning mystery into one mesmerizing South Sea dream."

—Carol Cassella, national bestselling author of *Oxygen* and *Healer*

"Seasoned with mystery and awash in the glory of the South Pacific, this stirring wartime romance explores the uncompromising power of long-lost love. Readers, pack your bags and set sail for enchantment in Sarah Jio's *The Bungalow*!"

—Sarah McCoy, author of *The Baker's Daughter* and *The Time It Snowed in Puerto Rico*

# The Bungalow

A NOVEL

Sarah Jio

**Doubleday Large Print
Home Library Edition**

A PLUME BOOK

This Large Print Edition, prepared especially for Doubleday Large Print Home Library, contains the complete, unabridged text of the original Publisher's Edition.

PLUME
Published by the Penguin Group
Penguin Group (USA) Inc., 375 Hudson Street, New York, New York 10014, U.S.A.

Penguin Books Ltd., Registered Offices: 80 Strand, London WC2R 0RL, England

ISBN 978-1-61793-492-6

**This Large Print Book carries the
Seal of Approval of N.A.V.H.**

**For Jason, with memories of our
own island bungalow.
I love you.**

Tuck a slip of paper into a flimsy envelope, seal it with a swipe of the tongue, then send it on its way. That letter might be handled by dozens of people and journey a thousand miles before reaching the intended mailbox, where it nestles anonymously between pages twenty-nine and thirty of some unwanted catalog, lying in wait for its unsuspecting recipient, who tosses the catalog, with its treasure tucked inside, into the recycle bin with a flick of the wrist. There, next to poorly rinsed milk cartons, an empty wine bottle, and yesterday's newspaper, a life-changing piece of mail quietly awaits.

That letter was for me.

# Prologue

"Hello?"

Startled, I opened my eyes at the sound of a familiar voice—pleasant, but sorely out of place. Jennifer, yes, my grand-daughter. *But where am I?* Or rather, why was she *here*? I blinked a few times, dis-oriented. I had been dreaming of sandy beaches and coconut palms—the place my unconscious mind always tries to visit, but this time I was lucky enough to find it in the archives of my memories.

He was there, of course—in uniform, shyly smiling at me as the waves fell into the shore. I could hear them—their violent crash, followed by the fizz of a million bubbles kissing the sand. Closing my eyes tighter, I found him again, standing there amid the fog of sleep that was lifting, too quickly. *Don't go*, my heart pleaded. *Stay. Please stay.* And he obediently appeared again with that beckoning grin, those arms outstretched to me. I felt the familiar flutter in my heart, the longing.

And then, in an instant, he was gone.

I sighed and looked at my watch, scolding myself. *Half past three.* I must have dozed off while reading. Again. Spontaneous sleepiness was the curse of the elderly. I sat up in my lounge chair, a bit embarrassed, and retrieved the novel I'd been reading before the exhaustion hit. It had fallen from my hands to the ground, spine side up, its pages fanned out in disgrace.

Jennifer walked out onto the terrace. A truck barreled by on the street, further disturbing the peace. "Oh, there you are," she said, smiling at me with her eyes, smoky brown, like her grandfather's. She wore jeans and a black sweater with a light green belt around her slim waist. Her blond hair, cut to her chin, reflected the sun's rays. Jennifer didn't know how beautiful she was.

"Hi, honey," I said, reaching my hand out to her. I looked around the terrace at the pale blue pansies in their simple terra-cotta pots. They were pretty enough, peeking their heads out of the dirt like shy, repentant children who'd been caught playing in the mud. The view of Lake Washington and the Seattle skyline in the distance was beautiful, yes, but cold and stiff, like a painting in a dentist's office. I frowned. How had I come to live here, in this tiny apartment with its stark white walls and a telephone in the bathroom with a red emergency call button beside the toilet?

"I found something," Jennifer said, her voice prying me from my thoughts, "in the recycle bin."

I smoothed my white, wispy hair. "What is it, dear?"

"A letter," she said. "It must have gotten mixed in with the junk mail."

I attempted to stifle a yawn, but it came anyway. "Just leave it on the table. I'll look at it later." I walked inside and sat down on the sofa, turning my gaze away from the kitchen to the reflection in the window. *An old lady.* I saw her every day, this woman, but her reflection never ceased to surprise me. *When did I become her?* My hands traced the wrinkles on my face.

Jennifer sat down next to me. "Has your day been any better than mine?" In her last year of graduate school at the University of Washington, she had chosen an unusual subject for a class-assigned article: an obscure work of art on campus. Donated in 1964 by an anonymous artist, the bronze sculpture of a young couple had a placard that read simply, *Pride and Promises*. Transfixed by the sculpture, Jennifer hoped to profile the artist and learn the story behind the work, yet an entire quarter's worth of research had turned up very little.

"Any luck with your research today, dear?"

"Nada," she said, frowning. "It's frustrating. I've worked so hard to find answers." She shook her head and shrugged. "I hate to admit it, but I think the trail's gone cold."

I knew something about being haunted by art. Jennifer didn't know it, but I'd spent the majority of my life searching in vain for a painting that I'd held in my hands a very long time ago. My heart ached to see it again, and yet after a lifetime of working with art dealers and collectors, the canvas eluded me.

"I know it's hard to let go, honey," I said delicately, knowing how important the project was to her. I tucked my hand in hers. "Some stories aren't meant to be told."

Jennifer nodded. "You may be right, Grandma," she said with a sigh. "But I'm not ready to let it go. Not yet. The inscription on the placard—it all has to mean something. And the box, the one that the man in the statue holds in his hands, it's locked, and the people in the archives don't have record of a key, which means"—she paused and smiled hopefully—"there may be something inside."

"Well, I admire your spirit, sweetheart," I said, clutching the gold chain around my neck, the one that held the locket I'd worn and kept safe for so many years. Only one other soul knew what was tucked inside beyond the protective guard of the clasp.

Jennifer walked back to the table. "Now,

don't forget this letter," she said, holding up an envelope. "Look at this gorgeous stamp. It's from"—she paused, reading the postmark—"*Tahiti.*"

My heart rate quickened as I looked up, squinting to see the letter in Jennifer's hands.

"Grandma, *who* do you know in Tahiti?"

"Let me see it," I said, inching closer.

I scanned the simple white envelope, damp from its brush with a milk carton and speckled with crimson dots from last night's cabernet. No, I did not recognize the handwriting, or the return address. *Who would be writing me from Tahiti? And why? Why now?*

"Aren't you going to open it?" Jennifer said, hovering over me in anticipation.

My hands trembled a little as I turned the envelope over again and again, running my fingers along the exotic stamp, which depicted a Tahitian girl in a yellow dress. I swallowed hard, trying to purge the memories that were seeping into my mind like rising floodwater, but mere mental sandbags could not keep them out.

Then, powerless to resist, I opened the envelope with one swift tear.

Dear Mrs. Godfrey,

Forgive me for my intrusion. It has taken me many years to find you. I understand that you were an army nurse stationed in Bora-Bora during the war. If I am correct, if you are indeed the woman I seek, I urgently need to speak with you. I was raised in the Tahitian islands, but have only now returned, with a mission to solve a mystery that has troubled me since girlhood. A horrific murder occurred on a quiet stretch of beach on Bora-Bora one evening in 1943 I am haunted by the tragedy, so much so that I am writing a book about the events that preceded a happening which, in many ways, changed the island forever.

I was able to locate the army employment records and I noticed that you were blocked out on leave that day, the day of the tragedy. Could you, by chance, remember something or someone on the beach that night? So many years have passed, but perhaps you recall something. Even a small detail may help in my search for justice. I pray that you will consider my request and get in touch. And, if you ever plan to visit the island again, there is something of yours I found here, something you might like to see again. I would love nothing more than to show it to you.

Yours Truly,

Genevieve Thorpe

I stared at the letter in my hands. Genevieve Thorpe. No, I did not know this woman. *A stranger.* And here she was, stirring up trouble. I shook my head. *Ignore it.* Too many years had passed. How could I go back to those days? How could I relive it all? I closed my eyes tightly, willing the memories away. *Yes, I could just ignore it.* It wasn't a legal inquiry or a criminal investigation. I did not owe this woman, this *stranger*, anything. I could throw the envelope into the garbage can and be done with it. But then I remembered the last few lines of the letter. "If you ever plan to visit the island again, there is something of yours I found here, something you might like to see again." My heart, already in poor condition, raced at the thought of it. *Visit the island again? Me? At my age?*

"Grandma, are you all right?" Jennifer

leaned in and wrapped her arm around my shoulder.

"I'm fine," I said, composing myself.

"Do you want to talk about it?"

I shook my head and tucked the letter safely inside the book of crossword puzzles on the coffee table.

Jennifer reached for her bag and began fumbling inside. She retrieved a large manila envelope, wrinkled and worn. "I want to show you something," she said. "I was going to wait until later, but"—she took a deep breath—"I think it's time."

She handed me the envelope.

"What is this?"

"Look inside," she said slowly.

I lifted the flap and pulled out a stack of black-and-white photos, instantly recognizing the one on top. "That's me!" I cried, pointing to the young woman dressed in white nurse's garb, with a coconut tree in the distance. Oh how I had marveled at the palms the first day I set foot on the island, almost seventy years ago. I looked up at Jennifer. "Where did you find these?"

"Dad found them," she said, eyeing my face cautiously. "He was going through some old boxes and these were tucked inside. He asked me to return them to you."

My heart swelled with anticipation as I flipped to the next photograph, of Kitty, my childhood friend, sitting on an overturned canoe on the beach, her feet kicked out like a movie star's. Kitty *could* have been a movie star. I felt the familiar pain in my heart when I thought of my old friend, pain that time hadn't healed.

There were several more in the stack, many of them scenes of the beach, the mountains, lush with flora, but when I reached the last photograph, I froze. *Westry. My Westry.* There he was with the top button of his uniform undone, his head tilted slightly to the right with the bungalow's woven palm wall in the background. *Our bungalow.* I may have taken thousands of photographs in my life, and so many of them were forgotten, but not this one. I remembered everything about the snapshot, the way the air had smelled that evening—of seawater and freesia, blooming in the moonlight. I could recall the feeling I had in my heart, too, when my eyes met his through the lens, and then there was what happened in the moments that followed.

"You loved him, didn't you, Grandma?" Jennifer's voice was so sweet, so disarming, that I felt my resolve weaken.

"I did," I said.

"Do you think of him now?"

I nodded. "Yes. I have always thought of him."

Jennifer's eyes widened. "Grandma, what happened in Tahiti? What happened with this man? And the letter—why did it affect you in the way it did?" She paused, and reached for my hand. "Please tell me."

I nodded. *What would be the harm in telling her?* I was an old woman. There wouldn't be many consequences now, and if there were, I could weather them. And how I longed to set these secrets free, to send them flying like bats from a dusty attic. I ran my finger along the gold chain of my locket, and nodded. "All right, dear," I said. "But I must warn you, don't expect a fairy tale."

Jennifer sat down in the chair beside me. "Good," she said, smiling. "I've never liked fairy tales."

"And there are dark parts," I said, doubting my decision.

She nodded. "But is there a happy ending?"

"I'm not sure."

Jennifer gave me a confused look.

I held the photo of Westry up to the light. "The story isn't over yet."

# Chapter 1

August 1942

"Kitty Morgan, you did not just say that!" I set my goblet of mint iced tea down with enough force to crack the glass. Mother would be happy to know that I hadn't spoiled her set of Venetian crystal.

"I most certainly did," she said, smirking victoriously. Kitty, with her heart-shaped face and that head full of wiry, untamable blond ringlets springing out of the hairpins she'd been so meticulous about fastening, hardly provoked anger. But on this subject I held my ground.

"Mr. Gelfman is a *married* man," I said in my most disapproving voice.

"James," she said, elongating his first name for dramatic effect, "is impossibly unhappy. Did you know that his wife disappears for weeks at a time? She doesn't even tell him where she's going. She cares more about the cats than she does him."

I sighed, leaning back into the wooden bench swing that hung from the enormous walnut tree in my parents' backyard garden. Kitty sat beside me then, just as she had when we were in grade school. I looked up at the tree overhead, its leaves tinged with a touch of yellow, hinting that autumn was imminent. *Why must things change?* It seemed like only yesterday that Kitty and I were two schoolgirls, walking home arm in arm, setting our books down on the kitchen table and making a dash to the swing, where we'd tell secrets until dinnertime. Now, at twenty-one, we were two grown women on the verge of, well, something—not that either of us could predict what.

"Kitty," I said, turning to face her. "Don't you understand?"

"Understand what?" She looked like a rose petal, sitting there in her dress brimming with pink ruffles, with those wild curls that were getting even more unruly in the late-afternoon humidity. I wanted to protect her from Mr. Gelfman, or any other man she intended upon falling in love with, for none would be good enough for my best friend—certainly not the married ones.

I cleared my throat. *Does she not know Mr. Gelfman's reputation?* Certainly she remembered the hordes of girls who had flaunted themselves at him in high school, where he had been Lakeside's most dashing teacher. Every girl in English Lit had hoped to make eye contact with him as Elizabeth Barrett Browning's "How Do I Love Thee?" crossed his lips. That was all girlish fun, I contended. But had Kitty forgotten about the incident five years ago with Kathleen Mansfield? How could she forget? Kathleen—shy, big breasted, terribly dim-witted—had fallen under Mr. Gelfman's spell. She hovered near the teachers' lounge at lunch, and waited for him after school. Everybody wondered about them, especially when one of our girlfriends spotted Kathleen in the park with Mr. Gelfman after dusk. Then, suddenly, Kathleen stopped coming to school. Her older brother said she'd gone to live with her grandmother in Iowa. We all knew the reason why.

I crossed my arms. "Kitty, men like Mr. Gelfman have only one objective, and I think we both know what that is."

Kitty's cheeks flushed to a deeper shade of pink. "Anne Calloway! How dare you suggest that James would be anything but—"

"I'm not *suggesting* anything," I said. "It's just that I love you. You're my best friend, and I don't want to see you get hurt."

Kitty kicked her legs despondently as we swung for a few minutes in silence. I reached into the pocket of my dress and privately clutched the letter nestled inside. I'd picked it up at the post office earlier that day and was eager to sneak away to my bedroom to read it. It was from Norah, a friend from nursing school who'd been writing me weekly accounts from the South Pacific, where she'd been serving in the Army Nurse Corps. She and Kitty, both hot-tempered, had a falling out in our final term together, so I chose not to bring up the letters with Kitty. Besides, I couldn't let on to her how much Norah's tales of the war and the tropics had captivated me.

They read like the pages of a novel—so much so that a part of me dreamt of taking my newly minted nursing degree and joining her there, escaping life at home and the decisions that awaited. And yet, I knew it was just a fanciful idea, a daydream. After all, I could help with the war efforts at home, by volunteering at the civic center or collecting tin cans and assisting with conservation projects. I shook my head at the thought of traipsing off to a war zone in the tropics mere weeks before my wedding. I sighed, grateful I hadn't uttered a word of it to Kitty.

"You're just jealous," Kitty finally said, still smug.

"Nonsense," I retorted, pushing Norah's letter deeper into my pocket. The sun, high in the summer sky, caught the diamond ring on my left hand, producing a brilliant sparkle, as arresting as a lighthouse's beacon on a dark night, reminding me of the unavoidable fact that I was engaged. Bought and paid for. "I'm marrying Gerard in less than a month," I said. "And I couldn't be happier."

Kitty frowned. "Don't you want to do something else with your life before you"—she paused as if the next few words would be very difficult, very displeasing to say— "before you become Mrs. Gerard Godfrey?"

I shook my head in protest. "Marriage, my dear, is not suicide."

Kitty looked away from me, her gaze burrowing into a rosebush in the garden. "It might as well be," she murmured under her breath.

I sighed, leaning back into the swing.

"Sorry," she whispered, turning back to me. "I just want you to be happy."

I reached for her hand. "But I will be, Kitty. I wish you'd see that."

I heard footsteps on the lawn and looked up to find Maxine, our housekeeper, approaching, tray in hand. In heels, she walked steadily across the lawn, requiring only a single hand to bear a laden silver platter. Papa had called her graceful once, and she was. She practically floated.

"May I fetch you girls anything?" Maxine asked in her beautiful, heavily accented voice. Her appearance had changed very little since I was a girl. She was petite, with soft features, great big sparkling green eyes, and cheeks that smelled of vanilla.

Her hair, now graying slightly, was pulled back into a tidy chignon, never a strand out of place. She wore a white apron, always clean and freshly starched to a remarkable stiffness, cinched tightly around her small waist. Lots of families in the neighborhood had servants, but we were the only household that employed a *French* housekeeper, a fact Mother was quick to point out at bridge parties.

"We're fine, Maxine, thank you," I said, weaving my arm through hers.

"There is something," Kitty said conspiratorially. "You can convince Anne not to marry Gerard. She doesn't love him."

"Is this true, Antoinette?" Maxine asked. I was five years old the day she came to work in our home, and after a quick once-over, she said declaratively, "You do not have the face of an Anne. I shall call you Antoinette." I had felt very fancy.

"Of course it's not true," I said quickly. "Kitty is just in one of her *moods*." I gave her a sideways glance of disapproval. "I'm the luckiest girl in Seattle. I'm marrying Gerard Godfrey."

And I *was* lucky. Gerard was tall and

impossibly handsome, with his strong jaw and dark brown hair and eyes to match. He was quite wealthy, too, not that it mattered to me. Mother, on the other hand, frequently reminded me that at twenty-seven he enjoyed the distinction of being the youngest vice president at First Marine Bank, a title that meant he would come into a fortune when he took over for his father. You'd have to be a foolish woman to turn down a proposal from Gerard Godfrey, and when he asked for my hand, under this very walnut tree, I nodded without a moment's hesitation.

Mother had been giddy upon hearing the news. She and Mrs. Godfrey had planned the union since I was in infancy, of course. Calloways would marry Godfreys. It was as natural as coffee and cream.

Maxine picked up a pitcher of iced tea and refilled our goblets. "Antoinette," she said slowly, "have I ever told you the story of my sister, Jeanette?"

"No," I said. "I didn't even know you had a sister." I realized that there were many things I didn't know about Maxine.

"Yes," she said quietly, looking thoughtful. "She loved a boy, a peasant boy from Lyon. They were madly in love. But our father and mother pushed her toward another man, a man who made a decent wage in the factories. So she parted with her farm boy and married the factory worker."

"How heartbreaking," I said. "Did she ever see him again?"

"No," she replied. "And she was miserable."

I sat up and smoothed my dress, blue crepe with a delicate belt on the bodice that was just a trifle too tight. Mother had brought it home from one of her European shopping trips. She had a habit of buying clothing too small for me. "Well, that's very sad, and I'm sorry for Jeanette. But this does not have any application to my life. You see, I *love* Gerard. There is no one else."

"Of course you love Gerard," said Maxine, reaching down to pick up a napkin that had fallen on the grass. "You've grown up with the boy. He is like a brother to you."

*Brother.* The word had an eerie pulse to

it, especially when used to describe the man I was going to marry. I shivered.

"Dear," she continued, catching my eyes and smiling, "it is your life and your heart. And you say there is no one else, and that may be true. I'm simply saying that maybe you haven't given yourself enough time to find him."

"Him?"

"Your one true love," she said simply. The four words rolled off her tongue in a natural, matter-of-fact way, implying that such deep, profound feeling was available to anyone who sought it, like a ripe plum dangling from a branch, ready for the picking.

I felt a chill come over me, which I blamed on the breeze that had just picked up, and shook my head. "I don't believe in fairy tales, or in knights in shining armor. I believe that love is a choice. You meet someone. You like them. You decide to love them. It's that simple."

Kitty rolled her eyes. "How horribly *unromantic*," she groaned.

"Maxine," I said, "what about you? Were you ever in love?"

She ran a cloth along the side of the tea

tray, wiping up the rings our goblets had left. "Yes," she said, without looking up.

Blinded by curiosity, I didn't stop to consider that maybe the memory of this man was painful for her. "Was he an American or a Frenchman? Why didn't you marry him?"

Maxine didn't answer right away, and I instantly regretted my line of questioning, but then she opened her mouth to speak. "I didn't marry him because he was already married to someone else."

We all looked up when we heard Papa's footsteps on the terrace. Puffing on a cigar, he crossed the grass toward the three of us. "Hi, kid," he said, smiling at me through his thick gray mustache. "I didn't think you were coming home until Tuesday."

I returned his smile. "Kitty talked me into taking an earlier train."

I had finished my college courses at Portland State University in the spring, but Kitty and I had stayed on for an additional two months of training to obtain our nursing licenses. What we'd do with these credentials was of great concern to our parents. Heaven forbid we actually use them.

Gerard, on the other hand, found the whole business of being engaged to a trained nurse, in a word, amusing. Our mothers didn't work, nor did any of the women we knew. He joked that the cost of hiring a driver to chaperone me to my hospital shifts would amount to more than any paycheck I'd ever make, and yet if donning the white cap and tending to the sick was what I wanted to do, he promised to support me.

In truth, I didn't know what I wanted to do. I'd chosen nursing because it stood in stark contrast to everything I'd grown to detest about the lives of the women I knew—Mother, who devoted herself to luncheons and the current state of ladies' hemlines; and my school friends, who had spent months luxuriating in Paris or Venice upon high school graduation, with nary a worry, save finding a rich husband so they could perpetuate the lifestyles of their youth.

No, I didn't fit that mold. Its confines stifled me. What spoke to me was nursing, in all of its gritty rawness. It promised to fulfill a part of me that had lain empty for the majority of my life, a part that longed to help others in a way that had nothing to do with money.

Maxine cleared her throat. "I was just leaving," she said to Papa, picking up the tray with one fluid swoop. "Can I get you anything, Mr. Calloway?"

"No, Maxine," he said. "I'm just fine. Thank you." I liked the way he spoke to Maxine, always kind and gentle, never cross and hurried, which was the way of Mother.

She nodded and made her way across the emerald lawn, disappearing into the house.

Kitty looked up at Papa with concerned eyes. "Mr. Calloway?"

"Yes, Kitty?"

"I heard about another wave of men being drafted"—she gulped—"for the war. I read about it in the newspaper on the train. Do you know if any from Seattle have been notified?"

"It's still very early, Kitty Cat," he said, using the name he'd given Kitty when we were in grade school. "But the way things are progressing in Europe, I think we'll see a great deal of men going off to fight. I just ran into Stephen Radcliffe in town and heard that the Larson twins are shipping out Thursday."

I felt a tightness creep up in my chest. "Terry and Larry?"

Papa nodded solemnly.

The twins, a year younger than Kitty and me, were going off to war. *War.* It hardly seemed possible. Wasn't it only yesterday that they were tugging at my pigtails in grade school? Terry was shy and had cheeks speckled with freckles. Larry, a bit taller and less freckled, was a born comedian. Both redheads, they were rarely seen apart. I wondered if they'd be allowed to stand next to each other on the battlefield. I closed my eyes as if to try to suppress the thought, but it lingered. *Battlefield.*

Papa read my mind. "If you're worried about Gerard shipping out, don't," he said.

Gerard was as strong and gallant as any man I knew, surely, but as hard as I tried, I couldn't imagine him anywhere but in a suit at the bank. And yet, as much as I wanted him spared from fighting, a secret part of me longed to see him in uniform, to see him stand for something other than dollars and cents.

"His family's position in the community

is too important," he continued. "George Godfrey will see that he isn't drafted."

I hated the conflict brewing inside my heart—the fact that I took comfort in Gerard's protected position and detested it at the same time. It wasn't right that men from poor families had to fight a nation's war while a privileged few dodged the draft for frivolous reasons. Sure, George Godfrey, a bank mogul now in failing health, was a former senator, and Gerard was the next in line to fulfill his duties at the bank. But even so, it was unsettling to imagine the Larson twins fighting in a European bunker in the dead of winter while Gerard rested comfortably in a heated office with a leather chair that swiveled.

Papa could read the anxiety in my eyes. "Don't let it worry you. I hate to see you worry."

Kitty stared at her hands in her lap. I wondered if she was thinking of Mr. Gelfman. *Will he join the war too?* He couldn't be more than thirty-eight, surely young enough for combat. I sighed, wishing I could will the war to an end. The ill tidings of conflict hovered, creeping in and spoiling even the most perfect summer afternoon.

"Mother's eating in the city tonight," Papa said, glancing toward the house with a look of uncertainty that had all but disappeared by the time his eyes met mine. "Will I have the privilege of dining with you ladies this evening?"

Kitty shook her head. "I have an engagement," she said vaguely.

"Sorry, Papa, I'm having dinner with Gerard."

He nodded, suddenly looking sentimental. "Look at you two, all grown up, with big plans of your own. It seems like only a moment ago that you girls were out here with your dolls."

Truth be told, I longed for those easy, uncomplicated days that revolved around paper dolls, dress-up, and tea parties on the terrace. I buttoned my sweater against the wind on my skin—winds of change.

"Let's go inside," I said, reaching for Kitty's hand.

"OK," she said sweetly. And just like that, we were Kitty and Anne again.

My eyes burned from the haze of cigarette smoke hovering like a low cloud over our table. The lights were dim in the Cabaña Club, the place everyone in Seattle went dancing on Saturday nights. I squinted, trying to make out the scene.

Kitty pushed a box wrapped in blue paper toward me. I eyed the gold ribbon. "What's this?"

"Something for you," she said, grinning.

I looked at her quizzically, and then at the box, and carefully untied the ribbon before peeling off the wrapping. I lifted the lid of a white jewelry box and pushed aside the cotton lining to reveal a sparkling object inside.

"Kitty?"

"It's a pin," she said. "A friendship pin. Remember those little rings we had as children?"

I nodded, unsure if the stinging in my eyes was from the smoke or the memories of simpler times.

"I thought we needed a grown-up version," she said, pulling a lock of hair away from her shoulder to reveal a matching pin on her dress. "See? I have one too."

I eyed the silver bauble, round and dotted with tiny blue stones that formed the shape of a rose. It glistened under the dim lights of the club. I flipped it over, where I found an engraving: *To Anne, with love, Kitty.*

"It's perfectly beautiful," I said, pinning the piece to my dress.

She grinned. "I hope it will be a symbol of our friendship, a reminder to us both that we'll never keep secrets from one another, that we'll not let time or circumstances change things between us."

I nodded in agreement. "I'll wear it always."

She grinned. "Me too."

We sipped our sodas and scanned the bustling club, where friends, schoolmates, and acquaintances reveled in what could be the very last Saturday night before whatever waited in the wings scooped them up. War. Marriage. The unknown. I swallowed hard.

"Look at Ethel with David Barton," Kitty whispered in my ear. She pointed to the two of them huddled together at the bar. "His hands are all over her," she said, staring a little too long.

"She ought to be ashamed of herself," I said, shaking my head. "She's engaged to Henry. Isn't he away at school?"

Kitty nodded. But instead of mirroring my disapproving gaze, her face told a different story. "Don't you wish someone could love you *that* much?" she said wistfully.

I scrunched my nose. "That, my dear, is not love."

"Sure it is," she said, planting her cheek in her hand. We watched the couple saunter hand in hand out to the dance floor. "David's crazy about her."

"Crazy, sure," I said. "But not *in love* with her."

Kitty shrugged. "Well, they have passion."

I retrieved the pressed powder from my purse and dabbed my nose. Gerard would be there soon. "Passion is for fools," I said, snapping the compact closed.

"Maybe," she replied. "But just the same, I'll take my chances with it."

"Kitty!"

"What?"

"Don't talk like that."

"Like what?"

"Like a *loose* woman."

Kitty giggled, just as Gerard arrived at our table with his friend Max, a colleague from the bank—short, with curly hair, a plain, honest face, and eyes for Kitty.

"Do share your joke, Kitty," Gerard said, grinning. I loved his smile, so charming, so confident. He towered over the table in his gray suit, adjusting a loose cufflink. Max stood at attention, panting like a German shepherd, eyes fixed on Kitty.

"You tell him, Anne," Kitty said, daring me with her smirk.

I cleared my throat, smiling deviously. "Yes, Kitty was just saying that, well, that she and Max made a better dance duo than the two of us, Gerard." I shot Kitty a victorious look. "Can you believe that?"

Gerard grinned, and Max's eyes lit up. "Now, we can't have her carrying on like that, can we, dear?" He looked toward the dance floor and held out his hand. "Shall we?"

The band began playing, and Max fumbled to his feet, grinning from ear to ear. Kitty rolled her eyes at me as she took Max's outstretched hand.

Gerard clasped his arms around my waist, smoothly, elegantly. I loved his firm grasp, his confidence.

"Gerard?" I whispered in his ear.

"What is it, sweetheart?" He was an excellent dancer—precise in the same way he was about finances, never missing a penny in his budgeting.

"Do you feel . . . ?" I paused to consider what, exactly, I was asking him. "Do you feel *passionate* about me?"

"Passionate?" he said, stifling a laugh. "You funny thing, you. Of course I do." He squeezed me a little tighter.

"Really passionate?" I continued, dissatisfied with his answer.

He stopped and lovingly pulled my hands toward his chin. "You're not doubting my love for you, are you? Anne, you must know by now that I love you more than anything, more than anything on earth."

I nodded, and closed my eyes. Moments later, the song stopped and another began, this one slower. I nestled closer to Gerard, so close I could feel the beat of his heart, and I was sure he could feel mine. We swayed to the clarinet's haunting melody, and with each step, I assured myself that we had *it*. Of course we did. Gerard was head over heels for me, and I for him. What nonsense these feelings of uncertainty were. I blamed Kitty for planting them.

*Kitty.* I glanced over at her dancing unhappily with Max, when, out of nowhere, Mr. Gelfman appeared on the dance floor. He walked straight toward her, said something to Max, and took her into his arms as Max, crestfallen, scurried away.

"What is Kitty doing with *James Gelfman*?" Gerard asked, frowning.

"I don't like it," I said, watching as Mr. Gelfman twirled her around the room like a doll. His hands were too low on her waist, his grasp too tight. I thought of Kathleen, poor Kathleen, and winced.

"Let's go," I said to Gerard.

"So soon?" he said. "But we haven't even had dinner yet."

"Maxine left some sandwiches in the icebox," I replied. "I don't feel like dancing anymore."

"Is it Kitty?" he asked.

I nodded. I knew there was no stopping Kitty now. She had made that much clear. But I'd be damned if I was going to watch my best friend give away her heart, her dignity, to a man who wasn't worthy of her—a *married* man who wasn't worthy of her. But there was more to the story, something my mind wouldn't acknowledge just then, though my heart already knew: I envied Kitty. I wanted to *feel* what she was feeling. And I feared I never would.

The doorman handed me my blue velvet coat, and I tucked my hand into the crook of Gerard's arm. Warm. Safe. Protected. I told myself I was very lucky.

On the drive home, Gerard wanted to talk about real estate. Would we buy an apartment in the city or something in Windermere, the opulent neighborhood of our youth, near our parents? The apartment would be closer to the bank. And how gay it would be to live on Fifth Avenue, he crooned. But the Buskirks would be selling their home this fall, the big Tudor with the four dormers in front. We could buy it and renovate; build a new wing for the help and a nursery for the baby. For the *baby*.

Gerard droned on and suddenly the air in the car felt warm. Too warm. The road blurred in front of me and the street lights multiplied. What was wrong with me? *Why can't I breathe?* Dizzy, I clenched the door handle to steady myself.

"Are you all right, darling?"

"I think I just need a little air," I said, rolling the window down.

He patted my arm. "Sorry, honey, am I overwhelming you?"

"A little," I replied. "It's just that there are so many decisions to make. Can we take them one at a time?"

"Of course," he said. "No more talk of homes for now."

He turned the car in to Windermere, passing the stately, lit columns flanking the entrance. Within was a well-tended sanctuary, where gardeners spent hours manicuring lawns and grooming flowerbeds, not a petal askew, and governesses tended to children in a similar fashion. We passed Gerard's parents' home, the gray gable mansion on Gilmore Avenue, and the Larsons' white colonial, with the clipped boxwood hedges and stone urns shipped from Italy. *What is wrong with me?* Here was a man who loved me, who wanted to give me a beautiful, comfortable life, a life I was accustomed to. I scolded myself.

Gerard parked the car in my parents' driveway, and we walked into the house and straight to the darkened kitchen. "Maxine's probably gone to bed," I said, looking at the clock. Half past nine. Maxine always retired to her downstairs quarters at nine.

"Would you like a sandwich?" I offered.

"No, I'm fine," Gerard said, consulting his watch, a Rolex—my gift to him on his twenty-fifth birthday.

We both looked up when we heard footsteps.

"Papa?" I said, peering around the corner, where I detected a female form coming down the stairs in the darkness.

"Mother?" I turned on the hallway light and realized I'd been mistaken.

"Your mother isn't home yet," Maxine said. "I was just stocking your bathroom with towels. Francesca wasn't here today, and I wanted you to have some for the morning."

"Oh, Maxine," I said. "Look at you worrying about *my towels* at this late hour. I will not hear of it! Please, get some rest. You work far too hard."

When she turned her head to look at the clock, I thought I detected a glint of moisture in her eyes. *Has she been crying or is it just the day's exhaustion?*

"I think I shall say good night," she said, nodding. "Unless you need anything."

"No," I said. "No, we're fine. Sweet dreams, Maxine." I wrapped my arms around her neck the way I had done as a girl, taking in a breath of her vanilla cheeks.

After she'd left, Gerard kissed me, gently, quickly. *Why can't he kiss me longer?* "It's getting late," he said. "I suppose I should be on my way too."

"Do you have to go?" I said, pulling him toward me, eyeing the couch in the living room with other intentions. *Why must Gerard be so practical?*

"We need our rest," he said, shaking his head. "Tomorrow's going to be a big day."

"A big day?"

"The party," he said, looking at me suspiciously. "Have you forgotten?"

Until that moment, I had. Gerard's parents were hosting an engagement party for us at their home, on that enormous lawn, trimmed so perfectly that it resembled the ninth hole at Papa's country club. There would be a band, croquet, ice sculptures, and platters of tiny sandwiches served by white-gloved waiters.

"Just put on a pretty dress and be there by two," he said with a grin.

"I can do that," I replied, leaning into the doorway.

"Good night, darling," he said, walking out to the driveway.

I stood there watching as his car motored away, until the sound of the engine was swallowed up by the thick quiet of the August night.

# Chapter 2

"Maxine!"

I opened my eyes, blinking a few times, trying in my deep state of grogginess to place the voice—loud, shrill, a bit angry, but mostly annoyed, and definitely frustrated.

*Mother.* She was home.

"I told you Anne would wear the blue dress today—why isn't it pressed?" The voice was nearer now, right outside my bedroom door.

I pushed the quilt aside and sat up, reaching for my robe before setting my feet down reluctantly on the cool hardwood floors. *Poor Maxine.* She didn't deserve to be shouted at. Again.

I opened the door. "Mother," I said cautiously. I knew better than to contradict her fashion decisions. I walked slowly into the hallway. "I thought I'd wear the red one today. The one you bought in Paris."

She smiled, a few paces away on the landing, yanking the drapes open with a vexed glance at Maxine. "Oh, good morning, dear," she said, walking toward me. "I didn't know you were up." She reached out her arms and cradled my face in her hands. "You look tired, love. Were you out late last night? With Gerard?" She always said his name with a tone of excitement, the way one might gush about a chocolate cream pie. It had occurred to me at least once that Mother might like to marry Gerard Godfrey herself.

I shook my head. "No, it was an early night."

She pointed to the puffiness under my eyes. "Then why the dark circles?"

"I couldn't sleep," I said.

Maxine approached timidly, with a dress on a hanger. "Antoinette," she said. "Is this the one?"

I nodded.

"I wish you wouldn't call her that, Maxine," Mother snapped. "She's not a girl anymore. She's a woman, and about to be married. Please use her given name."

Maxine nodded.

"Mother," I squeaked, offering my hand to Maxine, "I *like* to be called Antoinette."

Mother shrugged. A new pair of diamond earrings swung from her lobes. "Well, I suppose it doesn't matter now. Next month you'll be Mrs. Gerard Godfrey, the most important name of all."

I felt a prickly sensation in my underarms. My eyes met Maxine's, and we shared a knowing look.

"Must you wear the red dress, darling?" Mother continued, tilting her head to the right. She was a beautiful woman, far prettier than I would ever be. I'd known it since I was young. "I'm not sure it's your color."

Maxine looked Mother straight in the eyes, something she didn't do often. "I think it's perfect on her, Mrs. Calloway," she said, leaving no room for further argument.

Mother shrugged. "Well then, wear whatever you wish, but we need to leave for the

Godfreys' in two hours. You had better start getting ready." She was halfway down the hall when she turned back to Maxine and me. "And put your hair up, dear. Your profile looks so much more becoming that way."

I nodded in compliance. Mother subscribed to all the fashion magazines and attended the runway shows in New York and Paris each year. She cared a great deal about appearances, in a way that other mothers didn't—always designer dresses, perfect hairdos, the latest accessories. And for what? Papa hardly noticed. And the more clothes she amassed, the unhappier she seemed.

When Mother was out of earshot, I rolled my eyes at Maxine. "She's in a *mood*, isn't she?"

Maxine handed me the dress. Her eyes told me she was still smarting from Mother's dismissive tone. We walked back to my room, and I shut the door.

I draped the dress against my body. "Are you sure this one will look all right on me?"

"What's bothering you, Antoinette?" she asked. I could feel her eyes piercing my skin, demanding an answer I wasn't yet prepared to give.

I gazed down at my bare feet on the hardwood floor. "I don't know," I said, hesitating. "I worry that it's all happening so fast."

Maxine nodded. "You mean the engagement?"

"Yes," I said. "I love him; I really do. He's such a good man."

"He is a good man," she said simply, leaving room for me to continue.

I sat down on the bed and leaned my weary head against the headboard. "I know a person can't be perfect and all," I said, "but I sometimes wonder if I'd love him more, feel more deeply for him, if he'd do the right thing."

Maxine hung the dress up against the door. "And join the war?"

I nodded. "I just wish some things were different about him, about us."

"Like what, dear?"

"I want to feel proud of him the way the other women feel about their men joining the fight," I continued, pausing for a moment to think of other couples I knew. "I want to feel passionate about him." I giggled nervously. "Kitty thinks we don't have enough passion."

"Well," Maxine said expectantly, "do you?"

"I don't know," I replied, before shaking off the thought. "Listen to me going on like this. What a terrible fiancée I am even to speak this way." I shook my head. "Gerard is a dream come true. I'm lucky to have him. It's time I start playing the part."

Maxine's eyes met mine. I could see a fire brewing inside. "You must *never* talk that way, Antoinette," she said, making each word as clear and firm as she could muster with her heavily accented voice. "You can never play a part in life, especially not in love."

She wrapped her arm around my shoulders the way she'd done when I was a child, nuzzling her cheek against mine. "You be yourself," she said. "And never ignore what your heart is telling you, even when it hurts, even when it seems like following it will be very difficult or untidy."

I sighed and buried my face against her shoulder. "Maxine, why are you telling me this? Why now?"

She forced a smile, her expression

oozing regret. "Because I didn't follow my heart. And I wish I did."

Gerard's mother, Grace Godfrey, was a formidable woman in appearance. Her dark eyes and sharp features, which looked so handsome on Gerard, manifested in the female form as alarming, jarring. But when she smiled, the edges softened. As a child, I often wished Mother could be more like Mrs. Godfrey—practical, down-to-earth, despite her wealth and her position. In a time when women in her class offloaded much of the child rearing to hired help, Mrs. Godfrey did not. During their childhood, if one of the Godfrey boys skinned their knees, she'd shoo the nanny away and swoop in to bandage it herself, kissing the injured child gently.

"I don't know why Grace Godfrey doesn't let her nanny do her job," I overheard Mother complain to Papa when I was in grade school.

And true to form, as my parents and I walked across the lawn at the Godfreys' that afternoon, Grace could be seen assisting the waitstaff in carrying an ice sculpture—a large duck with three ducklings trailing precariously behind—from the terrace to a table on the lawn.

"Let me help you with that," Papa called out from behind me.

"Grace, be careful," Mother chimed in. "You'll put out your back."

Mrs. Godfrey relinquished her hold on the duck, which looked perilously on the verge of collapse, just as Papa dove in to assist.

"Thank you," she said, before turning to Mother. "Hello, Luellen, Anne. Isn't it a lovely day for a party?"

"Yes," I replied, peering up at the blue sky, a single fluffy white cloud its only resident. Tables covered the expansive lawn, and in every vase atop the lilac-colored table linens were five stems of purple hydrangeas. "It's . . ." I paused, suddenly overcome with emotion for the display of love for me, for Gerard, for our impending union. "It's all so beautiful."

"I'm glad you like it," Mrs. Godfrey said, entwining her substantial arm in mine. "Gerard's on the terrace waiting for you, dear."

I could see him in the distance, stretched out on a chaise longue, puffing on a cigar with his father. Smart, handsome, strong, he could have stepped from the pages of one of Mother's magazines. When he saw me, he stood up quickly and snuffed the celebratory smoke. "Anne," he called, waving, "I'll be right down."

I adjusted the sash on my dress, and Maxine's words rang in my ears: "You can never play a part in life, especially not in love." *But everyone plays a part, don't they? Mother. Papa. Kitty, in some ways. Even Maxine. Why should I be expected to behave any differently?*

Moments later I felt Gerard's arms around my waist. "You," he said, whispering in my ear, "are the most beautiful woman I have ever laid eyes on."

I blushed. "Do you really think so?"

"I know so," he replied. "Where did you get that dress? You are a vision."

"I wore it for you," I said. "I wanted you to—"

"Wait, is that Ethan Waggoner?" He squinted at the entrance to the garden as a man and his very pregnant wife walked through the gate. "Sorry to interrupt, sweetheart, but it's an old friend from college. Let me introduce you."

The afternoon was so filled with introductions and how-do-you-dos that I hardly saw Gerard, except for an occasional wave from across the terrace or a kiss on the cheek in passing. Engagement parties were not for the engaged.

As the dinner bell rang, I looked around for Kitty, realizing that I hadn't seen her all afternoon. *That's strange; she's known about the event for weeks.* Throughout dinner, her spot at the head table next to Gerard and me remained curiously empty. And when the band started to play the first song of the night, "You Go to My Head," I began to worry.

"Gerard," I whispered in his ear as we swayed on the dance floor, feeling what seemed to be a thousand pairs of eyes staring at us through the warm night air. I tried to ignore them. "Kitty hasn't shown up. I'm worried about her."

"She's probably just running behind schedule," he said, without a trace of concern. "You know Kitty."

True, Kitty was often late. But not *five hours* late—to the engagement party of her best friend. No, something was wrong. I felt it.

I rested my head on Gerard's lapel as he led me around the dance floor in perfect form. I closed my eyes and let him lead me, as I always did, never taking the reins for a moment, as I listened to the words of the song.

*You go to my head and linger like a haunting refrain. . . .* Did *Gerard* go to my head?

"Gerard," I whispered, "have you thought much about the war? About joining?"

He pulled back to look at me. "Sweetheart, if you're worried about me being drafted, please don't. Father's already taken care of that."

I frowned. "Oh," I said, pausing to choose my words carefully. "But, don't you ever worry that . . ."

"Worry about what?"

My thoughts were interrupted by motion, detected in the corner of my eye, at the entrance to the garden. Someone was waving, trying to get my attention. The lights from the dance floor blurred the periphery, but I squinted hard to bring the person into focus. *Kitty.* There she was, standing behind the garden gate. *Is it locked? Why isn't she coming in?* She dabbed a handkerchief to her eye. *No, something is wrong.*

The song ended and several other couples joined us on the dance floor. I leaned in close to Gerard and whispered, "Do you mind sitting this one out?"

He gave me a confused smile, but nodded, before I raced through the gate, where I found Kitty seated on the sidewalk, slumped over, head buried against her knees.

"Kitty, what happened?" I noticed her face first, the tear-smeared makeup down her cheeks, eyes red from crying.

"You must think I'm a terrible, terrible friend," she sobbed, burying her face again.

I smoothed her hair, tucking whatever stray locks I could back into her hairpins, but it was no use. Her curls were disheveled in a way I'd never seen before. "Of course I don't, dear," I said. "What's wrong? Tell me."

"I'm so sorry, Anne, for standing you up like I have," she sniffed. "You must consider me a wretched friend. And I am. I am a miserable, unworthy friend." More sobbing

ensued, and I pulled out a fresh handkerchief from the fold of my dress and handed
it to her.

"You are not an unworthy friend," I said.
"You are my dearest friend."

Kitty blew her nose, and looked up at
me with frightfully grief-stricken eyes. Her
gaze telegraphed sadness, that was certain, but also a glint of desperation. Here
was a woman on the verge of a drastic
move. I looked away.

"I arrived hours ago," she said. "But I
just couldn't come in."

"Why on earth not?"

She blew her nose again. "Because I
can't bear to see you off," she said.

"But I'm not going anywhere, Kitty."

"That's just it," she said. "You are. You're
getting married. You're changing. And I
know I should be happy for you, but all I
can think of is how I'm losing you."

"Oh, Kitty," I said. "You'll never *lose* me!"

She nodded. "But I will. And it's the way
it has to be. I just haven't gotten used to it
yet." She pointed to the party on the other
side of the hedge. "It's why I couldn't join
in tonight. I'm so sorry, Anne."

I reached for her hand. "No," I said firmly.

"You mustn't apologize." I used the hem of my dress to blot an errant tear from her cheek.

"Anne," she said, a little distantly. "There's something I need to tell you."

I let go of her hand. "What?"

"You're not going to like it."

"Tell me anyway," I said, bracing myself for whatever was coming.

"I've made a big decision—about my future," she said. She cleared her throat. "You're moving on, and so must I."

"Kitty, whatever do you mean?"

She took a deep, calming breath. "You remember the pact we made when we signed up for nursing school together?"

I nodded. "Yes. We swore we wouldn't end up like our mothers."

"Exactly," she said, staring straight ahead. "And that we wanted a different life, a more meaningful life."

I frowned. "Kitty, if you're implying that by me marrying Gerard I'm—"

"No," she said quickly. "I don't mean that at all. I'm just saying that it occurred to me that there is something *I* can do with my life, with my skills—something of great meaning. I've been thinking about it for a while now, ever since we first heard rumors of the war, but tonight, Anne, it's clear what I need to do."

I clenched my hands tightly in my lap.

"I'm going away," she said. "Far away—to the South Pacific. I'm joining the Army Nurse Corps to assist with the war efforts. I was downtown today at the volunteer registration center. Anne, they need trained nurses. They're desperate for them. This could finally be a chance for me to do something of value."

My heart surged with emotion. I thought of the stories recounted in Norah's letters about the islands—the muggy nights with the stars so close you could touch them, the beauty and the mystery, the fear of destruction, of war, lurking around every corner. The men. And though I'd only dared to dream about what it would be like, I had no idea that Kitty had been quietly making plans to go.

I kicked a pebble, sending it flying into the street. "Are you sure?"

"Yes," she said softly.

I sighed.

"Listen," Kitty continued. "You're getting married. Everyone's getting married, or going to school, or going somewhere. I won't sit here idly and watch while everything changes. I want to be a part of the change."

Yes, change was happening to both of us, whether we wanted to participate or not. The closer we came to it, the more painful it felt. And now that we were staring it in the eye, it produced an ache in my heart that I could not ignore.

"Mother hates the idea, of course," Kitty continued, "of me running off to an untamed island, to mingle with *savages*, to live among army men, but I don't care. I don't care what anyone thinks, except"—her tone became more cautious—"well, you."

I couldn't bear to think of Kitty out there either, but not because of the "savages" or the men, though the latter did concern me a fair amount. No, I couldn't stand it that Kitty was leaving, flinging herself to another part of the world—without me.

"I've been corresponding with Norah," I finally confessed.

Kitty looked displeased, but then her eyes brightened. "Isn't she in the South Pacific now?"

"Yes," I said. "She's been after me to sign up."

Kitty grinned. "Well, she's wasting her time on the wrong girl."

"Maybe not," I said quietly.

I thought about the wedding, just weeks away. All the little details ran through my mind like the frames of a film. My dress, French silk. The blue garter. A five-tier cake, with fondant. Doilies. Bridesmaid bouquets. White peonies and lavender roses. I shuddered. *How can I get married without Kitty standing by my side?*

I sat up straighter and nodded to myself. "I'm going with you," I said matter-of-factly.

Kitty beamed. "Anne! No, you can't mean that. What about the wedding? We'd have to leave in under a week, and the commitment is at least nine months, maybe longer."

I shrugged. "They need nurses, don't they?" My heart pounded—with excitement, with anticipation, and also with fear.

Kitty nodded through her sniffles. "They do," she said. "The recruiter says the action in the Pacific is heating up, and they're in dire need of nurses."

I smiled. "What kind of friend would I be if I let you set off on the adventure of your life without me?"

Kitty threw her arms around me, and we sat there on the sidewalk together for the next song, and then another. The music from the party sounded as if it might be a world away, and in some ways it was. The clipped laurel hedge represented the border between the certain and the uncertain.

"Gerard will never forgive me," Kitty said, "for stealing his fiancée away on the eve of his wedding."

I shook my head. "That's nonsense. You're not taking me prisoner. I'm going because I want to."

I looked over my shoulder at the party behind us. My decision would come with consequences; I knew that. Mother would be beside herself. Papa would warn against it. And Gerard . . . *Gerard*. I sighed. He would find this hard to take—his fiancée going off to a battle zone while he stayed comfortably at home. I knew he'd also be hurt, which is what worried me most of all. But I couldn't think about that, not now. If he loved me, truly loved me, he would wait—and if he wouldn't, well, then I'd cross that bridge when I came to it.

As each moment passed, I felt my resolve strengthen. I needed to go to the South Pacific with Kitty. Why, exactly? The answer was still hazy. And yet one thing was certain: In this new adventure, I would not be simply playing a part.

# Chapter 3

Kitty jabbed her elbow into my side, and I groaned, opening my heavy eyelids. "Look out your window," she said, squealing with delight. "We're almost here!"

It had been a forty-five-minute flight from an island to the north, where we'd arrived by ship. I'd been seasick for a full four days and longed to be on land again. I looked around the cabin of the small plane, so gray and mechanical. A place for men. Yet, other than the pilots in the cockpit and a single soldier, a tall, gangly fellow with strawberry-blond hair and a freshly pressed uniform on his way back from an extended medical leave, the plane was filled to capacity with nurses.

"Look!" Kitty exclaimed, holding her hand to her heart. "Have you ever seen anything more beautiful?"

I leaned over Kitty to have a look out the tiny window. I gasped as my eyes met the scene below—the impossibly light blue water against white sand and the lush, emerald-green hillside. I hadn't expected to catch my breath at the sight. Frankly, I hadn't expected much. Sure, Norah, now on a ship headed stateside, had talked of the islands' allure, but newspaper articles from home told a different story, one of an unrelenting tropical heat, squalor, and misery, where men fought in mosquito-infested swamps described in letters as "a living hell." And yet the view from the window didn't seem to fit that description. No, this island was something else, something entirely different.

My thoughts turned to Gerard and the look on his face when I boarded the plane—sad, unsure, a little frightened. He had been wonderful when I told him, the day after the party, that I was going. But there had been something concerning in his eyes too.

Of course, he tried to talk me out of going, but eventually he squeezed my hand and forced a smile. "I'll be here for you when you return. Nothing will change that," he said.

After a long talk before I left, we decided to postpone our wedding a year. Mother was devastated when she heard the news, running to her bedroom to weep. Papa was a little more difficult to read. I waited until the evening after the party at the God-freys', right before supper, when he was sipping a scotch in his study. Little beads of sweat had appeared on his forehead. "Are you sure you want to do this, kid?"

"I'm sure," I said. "I can't explain it other than it just feels *right*."

He nodded, then lit a cigar, puffing the smoke toward the open window. His eyes glimmered. "I wish I had your courage."

"Papa—"

"Well, that's that," he said abruptly, snuffing out the cigar in an ashtray and any emotion lingering in the air. "We don't want to miss dinner. Maxine is making *croque monsieur.*" And yet, Papa managed to take only one bite that night.

I straightened my dress. How had mine gotten so rumpled when Kitty's looked freshly pressed? I frowned. *Have I made a mistake coming here?* I folded my hands in my lap and eyed the landscape below—my new home, for a good portion of a year, at least.

Constance Hildebrand, the charge nurse who would be our superior on the island, stood up in the front of the plane and looked sternly at the group of young nurses. She was a portly woman with gray hair tucked severely under a nurse's cap clipped so tightly it looked painful. If she had a gentle side, she kept it under lock and key. "We are almost to the island," she said. It was loud in the airplane, and even though she spoke in a shout, I still had to read her lips to understand her completely. "Don't be fooled by its beauty; it isn't a place of luxury," she continued. "You will work harder and perspire more than you can imagine. The heat is harsh. The humidity is suffocating. And if the mosquitoes don't get you, the natives will. The ones close to the shoreline are friendly, but don't venture farther than that. Cannibal colonies still exist not far from the base."

I glanced at the other women near the aisle, wide-eyed and frightened, as Nurse Hildebrand cleared her throat. "I know you are tired, but there is work to be done," she said. "You will find your quarters, wash, and meet me in the infirmary at fourteen hundred hours. And, a word of warning: There will be a great many men watching your arrival, men who haven't seen women in a very long time, aside from the *wahine*." She shook her head for emphasis. "Do not oblige the men with eye contact. They must be made to behave like gentlemen."

One of the girls in the row in front of us whipped out her compact, dusting her nose with a bit of powder before applying a fresh coat of red lipstick.

Kitty leaned in toward me with a grin. "There are two thousand men on the island," she whispered. "And forty-five of us."

I frowned at Kitty. How could she let her mind turn to men when all I could think of were Nurse Hildebrand's chilling warnings? "Do you really think there are *cannibals*?"

"Nah," Kitty said confidently. "She's just trying to scare us."

I nodded to reassure myself. "Besides," I added, "Norah didn't say anything about mosquitoes in her letters."

Kitty nodded in agreement. "Meredith Lewis—you know, Jillian's sister—was on another island near here. She arrived with the first wave of troops and said the cannibal stories are all fiction."

But instead of comforting me, Kitty's words hit my heart like shrapnel. Meredith Lewis had been in Gerard's class in high school. She'd stood next to him in his yearbook photograph, and the memory made me long for home. My heart swelled with uncertainty, but the thoughts quieted as the plane began to shudder and jolt.

Kitty and I held hands as we touched down with a thud, speeding down a runway that appeared dangerously close to the ocean. For a moment, it seemed a very real possibility that we would catapult right into that great body of water like a speeding torpedo. I quietly crossed my heart and said a prayer.

"Here goes," I whispered under my breath a few moments later, as I filed in with the other women to exit the plane.

I felt Kitty's hand on my shoulder behind me. "Thank you for coming with me," she whispered. "You'll be glad you did, I promise."

One by one, we walked down the stairs onto the airstrip. The breeze hit my face—warm and humid, and when I took a breath, I could almost feel steam rising in my lungs. A nurse to our right, who had powdered her nose right before stepping off the plane, now looked dewy and shiny-faced, and I noticed a bead of perspiration roll down her cheek. I resisted the urge to retrieve the compact in my handbag, reminding myself that it didn't matter how I looked; I was engaged.

I looked across the airstrip and saw that Nurse Hildebrand was correct—about the men, at least. A sea of dark green uniforms swarmed like hornets. The bold ones whistled; others just leaned up against trucks behind lit cigarettes, staring.

"You'd think they had never seen women before," Kitty whispered, batting her eyes at a soldier in the front of the crowd, who puffed up his chest and smiled at us confidently. "He's cute," she said, a little louder than she should have.

Nurse Hildebrand turned to face us. "Ladies, allow me to present Colonel Donahue," she said, turning toward a man in uniform decorated with at least a dozen medals and pins. As he crossed the tarmac, his men moved into formation. A hush came over the crowd, and the nurses watched in fascination as he approached. The colonel was about forty, maybe older, with golden skin, dark hair with specks of gray, and undeniably striking eyes. He looked powerful in uniform, and a little frightening, I thought.

"Nurse Hildebrand, ladies," he said, with a tip of his hat. "I would like to formally welcome you to Bora-Bora. We are grateful for the service you are bestowing on the country, and I can assure you that your work will not go without a heartfelt thanks from the men stationed on this island, myself included." He turned to the men and shouted, "At ease," and the men erupted in applause.

"What a perfect gentleman," Kitty said in a whisper, without taking her eyes off of the colonel.

I shrugged. The sun felt even hotter now, its rays pelting us with an intensity I hadn't noticed when we first stepped off the airplane. It radiated off the pavement, causing heat to swirl around us, unrelenting. Kitty's body swayed slowly next to mine. At first I thought she was moving to the Ella Fitzgerald recording playing from a jeep nearby, but when I turned to face her, I could see that her cheeks had gone white, and her arms limp. "Kitty," I said, reaching for her hand, "are you all right?"

Her eyes fluttered just as her legs buckled underneath her body. I was able to catch her as she fell, but her bag, overstuffed with dresses too formal for the island, was the real saving grace, cushioning her head against the unforgiving tarmac. She lay in a crumpled heap on the hot cement airfield with her head in my lap.

"Kitty!" I screamed, instinctively pulling

the hem of her blue dress lower on her legs.

"Smelling salts!" Nurse Hildebrand ordered, pushing through the circle of hovering women. She produced a green glass vial and held it under Kitty's nose. "The sun has gotten to her," she said without emotion. "She'll become accustomed to it in time."

Colonel Donahue appeared at Nurse Hildebrand's side. "Get her a stretcher!" he shouted to a man near the airplane. "And quick."

"Colonel Donahue," Nurse Hildebrand said, "we're dealing with a simple case of heatstroke. She'll be fine, this one."

He eyed Kitty with a possessive look. "Just the same, I'd like to make sure she's comfortable."

"Suit yourself," Nurse Hildebrand replied.

Two men appeared moments later with a stretcher and lifted Kitty, now conscious but groggy, onto it.

"Anne," Kitty said, turning to me, "what happened?"

Colonel Donahue swooped in by her side before I could respond. "It's always the prettiest ones who faint in the tropics," he said with a grin.

I didn't like his tone, but Kitty beamed. "How terribly embarrassing. Was I out long?"

The colonel smiled in return. The crowd around us was so thick I could no longer see through it. "Just long enough to miss the news that we're having a dance tonight in honor of your arrival," he said, phrasing the statement as if the dance might be solely for her.

Kitty smiled, much too flirtatiously to address a ranking colonel. "A dance?" she muttered weakly.

"Yes," he said, "a dance." He turned to face the crowd. "You heard that right, men, tonight at twenty hundred."

"Thank you," Kitty said, unable to stop smiling.

"My pleasure," he replied gallantly. "I'll just ask for one favor."

"Of course," Kitty said, still beaming.

"That you save a dance for me."

"I'd love to," she replied dreamily as the men began wheeling her through the crowd.

Kitty always knew how to make an entrance.

The rest of the crowd began moving. I looked down at my suitcase and Kitty's enormous bag and groaned. The men had scattered, and now I was left to carry both.

"Can you believe that?" a woman said from behind me. I turned around to find one of the new nurses. Her soft auburn waves resembled Rita Hayworth's in *Life* magazine, but that was where the similarity ended.

"I'm sorry?" I said, unsure of her meaning.

"Your friend pulled quite a stunt there to get the colonel's attention," she said, smirking. A bit of lace protruded above the top button of her dress. I wondered if the reveal was purposeful.

A second later, another nurse, this one with shiny dark hair and a meek smile, appeared at her friend's side with a look of agreement.

"Oh no, no," I said. "You're not implying that Kitty fainted intentionally, are you?"

"It's exactly what I'm saying," the auburn-haired nurse replied, clearly the alpha of the pair. "Scenes like that don't happen *spontaneously*. She staged it."

"She most certainly did not," I said in

protest. "If you ask me, I think you're jealous."

The dark-haired nurse gasped, as the other woman shrugged confidently. "You'll thank us someday," she said.

"For what?" I asked suspiciously.

"For warning you of what your little friend is capable of. I wouldn't trust that one as far as I could throw her around any man of mine."

I shook my head and continued walking, as fast as I could with two heavy bags, one more so than the other.

"How rude of us," the auburn-haired nurse spoke up. But the apology I had anticipated wasn't coming. "I almost forgot to introduce myself. I'm Stella, and this is Liz," she said, pointing to her brunette friend.

I kept walking, disregarding the introduction.

"And you are?"

"Anne," I barked, marching onward without turning around.

⌘

Our quarters in the nurses' barracks were simple, meager at best, just two crudely constructed beds, a dressing table, and one closet for the two of us to share. The flimsy cotton drapes, discolored to a pale yellow from the hot sun, seemed inadequate to block the light or the men's line of vision. I arrived to find Kitty standing on one of the beds, hammering a nail into the wall. "What do you think of this spot for a picture?" she asked, tilting her head a little. "I was thinking of hanging a photo of Mama and Papa."

I set her bag down with a thud and wiped my brow. "I think it's fine," I said blankly. "You're feeling better, I see."

"Yes, thanks, dear," she said. "I feel badly for leaving you in the crowd like that. But Colonel Donahue insisted."

I was beginning to dread the sound of *the colonel*'s name, but I was careful not to let it show. "I'm just glad you're OK."

Kitty flitted like a spring bird around our little second-story room, chattering on about how we'd fix the place up. A spare sheet would make a perfect valance, she crooned, and we'd certainly be able to locate a coffee table, somewhere, for tea. *Certainly.* And the walls, weren't they such a lovely, soothing color? *Yes, infirmary beige—very soothing.*

In my view, however, the room was dank and strange. The two navy-blue-and-white-striped mattresses were bare and speckled with visible stains. Stacks of threadbare linens sat folded in neat little piles atop each. I longed for Maxine then, even though the thought made me feel childish. She'd have jumped in and made the beds, settling each of us with a calming cup of tea.

I was on my own now.

"Anne, can you believe there's going to be a dance tonight? A dance! And Colonel Donahue wants to dance with *me*!"

There was that name again. *Why does it affect me so? Do I distrust his intentions, or are my feelings misplaced?* I remembered what Stella and Liz had said on the tarmac. They were jealous. I hated to think that I was too.

Kitty had a way with men that I would never have. I thought of Gerard and twisted my engagement ring around my finger, which was swollen from the heat.

"Yes, won't that be fun?" I chimed in, working hard to sound cheerful.

"I'm going to wear my yellow dress," Kitty said, running to her suitcase. She looked great in yellow, especially in the dress she held up for my approval. I'd seen her wear it a half dozen times—on the last occasion with Mr. Gelfman's arms wrapped tightly around the bodice. Funny, she'd been so heartbroken about the man when we left Seattle, but the island seemed to have erased her memory. I vowed to keep mine intact.

Kitty looked into the mirror, pressing the dress to her body, smoothing out the wrinkles, which the island humidity would soon erase. "I don't know," she said. "Maybe I should wear the blue one, the one we bought at Frederick and Nelson's last spring. It's a bit more conservative, I guess."

I shook my head. "No," I said, thinking of Liz and Stella. I was determined to prove—to myself, anyway—that I was not jealous, that I was being the best friend I could to Kitty. It's why I followed her here, I reminded myself. "Wear the yellow one. You look stunning in it."

Kitty would be the most beautiful woman at the dance. She'd have the time of her life. And I'd be happy for her.

The infirmary, a white building with a red cross painted above the entryway, smelled of soap and ipecac, with a touch of rubbing alcohol thrown in for good measure. Kitty and I, the last two to arrive that afternoon, nestled into the circle of women watching Nurse Hildebrand as she demonstrated, on a nurse's arm, the art of wound care in the tropics. Bandages were to be wrapped, she said, counterclockwise, not too tight, but snug enough to stop the bleeding. "The wound needs to breathe," she said. "Too much or too little air, and you get infection." She paused, looking out through the windows at the distant hills. "Especially in this godforsaken place."

We spent the rest of the session rolling bandages into tight little bundles, then tucking them away in crates pulled off the plane. I laid out the big bolts of taupe linen on the table, trying not to dwell on the wounds they would one day cling to. Kitty took one end, and I another. After an hour, my fingers ached.

We worked in silence, mostly in fear of Nurse Hildebrand, for we all had plenty to say. But when she left to attend a matter in the mess hall, the women began to find their voices.

"She's a tough one, that Nurse Hildebrand," said a woman to our left. A few years older than Kitty and me, she had hair the color of straw, freckles dotting her nose, and large, friendly eyes. Her smile revealed crooked teeth, which she tried, unsuccessfully, to keep hidden behind pursed lips.

"She is," I said in agreement. "I don't understand—if she hates this place so much, why did she volunteer?"

"She has a past here," she said.

"What do you mean, 'a past'?"

"All I know is what another nurse told me on the mainland." She lowered her voice to a whisper. "She was here before, a very long time ago. And something bad happened."

"What happened?"

"I don't know exactly, but it's some kind of scandal."

"You can't mean that she's a criminal!" Kitty exclaimed.

The woman shrugged. "Who knows? But I wouldn't want to be caught on Nurse's bad side," she said. "I'm Mary," she continued, nodding to Kitty and me.

"I'm Anne."

"And I'm Kitty."

Mary tucked another rolled bandage into the crate on the table. "What brings you here?"

Kitty opened her mouth, but I spoke first. "Service to our country," I said simply.

Mary smirked. "Isn't that what we all say? No, why are you *really* here? We're all running from or searching for something. What's your story?" She looked down at my engagement ring, perhaps because I was tugging at it.

But this time, Kitty responded before I could. "Anne was engaged," she began, but I cut her off.

"*Is* engaged," I corrected her.

"Yes, Anne *is* engaged, but she delayed the wedding to come with me." Kitty nuzzled her shoulder against mine, a gesture of gratitude. "I was in a horrible romantic mess before we left. I felt I needed to escape."

"Me, too," Mary said, holding up her bare left hand. "My fiancé broke off our engagement. He came by one day and told me he didn't love me. Now, what were his exact words, again?" She looked up at the ceiling as if to scan her memories. "Yes," she continued. "He said, 'Darling, I love you but I am not *in love* with you.' If that wasn't enough, he then announced that he was going to marry my best friend. Apparently they'd been seeing each other for months. I'll be honest, girls, it almost sent me to the loony bin, that ordeal. When I was coherent enough to think about my next move, I knew I had to leave town. I wanted to go to the farthest corner of the world to dull the pain. Our wedding was going to be in the fall, at the Cartwright Hotel in San Francisco." She looked down at her hands and sighed. "It was going to be *grand*."

"I'm so sorry," I said.

"Thank you," she replied. "I don't mind talking about it now, not really." She began working on another bandage roll. "We were going to move to Paris," she continued. "He was—well, is—joining the Foreign Service." She shook her head wistfully. "I should never have fallen in love with Edward. Mother was right. He was much too good-looking for me." She shrugged, replacing the hurt in her eyes with practicality. "And now I'm here. And you?" She looked at me. "Do you love the man you're going to marry?"

"Of course I do," I said a little more defensively than I had planned.

"Then why are you here and not at home with him?"

*Why* am *I here and not home with him? Is the answer really that simple?* I pondered the question for a moment. *Is it adventure that I, like Kitty, seek? Am I listening to Maxine's words and giving myself a chance to wait for something—God help me, for* someone—*to come along before I seal my fate?* I shook my head, destroying the thought. *No, I am here for Kitty. Yes, that's it, plain and simple.*

"Because my friend needed me," I said, squeezing Kitty's hand.

"That's sweet," Mary said. "You're lucky, you know—to have each other. I don't have a friend like that."

Kitty, ever the generous spirit, smiled warmly at Mary. "You can have us."

Mary's charming grin revealed her imperfect teeth. "I'd like that," she said, tucking another bandage into the crate. We'd rolled at least a hundred, give or take. It was a small feat, yes, but I was proud of our accomplishment. A mountain of bandages on our first day on Bora-Bora. We were *doing something*. We were really living.

The nurses had two designated tables in the mess hall, a plain building with long cafeteria tables packed in rows. We were not to eat with the men, said Nurse Hildebrand. Even so, we were aware of their every move, as they were of ours. Their eyes bore into us as we ate—Spam and beans.

"This food is *awful*," Mary said, stabbing a green bean with her fork and holding it up to the light. "Look, this thing is petrified."

"We'll come home perfectly thin," Kitty said, smiling, ever the optimist.

Stella and Liz sat across from us, but after their comments about Kitty earlier in the day, I dismissed their presence. "Well, well," Stella said with dramatic flair, pointing to a corner table where three men sat. "Get a load of that!"

Mary and Kitty, unaware of my grudge,

turned to see what the fuss was about. "He's the spitting image of Clark Gable," Kitty said in agreement. "I wonder who he is?"

"His name's Elliot," Stella said. "The corporal who carried my bag today introduced us. Isn't he dreamy?"

Mary nodded. "Very," she said, swallowing a bite of Spam with a strained gulp.

"It's too bad, though," Stella continued. "Word is that he's deeply in love with a woman back home. A married woman."

Our eyes widened in unison.

"He could have his pick of women here," she went on, shaking her head, "and yet rumor has it that he spends his leave holed up in his bunk writing in his journal, brooding about her."

"How romantic," Kitty said dreamily.

I nodded. "A man who loves a woman that much is very rare."

"Or very stupid," Stella rattled back. She went on about her plan to capture Elliot's attention, while I picked at my plate.

I took another look at the table, where this man, Elliot, sat. He did resemble Clark Gable. Handsome, with dark eyes and thick ebony hair that came to a curl at the front. Yet my eyes were drawn instead to another, seated to his left. Tall, but not nearly as built, with lighter, wispier hair and sun-kissed skin with a dusting of freckles. His left hand shoveled food into his mouth while his right cradled a book, one he was clearly engrossed in. As he turned the page, he looked up. His eyes immediately met mine, and the creases of his mouth formed an instant smile. I quickly snapped my head back around. *What has gotten into me?* I instantly regretted the breach of decorum.

I felt my cheeks burn as I forced a bite of Spam, trying my best to avert the gag reflex rising in my throat. Stella had seen the exchange, and she shot me a mocking glance, but I turned away, willing myself to regain composure.

❧

Tropical nights were better than tropical days, I decided, even if there were mosquitoes. The break from the sun made the air more agreeable. And then there was the cool mist wafting off the sea, and the stars, those luminous stars, so close you could almost reach out and pluck one from the indigo sky.

Kitty and I walked arm in arm along the gravel path to the center of camp to join in the evening festivities, she in her yellow dress and I in my red one. Kitty had urged me to wear something more daring, and at the last moment, I'd conceded.

It wasn't much of a walk, maybe the equivalent of five city blocks, but it felt like a great distance in heels. We passed the infirmary and noticed an interior light shining. *Is Nurse Hildebrand inside?* We scurried past swiftly. As we neared the men's barracks, Kitty and I pretended not to hear the whistles from the men smoking outside.

A safe distance past, Kitty tugged at my arm. "Look," she said, pointing to a large green shrub erupting in the most breathtaking blossoms.

"They're beautiful," I said. "What are they?

She picked a red bloom from the bush. "Hibiscus," she said, tucking the flower behind her right ear, before offering one to me. "In French Polynesia, when your heart is taken, you wear the flower in your left ear," she said. "When it's not, you wear it in your right."

"How do you know that?"

Kitty grinned. "I just do."

I stared at the enormous bloom in my hands; its crinkly petals were a brilliant shade of crimson. "Then I must wear it in my left," I said, dutifully tucking the flower behind my ear.

"How lovely," Kitty said, pointing to a makeshift dance floor in the distance. It had been cobbled together from plywood. "Fairy lights."

Strands of tiny white lights hung above, crisscrossing the rafters constructed of palm fronds. Men huddled together on the sidelines, whispering among themselves, as a group of nurses made their way across the lawn. Five musicians took to the stage, tuning their instruments while an announcer wielded a microphone.

"I would like to welcome the corps of nurses to our little island," the announcer said. "Let's show them a good time, lads."

There was a round of cheering and applause before the band started, and for a moment, no one moved. "What are we supposed to do?" Kitty whispered. Her breath tickled my shoulder.

"Don't do anything," I said, wishing I had stayed behind in the room with a book.

Stella and Liz ventured forward a few steps, and two of the men followed suit, one bolder than the other. "May I have this dance?" a soldier with a southern accent and a swagger in his step said to Stella. The other sidled up to Liz. Both women obliged.

"Look at them," I said to Kitty. "So fast."

Kitty was too distracted to hear me. I knew whom she was looking for. Suddenly, though, a man approached us—well, approached Kitty. I recognized him from the morning on the airstrip. "I saw your flower," he said, bowing in an exaggerated way. Men did strange things around Kitty. "I'm Lance," he said, extending his hand to her, and she relinquished hers, allowing him to lay a mock kiss upon it.

I rolled my eyes. He was tall and athletic, with hair a forgettable shade of brown, sharp features, and a coy smile that made me distrust him instantly.

"I'm Kitty," she said, clearly flattered.

Lance grinned. "Would you like to dance?"

Kitty nodded, and he whisked her off to the dance floor, leaving me alone on the sidelines. I tapped my foot to the music. It was a fine band—for the middle of nowhere. I felt prickles on my arm when I heard a clarinet play the introductory lines to "A String of Pearls." I'd last heard the Glenn Miller tune on the Godfreys' lawn. At our engagement party. I sighed, suddenly feeling lonely. Out of place. Awkward. I tugged at my dress. I unfastened a wayward pin in my hair and clasped it back into place. *Where is Mary?* I looked around, but saw only strange men staring at me. *Thank God for the flower.*

But oblivious to the ring on my finger or the code of the flower, a man approached me. His shirt looked wrinkled, and I could smell alcohol on his breath even before he opened his mouth. "Care to dance?"

"Thank you," I said politely, "but no. I think I'll sit this one out."

"You're much too pretty to be a wallflower," he protested. "Besides, I'm tired of *wahine*. I want to dance with a real American woman." He pried my hand from my side and led me out to the dance floor.

"Well, you see," I said, startled by his bravado, "I think I better not."

"Nonsense," he said, grinning. I could smell the sour odor of beer—too much beer—on his breath.

He pressed his cheek against mine and I could feel the scratchy stubble on his jawline. "You're pretty," he said, as the band struck up a melody. *Please, not a slow song.* His hands were hot and moist on my dress, and his embrace suffocating, yet I willed myself to endure; I could not cause a scene. I would have to make it to the end of the song.

But, to my horror, the song ended and another man approached, presumably a friend of my dancing partner's, and as the tempo hastened, I found myself caught between them. One twirled me by the arm, spinning me into the other. I bobbled back and forth like a ball on a tether. I looked around desperately for Kitty, and spotted her tucked into the arms of Lance. She looked happy, amused. *Don't cause a scene.* I felt a hand brush my breasts. *Whose?* I froze, even though my legs were still moving. My eyes darted from left to right, and another hand cinched my waist, this one firmer. The room began to spin, or maybe I began to spin. Men were all around me. Hot, sweaty. The humid air was thick. I felt my voice rising up in my throat, but nothing came out. And then, there was scuffling and a loud thud. Someone fell to the ground. The music stopped, and a crowd formed around my original dancing partner. Blood trickled from his nose. He was out cold.

I pushed my way through the crowd off the dance floor, self-consciously keeping my head down. I felt guilty, even though I'd done nothing wrong. I didn't want to be followed. I darted for the path back to the barracks, quickening my pace to a light jog when I passed the men's barracks. I felt tears welling up in my eyes as the wind whistled through the palms overhead. It was a lonely sound, so foreign, so strange. I missed the walnut tree. I missed Seattle.

Spooked by a sound in the bushes, I instinctively turned to the infirmary instead of continuing on. The poorly lit path and the island night seemed impossibly dangerous without Kitty by my side. *Kitty.* I worried about leaving her there. She'd be fine, though; Lance looked decent enough. Or so I convinced myself.

A light shone inside, and I expected to find Nurse Hildebrand at her desk. Seated there instead was a man, the very man I'd seen in the mess hall at dinner.

He smiled, and I offered a startled smile in return.

"Hello," he said from across the room. "Don't let me frighten you. I'm just looking for a bandage. I thought I could find one in here, but you all must have the place soldier-proofed."

I squinted, and could see that his hand was bleeding. I ran over to the box of bandages I'd rolled that afternoon. "Here," I said, pulling one out, "let me help you."

I told myself not to be embarrassed. I was a nurse. He was a patient. There was no reason to feel odd about the interaction, no reason to feel awkward about being alone with this man after dark.

"What happened?" I asked, dabbing his wound with gauze I'd soaked in rubbing alcohol.

He winced, but continued smiling. "You didn't see?"

"See what?"

"I couldn't bear to watch Randy Connors have his way with you on the dance floor," he said.

"Randy Connors? Have his way with me? I beg your pardon—"

"What? His hands were all over you."

He'd stated an obvious fact, but still I looked down at my feet, ashamed.

The soldier lifted my chin with his hand. "It's why I punched him."

I grinned. "Oh," I said, trying my best to compose myself. *Does he notice the tears in my eyes?* "It was you. Well, then I owe you my gratitude."

"You'll have to forgive the men," he said. "They haven't seen women like you all in months, some longer. We've been on this rock a long time."

I remembered the word the soldier had uttered, *wahine*. It had sounded dirty and harsh on his breath.

"Do you happen to know what *wahine* means?"

His eyes twinkled. "Why yes," he said. "That's Tahitian for *woman*."

I nodded. "Well, I don't care if these men have been away from women for a century. It's no excuse for barbarism."

"It's not," he said. "Which is why I avoid most of them. There are a few decent men here. You must learn to be direct with them. At home you can play coy; you can expect decorum and genteelness. Not here. The tropics bring out the savage in all of us. The island dulls your inhibitions. It changes you. You'll see."

"Well," I said dismissively, wrapping his knuckles with a linen bandage in just the way Nurse Hildebrand had instructed. "I, for one, don't believe that something can change you unless you *want* to be changed. Haven't you ever heard of free will?"

"Sure," he said, looking very amused. "I'm just saying that this place has a way of revealing the truth about people, uncovering the layers we carry and exposing our real selves."

I fastened the bandage with an aluminum bracket, and exhaled. "Well, I'm not sure about that," I said. "But you're all fixed up."

"I'm Westry," he said, extending his bandaged hand. "Westry Green."

"Anne Calloway," I replied, shaking his hand gently.

"See you around." He headed to the door without lingering.

"See you around," I said, catching a glimpse of red in his left hand. As the door clicked closed behind him, I reached up to my ear. The hibiscus was gone.

# Chapter 4

"What time did you come in last night?" I asked Kitty the next morning from my bed across the room. I'd been awake reading for at least two hours, waiting for her to stir.

She took one look at the clock, then pressed her head back into her pillow. "Late," she said, her voice muffled by down stuffing.

"It's nearly nine," I said, remembering our good fortune to have arrived on the island on a Friday. Saturday was our only day of leave. "I won't let you sleep away our only day off. Come on, let's get dressed!"

She yawned and sat up. "I can't believe it's nine already."

"Yes, sleepyhead," I said, walking to the closet. I wanted to explore the beach today and I'd need to wear something light.

Kitty stood up quickly. "I have to hurry," she said. "Lance is taking me into town for the day."

My heart sank, and Kitty could tell.

"You can come too," she offered. "He invited you."

"And be the third wheel?" I shook my head. "No thanks. You go on your own."

Kitty shook her head, unbuttoning her nightgown and letting it fall to the floor, exposing her breasts, two perfect spheres. "You're coming with us," she said. "A few others are going too. Lance is taking a jeep. Elliot's coming, and Stella."

"What?" I said. "How did she wrangle him into going?"

"She didn't," Kitty said. "Lance did."

I pulled the curtains closed to hide Kitty's naked body from prying male eyes. "Is anyone else coming?" I thought of Westry.

"I think that's it," Kitty said, looking into the closet. "Wait, is there someone you were thinking of?" There was a hint of teasing in her voice.

I shook my head. "I was only thinking of Mary."

Kitty didn't look up from the closet.

"I didn't see her last night, did you?"

"No," she said, pulling out a powder blue dress with short sleeves. "What do you think of this one?"

"It's fine," I said, less concerned about Kitty's wardrobe than the safety of our new friend. "Don't you think we ought to check with Nurse Hildebrand to see if Mary's all right?"

Kitty shrugged, holding up a pair of tan heels for inspection. "Yes or no?"

"No," I said. "Wear the blue ones. Your feet will thank me later."

She clasped her bra and stepped into a white silk slip, before putting on the dress.

"Tell me about Lance," I said a little cautiously, zipping her up. "Do you like him?"

"Yes," Kitty said, though I thought I detected a note of hesitation in her voice. "He's great."

"Did you ever dance with the colonel last night?" I asked, selecting a glaringly simple tan dress from the closet.

Kitty nodded. "I did," she said, smiling. "And it was divine. Lance wasn't too happy, but he could hardly challenge his superior."

I took a look at myself in the oval mirror on the wall. My cheeks were flushed from the morning heat and my hair looked limp. In a battle with the humidity, the humidity had won. I shrugged and pulled it back into a clip. I'd be wearing a sun hat anyway.

"Ready?" Kitty said, grabbing her handbag.

I stared back at her. Her cheeks were rosy, not ruddy like mine. Her hair, curlier and wilder than ever, looked alluring the way she wore it, pinned to the side.

The tropics became her.

"Ready," I said, following her out the door.

Lance drove much too fast. Kitty was unaffected, however, looking gay in the front seat while Stella, Elliot, and I were squeezed into the back like pickles in one of Maxine's canning jars. My legs began to sweat on the hot canvas seat, and I clutched my hat as Lance gunned the engine. The pothole-littered gravel road that encircled the island wasn't for the faint of heart. The dust was thick; I wished I'd brought a scarf.

"First to town center," Lance said, sounding like an overzealous tour guide. "And next, to the beach."

Kitty let out a little cheer, and Stella eyed Elliot, whose gaze remained fixed on the road ahead. "Do you get into town much?" she asked him sweetly.

He didn't respond.

"I SAID," Stella repeated, louder this time, competing with the engine noise, "DO YOU GET INTO TOWN MUCH?"

Elliot looked at us, at first startled, then confused, as if he wasn't sure which of us had spoken and why in such a shout.

"No, not often," he said briefly, before turning his gaze back to the road.

Stella huffed and folded her arms across her chest. The air smelled of dirt right after a rain, mingled with a sweet, floral scent I didn't recognize.

"You see that?" Lance said, pointing to a gated property to our left. He slowed the jeep, and I was glad to let go of my hat for a moment. My arm was beginning to cramp. "It's a vanilla plantation. Almost all the vanilla in the world comes from this island."

I wasn't sure if this bit of trivia was true, or if Lance had just thrown it in to impress Kitty, but the idea of seeing a real, working vanilla plantation was incredibly exciting. I thought of Maxine. Was she happy living in the Windermere home day after day, waiting on my parents with little more than a "Thanks, Maxine" or "That will be all, Maxine"?

"An American owns the place," Lance continued. "He married an island girl."

Stella's eyes widened. "I thought they were all cannibals."

Elliot took his eyes off the road and gave me a knowing look before settling back into his quiet mind.

Lance continued on. Makeshift homes, constructed of scrap lumber, dotted the roadside, tucked in under the lush palms. Occasionally we'd spot a rooster or chicken pecking about, or a child running nude in front of one of the dwellings, but never an adult, and I was curious to see one of these natives that Nurse Hildebrand spoke of.

The jeep wound around the north side of the island and past a small turquoise cove with a ship anchored a way out. It might have been pulled from a page of *Robinson Crusoe*. Moments later, Lance pulled over to the side of the road. "Here we are," he said.

I stepped out onto the dusty ground and turned my gaze to the busy scene ahead, where one might never guess there was a war going on mere miles from the shore. There were rows of tables cluttered with exotic fruits and vegetables, handmade necklaces, packs of cigarettes, and bottles of Coca-Cola. The scantily dressed shopkeepers, with their olive skin and enigmatic eyes, sat behind their tables looking vaguely bored, or sleepy, or both, as soldiers buzzed about spending their hard-earned cash on whatever trinket caught their eye.

"Look," said Stella, gasping. She pointed to a native woman walking toward us. Bare-breasted, she wore her hair twisted into a single braid that rested between her breasts. A swath of green fabric hung around her waist, tied loosely, dangerously so. I noticed the flower in her left ear as she walked right up to us as if she knew us. I tried to look away, but her breasts, with nipples so dark, lured my eyes with magnetic power. Her presence had the same effect on Stella, Kitty, Elliot, and especially Lance.

"Mr. Lance," the woman said, setting down the bag she had been carrying. Her thickly accented voice was sweet and soft. She was maybe eighteen, possibly younger. Her breasts dangled and swayed as she bent down to the bag and produced a pack of Lucky Strikes. "Your cigarettes," she said, offering him the pack.

**How does Lance know this woman, or rather, woman-child?**

"Thank you," Lance said. Kitty eyed him as he tucked the pack into his shirt pocket. "*Atea* here is the only shopkeeper who can track down my Lucky Strikes. She saves a pack for me every Thursday."

Atea looked proud standing there, bare chested, not the least bit modest. Her eyes sparkled. She gazed at no one but Lance.

"Are you coming today?" she said, unaware of the awkward stiffness in the air.

"Not today, Atea," he said, dismissing her

with a self-conscious nod. "You be a good girl and rustle me up some more, if you can. I'll be back in a few days." He tucked a coin in her hand and then reached for Kitty's arm. "Now, let's go see the rest of the market."

"That was strange," Stella said, leaning in to me a few moments later.

It *was* strange, but I wasn't going to discuss it with her, not when Kitty might overhear. "What's so strange about Lance buying cigarettes from a female?" I said instead.

Stella smirked and continued on, stopping at a table of brightly colored beads.

"You OK?" I said to Kitty, once Lance was a safe distance away.

"Of course," she said. "Why?"

*Good. She wasn't upset by the interaction. Then I'll just leave it alone.* "Oh, nothing," I said. "Just wanted to make sure the heat wasn't getting to you."

She took a deep breath of the humid island air and smiled. "I'm having the time of my life," she said gleefully.

Stella laid a blanket out on the beach, careful to secure a spot next to Elliot. "I'm starved, are you?" she said, attempting to catch his attention, but he merely shrugged and muttered, "I ate a big breakfast," before leaning back against a large piece of driftwood wedged into the sand, snuffing out all further conversation by pulling his hat over his eyes.

We'd driven back around to the other side of the island, close to base. Though we selected a spot beneath the shade of a palm for our picnic, the white sand still radiated heat. I shifted my legs uncomfortably as Kitty set out a loaf of bread, a cheerful bunch of miniature bananas, four bottles of Coca-Cola, and a wedge of cheese—our improvised lunch cobbled together at the market.

We ate in silence at first, watching the waves crash onto the shore. Then Kitty pointed to the sea and said what we all felt: "It's hard to believe there's a war happening out there. This corner of the world is too beautiful for destruction."

I nodded, helping myself to another banana. They tasted different than the bananas at home, a little tarter, with a hint of lemon. "But there is," I said practically.

"And a serious one, at that," Lance added. "Just yesterday, the Japs shot down three of our planes."

Stella looked worried. "Do you think we'll see fighting right here on the island?"

"I think we might," Lance said gravely. "Colonel Donahue doesn't see it that way, though. He's a fool. I tell you, we'll be all asleep in our bunks when the Japs fly over, bombarding us when we least expect it."

Kitty looked up with concerned eyes, then shook her head. "Colonel Donahue will protect this island."

Lance shrugged. "If you say so." He smirked, before muttering, "I could run this operation better blindfolded."

The statement was too boastful for a man of twenty-five, but Kitty must have been unaffected by his arrogance, because she laid her head lightly in his lap. I could tell by his smile that he liked it.

Elliot began to snore. Stella brooded.

"I think I'll take a walk," I said, standing. Kitty's eyes were closed in pretend slumber as I adjusted the brim of my hat and kicked off my shoes. "I'll be back," I said, though I don't think anyone looked up.

I walked down the beach, stopping occasionally to examine a rock or a shell, or to
marvel at the growth patterns of the palms,
reaching out to the sea in horizontal fashion. Years of wind and tropical storms had
sculpted their trunks, but I liked to think
they grew that way because the sea was
calling. It made me remember what Westry had said about the island changing
people. *Will I be able to resist its force?*

I strengthened my footing in the sand
and charged onward. After the morning at
the market, it felt good to be alone with my
thoughts and the quiet lull of the waves
on the shore. The deserted beach seemed
to stretch toward infinity. I walked closer to
the water, relishing the feeling of the cool,
sea-kissed sand on my feet. Each step left
an inch-thick indentation.

A seabird squawked from its perch on a
rock a few feet away, which is where I first
noticed another set of footprints, fainter,
older, but still relatively fresh. *Whose?*

*It would be silly to follow them*, I told
myself. *What if they're a native's? A cannibal's?* I shook my head. *I'm alone. I
should turn back.* And yet, they lured me

farther down the beach, beyond the bend. *Just a few steps farther.*

The footprints stopped at a crumpled beige blanket, anchored to the sand by nothing but a book. I recognized the fabric instantly because I had the same standard military-issue on my bed in the barracks. *But who was here?*

I turned quickly when I heard a rustling sound in the thick brush behind the palms at the edge of the beach.

"Hello there," said a man appearing out of nowhere a few hundred yards away. He carried a large palm frond that shrouded his face, but when he moved it aside, I could see that it was Westry.

"Hello," I said, a bit surprised, but grateful to have avoided an encounter of a grimmer nature.

"Are you following me?" he said teasingly.

I felt foolish, then irritated. "Of course not!" I said, my voice thick with pride. *I can't have him thinking I'm chasing after him.* "I was merely taking a walk—which reminds me, I need to be going. My friends are expecting me."

Westry smiled. "Oh, don't go," he said, pushing the base of the palm branch into the sand and then sitting under it. "Look, the perfect shade. Won't you sit down? Just for a minute?"

His smile was impossible to resist. I hesitated, then felt the corners of my mouth turn upward, without my permission. "All right," I said, grinning in spite of myself. "Just for a minute."

"Nice day," he said, leaning back on his elbows.

"Quite," I said, pulling the hem of my dress lower on my legs.

"What brings you to my beach?"

"*Your* beach?"

"Yes," he said matter-of-factly. "I discovered it."

I let out a little laugh. "You're really something."

"It's all virgin coastline, you know," Westry continued. "Of course, the natives have been here forever, and it will always be theirs. But the rest of the world isn't onto it. For now, this little slice of heaven is mine." He looked at me. "Well, ours. I'll let you have half."

"Well, that's awfully generous of you," I said, playing along.

"Do you know what I'm going to do, after the war's over?"

"What?"

"I'm going to buy this stretch of beach," he said earnestly. "As much as I can afford. I'm going to build a house and raise a family, right here. My wife and I, we'll watch the sun rise every morning from our porch and listen to the surf crash onto the shore at night."

"It all sounds terribly romantic," I said. "But I think you're bluffing. You'd actually want to live *here* after"—I pointed out to the Pacific, where Japanese warships may have been taking up residence at that very moment—"after all this? After the war?"

Westry nodded. "Sure," he said. "It's paradise."

It *was* paradise, I reminded myself. "But don't you have a life waiting for you at home?"

"No," he said, without hesitating. "But *you* do."

It wasn't a question, but a statement. He'd seen the ring on my finger.

"I do," I said honestly.

"Do you love him?"

"What kind of question is that?"

"A simple one," he said, grinning. "So, what's the verdict?"

"Of course I love him," I said, looking away. *Why does he have to stare at me that way?*

"Is he a good man?"

I nodded. "I wouldn't marry any man who wasn't."

The waves crept in closer to the blanket, prompting Westry to stand up, and I followed. "We better shift our camp a bit, or else Old Man Sea is going to swallow us up."

I smiled. "I really should be getting back. My friends are waiting for me."

Westry nodded. "I'll walk you."

The shoreline looked different in reverse, perhaps because I was seeing it through Westry's eyes now. I imagined his life on the island years from now, with a house and a wife, and two or three barefoot children, and smiled to myself.

"How's your hand?" I asked.

He held it up, and I took it in mine, feeling a flutter deep inside that I told myself to ignore.

"I think I'm going to pull through," he said mockingly.

"It's filthy," I scolded. "You really must let me change the bandage when we get back. You'll risk infection."

"Yes, nurse," he said playfully.

Moments later Westry gestured toward something in the brush line, where palms grew thick. We walked closer and stopped, just as the beach ended and vegetation began. Birds sang and animals howled under the cover of shady green plants with gargantuan leaves, just as I'd always imagined a jungle.

"Do you see that?"

I shook my head. "What?"

"Look closer," he said.

"No," I whispered, "I don't see anything."

Westry reached for my hand, and I took it, only because I feared danger lurking, and I followed him a few paces beyond the beach, which is when I finally saw what he did: a thatched-roof hut, just beyond the thicket. Though constructed in as makeshift a manner as the homes along the roadside, this one had a charm all its own. The exterior was built of bamboo canes, into which someone had painstakingly cut holes to approximate ocean-facing windows. A small door dangled from a single hinge, creaking in the afternoon breeze.

"I don't know if we should be here," I whispered.

"Why not?" he said, grinning mischievously. "Now that we've found it, we have to see what's inside."

Before I could protest, Westry set foot on the little step to the front door. The sound of his shoe striking the wood startled me, and I jumped back a few feet.

He lifted the collapsing door off its lone hinge and set it down on the sand, peering inside before turning to me with a wink. "All clear."

He helped me up the step, and we surveyed the place in silence. The interior walls, made of woven palm branches weathered to a light shade of caramel, had been beautifully strung together in a V-shaped pattern. They provided a perfect backdrop to a dark mahogany chair paired with a small desk containing a single drawer. Westry reached for its handle and pulled out a book, some French coins and bills, and a piece of paper, yellowed and curled from the humidity. He held it up so I could have a look. "Can you read French?"

I shook my head. "I wish I'd paid more attention in school."

"Me too," he said, slipping the paper back in the drawer.

The bed, big enough for just one person, looked tidy, even with a layer of dust on top, as if someone had woken up one morning and tucked the linens in place in anticipation of a return that never occurred.

My eyes darted around the space, landing anywhere but on Westry's face. Here I was, an engaged woman, alone in a bedroom with a soldier I knew nothing of.

My reverie broke when a spider the size of my palm crawled out from under the desk and raced out the open doorway, causing me to leap on top of the bed in terror. "Did you see that thing?" I shrieked, certain that another would jump out at any moment.

"They're harmless," Westry said, grinning. "Plus, they eat the mosquitoes, so we ought to lay out a buffet table for the critters."

I cautiously stepped down from the bed. "Who do you think lived here?"

Westry looked out at the sea. "My best guess?" He turned back to the bungalow, studying it carefully. "A shipwrecked sailor."

I nodded. It sounded plausible enough. "But what happened to the ship?"

"Maybe it sunk."

"So how did he recover the paper and"—I opened the desk drawer and pulled out the book with its dark brown leather cover— "and this book?"

Westry touched his index finger to his chin, as if to ponder the fate of our ship-wrecked sailor. "Maybe he had a knapsack packed with a few rations." He pointed to the lamp on the desk. "A lantern, this book, a tin of biscuits. And he managed to find a piece of wood to drift on until he reached the island."

"The book would have gotten wet," I said.

"So it may have," Westry conceded. "But he might have let it dry in the sun." He fanned the book's pages, and sure enough, they were covered in water stains. "See?"

I nodded. "But where was he heading? He was clearly French."

"And poor," Westry added, pointing to the small stash of coins in the drawer.

"Could he have been a pirate?"

Westry shook his head. "Domestic trappings would hardly hold the interest of a pirate."

I eyed the curtains on the windows, ragged from the weather, yet still a brilliant burgundy, as if the fabric had been soaked in wine.

"OK, so he's a poor, shipwrecked, French sailor who likes to read," I said.

"And likes to drink," Westry added, holding up a dusty green glass vessel, sealed with a cork. "Red wine."

"And appreciates art," I said, pulling away a scrap of burlap that covered a painting hanging over the bed. The canvas depicted an arresting scene: a bungalow, just like the very one we found ourselves in, nestled between impossibly blue water and a hibiscus bush flowering vibrant yellow. Two figures stood in the distance.

"My God," Westry gasped. "It's beautiful."

I nodded. "Do you know much about art?"

"A little," he said. "Let me have a closer look." He stood up on the bed to gaze at the painting. "It looks"—he scratched his head—*familiar* somehow."

Mother had prided herself on teaching me about the French impressionists, and yet, I feared my artistic knowledge was still woefully inadequate. Even so, I reveled in the potential of the discovery.

"Do you think the artist lived *here*?"

"Maybe," Westry said, his eyes still fixed on the painting. "What year was that book printed?"

I thumbed the opening pages of the book for a date. "Here, found it. Copyright 1877."

"It might have been one of the master impressionists," he said.

"You can't be serious," I said, in awe.

"Well, it's as possible as anything," he replied, grinning. "I'm almost certain I've seen this one in books before, or maybe something similar. And this island, all of these islands in the Pacific, they were popular among the French artists. It could have been any one of the greats." His eyes were wild with excitement. "You know what this means, don't you?"

"What?"

"We have to protect this place."

I nodded. "But how?"

"It will be our project," he said, "while we're here. We'll restore it."

"It does need a good scrub."

"And a new door," Westry added.

"And the curtains are rags," I said. "I can make new ones."

"So you're in?" He was looking at me with slightly mischievous eyes.

*Why not? It will pass the hours Kitty spends with Lance.* "I'm in," I said. "But how will we ever find the time, and how will we get here?"

"We'll walk," he said simply. "The base is less than a half mile up shore. You can slip out and be back before anyone knows you've even left. There's a trail that leads up to the road, so I'll bring the tools and the wood out in a jeep, of course. It will take some planning, but we'll figure it out."

Westry turned to the door and a weak floorboard creaked and bowed from the pressure of his foot. He knelt down and pulled it up, exposing the rickety subfloor and a small alcove just below the surface. "Here," he said. "This will be our 'mailbox.' I'll leave you letters when I'm here without you, and you can do the same."

My heart leapt with excitement—for the bungalow, for the artist, for the prospect of letters tucked under floorboards, but especially for this man who held the key to it all.

Westry wrapped the painting in its burlap covering and carefully slid it under the bed for safekeeping.

"There's just one thing," he said.

"What?"

"We can't tell a soul about this place, not anyone."

It pained me to think of keeping a find this marvelous from Kitty, and yet, I couldn't imagine her here in the bungalow, a place that already felt special to me, sacred, even after only a few minutes. I touched my hand to Kitty's pin, and felt a pang of guilt. *Is it wrong to want to harbor this little hut to myself, especially after we've vowed not to keep secrets from each other?*

"What do you say?" Westry continued.

I let my hand fall to my side and nodded. "Cross my heart," I said, convincing myself that Kitty didn't need to know—not yet, anyway. "I won't tell a soul."

"Good. Shall I walk you back?"

"Yes," I said. "They're probably wondering if I drowned."

"Or got eaten by a shark," he added, grinning.

The beauty of the island wasn't limited to its turquoise waters or green hills. That was mere surface beauty. The real awe of the place was evident in its stories. There was one waiting beyond every curve of the shore.

# Chapter 5

"Westry seems nice," Kitty said as soon as we'd shut the door to our room later that day.

"He's all right," I said vaguely, taking off my hat and placing it on the top shelf of the closet.

"Where's he from?"

I shrugged. "Not sure. We only spoke for a moment. He was kind enough to walk me back."

I could sense Kitty's grin, even without looking up to confirm it. "Seems like you and Lance are getting along fine," I said, changing the subject.

"Yes," Kitty replied, leaning back against the headboard of her bed. "I do like him. Very much. It's just"—she paused and shook her head—"it's just, well, I don't care for the way he speaks of Colonel Donahue. Don't you think he should show him more respect than he does?"

I shrugged. I hadn't yet determined the lesser evil for Kitty: the cocky soldier or his overbearing superior.

"Well," Kitty continued, "I suppose it's a small detail. Lance has so many stand-out qualities."

*Like his bravado. His philandering with the island women. His smug attitude.* "Yes," I said instead. "So many."

"Anne," Kitty said, a little shyly. "I haven't had a chance to tell you, but on the night of the dance, Colonel Donahue—"

We both looked up, startled, when we heard a loud, rapid knocking at the door.

"Yes," I said, turning the knob.

Liz stood outside, panting and out of breath. "It's Mary," she said. "In the infirmary. Come quick."

We followed Liz down the stairs and out the barracks door, picking up a brisk pace once we reached the pathway outside. The infirmary wasn't far, but we arrived at its entrance wheezing from the sprint.

Inside, Nurse Hildebrand hovered over Mary's bed alongside Dr. Livingston, a middle-aged physician with thinning hair and spectacles. Mary looked unnaturally pale. Her eyes were closed, but the shallow rise of her chest told us she was still breathing.

"Dear Lord," I whispered. "What happened?"

The doctor produced a syringe and injected a clear liquid into Mary's arm; she didn't flinch when the needle pricked her skin.

"One of the women found her in her room," Nurse Hildebrand said, "collapsed by the bed. She'd been there at least sixteen hours. Malaria. Must have contracted it on her first day on the island."

"Malaria," I repeated. The word sounded so foreign, and yet the disease was right here, threatening to take the life of a terrific girl, one we'd just begun to know, a girl who had her whole future ahead of her, who had come to the South Pacific to start over, not to die.

"The fever broke," Dr. Livingston said,

"but I'm afraid it weakened her heart. The only thing we can do now is wait."

My hands trembled. "But she's going to make it," I said. "She's going to pull through. She has to pull through."

Dr. Livingston looked away.

I thought of Mary, poor Mary. Tall, perhaps a little too tall. Teeth a bit crooked. Heart broken. Her fiancé had left her and she had felt alone; she'd told us so. *No, I will not let her die alone.*

"Kitty," I said, "will you run back to the barracks and fetch my reading glasses and anything you can find to read? Bring the damn *War Digest*, if that's all there is—whatever you can find."

Kitty nodded.

"We're going to hold vigil," I said. "May I pull up a bed and stay next to her tonight?" I asked Nurse Hildebrand.

She nodded in approval.

Kitty returned with two magazines, three books—two from Liz and another from Stella—a copy of the *War Digest*, and a nursing textbook, just in case.

"Good," I said, examining a book with a tattered spine. "We'll take shifts reading to

her. We won't stop until she regains consciousness, or . . ."

Kitty reached for my hand. "Anne, you
can't save her if she's—"

"I won't let her die alone," I said, wiping
away a tear. "Nobody deserves that."

Kitty nodded.

I set down the book and picked up a
copy of *Vogue* with Rita Hayworth on the
cover. I turned to the first page, and began
reading an advertisement: "Why not get a
lovely figure for spring? If you want to dress
inexpensively, and be able to wear standard
fittings with charm and distinction, start
now to get rid of that accumulated winter
fat. With the help of nightly Bile Beans
you can 'slim while you sleep' safely and
gradually . . ."

I read for four hours, every word on every
page in front of me, until my eyes began to
blur. Kitty read next, turning on a little lamp
on the table next to the gurney when the
sun set, then passing the torch back to
me a few hours later after her voice became
hoarse.

We'd covered three magazines and three
quarters of a novel by the time the sun's
morning rays first shone through the infir-

mary windows, which is when Mary's eyes began to flutter.

She opened them slowly, then shut them again, and we watched with great anticipation as the next minute passed, and then the next, before she moved her arm, and then her legs, and then her eyes again, this time opening them and looking straight at me.

"Where am I?" she said weakly.

"In the infirmary," I replied, tucking a strand of her blond, straw-like hair behind her ear. "You've been stricken with malaria, dear," I continued, choking back tears. "But you're going to be fine now."

Mary looked around the room, then at Kitty and back to me. "I had the strangest dream," she said. "I kept trying to walk toward a bright light, and there was this voice always there. It kept luring me back."

"Did you turn around?"

"I didn't want to," she said. "I wanted to keep walking, but every time I took a step, the voice beckoned."

"Good," I said, holding a glass of water to her lips before tucking her cold arms back under the blanket. "Dear, we have all the time in the world to talk about it, but you need your rest now."

Our care of Mary didn't compel Nurse Hildebrand to congratulate us on our nursing skills, but she did excuse us from duty that day, and Kitty and I welcomed the opportunity to rest.

I slept until noon, when the sound of the lunch bell ringing from the mess hall woke me. My stomach growled, yet my exhaustion persisted and I was tempted to stay in bed.

"Kitty?" I said, without lifting my head. "Are you awake?"

I turned my heavy head expecting to see her fast asleep, and instead found her coverlet pulled tightly up over her bed and the two pillows fluffed and neatly stacked against the headboard.

*Where is she?* I sat up and stretched, then noticed a note on the dressing table.

Anne,

I didn't want to wake you. I left at 10 to go canoeing with Lance. I'll be back this afternoon.

Love,

Kitty

Boating with Lance. Of course, it was a perfectly normal thing for her to do, and yet I felt uneasy. *We were granted the day off only hours ago, so when did she have time to make plans with Lance?* I thought of the bungalow, and realized our little dormitory room was already thick with secrets.

The lunch bell rang a second time—the last call. If I dressed and ran quickly I could make it in time. But I saw a shiny red apple on the nightstand and thought of a much better idea.

☙

I slung over my shoulder a knapsack packed with the apple, a bit of bread Kitty had brought back from the mess hall, and a canteen filled with water, then I snuck past the entrance to the infirmary, stopping briefly to glance through an open window to where Stella and Liz and a few of the other nurses were working. They looked bored, at best. A few fussed over a lightbulb that needed changing, and a small group hovered over the only patient in the building, a man who looked like he had nothing more than a skinned knee. His smile indicated his enjoyment.

This wasn't the wartime life I'd expected. And yet, change was coming. I'd heard a rumor that Colonel Donahue had an operation planned, something big. I wondered how it might affect our work, our world.

I made my way to the path that led to the beach. Westry had said the bungalow was just a half mile north of the base. I hoped he was right.

I walked fast, and looked over my shoulder more than a few times. *What would people think of me sneaking away from the base like this, alone?* It didn't feel like something Anne Calloway would do.

Just around the bend, I began to make out the thatched roof of the bungalow, nestled in the thicket, just as we'd left it. As I grew nearer, I could hear the sound of a saw zigzagging.

My heart pounded in my chest. *Westry is here.*

"Hello," I said, knocking ceremoniously on the place where the door had once hung precariously. "Anyone home?"

Westry looked up, wiping his brow before brushing sawdust off his hands. "Oh, hi," he said. "Are you real or a mirage? I've been out here all morning without water, and I can't tell if I'm hallucinating or if there's really a beautiful woman standing in the doorway. Please tell me it's the latter."

I grinned. "You're not hallucinating," I said, pulling the canteen out of my bag. "Here, drink."

Westry took a long gulp, then exhaled, handing the canteen back to me. "I've almost got the door in working order," he said. "It didn't fit on the doorframe. The weather must have warped it. I had to take an inch off the side. See? I rustled up some old hinges from the supply yard." He held up the hardware proudly, as if it were treasure. "Our bungalow needs a proper, working door."

I smiled. I liked to think of it as *our* bungalow.

I pulled a box of Borax and some rags from my bag. "I thought I'd give the place a shine," I said.

"Glad you could join the work party," Westry said, turning back to his saw.

By three, the floors were fit to eat from, and Westry had the door fastened in place.

"I almost forgot," he said, plucking a scuffed brass doorknob from his knapsack. "It will just take me a second to fit it."

I watched him attach the knob, carefully fastening the screws in their holes.

"Our key," he said, holding up a shiny piece of steel. "Now, if we can just find the right hiding place for it."

I pointed to the open-air windows. "But anyone who wants in can just climb on through."

Westry nodded. "Sure. We'll get the windows installed soon enough. Besides, every home needs a proper, working lock. But where to hide the key, that's the question."

I followed him outside the hut, and we looked around near the front step. "How about here?" I suggested, pointing to a spot in the sand. "We could bury it."

Westry shook his head. "It's the first place someone would look. It's like the welcome mat—every crook knows to go there first." He paused as an idea struck. "Wait," he continued, running back inside and returning with a book he'd pulled from his bag. "We'll use this."

"A book?"

"Yeah," he replied, pulling out the ribbon attached to the spine. Its purpose might have been to mark the page for a reader, but Westry had other plans. He tied the ribbon securely around the lip of the key, tucking it into the book. "There," he said, sliding the book below the step. "Our secret spot."

The waves were crashing loudly now. "The tide's coming in," he said. "Want to watch it with me?"

I hesitated. "I probably should be thinking about walking back." I hadn't left a note for Kitty, and I worried that she could be concerned.

"C'mon," Westry said. "You can stay a few more minutes."

"All right," I said, caving. "Just a few."

"There," he said, pointing to a piece of driftwood a few paces ahead on the beach. "Our perch."

He grabbed the wine bottle he'd found in the bungalow the day before and a tin cup from his knapsack and sat down next to me in the sand, our heads resting comfortably on the driftwood that had been smoothed into submission by the pulverizing surf. "A toast," he said, pouring the ancient wine into the cup. "To the lady of the bungalow."

He extended the cup to me, and I took a cautious sip, my face involuntarily contorting. "To sour hundred-year-old wine."

A bird sang in the distance as we sat together, mesmerized by the waves.

"I don't know anything about you," I said, turning to him a little abruptly.

"And I don't know anything about you," he retorted.

"You start."

Westry nodded and sat up. "I was born in Ohio," he began. "Didn't stay there long. Mother died of scarlet fever, and I moved west with my father, to San Francisco. He was an engineer, worked on the railroads. I tagged along with him, attending a different school every month."

"Far from a proper education," I said.

Westry shrugged. "I got a better one than most. I saw the country. I learned the way of the railways."

"And now what? After all of this, you said you wanted to come back here, to the island, but surely you have other aspirations, other things to attend to first?"

Westry's eyes were big and full of life, full of possibility.

"I'm not sure, exactly," he said. "I may go back to school, become an engineer, like Pop. Or maybe go to France, and learn to paint like the great impressionists. Or maybe I'll just stay here," he said, motioning with his head toward the bungalow.

"Oh, you can't do that," I said. "What a lonely life that would be!"

"Why would you call it lonely?" he countered. "I'd have everything I could possibly want. A roof over my head. A bed. The most beautiful scenery in the world. Some might call that paradise."

I thought about what he'd said about settling down and raising a family right there on the stretch of beach before us. "But what about companionship?" I said a little shyly. "What about . . . love?"

Westry grinned. "Easy for you to say. You already have that."

I looked at my feet, burrowing the tip of my shoe into the sand, which was so hot I could feel it radiating beneath the leather.

"Well," he continued, "I suppose I'll find her. Out there somewhere."

"What if you don't?" I asked.

"I will," he said, smiling at me confidently.

I turned away quickly.

"Now," he said, "let's hear about *you*."

I tugged at a loose thread on my bag until the silence felt strange. "Well, there isn't much to tell."

"I'm sure there is," Westry said with a leading smile. "Everyone has a story."

I shook my head. "I was born in Seattle. I lived there all my life. I got my nursing license, and now I'm here."

"And there you have it," he said dramatically. "An entire lifetime in three sentences."

I felt my cheeks get hot. "Sorry," I said. "I guess my life isn't quite as exciting as yours."

"I think you're bluffing," he said, sizing me up with his eyes. "The man you're engaged to," he continued, pointing to the ring on my hand, "why didn't you marry him before you left?"

*How dare he ask me such a question?* "Because I . . ." My voice trailed off without an answer. I thought of all the practical reasons: I didn't want to rush things; because Mother wanted a big affair at the Olympic Hotel; because . . . ; and yet, none were satisfactory. If I'd wanted, I could have marched down to City Hall, just like Gerard had suggested, and made it official. I could have become Mrs. Gerard Godfrey without a yearlong odyssey to the South Pacific as a hurdle that stood between us. *Why didn't I?*

"See?" Westry continued. "You do have a story."

"I assure you," I retorted, "you've created drama where there is none."

Westry winked. "We'll see."

⌒🐾

Kitty wasn't in the room when I returned, so when the mess hall bell rang, announcing dinner, I walked out of the barracks alone, making a quick stop in the infirmary to check on Mary, whom I was happy to find sitting up and sipping orange juice through a straw.

"Hi, Anne," she muttered from her bed. Her voice, still quite weak, had perked up. There was strength in it that hadn't been there this morning.

"Hi," I said. "I'm headed to dinner. I was just wondering if I could bring you anything. You must be tiring of the liquid diet."

"I am," she replied. "A roll and a few packages of butter would be divine."

"I'll take care of it," I said, smiling.

I walked back out to the path that led to the mess hall, passing the hibiscus bush where Kitty and I had plucked flowers that first night. I kept walking until I could see the recreation dock. A dozen canoes bound by rope tethers bobbed on the water, waiting for off-duty soldiers to take them out to sea. Few did, even though Bora-Bora was a relative safe haven from enemy attack—so far.

I looked closer and spotted two figures climbing out of a canoe. The tousled curls could have belonged to no other but Kitty, but the man helping her onto the dock wasn't Lance. I gasped when I saw instead the face of *Colonel Donahue*. She smiled sweetly at him as he stowed the paddles inside the canoe. They walked together, arm in arm, back up to the lawn, where he bid her adieu, and Kitty hurried along the trail back to the women's barracks.

*Should I run after her?* I decided not to; after all, she hadn't told me the truth about her date, and it was most likely because she thought I'd disapprove, *and I did*. But I couldn't have her thinking I was spying on her. No, she'd tell me in her own time. Instead, I turned back to the mess hall and spoke to the cook about getting a tray made up for Mary.

"How's Lance?" Stella coyly asked Kitty at breakfast. *Did she see her with the Colonel too?*

"Fine," Kitty said, picking at her scrambled eggs and grits, both the consistency of rubber. "We're seeing each other tonight."

Stella shook her head jealously, a gesture that might have put me on the defensive the day we met, but I had come to learn quickly that it was merely Stella's way. "My, do you have luck with men," she said, before sighing in defeat. "I've given up on Elliot. His head is much too tangled up with that woman from back home. He's either by himself taking photographs on the beach or holed up in the barracks writing poetry about her. She must be something else, that woman. Anyway, I met an airman last night. His name is Will, and he isn't half bad."

Liz approached our table with a tray and set it down. "Is Mary still on the mend?"

"Yes, thank God," I said. "She's much stronger today."

Liz gazed intently at an envelope she held in her hand. "This came for her today," she said cautiously. "And I can't help but notice the name on the return address. Didn't she say her ex-fiancé's name was *Edward*?"

I nodded. "Let me see it."

I held the envelope up to the light, unable to make out anything significant, just that the sender was indeed Edward. Edward Naughton, with a return address in Paris.

"Anne!" Kitty scolded. "You shouldn't read her mail. It's private."

"I will if I think it's going to compromise her recovery," I said. "Listen, if this man could leave her, almost at the altar, and send her into such a tailspin that she banished herself to a far-flung island on the other side of the world, imagine what a letter from him could do to her."

The other women nodded in agreement, and Kitty softened.

"Look," I said, "I'm not going to read it; I'm merely tucking it away until she's ready. Her heart is weak. She needs to regain her strength first. I won't let this letter conflict with her recovery."

"All right," Kitty said. "But you really shouldn't meddle when it comes to love."

**Is she giving me some kind of warning about her own life?**

I scrunched my nose in displeasure and tucked the envelope into the pocket of my dress for safekeeping. "I'm not *meddling*," I said directly to Kitty. "This is a matter of health."

Kitty pushed her plate aside. "Well, girls, I don't think I can stand another bite of these overcooked eggs. I'm heading to work. Nurse Hildebrand says we've got a live one coming in today."

I stewed about Kitty's comments as we walked to the infirmary that morning, but forgot about the interaction entirely when we got word that a medic had radioed from another island that a wounded pilot was en route. The pilot would be our first real patient, aside from Westry, who was mine alone.

The airman arrived at a quarter past ten. It was as serious a case as any one of us could have imagined—shrapnel wounds to the head. Kitty, first to wheel the soldier into the operating area, worked alongside the doctor with steady hands, removing bits of blood-covered metal and piling them on a plate beside the operating table. Liz excused herself to vomit, yet Kitty didn't flinch. She handled the procedure with such skill and ease that the doctor requested she stay on for another hour to assist with the patient's care. She quickly agreed.

After our shift ended, I walked back to the barracks, eager to escape the sterile infirmary and relax in the comfort of the bungalow. I packed a little bag and tucked in scissors, a needle and thread, and a bolt of pale yellow fabric I'd found in a trash barrel outside the infirmary. Perfect for curtains, I'd thought, snatching it up before the enlisted men could haul it away with the garbage collection.

Westry wasn't inside when I arrived, so I retrieved the key from the book, remembering how he'd thought of the hiding place, and unlocked the door, setting my bag down on the old mahogany chair.

I immediately got to work on the curtains, measuring the width of the windows and calculating the length and width of each panel. I laid out the fabric on the floor, shooing a baby lizard away as I did, and commenced cutting. I listened to the birds' songs as I hemmed the curtains. I didn't have an iron to press them, but the seams would be fine for a beach hut, and in time, the warm, misty air would soften their creases.

As I stitched, I thought of Westry, so spirited and spontaneous, so unlike Gerard and his consistent, measured ways. *Why can't Gerard be more free, more of a lover of life?* And yet, as I pushed my needle and thread through the fabric, I realized the concerns I had harbored about him in Seattle seemed only to fester in the tropics. In particular, his ability to sidestep the war gnawed at my conscience. *Why didn't he disagree with his father's wishes and do the honorable thing?*

I remembered the painting resting under the bed as I fitted the rod into the first set of curtains on the window. I wondered about the subjects of the canvas, but mostly I wondered about the artist.

*Who lived here so long ago? A man like Westry, with adventure in his soul?* I pictured Westry spending the rest of his days here on the island. Maybe he'd marry a native girl, like the one we'd met with Lance and Kitty at the market. *What was her name? Yes, Atea. But would he be happy then? Would a woman like that make him happy?* I grinned. *Yes, happy in* one *way, certainly, but would they be on the same intellectual plane?* Passion fades, yet love lives on. It's what I wished Kitty would come to believe.

Darkness fell on the bungalow just then, and I looked out the open-air window at gray, rain-soaked clouds looming in the sky, ready to drench the land below, whether it obliged or not. I scanned the beach, hoping I might see Westry bounding toward the bungalow, which is when I remembered the mailbox, or rather, the creaky floorboard in the corner. I walked over and lifted it, peering inside, and a white envelope caught my eye.

I tore it open with anticipation.

Dear Mrs. Cleo Hodge,

I suppose you're wondering who Mrs. Cleo Hodge is. Why, my dear, she is you. We need code names in case we're found out. Let's not forget, we are living in war times. So, you will be Cleo. I will be Grayson. What do you think? I considered the surname Quackenbush, but we'd fall to our knees in laughter every time we'd address each other and get nothing done. So, we shall be the Hodges, unless you have a better suggestion.

Yours,

Mr. Hodge

P.S. Look in the desk drawer. A surprise is waiting.

I giggled to myself, opening the drawer to find an orange. Its shiny, dimpled skin looked brilliant against the darkness of the mahogany drawer frame. I held it to my nose and inhaled the floral citrus scent before turning the letter over and writing a message to Westry:

Dear Mr. Grayson Hodge,

Today, I have been hard at work on the drapes, which I hope you will find satisfactory. Do you think we need a rug? A nice oriental? And how about a bookshelf and a place to sit, other than the bed? Perhaps, if we are lucky, a sofa will wash up on the shore. Thank you for the orange; it was perfect.

Yours,

Mrs. Hodge

P.S. Your imagination is uncanny. Where on earth did you come up with the name "Quackenbush"? I can hardly contain my laughter.

I tucked the note in the space below the floorboard and locked the door behind me. The wind had picked up since I had arrived, and the clouds overhead, now even darker, threatened rain. I hurried along the beach, nibbling on sections of the orange as I went.

I startled when, not far from the bungalow in the brush above the beach, I heard a rustling sound, causing every muscle, every tendon in my body to freeze. *What was that? Is someone following me?*

I took a few steps toward the jungle line, and waited. *There it is again, that sound. Rustling, and faint voices.* I crept closer, taking cover behind the base of a very large palm, and squinted. Two figures stood in the shadows of the lush jungle brush, one male, one female. Then I saw the telltale sleeve of an army dress shirt, and a bare female leg. I shrank back behind the palm before tiptoeing again onto to the beach and quickening my pace to a sprint, looking over my shoulder at every turn.

Once inside the room, I was disappointed to see that Kitty wasn't there waiting.

# Chapter 6

"Can you believe it's been two months since we arrived?" Mary marveled, her cheeks tinged a rosy pink. It was good to see the color, the life back in her face. She had insisted that Nurse Hildebrand let her work morning shifts instead of making her continue on bed rest. Despite intermittent trembling in her hands, Mary continued to gain strength, and she eagerly volunteered to assist me in a round of immunizations that morning.

"I know what you mean," I said. "It sometimes feels as if we arrived only yesterday." I paused to count the vials of vaccine we'd be giving the men after breakfast. "Yet, so much has happened already. I hardly feel like the same girl who stepped foot on that tarmac the first day."

Mary nodded. "Me too. It's hard to imagine life back there."

I sighed. "I've almost forgotten what Gerard's voice sounds like. Isn't that terrible?"

"Not really," Mary said. "You still love him."

"Yes, of course," I said with extra emphasis, feeling guilty for not yet taking the time to write him.

"I've almost forgotten Edward's voice," Mary added. "But that's definitely not terrible." She grinned, and I nodded in agreement.

I remembered the letter I'd been keeping from her. *Is she ready yet?* I listened to her hum as she unwrapped the packages of vaccine and set them on the trays. *That letter could spoil everything.*

"Where's Kitty?" Mary asked. "I thought I saw her here earlier this morning."

"Oh, she's here," I said. "We walked down together."

"No," Nurse Hildebrand grumbled. "She

said she wasn't feeling well, so I sent her back to the barracks."

*That's odd. She looked fine this morning.* I tried not to let my mind wander, but Kitty had been behaving strangely, almost since the moment we'd arrived on the island—saying she was going somewhere and turning up in another place; promising to meet me at breakfast or lunch only to disappear. She rarely spoke of Colonel Donahue, and I hadn't mentioned witnessing their boat trip. That ship seemed to have sunk, yet she spent far too much time with Lance. Yesterday they stayed out until nearly midnight. Jarred from slumber, I'd eyed the clock sleepily when she finally stumbled into bed.

"She must have caught the virus that's going around," Mary said. "A terrible stomach illness."

I didn't believe that Kitty had a stomach illness. No, something else was going on. Our shifts in the infirmary didn't leave room for meaningful conversation, now that more wounded men were arriving from nearby islands, where the fighting was thick. They trickled in slowly, but the cases were grim.

Knife wounds. Gunshots to the abdomen. And just yesterday, a nearly severed leg that needed an immediate amputation. The somber work of caring for fallen soldiers consumed our days, and when our shifts ended, we'd scatter like mice to our favorite hiding places. But where was Kitty's?

I thought about the other nurses. Stella had begun spending a lot of time in the recreation hall, where she'd taken a new interest in shuffleboard, or rather, in Will, who played shuffleboard. Of course, Liz dutifully tagged along. Mary, with little energy after a shift in the infirmary, went back to the barracks to read or write letters to friends at home, while I snuck away to the bungalow. Sometimes Westry would be there, sometimes not, but I always hoped to find him.

"Mail's here!" one of the nurses cried from the front door of the infirmary.

I left Mary with the vaccines and ventured over to the wooden crate filled with letters and parcels. Mail deliveries had been sparse. But this was a mountain of mail. It spilled out on the floor when I pushed

the crate closer to the table—so many letters, like covert submarines, infiltrating our
private world.

Stella received five; Liz, three; and Kitty,
just two, both from her mother. And then I
saw one addressed to me and I felt a familiar tugging at my heart when I recognized
the handwriting. *Gerard.*

I opened it discreetly, prepared to tuck it
away the moment Stella or another nurse
crept up.

My love,

The leaves are turning colors here, and
I miss you so. Why did you have to go
again?

Seattle is the same, just as you left it,
only it's lonelier without you. I suppose
the war has something to do with the
loneliness factor. It's all anyone can talk
about. I worry about you out there. There
will be great action in the Pacific. I pray
that your island will be shielded from it.
The military minds who I've spoken to
here believe it will be untouched. I pray
they are right.

The war has taken the best of us. It's a ghost town at the Cabaña Club. You wouldn't recognize the place. Every able-bodied man has either joined up or been drafted, and I wanted you to know that even after all Father has done to protect me from the fight, I can't help but wonder if I should join too. It would be the right thing to do. The next wave of troops ships out on the 15th of October, and I'm thinking about voiding my exemption and going with them. I'd be spending two weeks in basic training at a base in California before heading to Europe.

Please do not worry about me. I will write you often to tell you how I am, and will dream of the day when we are reunited.

I love you with all my heart and think of you more than you know.

Yours,

Gerard

I held the letter to my heart and blinked hard. As much as I reveled in his burst of patriotism, I hated to think of him in danger, and cringed when I thought about the lapse in time between his sending the letter and my receiving it. *Could he be on a battlefield right now? Could he could be . . . ?*

I felt an arm on my back after I'd slumped over in my chair, trying to hide my tears from the other women. "What's the matter, dear?" Mary asked softly.

"It's Gerard," I said. "I think he signed up."

Mary patted my back as my tears dotted the crumpled paper in my hands, smearing Gerard's beautiful handwriting into patches of muddled black ink.

❧

"What do you think it would be like to be a military wife?" Kitty asked me that night before bed. She sat in a pink cotton nightgown on top of her bunk, brushing her blond curls—and clearly feeling just fine—as I tried, unsuccessfully, to read.

I set the book down. "You can't be saying you're already thinking of marrying Lance, are you?"

Kitty didn't answer; she just continued brushing her hair. "I suppose the lifestyle could have its benefits," she said. "All the traveling and the excitement."

"Kitty, but you've only just met him," I said.

The evenings were the only time we talked anymore—at least, those evenings when Kitty wasn't out with Lance.

Kitty set her brush down on her bedside table and climbed into her bed, pulling the coverlet up to her neck, before turning to me. "Anne," she said. Her voice was childlike, curious, naive, tremulous. "Did you always know that Gerard was the one?"

The question caught me off guard in a way it wouldn't have in Seattle. "Well, yes, of course I did," I said, remembering his letter from earlier today. My devotion to him swelled. "I just knew."

Kitty nodded. "I think I have the same feeling," she said, turning her head to the wall before I could question her. "Good night."

Westry had been away on a mission to another island for thirty days, and when he returned on November 27, I waited near the men's barracks, pretending to gather hibiscus, in hopes of meeting him on the pathway. It was Wednesday, the day before Thanksgiving, and the buzz in camp revolved around two things: turkey and cranberry sauce.

"Hey, you, nurse!" one of the men shouted from a third-story window. "Do you think we'll get a bird?"

"Do I look like the cook?" I said sarcastically.

The soldier, barely nineteen, if that, smirked and recoiled. It had taken me months to become comfortable with the ways of men and war. No longer shy, I grunted at those who grunted at me and greeted inappropriate remarks with retorts that leveled the playing field. Mother would have been beside herself.

Twenty minutes of flower picking resulted in no Westry sighting, so I retreated to the barracks with a heavy heart and a bag full of hibiscus.

"The mail came," Kitty said, tossing an envelope on the bed. "It's from your mother."

I shrugged and tucked the envelope into my dress pocket as Kitty peeked into the flower-filled bag I'd set by the door. "They're gorgeous," she said. "Let's get them in water."

She plucked the blossoms from the bag and arranged them, one by one, in the water glass on her dressing table.

"They'll never keep," I said. "They're a terrible cutting flower. They'll wilt by morning."

"I know," she said. "But don't they look so pretty *right now*, just as they are?"

I nodded. I wished I could see the beauty in the moment the way Kitty did. It was a gift.

She stood back and marveled at the makeshift vase, packed with bright red blooms that would be limp by the time we came back from dinner, before glancing at her bedside table. "I almost forgot," she said. "I also got a letter from home. From Father."

Kitty tore the edge of the envelope and pulled out the letter, reading at first with a grin. But then a frown appeared, and a look of shock. Tears began a slow trickle down her cheeks.

"What is it?" I asked, running to her side. "What does it say?"

She threw herself on the bed, burying her face in the pillow.

"Kitty," I persisted, "tell me."

She didn't budge, so I picked up the pages of the letter that had fallen to the ground and read it myself, in the words of her father.

> You should know, love, that Mr. Gelfman left for war in September, to Europe, and I'm afraid he was killed. I know this news is going to be hard for you to hear. Your mother did not want me to write of it, but I felt you should know.

I tucked the letter into Kitty's dressing table. *The damned mail. Why does it come and haunt us the way it does? We were getting along fine until the letters started arriving.* "Kitty," I said, leaning my face into hers. "I'm so sorry."

"Just let me be," she said quietly.

"I'll bring dinner up for you," I said, hearing the sound of the mess hall bell.

"I'm not hungry," she whimpered.

"I'll bring it anyway."

I heaped a pile of mashed potatoes on my plate and, with the cook's permission, I got an extra plate for Kitty, followed by sliced carrots and boiled ham that looked curled and dry under the warming lights. Still, at least it wasn't canned. I was glad of that.

Stella and Mary waved at me from the nurses' table, and I nodded and walked toward them. "I'm just grabbing a tray for Kitty and myself, to take back to the room. Kitty got a letter from home today. A bad one."

Mary frowned. "I'm sorry to hear it," she said. "Can you sit for a minute, though? You can't juggle both of those trays on the path back. You'll trip. Why don't you eat first?"

I thought it over, then agreed, sitting down next to Mary.

"They say there was a fight in the barracks today," Stella said in a hushed voice. "This island's really wearing on the men."

"It's wearing on all of us," I replied, attempting to cut the tough slice of ham with a dull knife.

Stella nodded. "I saw Lance at the

market yesterday. He had his arm around that girl, that native."

I was grateful Kitty wasn't present. She'd experienced enough heartbreak for one day. "You mean *Atea*," I said. "She has a name." It irritated me that Stella held the island's indigenous population in such low regard.

"I guess that was her name," she said with a shrug. "Lance sure has a thing for her."

Mary looked doubtful. "Oh, Stell," she said. "Just because he gets his cigarettes from her doesn't mean he's carrying on with her."

Stella shrugged. "I'm just telling you what I saw."

**Poor Kitty. I won't tell her. Not yet. She needs time.**

"All right, girls," I said, retrieving Kitty's tray, "I'm off to deliver a meal."

"Good night," Mary said.

Stella nodded and sank her teeth into a biscuit.

I waved flies from the tray as I followed the trail, pausing for a moment in front of the men's barracks, hoping, in vain, to find Westry gazing down from a window. Was his bunk on the second floor or the fourth? I scanned the second floor and my eyes stopped at an open window toward the middle of the building. There was rustling and movement inside. *A fight.* "Yes, sir!" a voice rang out. "Please, sir!" It was *Westry's* voice.

*My God! He's hurt. He's being beaten.* I set the tray down on a bench and walked to the entrance to the barracks. I had to help him. But how? Women weren't allowed inside. I stood on the steps in desperation, listening to the sound of flesh pounding flesh and furniture breaking. *Stop. It has to stop.*

A moment later, it did. A door slammed, then heavy footsteps pounded in the hallway and down the stairs to the entrance of the barracks. My stomach turned when Colonel Donahue appeared in the doorway, clutching a bloodied hand. I shrank back against the hibiscus and watched as he walked directly to the infirmary.

My heart raced. "Westry!" I called out, in a panic. "Westry!" I said louder, pitching my voice into the open window.

There was only silence, and I feared the worst.

I ran to the mess hall, where many of the men were still eating, and found Elliot at a table near the entrance. His eyes met mine, and I motioned for him to come over.

"What is it, Anne?" he said, releasing a cloth napkin from his collar.

"It's Westry," I whispered. "He was beaten. By Colonel Donahue. He's in his room. He may be unconscious." My words shot out of my mouth like rapid fire.

Elliot's eyes widened. "I'll go," he said, pushing through the double doors and sprinting out to the trail.

I waited outside the barracks for a long while, alternately pacing and peering up at the second floor, trying to catch a glimpse through the window. Then I heard the door open and Elliot stepped outside.

"He's been beaten pretty bad," he said. "A laceration across his forehead's going to need stitches."

"Why won't he come down, then?" I said.

"He won't," Elliot continued.

"I don't understand. Why did Colonel Donahue do that to him?"

"He won't talk about it," he said, looking down the trail where the colonel had exited. "But something bad must have happened. Something's not right."

I rubbed my hand along my forehead. "Can you stay with him, then? Make sure he's OK, try to get him to go to the infirmary to get stitched up?"

Elliot nodded. "I'll do my best," he said, turning back to the door.

"Thanks," I replied. "And Elliot?"

"Yes?"

"Tell him I miss him."

Elliot grinned. "He'll like that."

Kitty's dinner tray was cold by the time I returned to the room, but it didn't matter. She still refused food.

"Can I do anything for you, dear?" I said, stroking her soft curls.

"No," she said meekly. "I just need to be alone."

"Yes," I replied, a little hurt. "I understand."

The sun had set, but the moon overhead provided an alluring amount of light. I eyed my knapsack. *The bungalow.* It's where I needed to be; my heart felt it.

"Kitty," I said softly, tucking a book into my bag. "I'm stepping out for a while."

She didn't answer, but I didn't fault her.

"I'll be back soon," I said, closing the door behind me.

The wind blew stronger than it usually did, tousling my hair as I trudged along the sand toward the bungalow. When I arrived, I unlocked the door and lay down on the bed. The new quilt I'd brought last week, found on the top shelf of our bedroom closet, felt warm and comforting on my weary body. I didn't bother checking the mailbox. Westry hadn't been back long enough to visit, and now he was holed up in the barracks nursing his wounds. I shuddered at the thought of Colonel Donahue's brutality. *Why did he hurt him so?* Whatever the reason, I was sure Westry hadn't deserved it.

I propped up the pillow behind my head and pulled out the letter from Mother that I'd tucked inside my pocket earlier.

My dearest Anne,

I write with a heavy heart, for it is I who must relate the most terrible news to you. Believe me, I pondered, for a very long time, whether to write you with this news or wait until you return. But, I feel you must know.

I am leaving your father. The circumstances are much too grave to discuss in a letter, but I will only say that despite our separation, I will love you as much as I always have. I will explain everything when you come home.

May your marriage to Gerard be more love-filled than mine has been.

I love you dearly and I hope this news doesn't hurt too much.

With love,

Mother

I felt the sting of salty tears in my eyes. *She's leaving Papa. Poor Papa. How could she?* "May your marriage to Gerard be more love-filled than mine has been." *What kind of rubbish is that?*

I heard a sound outside on the beach, followed by the slow creak of the bungalow door opening. My heart calmed when I saw Westry's face.

"I hoped you'd be here," he said, grinning.

"Look at you!" I exclaimed, ignoring my

inhibitions and running to his side, where I instinctively reached my hand out to caress his cheek. "Why did Colonel Donahue hurt you?"

"Listen," he said firmly, "I need to make myself clear. You did not see Colonel Donahue today."

"But I did—"

"No," he said. "You didn't."

"But Westry, why?"

He looked conflicted and pained. "Please, don't ever mention it again."

I frowned. "I don't understand."

"It has to be this way," he said. "You'll understand someday." His face caught the light and I could see the severity of his wounds.

"You must let me take you to the infirmary."

Westry flashed a devious smile. "Now, why would I do that, when I have my very own nurse right here?"

I grinned, reaching for my knapsack. "Well, I should have a first-aid kit in here somewhere." I riffled through the bag until I found the little white case stocked with nursing essentials, then removed the suture set. I opened a white packet, pulling out an alcohol-soaked square of gauze. "This might sting a little."

I took his hand, feeling the familiar flutter inside when our skin touched, and led him to the bed. *What does it matter if we both sit here?* "Now," I said when we were seated, "hold still."

Elliot had been right. The laceration on his forehead was deep, and I doubted my ability to stitch it up. "It looks bad," I said, dabbing the wound with the gauze. Westry flinched but didn't say anything.

"You know," I said nervously, "we have a topical numbing cream at the infirmary. Let's go there. It will be less painful for you."

I began to stand up, but Westry reached for my hand and pulled me back. "I don't want to go," he said. "I want to stay. Right here."

His eyes were intense, tender. I nodded and picked up the suture set. "All right, but this may hurt a bit."

Westry stared at the wall ahead as I made one stitch and then two. A third was all I needed to close the gap. I tied it firmly then snipped the edge. "There," I said. "Now, that wasn't too bad, was it?"

Westry shook his head. "You're a natural,

Cleo Hodge," he said teasingly, gazing into my eyes with a look of concern. I smiled, then quickly turned away.

"You've been crying," he said. "Why?"

I thought of the letter from Mother. "Just some disturbing mail from home."

"What did it say?"

I hesitated. "It was from my mother. She's"—I choked back the tears that were coming again—"she's leaving my father."

He reached out and pulled me toward him; his arms wrapped around my back, and the side of my head nestled into his chest. I felt protected, encircled. "I'm so sorry," he said. His words reverberated in the little bungalow, floating on the air for some time, for neither of us spoke again for a great while.

I looked up to face Westry. He was here. Present. Now. And in that moment, nothing else mattered.

His hands moved up my arms, along my shoulders toward my neck and to my cheeks, where they pulled my face toward his. I felt something new stir inside me. Westry pressed his lips against mine so delicately, so perfectly. He pulled me closer, weakening any lingering resistance.

He held me in his arms, cradling me. November 27. It was an insignificant date, just a blip on the calendar. But it was also a life-changing occasion. It was the day I started loving Westry.

# Chapter 7

The sun beat down without reprieve, which seemed unfair, given that it was Christmas Eve. At home, Mother would be trimming an enormous fir tree in the entryway. I could almost smell the evergreen, even if it was a figment, both because there were only palms in sight and because Mother had moved out of the house. Her most recent letter indicated that she'd taken an apartment in New York.

I thought of how jolly Papa was this time of the year, offering big mugs of mulled cider to carolers, stuffing Maxine's pastries and cookies into his mouth at every turn.

*Maxine.* I'd wondered more than a few times why she hadn't written. The mail had slowed altogether, though, and the women waited expectantly every afternoon, hoping to catch sight of a jeep barreling across the lawn with a special delivery.

I hadn't heard from Gerard, which concerned me most of all. His silence had been welcome in some ways, leaving a place for my feelings for Westry to grow undisturbed. And yet, I worried about him every day, imagining him on a cold foreign battlefield, fighting for America. Fighting for me.

Kitty had grown to accept the death of Mr. Gelfman, though she didn't talk about it. Instead, she seemed to invest every fiber of her being in Lance. She frequently slipped off to meet him and stayed out much too late. But who was I to judge?

And suddenly it was Christmas Eve. I had time to head to the beach before the candlelight service at the chapel later that night, so I snuck away before Nurse Hildebrand could recruit me to help unpack the new shipment of supplies.

I was disappointed to find the bungalow empty. Westry had been on three missions in the past month, and I'd seen very little of him. I checked the mailbox under the floor-board, and giggled when I found an enve-lope waiting for me.

My darling Cleo,

Merry Christmas, my dear. I'm sorry we haven't seen much of each other lately. My commanding officer seems to have taken on all the qualities of a slave driver. I had hoped to meet you here this morn-ing, the only time I could break away, but no luck. So I will leave your Christmas present here for you to find. Maybe some-day we'll have a real Christmas together.

Yours,

Grayson

My eyes welled up with tears as I read the last line over again. "Maybe someday we'll have a real Christmas together." *Will we?* The idea was frightening and exciting at the same time. My fingers worked fast to untie the red ribbon from the little box wait-ing below the floorboard, wrapped beauti-fully with tinfoil he must have stolen from the mess hall. I lifted the lid and found a gold, oval locket on a delicate chain. The inside was empty, but on the back, the inscription read: *Grayson and Cleo*.

I smiled, clasping the chain around my neck proudly, before producing a pen and a notebook from my bag.

My darling Grayson,

Thank you for the necklace. I love it. Do you know that in my 21 years, I have never owned a locket? I have always wanted one, and I will be very proud to wear it. In fact, I don't think I shall ever take it off. My mind is filled with ideas about what to put inside. You'll have to help me decide.

I miss you so much, but being here helps. For even when we are apart, I can find you here. Your presence lingers in these four walls, and it warms me.

Merry Christmas.

With love,

Cleo

The mail arrived that evening, just before the Christmas Eve service. I eyed the crate with suspicion and caution, especially after Mother's last letter, which had been so surprising, so jarring. Leaving Papa with no explanation. Surely there was more to the story.

"Just one for you today, dear," Mary said, handing me a light pink envelope.

*Pink.* I felt my heart lighten. *Definitely not from Gerard.* I hated myself for feeling a sense of relief. It wasn't that I *didn't* want to hear from him. No, it was more complicated than that. I looked at the handwriting, so elegant, so perfect, and the return address on the envelope. *Maxine.* I tucked the envelope in the pocket of my dress and turned to the door. But when I heard church bells chiming from the chapel in the distance, I turned back around to see Nurse Hildebrand consumed in paperwork at her desk. *What will she be doing on this strange island, all alone, on Christmas Eve?* She never spoke of family, and if what the girls said was true, her past hadn't been a happy one. *She must be lonely this time of the year.* It was true that she hardly smiled or opened her mouth unless it was to bark orders at us. But it was Christmas. No one could be alone on Christmas. *Has anyone invited her to the candlelight service?*

I approached Nurse Hildebrand quietly. "Excuse me, Nurse Hildebrand," I began cautiously. "I'm leaving for the night. It's Christmas Eve—"

"I'm aware of the date," she snapped.

I nodded submissively. "It's just that I wanted to, er . . ."

"Make your point, Nurse Calloway," she said. "Can't you see I'm busy?"

"Yes," I said, "I'm sorry. It's just that I wondered if you knew about the candlelight service tonight. I thought you might like to attend, that's all."

She turned away from her files and looked at me for a moment—a good, hard look of amusement and maybe confusion, too.

"Run along, Nurse Calloway," she said briskly. "Your shift is over."

I nodded and walked back to the door, trying to hide my disappointment. *What does it matter?*

❧

Kitty had promised to go with me to the service that night, but she wasn't in the room when I got back. After fifteen minutes of waiting and no sign of a note of explanation, I gave up and went to the closet to find something to wear, which is when I noticed that her yellow dress was missing—the one that clung to her body a little too suggestively. *Where is she going in that dress?* I chose a simple blue frock for myself, then retrieved Maxine's letter.

My dear Antoinette,

How are you, my dear? My, how I have missed you. The home isn't the same with you away. It's lonelier. It lacks life.

So much has changed since you left, and I'm afraid I don't know where to begin. But, we have always been honest with one another, so I will start with the truth. Bear with me, because the next few sentences may be very hard to take.

You must know, my dear, that I have loved your father for a very long time. It has been a love that I have fought, with all of my might, with all of my soul. But, you can't fight love. I know that now.

I never intended for this love to tear your family apart. And for many years,

I was successful at hiding my feelings away, bottling them up so efficiently that even I was fooled. And yet, when I learned that your father returns my love, it pried open that cork that I'd been so diligent about keeping intact. It changed everything.

I do not know if you will ever speak to me again, or look at me in the same way you once did, but I pray that you will find it in your heart to forgive me. Your father and I want nothing more than your blessing.

After the war, we're going to France to be married. I know this probably sounds so strange and sudden. Give it time, dear Antoinette. For in time, I pray that we can be a family again.

With love,

Maxine

The pages drifted out of my hands, effortlessly, and fell onto the quilt on my bed, where I stared at them, studying Maxine's cursive. *Why does she loop her y's in such a strange way?* And that stationery, with the embossed edges—it was Mother's. *Who does she think she is? The lady of the house?*

Maxine and Papa. It didn't add up. *Have they loved each other my entire life? Did my mother know? No wonder she has been so cruel to Maxine—Papa's mistress living under her own roof. Poor Mother! How did I not notice it? How have I been so naive?*

I picked up the pages, crumpling them into a tight ball and tossing it into the wastebasket. I didn't need to read it again. I didn't want to see it again. And when I walked out to the hallway outside the room, I startled myself with the force with which I closed the door.

If Kitty wasn't coming, I'd go to the service alone. I couldn't stay in on Christmas Eve thinking about Papa and Maxine roasting chestnuts together back at home. I shook my head, and made my way down to the foyer. But before I could push open the doors and step outside, my ears perked up. Someone in a room upstairs must have found a radio, and even rarer, a signal out across the great blue ocean that carried the sweet, beautiful, pure sound of "O Holy Night" sung by Bing Crosby. My knees weakened as I listened to the song drifting over the airwaves like a warm breeze, comforting me, reminding me of Christmases in Seattle. With cider. Carolers. An enormous fir tree in the entryway. Papa smoking by the fire. Mother fussing about wrapping gifts. Maxine's sweets, though I didn't have the taste for them now. And Gerard, of course. I couldn't forget Gerard.

"Makes you feel sentimental, doesn't it?"

I turned around upon hearing Stella's voice behind me. "Yes," I said. *If she only knew.*

Her face appeared softer in the dim light of the entryway. *Has the island changed her?* "It hardly feels right," she continued. "No snow. Not even a tree. For the first time, I'm homesick. Really homesick."

"Me too," I said, locking my arm in hers. We stood there listening until the song ended and the radio frequency became garbled—the moment lost forever, swallowed up by the lonely Pacific.

"Are you going to the service?" Stella asked.

"Yes," I said. "I was just coming back to get Kitty. We planned to walk over together."

"Oh, I almost forgot to tell you," she said.

"Tell me what?"

"Kitty asked me to pass along a message that she's terribly sorry, but Lance had some special Christmas date planned for her tonight and she won't be able to attend."

"A *date*? On *Christmas Eve*?"

Stella shrugged. "You'd know better than I would. Seems like those two are spending an awful lot of time together, doesn't it? Every time I pass Kitty in the hallway, she says she's off to see Lance. Lance this, Lance that. But if you ask me, he's hardly worthy of her affection. The man is dangerous."

"Dangerous?"

"Yes," she said. "Everyone knows how he carries on with the *native* girls. Besides, that man has a temper the size of the USS *Missouri*."

I remembered the way Atea had looked at him, and the instinct I'd had about him shortly after. But I hadn't seen his temper flare. Could he really be *dangerous*?

"Well," I said, "he may have a wayward eye, but it's Kitty's prerogative. I've tried to get through to her about men before, and believe me, it doesn't work."

"You're a good friend, Anne," Stella said, eyeing me with a look of admiration.

I thought of my secrets. "Not as good as I should be."

"Want to head over to the chapel with me?" she asked, glancing at the clock in the hallway, which read a quarter past seven. "Mary and Liz are already there setting up. We can go meet them."

I smiled. "I'd love to."

As we walked outside, the radio's signal regrouped and began transmitting a weak version of "Silent Night" sung in a foreign language I didn't recognize. It sounded strange and lost, which was exactly how I felt.

⸎

Once inside the little chapel adjacent to the mess hall I let out a gasp. "Where on earth did they get a tree?" I eyed the fir standing at attention near the piano. "A Douglas fir, in the tropics?"

Mary grinned. "It was our big secret," she said. "The Social Committee has been planning it for months. One of the pilots brought it over with the supplies last week. Nobody thought of decorations so we had to get creative. The men deserve a tree on Christmas."

The choir began warming up to our left, as I looked at the fir tree, adorned with tinsel—handmade from finely cut tin foil—and red apples on each bow. Some of the women must have loaned out their hair ribbons, as there were at least two dozen white satin bows from top to bottom.

"It's beautiful," I said, blinking back a tear.

Mary draped her arm around me. "Everything all right, Anne?"

The choir, which was nothing more than a group of volunteer soldiers cobbled together by a lieutenant who was a music teacher back home, began singing "O Come, All Ye Faithful," and the hair on my arms stood on end. I closed my eyes and could see Gerard's face smiling at me with his kind, trusting gaze. Maxine and Papa looked on too, beseeching me for forgiveness as Kitty waved in the distance. And Westry was there in the midst. He stood on the beach, watching them all. Waiting.

I felt my legs weaken and my body sway, as Mary pulled me toward a pew. "You need to sit down," she said, fanning my face with a hymnal. "You're not looking good." Then she snapped, "Stella! She needs water."

The room seemed blurry and the choir sounded as if it were singing the same lines over and over again. *O come let us adore him, o come let us adore him; O come let us adore him . . .*

Somebody handed me a mug and I took a sip, letting the water seep down my throat. "Sorry," I said self-consciously. "I don't know what happened."

"You're working too hard," said Mary. "That's what happened. I'm going to speak to Nurse Hildebrand about this. Look at you. Pale, thin. Did you eat dinner tonight?"

I shook my head.

Mary searched inside her purse until she found a candy bar. "Here," she said. "Eat this."

"Thank you."

Men began filing in, removing their hats at the door, and Stella nestled in next to us, followed by Liz. Partway through the service, I turned around to see if Kitty had come late, but instead I noticed Nurse Hildebrand seated in the back. She had a handkerchief in her hand, but quickly stuffed it into her dress pocket when her eyes met mine.

Shortly after the candles were lit and the choir began "Hark! the Herald Angels Sing," I heard some commotion and turned toward the back of the chapel. A door slammed. People shuffled in their seats. A nurse in the pew behind us let out a loud gasp.

"What's going on?" I whispered to Stella, unable to get a good view of the scene through the crowd.

"That's what's going on," she said smugly, pointing at the center aisle.

There, walking toward us, was Atea— bare-breasted, beautiful Atea, with tears rolling down her face. She looked just as striking as she had the day at the market, though now her face was clouded in distress.

"Where is he?" she screamed, looking from left to right, scanning the pews. "Why he not here?"

One of the men stood up and took her arm. "Don't you see that you're disturbing this Christmas Eve service, miss?"

She wrenched her arm away from him. "Don't touch me! Where is he? He lie. I find him. I tell everyone."

The soldier regained his grip, this time tighter, and attempted to pull her toward the door. Atea screamed.

"Stop!" I shouted, waving my arms. I felt the blood rush from my head, but I steadied myself on the side of the pew. "I know this woman. Let me speak to her."

No one seemed to object, so I walked over to Atea and smiled warmly. Her big brown eyes, red from crying, searched my face for understanding, for trustworthiness.

"Would you like to talk outside?" I asked as if we were the only two people in the building.

She nodded and followed me through the double doors outside. We walked in silence along the gravel pathway that led to the beach. The wind was brisk, but neither of us minded.

Atea led me to a log on the beach, and we both sat down.

"I am fear," she said.

"You mean, you're *afraid*?"

She nodded.

"What, dear? What are you afraid of?"

"Him," she said simply.

*Lance.* My cheeks burned with anger. Stella had been right.

I nodded. "What did he do to you, Atea?"

"He hurt me," she said, pointing to a bruise on her wrist and another on her upper arm, purple and black.

"I'm so sorry," I said. "But why did you come here, to the chapel, tonight?"

Her eyes swelled with tears. "I tell everyone what he did," she said, "then he no hurt me again."

"Atea," I said, "you must leave this base. If he wants to harm you, he'll find a way. You must leave and stay far away."

She looked confused. "Where can I go?"

"Do you have someone you can stay with? Your mother? A grandmother? An aunt?"

Atea shook her head. "No," she said. "I have no one, except Tita."

"Who is Tita?"

"The oldest woman on Bora-Bora. She take care of all of us."

I nodded. Suddenly my own problems seemed unimportant. "Well," I said, "you can't stay here."

She looked unsettled about something. "But what will I do when he comes?"

"What do you mean, 'when he comes'?"

"He will come."

I patted her arm. "See that white building in the distance, and the window on the corner of the second floor, just near the palm?"

"Yes," she said meekly.

"That's my room. You call up to me when you need something, when you're afraid. We always leave the window open. I'll hear you."

She searched my face with her big, trusting eyes. "What if you not there?"

"Then run down this beach," I said, pointing my finger toward the shore. "About a half mile up there's a bungalow, a little hut a few steps into the thicket. The door is locked, but you'll find the key under a book beneath the steps. No one knows about it here. You'll be safe there."

Atea's eyes grew big. "The artist's home?"

I shook my head, confused. "I'm not sure I know what you mean."

"Yes, the painter. No one goes there. Tita say it's haunting."

**"Haunted?"**

"Yes."

"And do you believe it's haunted?" I asked.

Atea shrugged. "Maybe, but I go there if I must."

"Good girl."

Atea smiled.

"You're going to be fine," I said. "Everything will be fine. I'll see to that."

"Really?" Her eyes searched mine. She looked so beautiful, yet so innocent and afraid. I vowed to protect her. I'd speak to Westry about Lance. I'd make sure he never hurt her again.

"Really," I assured her.

She exhaled deeply and stood up to leave.

"Atea, there's something else," I said. "If you see Lance, you mustn't tell him about your visiting the base, or your chat with me. It will only anger him."

She looked confused, but nodded.

"Good night," I said.

"*Taoto maitai*," she said before disappearing into the moonlight.

# Chapter 8

The morning sun was bright, streaming through the window with such force that two aggressive beams of light pushed through the curtains and danced unabashedly on the closet door. Kitty and I watched the rays from our beds.

"Can you imagine having a bright morning like this in Seattle—in January?" I said, turning to Kitty.

"No," she answered in a flat voice. "I miss the cold. I'm tired of all this sun."

"I don't know that I could ever tire of it," I said, sitting up and reaching for my robe draped over the foot of the bed. "Kitty? Can I confide in you?"

"Yes," she replied.

"I'm worried."

"Worried about what?" Her eyes looked tired, but not just because it was early. Deep exhaustion punctuated her face. We hadn't spoken of Lance since Christmas Day, when I'd told Kitty about what Atea had said. I'd warned her about Lance and yet the news hardly fazed her. Things were over between the two of them, or so it seemed. As each day passed, she grew quieter and more introspective, and I grew more concerned. Had Lance hurt her in the same way he'd hurt Atea?

"I'm worried that this island has changed us," I said.

Instead of looking at me, Kitty looked *through* me, right on to the wall behind my back. "It *has* changed us," she said simply.

"Kitty, it's just that I—" I stopped when I heard a sudden knock at the door.

"Who is it?" I called out.

"It's me, Mary."

I cinched the tie on my robe and opened the door to find Mary rosy cheeked and beaming. "Morning, lovelies," she said, poking her head into the room to catch Kitty's eye, with little success.

Mary had regained her strength after her bout with malaria, and she now hummed in the infirmary while the rest of us grumbled. Stella said Mary had been seeing a man named Lou, though Mary hadn't let on yet. I hoped it was true. She deserved happiness.

I felt a pang in my heart just then. *The letter. Mary's letter, from her ex-fiancé.* I looked at the shoe box under my bedside table, remembering that I'd hidden it there, promising myself I'd give it to her when I felt she was ready. I lifted the lid and reached inside the box and Gerard's most recent letter fell out onto the floor. My cheeks flushed and I hurriedly stowed it away. *How could Mary face her past if I couldn't even face mine?*

"I wanted to invite you to a little soiree tonight," Mary continued. Her eyes sparkled the way eyes do when one is in love, or rather, in *new* love. "A group of us are getting together tonight for a cookout on the beach. Stella, Liz, a few of the other nurses, and some of the men too. We're all piling into a truck at seven thirty for Leatra Beach. I think Westry's coming too, Anne."

She gave me a knowing look that I did not return. I hadn't spoken to Westry in three weeks, and I feared there was a silence growing between us. Sure, his commanding officer had kept him busy. Very busy. But I hardly found him in the bungalow anymore, even when I knew he was off duty.

Leatra Beach. It was just a stone's throw from the bungalow. Our bungalow. I felt my chest tighten. *What am I worried about?* Of course, no one would find it. No one knew it was there, except Westry and me. In fact, it sometimes felt that the little hut was visible only to us. And we spoke of that very thing the last time we were together there, when we'd spotted a soldier passing by on the normally quiet beach. The sound of his whistling sent shivers down my spine. Would he see the bungalow? Would he see us? I realized then how very much I loved this private little world of ours, and how much I hoped to keep it that way.

"Someone's coming," I had whispered in a panic to Westry.

We watched from the window that looked out upon the beach as the man stumbled along the white sand. Probably drunk. The soldiers drank too much, and the island heat only amplified their intoxication.

"The coast is clear," Westry said a few moments later. "He didn't see us."

*But why didn't he see us?* The bungalow wasn't too far off the beach, only loosely hidden by palm fronds. Anyone with an ounce of curiosity would see it on second glance. So why hadn't others found it? How had it gone unnoticed after all these years and with an army base populated by a couple thousand men just down the shore? These were the questions that made me wonder if the bungalow was merely a figment. Our figment, a mirage in the French Polynesian sun custom made for Westry and me.

"So," Mary said expectantly, "will you come?"

I glanced back at Kitty. She looked disinterested, distant. "I'll go," I said hesitantly, "but only if Kitty joins me."

Kitty looked startled. "Oh, no," she said, shaking her head. "No, I can't."

"Why not?"

Kitty provided no explanation, just silence.

I folded my arms and forced a grin. "See? You don't even have a good excuse," I said, before turning back to Mary. "We're going."

"Perfect," she said. "Meet us down in the parking lot at seven thirty."

Kitty joined me, reluctantly. I took a good, long look at her before we left the room. What had changed about her? True, the color had left her cheeks, and her hair, always wild, was even wilder now, untamable. She didn't even stop to catch her reflection in the little oval mirror in our bedroom. And if she had, I wasn't certain that she'd even be able to see the change. It wasn't only her hair, but her figure. Last week, I'd heard Stella whispering to Liz in the mess hall about Kitty taking a second helping of mashed potatoes. "She's going to go home fifteen pounds heavier," she had said. Kitty did look plumper now, but her beauty still shone through the mussy hair, pale cheeks, and rounder appearance. Kitty would be beautiful no matter what.

"You look pretty," I said as we walked out of the barracks that evening.

"No I don't," she said. I didn't like the defeat in her voice.

"Stop it," I chided her. "I wish you would snap out of this mood you're in." I turned to face her. "I miss my old friend."

Kitty stopped suddenly on the trail, and when I looked up, I could see why. Colonel Donahue was approaching. He tipped his cap at us, but didn't say a word. A sick feeling came over me as I remembered the incident with Westry. That incident had made me despise the colonel, but seeing the way he dismissed Kitty, without so much as a "Hello, how are you, Kitty?"—especially after the interest he'd taken in her when we'd arrived months ago—well, it made me fume. He was rumored to be seeing one of the other nurses—quiet, with dark hair and a figure that rivaled a pinup girl's. *He ought to be ashamed of himself.*

When the colonel was a safe distance away, I turned to Kitty. "I've never liked that man."

Kitty looked sad, which made me wonder if I'd said the wrong thing. "I didn't mean to—"

She reached for my hand and squeezed it tightly. "It's all right, Anne. You don't need to apologize. It's just that . . ." She paused, as if to collect her thoughts, or maybe to consider if anyone was listening from an open window in the distance. The men's barracks were nearing. "It's nothing."

"I wish you'd tell me," I said. "Are you sad about the colonel's new girlfriend? Stella says she's a real dimwit. Or is it Lance? Kitty, did something happen? Did he hurt you?"

She shook her head. "Anne, please don't."

"All right," I said, "but will you tell me when you're ready?"

Kitty nodded, but I feared it was an empty promise.

Just ahead, I spotted some of the men and women piling into a truck. Stella was there, with Will by her side, as was Liz, and Mary, with her new beau, Lou.

Kitty and I climbed in. "Hi," I said, taking a seat next to Mary.

She beamed. "I'm so glad you two could come. Liz sweet-talked a mess hall cook into joining, and look at the loot!"

Mary pointed to a chest of ice with chicken and potato salad and corn for roasting. Another cooler held an enormous quantity of beer. I looked around the vehicle shyly, trying not to make eye contact with the men. There were many faces I didn't recognize, eager faces. And Lance was there, seated next to a blond nurse. *What's her name? Lela, yes.* I shuddered when I thought of Atea, poor Atea. Lance had used her, and hurt her. Perhaps in the same way he'd used Kitty. I hoped Kitty didn't see the way he was talking to the woman, flirting with her.

I refused to watch them; instead, I searched the vehicle for Westry. *Did he come?*

Mary must have read my mind. "Looks like he didn't make it," she whispered. "I'm sorry."

I shrugged. "Don't be," I said, tugging at my engagement ring. "There's nothing between us. Nothing at all."

I held on to Kitty as the truck sped along the bumpy island road. Each pothole punctuated the shame I felt. *How did I, an engaged woman, let myself become emotionally involved with Westry? I barely know him. What has this island done to my judgment?* Kitty stared ahead. When the truck came to a stop a few minutes later, pulling up onto the beach, everyone but Kitty stood up.

"Kitty," I said, "let's go."

She nodded dutifully, rising as if it were an exhausting endeavor. Lance helped Lela out of the truck, scooping her in his arms and then plopping her onto the sandy ground. She giggled and batted her eyelashes at him. Kitty quickly looked away. *Was I wrong to bring her here?* I hardly wanted to be here myself.

Mary led the procession onto the beach, telling the men where to set out the blankets, the fire for the cook, the beverage station, and the radio. There were oohs and aahs when a lance corporal named Shawn pulled out a gray radio and extended its antenna. Even Kitty smiled a little. None of us were immune to the power of music.

"Now," Mary said, as the men and women found their places on the blankets. "If I can just get a signal." She worked on the tuner for some time, stopping momentarily when she heard the faint sound of a man's voice—an Australian accent—relating war news with such speed and intensity, I felt my body respond in kind.

"Japanese bombers stormed the north shore today, leaving a wake of death and destruction." We all leaned in closer to hear more. "Casualties are estimated in the hundreds, many of them women and children." She quickly turned the dial. After a few seconds, the static parted to reveal a crystal-clear signal coming out across the ocean. The melody was soft and sweet, haunting. "How strange," Mary said. "We're picking up a French station."

The words were foreign, the melody unfamiliar, and yet it entranced me, and everyone else who was huddled together on the beach. Stella leaned in closer to Will. Lou reached for Mary's hand and asked her to dance. A few other nurses paired up with men I didn't recognize, even Liz. And Kitty didn't object when a soldier sat down beside her. She even grinned, biting into an ear of corn with gusto. The melody aroused a longing in my heart that I tried to squelch, a longing for Westry. I turned my gaze toward the ocean and the stretch of beach that led to the bungalow. It was getting dark now. *I shouldn't.* Besides, he wouldn't be there anyway. But as the music played on, the bungalow's pull became stronger, until I could no longer resist it. I stood up and walked quietly toward the beach. *I could just slip away for a half hour. No one would know. No one would miss me.*

I walked quickly, glancing back several times, just to be sure that no one followed. I slipped into the thicket and made my way to the steps of the bungalow. *There it is. Our bungalow.* The sight soothed me. I knelt down and felt around under the steps for the book and the key, but I heard the door creak open in front of me. I looked up, and there, standing in the dim light, was Westry.

A faint shadow punctuated his jawline, and his wet hair and unbuttoned shirt suggested that he'd just returned from a swim. He smiled. "I was hoping you'd come tonight," he said. "Did you see that moon?"

I nodded, gazing up at the sky, where an orange-tinged full moon dangled on the horizon, so close it almost kissed the shore.

I took a step closer. "I've never seen anything like it."

"Come in," he said, reaching for my hand. "I have something for you."

He closed the door behind us, and I sat down on the bed. I felt the pulse, the electricity in the air. I knew he felt it too.

"Look," he said, holding up a radio. "I got a signal." He turned the dial and there was that sound again—that beautiful, haunting foreign melody.

"Listen," he said, shaking his head. "French."

I closed my eyes and swayed to the music.

"This song," he said, "do you know it?"

I listened intently for a few moments, then shook my head. "No, I don't think I do."

"It's 'La Vie en Rose.'"

I raised an eyebrow. "How do you know it?"

"I heard it shortly before I left for the war," he said. "A friend of mine works for a record label. No one knows the song yet, at least not anyone back at home. They're testing it on the radio before they release a record. But it's going to be a huge hit. Mark my words. Just listen." He sat down next to me. Our arms brushed, and I could feel the warmth of his body.

"What does it mean?" I asked, feeling Westry's gaze on my face. I stared ahead at the radio.

He took a breath. "It means, *Hold me close and hold me fast; The magic spell you cast; This is la vie en rose; When you kiss me, heaven sighs; And though I close my eyes; I see la vie en rose; When you press me to your heart; I'm in a world apart; A world where roses bloom; And when you speak; Angels sing from above.*"

"It's beautiful," I said, still unable to look at him. My hands began to tremble. I tucked them under my legs.

Westry stood up. "Will you dance with me?"

I nodded, taking his hand.

He held me close as our bodies swayed to the music, keeping his arms low on my waist, a perfect fit. I nestled my cheek into his chest.

"Westry," I whispered.

"You mean Grayson?"

I smiled. "My dear Grayson."

"Yes, Cleo?"

"Well, that's just it. I am Cleo; you're Grayson. But are we only pretending? Is this *real*? Why is it that when we're here together," I said, "everything feels so right, so perfect? But when—"

"When we're out there," he said, interrupting me, pointing toward the window, "it's different?"

"Yes."

"Because it is," he said simply. "This is our paradise. Out there, well, it's complicated."

"And that's just it," I said. "I almost didn't come tonight because I feared that you were growing distant. That night with Colonel Donahue—why haven't you spoken of it?"

He put his finger to my lips. "Would you believe me if I told you I was protecting you?"

I looked at him, confused. "Protecting me? From what?"

"It's a crazy world out there, Anne. War. Lies. Betrayal. Sadness. It's all around us." He cradled my head in his hands. "Next time you worry that I am growing distant, come here. Come to the bungalow and you will feel my love."

Love. *Westry loves me.* It was all that mattered. I pressed my body closer to his and felt something akin to hunger welling up inside, an unfamiliar longing I'd never felt with Gerard. *Passion. Is this what Kitty meant?*

Westry took a step back for a moment. "Look at you," he said. "You are a vision. I'm going to take your photograph." He retrieved a camera from his knapsack, and instructed me to lean against the far wall. "There," he said after the flash went off. "Perfect."

"Now you," I said, lifting the camera from his hands. "I want one of you. I want to remember this night, this moment."

He obliged, leaning against the wall as I had done. I stared at his eyes through the lens, hoping to memorize the moment forever, before I clicked the button.

I set the camera down on the desk, and Westry lifted me in his arms and laid me on the bed, so effortlessly I felt like a feather in his grasp. I ran my hands along his arms. They were strong and firm. His lips touched mine, and my heart rate quickened as I took in the familiar scent of his skin, breathing it in, letting it intoxicate me. I unbuttoned his shirt completely and ran my fingers along his chest. His muscles quivered a little at my touch and he smiled. Something in me trembled too as he reached for the zipper of my dress. He undressed me with such delicate, loving hands, caressing my skin, and kissed me with such intention, I wondered if he'd dreamt about this moment a thousand times before, as I had done.

Our bodies fit together like they were made for each other. *Meant* for each other. I closed my eyes, vowing to remember every second, every breath, every sensation, and when it was over, we lay snugly in each other's arms, his warm chest pressed against mine. Our hearts beat in sync as the waves crashed into the shore outside the bungalow.

"Westry," I whispered.

"What is it, my love?"

"What will happen after all of this is over?"

"You mean, after the war?"

"Yes," I said. "When we go home."

"I wish I knew," he said, kissing my forehead.

I felt the cool gold of my engagement ring against my skin, and I instinctively pulled away from Westry.

"You're thinking of him, aren't you?"

I sighed. "It's all so complicated."

"Not when love is so certain," he said.

For Westry, it was that straightforward. We loved each other. That was that. And yet, I had made a promise to Gerard.

Gerard, who might be fighting for his life on a battlefield right now. Gerard, who was waiting for me to be his wife. *How could I do this to him?*

I looked up at Westry. As I gazed into his eyes, my resolve strengthened. I loved this man with every ounce of my being. I kissed him softly, and laid my head back on his shoulder. We listened to the French songs on the radio for a long time, forgetting people, places, even time, until my eyes grew heavy.

It may have been minutes or hours later, but I bolted out of bed when I heard the snap of a twig outside. I hurriedly dressed, fussing with the zipper on my dress as I peered out the window, where I could see a shadowy form on the beach.

"Who do you think it is?" I whispered to Westry, who quickly rose from the bed, slipping on his trousers and sliding each arm through the sleeves of his shirt. He didn't stop to button it before opening the door. I followed close behind, realizing that I had no idea what time it was. Kitty and the others must have been panicked.

"Who's there?" Westry called out to the figure in the distance.

"It's me," said a familiar voice. "Kitty." We pushed past the thicket, and the light from the moon revealed her face. I could see that she was frightened. "Anne? Is that *you*?"

"Yes," I said, suddenly aware that my hair was askew. *Did I zip my dress all the way? What would she think seeing Westry standing there half-dressed?*

"Oh," she said when she noticed Westry beside me. "I—I didn't mean to interrupt; it's just that we were getting ready to leave, and we couldn't find you."

"I'm sorry, Kitty," I said, a bit embarrassed. "I must have lost track of time."

Kitty couldn't see the bungalow from where she was standing, and I was glad of it.

"I was just leaving," I said, turning to Westry. My God, he was handsome. I didn't want to leave. I wanted to stay with him here, maybe forever. "Good night, Westry," I said.

"Good night, Anne," he replied, smiling a secret smile.

Kitty and I walked in silence up the beach, until she finally spoke. "You love him, don't you?"

"Kitty!"

She nestled her hand in mine. "It's OK," she said. "I don't care who you love. I just want to see you happy. Are you?"

I looked up at the moon overhead and then back toward the stretch of beach that led to the bungalow. "Yes," I said. "I've never been happier in my entire life than at this moment."

The bumpy road home barely disturbed any of us. Not Stella, with her head resting comfortably in Will's lap; or Mary, deep in conversation with Lou; or Kitty, lost in her own thoughts; and especially not me, with a heart that swelled with such true and perfect love. But with it came a great heaviness, for I had to make a decision. Soon, I feared.

# Chapter 9

"Did you hear?" Liz said at breakfast. "The men are shipping out. Almost all of them. There's some big fight on an island south of here. It's going to be serious."

My eyes met Mary's. I could see the concern for Lou in her eyes and wondered if she could detect the fear I felt for Westry.

"Colonel Donahue is leading them out this evening," Kitty said, with little emotion, as if she was reading the *War Digest* verbatim.

"Does anyone know who's going?" I asked, hoping the panic I felt wasn't evident in my voice.

"Yes," Stella said, pulling out her handkerchief. "Go look at the list." She pointed to the bulletin board outside the mess hall. "I saw Will's name on it earlier."

"Stella, I'm so sorry," said Liz.

I turned to Mary. "Will you go look with me?"

She nodded, and we walked somberly outside to the board. There it was. His name, halfway down, in black ink. Westry Green. Lou's was there too. Mary gasped, and we clutched each other tightly.

"We have to find them," she said. "We have to say good-bye before . . ."

"Let's be confident," I said. "Let's think positively. They need that from us."

"Anne," Mary muttered, "I can't bear to lose him."

"You shouldn't talk that way, dear," I said, patting her arm. "It's bad luck."

I'd already worked the early morning shift in the infirmary, so I didn't feel guilty about sneaking out after breakfast to make a quick trip to the men's barracks, where I gazed up at Westry's window. The room, or what I could see of it from standing on a bench outside, looked empty—a tightly made bed and a coat missing from the hook near the door. *Has he already left?* Liz had mentioned earlier that a squadron had already departed. *Is Westry with them?*

I said good-bye to Mary and walked quickly to the beach, and once I'd rounded the bend, I started to run. *Maybe he's at the bungalow, waiting for me. I can see him before he leaves, if I run fast enough.* My shoes filled with sand as I sloshed along the beach—sand that had never felt so heavy, so stifling. *Can it be trying to keep me from Westry, to hold me back?* I tripped on a piece of driftwood and clutched my aching knee before standing up again and resuming my pace. *Faster. Run faster.* Each second counted.

I pushed through the brush and finally made my way to the front step of the bungalow. The morning sun shone on its palm walls, streaming light all around it. I reached for the doorknob, praying that it would be open, praying that Westry would be inside. But my hand was met with a sharp click. Locked. Westry wasn't there. I was too late.

I pulled out the key and let myself in anyway, sitting down in a heap of disappointment on the chair by the desk. The little room immediately comforted me. I could sense his presence, just as he'd said I would. I searched my memories for his exact words, and found them tucked away in my heart: "Next time you worry that I am growing distant, come here. Come to the bungalow, and you will feel my love." Yes, I could feel his love. It enveloped me.

I lifted the floorboard and my heart warmed when I saw a letter inside.

My darling Cleo,

I have to leave now, my dear. I am shipping out to Guadalcanal for what the CO calls "serious combat." The men don't know what to expect, nor do I. After all, we've been sitting pretty on this rock for so long. We were almost fooled into thinking we were on vacation. It's about time we fulfill our jobs, to do what we came here for. To fight.

I stopped by the infirmary this morning to say good-bye, but you were busy, and I hated to disturb you. I watched you work from the window for a few minutes. My, you are beautiful. The way you move. The way you talk. I have never loved as I love you.

I don't know how long I will be gone. Maybe days. Maybe months. But I pray that you will hold the memory of last night in your heart, as I will. I pray that you will think of me and wait for me. For I will return, and we will be reunited. And when the war is over and done with, we will never part.

Remember me, la vie en rose, my darling.

Yours forevermore,

Grayson

I wiped away tears, then ran outside to the shore as a squadron of airplanes flew overhead in formation. I blew a kiss out into the sky.

He'd come back. He had to.

The days passed with very little news from the war front. The men who had stayed seemed preoccupied and on edge, perhaps guilty that they weren't out fighting too, or ashamed that they hadn't been chosen for such an important mission.

The Allies were closing in on the Japanese in the Pacific, and this was a critical battle to protect New Zealand, Liz had explained. Liz knew more about the war than any of us. She said the Japanese had planned to colonize New Zealand, to rape and kill. And while the allies had taken Guadalcanal, pockets of enemy forces remained scattered throughout the South Pacific. We had to win. If we didn't, well, no one talked about that, but it weighed heavily on our minds.

Every day more injured men were wheeled off airplanes. Some came in on stretchers, dazed and bloodied, mute, as if what they had seen had robbed them of their voices, their sanity. Others had such severe injuries—severed legs, missing arms, shrapnel in the eyes—that they moaned for morphine, and we gave it to them as quickly as our hands could inject needles into their pain-ravaged skin.

The steady stream of men kept us busy in the infirmary, making us wonder if the battle was going according to plan. Nurse Hildebrand, who directed us with such emotionless precision, seemed almost mechanical. "Liz!" she shouted. "Go to the storeroom and get a fresh supply of bandages. Can't you see that we're almost out?

Stella! Come here and help me get this one prepped for surgery. Kitty! The man over in bed nine needs morphine. Quickly now."

She operated with the force of a drill sergeant, and rightly so. This was the most intense work any of us had ever done. And in it, emotions ran high. As each man was wheeled into the infirmary, the women crowded around to check for a familiar face.

And on one morning in early April, we heard a commotion at the entrance, where a man shouted, "I need a nurse here, fast!"

I saw a pilot standing in the entryway holding a bloodied soldier in his arms. "There wasn't time to wait for a stretcher so I brought him in myself," he said. "He bled out on the plane. I'm not sure what you can do for him, but work fast. He's a good guy."

I wheeled a stretcher to the entrance and helped the pilot lay the man on top. Though blood covered his face and neck, I recognized him in an instant. *Dear God, it's Will. Stella's Will.* "I'll take him from here," I said. "Thank you, lieutenant."

"There are more coming," he said gravely. "Just heard on the radio. It's bad out there. Lots of men down."

My heart filled with terror as I took Will

over to the operating room, where Dr. Wheeler was washing his hands. "Doc!" I yelled. "This one needs you now."

I motioned for Mary across the room.

"It's Will," I whispered once she was near. I pointed to the operating room. "He's badly hurt. Where's Stella?"

She gestured toward the far corner of the infirmary, where Stella was working with Nurse Hildebrand on a leg splint. The soldier moaned as they adjusted his knee, moving it into place. "We have to tell her."

"No," I said. "We need her. We need every able-bodied nurse on this island right now. The lieutenant said more are coming. Maybe Lou. Maybe Westry. We need to keep working. We can't stop to grieve."

She nodded solemnly. "I'll do my best to keep her away."

"Thanks," I said. "I'll keep an eye on him. If anything changes, I'll bring her over."

An hour later twenty-three more men came, and then nine more, and then another eleven. Three died. More were stabilized and sent on homeward-bound planes for care we couldn't administer.

"What a bloody mess," Liz said, dabbing her eyes with her handkerchief. The intensity was getting to her, and to all of us.

"Are you OK?" I asked, patting her back. "I can speak to Nurse Hildebrand and see about you getting some leave."

"No," she said, straightening her white uniform. "No, I can do this. I have to."

I glanced over at Kitty, where she worked feverishly with another nurse on a man who had just been brought in. I could see by the bandages they were reaching for that it was a head injury. A serious one. Kitty's fingers moved fast, dabbing the man's forehead with alcohol. He winced. She wrapped a bandage around his head, but she swayed a little as she did. Something was wrong. Then Kitty's legs buckled, just as they had on the tarmac that first day on the island. She fell to the floor, but this time, nothing blunted her fall.

I ran to her side, fanning her face. "Kitty, Kitty! Wake up. You fainted."

Liz handed me a vial of smelling salts. I held them to Kitty's nose, and a moment later, her eyes opened.

"I'm so sorry," she said. "Look at me. There are men here who are really in trouble, and I can't even manage to stand."

"You need to rest," I said. "I'll help you back to the room. Nurse Hildebrand will understand."

"Yes," she said. "But I won't let you walk me. You're needed here. I can go myself."

"All right," I conceded. "But be careful."

Kitty made her way outside, and I turned back to the rows of men waiting for medicine, for a bandage, for surgery, or just to die.

"We have to tell her," Mary said over my shoulder. "Doc says he may not make it."

I nodded. "Will you come with me?"

We walked over to Stella, who was searching a cabinet. "You'd think they'd restock this damn thing," she said, standing up. "Have you seen any iodine in this godforsaken place?"

"Stella," Mary said, "I need you to sit down."

"Sit down?" she shook her head suspiciously. "Now, why would I do that?"

"Will," I said, helping her into a chair. "He's been hurt. Badly hurt."

Stella gasped and covered her mouth with her hand. "No, no," she said. "No, I don't believe it." She looked at me, then at Mary. "Where is he?"

Mary pointed to the operating room. "Dr. Wheeler is with him now, but they don't know if he's going to pull through."

Stella ran across the room, and we followed close behind.

"Will!" she cried. "Will, it's me." She knelt down by the gurney, draping her arm lightly over his chest. "It's me, Stella."

Will didn't move. His breathing was shallow. "Doc, you're going to save him, right? You have to save him."

Just then Will's eyes opened. They fluttered and closed again.

"Will!" Stella cried. "Will, come back to me."

He opened his eyes again, and then his mouth, and said weakly, "I'm here, Stell. I'm here."

Dr. Wheeler took off his glasses. "By golly," he said. "He's conscious. This boy may make it after all."

Stella, oblivious to the tears streaming down her face, clutched Will's hand in hers. "You're going to pull through. Oh, Will!" She nestled her face in the crook of his neck.

Mary and I dried our eyes. Will had a chance. Thank God for that. But what about Lou and Westry? What about the other men? Would they have the same good fortune? Would we?

We worked until the shift change at eleven p.m. But even then, many of us, including me, didn't want to leave. *What if Westry comes through the doors of the infirmary? What if I miss him?* Still, Nurse Hildebrand forbid us to stay. "You're too tired, and you're getting sloppy," she said.

She was right. Liz had forgotten to give meds to a patient, and I had reported incorrect information to Dr. Wheeler about a sergeant's injuries. It was the head wound in bed nineteen, not the leg injury in seven, that needed his attention. Nineteen. Seven. Twenty-three. Four. The beds, the numbers, the men—they all blurred together, and when I closed my eyes, all I could see was a deep red shade of blood.

As I opened the door to the barracks, I realized I hadn't thought of Kitty at all since she had left. *Is she OK?* I rushed up the stairs to the room, where I found her in bed, sleeping.

"Kitty," I whispered, "how are you feeling, honey?"

She rolled over and looked at me. "I'm

all right," she said. "But how are the men? How are things down there?"

"It's crazy," I replied. "Will came in, badly hurt. But we think he's going to be all right."

"Good. And Westry? Any word?"

"Nothing yet," I said, feeling tears form in my eyes again.

"Mail came. I put a letter for you on your bed."

"Thanks," I said. "Night, Kitty."

I picked up the envelope and stood by the window so I could read the return address in the moonlight without disturbing Kitty. *It's from Gerard.*

My love,

I haven't heard from you, and I hate to even mention it, but yesterday, I was overcome with fear. I just felt that something was wrong. Of course, I don't want to believe it, but something in my heart flinched. Did something happen? Are you safe? Please write and tell me you are.

I am in France with the 101st Airborne Division, so far away from home, so far away from you. The conditions are tough here, as they are everywhere, I imagine.

Men are dying right and left. But I have that card you made for me, the one with the little red heart on the cover, tucked into my jacket pocket. I believe it brings me luck. I will come home to you, Anne. I promise.

Yours,

Gerard

I wept as I tucked the letter back into the envelope, then reached for my stationery set, light blue, embossed with my initials, AEC. Anne Elizabeth Calloway. I had intended to write many letters home, to Mother, to Papa, to Maxine, and especially to Gerard, but the little letter set hadn't gotten much use, and I was ashamed that I hadn't taken more time to write Gerard. I sat down to compose a letter, even if I didn't know what I'd say.

Dear Gerard,

I wanted you to know that I am well and fine. The mail has been backed up here, so I am only now receiving your letters.

I paused, considering the lie. A white lie.

I'm so busy here, or else I'd have written more. When we're not working we're sleeping; when we're not sleeping, we're working.

Another lie.

I think of you often, and miss you.

With love,

Anne

"You know what we need to do to pass the time," Stella suggested at the mess hall one morning in early May.

"What?" Mary asked, feigning interest.

"A knitting circle," she said.

"Easy for you to say," Mary snapped. "Your Will is right here, safe and sound. And you think *yarn* is what *we* need?"

Stella looked wounded.

"I'm sorry," Mary said. "I didn't mean that."

"It's OK," Stella replied. "I was only thinking that it might busy us in the evenings when all we do is listen for news on the radio."

"It's not a bad idea," I chimed in.

"I'm sure the natives could use blankets," Mary added. "For the children. We could make them."

"I'll join," Kitty said.

"Me, too," said Liz.

"We could start tonight, after our shift's over," Mary offered.

Stella smiled. "Good. I'll gather the supplies. We can meet in the rec hall."

Stella had been right. It was yarn that sustained us those next couple of weeks. We made one blanket, and then two. By the third and fourth, we were already planning the fifth: green and yellow yarn, a palm motif in the center.

"I wonder who will sleep under these?" Liz asked, running her hand along the edge of the first blanket we'd completed. "As insignificant as a blanket is, it's nice to be doing something for the people of this island."

We all nodded.

"Do you ever wonder what they think of all of this?" she continued. "One day, their peaceful oasis in the middle of the sea becomes the center of a raging war?"

"It must be terrifying for them," Mary replied. "I wish we could do more than give them blankets."

"But blankets are something," Liz said.

I thought of Atea, all alone and perhaps even in trouble. She might be able to use one, and if not, she'd know others who could.

I looked up at the circle of women, knitting needles clinking together. "I can take them to a woman, a native, I know who can use them," I offered. "I'll bring them to the market tomorrow."

"Nurse Hildebrand?"

"What is it?" she snapped without looking up from her desk.

"May I have permission to take an extended lunch?"

She pulled her spectacles lower on her nose. "And what is it that you intend to do?"

"Well, the nurses and I have been kitting blankets," I explained. "It's kept us busy in the evenings when we'd just be worrying—"

"Make your point, Nurse Calloway," she said sternly.

"Yes," I said, "I'm sorry. My intention is

to deliver the blankets to the market today, to give them to some of the islanders who could use them."

"Blankets?" she said, a little mockingly.

"Yes, ma'am," I said. "Blankets."

She shook her head, then shrugged. "Well, I don't see the harm. Be sure that you're back by half past two. We're getting a shipment, and we'll need all hands on deck."

I smiled. "Thank you, Nurse Hildebrand, thank you. I will."

The market seemed quieter than usual, eerily so. Since most of the men had been deployed in the fight, fewer islanders turned up to sell their wares, but I hoped Atea would be there. I needed to talk to her.

It had been months since I'd seen her, since that fateful Christmas Eve scene at the chapel, and I'd worried about her. The blankets were merely an excuse to make sure she was all right.

"Excuse me," I said to a toothless woman holding an infant at a nearby table stacked with bananas and a few clumps of dusty, exotic-looking salad greens. "Have you seen Atea?"

The woman eyed me skeptically. "She no here," she said dismissively.

"Oh," I said, holding out the blankets. "It's just that I wanted to give her these."

My gesture changed the woman's demeanor. She softened, pointing to a hill a few hundred yards away. "She with Tita. Green house. You find her inside."

"Thank you," I said, turning toward the hillside. I had less than an hour before the truck returned to camp, so I walked fast along the pathway that led to the hill the woman had indicated. Dirt caked my ivory patent-leather pumps, but I didn't mind. I swatted a mosquito from my arm and started on the trail into the thicket. It was darker under the cloak of the tropical forest, and I almost didn't see the little green house ahead, for it blended into the hillside as if it were part of nature. *That must be it.*

A bicycle leaned up against the side of the small one-room home, which appeared to be constructed of scrap wood and treasures that had washed up from the sea. A chicken squawked a few feet away, startling me as I lifted my fist to knock on the door. *Am I foolish coming here like this?*

An old woman appeared in the doorway,

her gray hair fashioned into a single tidy braid.

"I'm here to see Atea," I said meekly, holding up the basket of blankets.

The woman nodded and muttered something in French, or maybe Tahitian, that I could not understand. I heard footsteps from behind the door.

"Anne!" Atea said, poking her head around the old woman. "You come!" She looked different then, which might have been because she was wearing a dress, one that was about five sizes too big for her small frame. It appeared to have been plucked from the Sears Roebuck catalog circa 1895. I wondered why she wore it when she'd been so comfortable with hardly a swatch of clothing before.

"Yes," I said. "I'm sorry to intrude. I—I wanted to make sure you were safe. And I wanted to give you these."

Atea took the basket from my hands and gasped. "They're beautiful. For me?"

"Yes, and for anyone else you think can use them," I said, smiling. "How have you been?"

She looked conflicted about answering

the question. "Come in," she said instead. "This is Tita."

The old woman nodded.

"Pleased to meet you, Tita," I said. "I'm Anne."

Atea directed me to a grass-woven chair, and I sat. Moments later Tita produced a mug containing something warm. "Tea," she said. "For you."

I thanked her and took a sip. The beverage was sweet and spicy at the same time.

"It's good," I said. "What is it?"

"Kava," Atea said. "It calm you."

I nodded. Atea was right. Each sip had a soothing and somewhat dizzying effect. Everything softened around me. Minutes later, the sharp edges of the jagged window frame looked polished and the dirt floor I'd noted when I walked in began to take on the appearance of a soft oriental rug.

"Is this her?" Tita asked Atea.

Atea nodded.

Tita moved to the chair next to me. "You are the one who found the artist's home?"

Confused at first, I remembered what Atea had said on the beach so many months ago—a detail I had forgotten to share with Westry. "Yes," I said, "if you mean the bungalow."

Tita gave Atea a knowing look. "There is something you must know about this bungalow," the old woman said. Her eyes were so arresting, I could not look away. "According to legend, whoever steps foot in it will face a lifetime of"—she paused as if to consider the right word—"heartache."

"I'm not sure I understand what you mean," I said, setting the mug down on a little wooden table to my left. A fog seemed to appear in the room, and I wondered what was in the tea.

"Bad things happen there," she said.

I shook my head. No, she had it all wrong. *Good* things happened there. It was our beloved hideaway, the place where I had grown to love Westry. *How could she say this?*

"Like what?" I asked, finding my voice.

"Things too dark to speak of," she whispered, casting her eyes to a crucifix that hung on the wall.

I stood up abruptly and the room seemed to move. "Well," I said, steadying myself on the edge of the chair. "Thank you for the tea. But I really must be going." I turned to Atea. "Take care of yourself, dear. And please, remember my offer if you need assistance."

She nodded and eyed Tita cautiously as I reached for the door handle.

"Wait," I said, turning back around. "You said the bungalow once belonged to an artist. Do you happen to know who?"

Tita looked at Atea and then at me again. "Yes," she said with wistful eyes. "His name was Paul. Paul Gauguin."

꧁

The following night, Mary passed out the yarn in the rec hall just as the onslaught began. We looked up when we heard a rush of men coming through the door. "Nurses, come quick!" one shouted. "You're needed in the infirmary. It's a plane full of wounded men. Too many this time."

I dropped my knitting needles and ran with the other women along the path to the infirmary, where Nurse Hildebrand was shouting orders. "Kitty, you'll stay with me and assist Doc Wheeler. Stella, you'll handle beds one through eleven. Liz, take beds twelve through nineteen. Mary, Anne, you two work receiving. Keep it orderly.

There will be a lot of misery tonight. But it's why we are here. Nurses, find your strength. You will need to draw upon it hours from now."

We all scattered to our stations, and when the men began coming, it was like nothing we'd seen before. The wounds were more critical, the screaming louder, the intensity stronger than in past days.

Mary and I worked the doors, directing traffic and admitting the men, many of whom shrieked and pleaded for help, some weakly, others with such force that it was terrifying to witness. A young soldier with a head injury pulled my arm so hard he tore the sleeve of my dress. "I want my mama!" he screamed. "Mama! Where is Mama?"

It was harrowing to witness. All of it. The blood and the misery and the pain, and especially seeing men reduced to children in their suffering. But we kept on. We drew upon on our reserves of strength as Nurse Hildebrand had instructed. And when that ran out, we found more.

It was two thirty in the morning when the last plane came in. Nine men where wheeled into the infirmary. I heard Mary scream at the door. The horror in her voice told me why.

I ran to her side, and there on the stretcher lay Lou—limp, lifeless, and very badly burned.

The soldier at the door shook his head. "I'm sorry, ma'am," he said. "This one died on the way over. We did all we could for him."

"No!" Mary screamed, shaking her head violently. "*No!*"

She ran to the soldier and gripped his shirt in her fists. "Did you not try to help him? Did you not do anything?"

"Ma'am," he said, "I assure you, we did everything we could. His wounds were just too great."

"No," Mary said, falling to her knees. "No, this can't be." She stood up and lay her head on Lou's chest, sobbing into his blood-soaked shirt. "Lou, Lou!" she cried. "No, no, Lou. No."

Liz ran to my side. "We have to stop her," she said. "Will you help me?"

"Mary," I said. "Mary, stop. He's gone, dear. Let him go."

"I won't!" she screamed, pushing me away. Her face was covered in Lou's blood. I gestured to Liz for assistance.

"Honey," I said, taking her left arm in my hands. Liz took her right. "We're going to take you to bed."

"No," Mary moaned.

"Liz, grab the sedatives," I said.

She nodded and handed me a syringe. Mary hardly flinched as I jabbed the needle into her arm. Moments later, her body went limp.

"There," I said, letting her down softly onto a nearby bed. The sheets had a smudge of blood on them. Someone else's blood. But there wasn't time to change them. "Lie down, dear," I said, wiping Lou's blood from her face with a damp cloth. "Try to rest."

"Lou," she muttered weakly before her eyes closed.

I watched her breathing for a few minutes, thinking about how unfair this was. After all she'd been through, she had found love again, only to lose it in such a tragic way. It wasn't right.

Kitty and I walked back to the barracks together in silence. We had now seen war, or, rather, the aftermath of war—its ugliness, its cruelty.

We fell into our beds and listened to the airplanes flying overhead for a long time. I prayed for Westry, and I wondered who Kitty was praying for, or thinking of.

"Anne," Kitty whispered to me after the skies had been quiet for some time. "Are you still awake?"

"Yes."

"I have to tell you something," she said. "Something important."

I sat up. "What is it?"

She sighed, looking at me with eyes filled with sorrow, with hurt that I could not understand. "I'm pregnant."

# Chapter 10

I gasped, running to her bed. "Oh, Kitty!" I cried, shaking my head in disbelief.

"I've known for a while now," she said, her eyes welling up with tears. "I've been so afraid to tell you."

"Why would you be afraid, Kitty?"

She exhaled deeply. "Partly because I feared admitting it, even to myself, and also because I knew it would disappoint you."

"Disappoint *me*?" I ran my fingers through her curls and shook my head. "No, I'm only disappointed that you've had to carry this burden alone."

Kitty pressed her face against my shoulder and wept so intensely her body shook with grief. "I don't know what to do," she cried. "Look at me." She indicated her belly, which was obviously swollen. "I've been hiding under girdles for months. I can't go on like this anymore. Everyone will notice before too long. The baby's coming in a month, maybe sooner."

I gasped. "We'll speak to Nurse Hildebrand," I said.

"No!" Kitty pleaded. "No, we can't go to her. Please, Anne."

"It's our only option," I countered. "You can't be working such long hours in your condition, and the baby will be coming soon. We must plan for that."

Kitty looked frightened and lost. I knew by the expression on her face that she hadn't considered the reality of what lay ahead—delivering a child on an island thousands of miles away from home, unwed, in disgrace, uncertain.

"All right," she said. "If you think it's best, tell her. But I can't bear to be there when you do."

I kissed her forehead and smiled. "You don't have to, dear," I said. "I'll take care of everything."

There was little time the following day to find even a minute alone with Nurse Hildebrand, but by the final hour of my shift, I had managed to run into her in the storeroom.

"Nurse Hildebrand," I said, quietly closing the door behind us. "May I speak to you about something?"

"Yes, Anne," she said without looking up from the crate she was unpacking. "Quickly, please; I must get back."

"Thank you," I said. "It's about Kitty."

Nurse Hildebrand nodded. "I already know," she said simply.

"What do you mean, you know?"

"Her pregnancy," she replied without emotion.

"Yes, but I—"

"Anne, I've been a nurse for a very long time. I've delivered babies and had children of my own. I know."

I nodded. "She needs your help," I said cautiously. "The baby's coming soon, and she can't keep working like this."

For the first time, Nurse Hildebrand turned to me. Her face softened in a way I hadn't known it could. "Tell her not to worry about the work here. If the others ask, I'll say she has a bout of the fever going around, that she's been quarantined. You'll need to bring her meals up to her. Can you manage that?"

"Yes," I said, smiling. "Yes, of course."

"And when the time comes, come to me."

I nodded. "But what will become of the baby, after—"

"I know a missionary couple who will take the baby," she said. "They live just over the hill, on the other side of the island. They are good people. I'll speak to them in the morning."

"Thank you, Nurse Hildebrand," I said with such emotion, tears fell from my eyes. "I didn't expect you to be so—"

"Enough," she said. The softness, now gone from her face, was replaced by the stern expression I knew so well. "It's time to get back to work."

❧

The day Mary left the island was sad for all of us, particularly for Kitty, who remained trapped in the barracks, unable to join the other nurses on the airstrip for her farewell.

The island had been hard on Mary, perhaps harder on her than on any of us. It had given her malaria and nearly taken her life, and then it broke her heart.

"Farewell, friend," Stella said to her.

"We'll never forget you, dear," Liz chimed in.

Mary looked like a shell of a woman standing there before the open door of the plane, thinner than ever, with wrists still bandaged from her self-inflicted wounds, the wounds that had almost ended her life.

She retrieved a handkerchief from her bag and dabbed her bloodshot eyes. "I'll miss you all so much," she said. "It doesn't feel right to leave. You've become my dearest friends, my sisters."

I squeezed Mary's hand. "It's your time, dear. Go home. Take care of yourself." I remembered the letter from Edward, which was now in my pocket. I hadn't anticipated keeping it from her this long. Was she ready to read it now? It didn't matter, I reasoned. The letter belonged to her.

"I guess this is it," she said, reaching for her bag.

The other women choked back tears as Mary turned toward the plane.

"Wait," I said. Mary looked back at me with a confused expression.

I pulled the letter from my pocket and tucked it in her hand. "This arrived," I said, "for you. I hope you will forgive me for keeping it from you. I wanted to protect you from any more pain."

Mary's eyes brightened when she saw the name on the return address. "My God," she gasped.

"I'm so sorry," I said, stepping back.

Mary extended her hand to take mine. "No," she said. "Don't be. I understand. I do."

"I'll miss you so much," I said, wishing that things could be different—for her, for Kitty, for all of us. "Promise you'll look me up in Seattle when the war's over?"

"I promise," she said. And with that, Mary and her letter were gone from our lives—forever, perhaps. And the island was lonelier because of it.

For a long time it felt like Westry might never return. The island was different without him, especially now that Mary had left and Kitty was bedridden. But then one morning in late May while working in the infirmary, we heard the loudspeaker at the center of camp announcing that the men had returned.

"Go," Nurse Hildebrand said to me.

I didn't stop to thank her; instead I ran out to the pathway and didn't pause until I'd reached the edge of the airstrip. Men trudged with heavy bags and even heavier hearts toward camp. Lance, Colonel Donahue, and some of the other men I knew. *But where is Westry?* I looked around for a familiar face. Elliot had gone home earlier with some of the other men whose service was up. *Would someone else know of Westry's whereabouts?*

"Have you seen Westry?" I asked an unfamiliar soldier. His head hung low.

"I'm sorry, ma'am," he said. "I don't know him."

I nodded, then noticed one of Westry's bunkmates from the barracks. "Ted," I said, approaching him. "Where's Westry? Have you seen him?"

He shook his head. "Sorry. Not since yesterday."

"What do you mean?"

"He was on the front lines, and . . ."

My heart raced. "What are you saying?"

"He wasn't on the plane with us."

"What does that mean?" I cried. "That he isn't coming home? That you just left him there?"

"There's another plane coming in to-night," he said. "Let's pray that he's on it."

I nodded as Ted tipped his cap at me and filed back in line with the men making their way back to camp, eager for a hot meal and a soft bed.

I clutched the locket that stood guard around my neck, hoping that wherever Westry was, he could feel my love. I would will him home. I had to.

A chill filled the air that night, unusual for May in the tropics. I shivered as I walked along the beach, a foolish move given Kitty's state. She'd been having mild contractions for days now, but she assured me they weren't serious. Even so, I promised her I'd only be gone an hour. I felt guilty about leaving, but I needed the comfort of the bungalow now more than ever.

I unlocked the door and draped the quilt around me, listening for airplanes over-head. *Is he coming? Please, God, bring him home.*

But instead of footsteps on the sand, I could only hear rain—just a few drops at first and then a hundred, a thousand. The sky appeared to have opened up, dumping

its contents right on the roof of the bungalow.

I opened the door, extending my hand
outside to feel the raindrops, like firm kisses
on my skin, beckoning me outside. I took
another step, and looked up to the sky,
eyes closed, letting the warm drops cover
my face, my hair. Moments later my dress
was soaked. I unfastened the buttons on
the bodice as the rain seeped down beneath my slip. And then, out of the corner
of my eye, I saw a figure. It was faint at first
and blurred in the distance. I walked closer,
unafraid, pushing my way through the rain,
like a curtain of beads extending from the
sky, until I could make out his face, thin
from months of fighting, and hungry for the
love I desperately wanted to give him.

Our bodies collided, fitting together perfectly as his bag dropped to the sand. "Oh,
Westry!" I cried. Even in the dark, I could
see the scratches on his face and his
ripped, mud-stained uniform.

"I came directly here," he said.

"Oh, Westry!" I cried again, pulling his
lips toward mine.

He ran his hands along my dress, tugging at the fabric as if to make it disappear.

I leapt into his arms, wrapping my legs around his body, kissing him again and again, before he smiled and gently set my feet down on the sand.

He reached inside his bag. "Let's do this the right way," he said. "Ever seen a proper military shower?"

Westry pulled out a bar of soap. "When we were on the ship, this is how we bathed," he said. "Right out on the deck, in the tropical rain."

I reached for his collar, running my hands down his shirt, unfastening each button as quickly as my fingers could move, until my hands caressed his bare chest and the dog tags hanging from his neck.

He slipped out of his trousers and lifted my dress over my head. We stood there for a moment, without a stitch of clothing, in the warm rain, until Westry moved toward me, running the ivory bar of soap along my neck. I gasped as he touched it to my breasts, lathering my skin with bubbles.

I moved in closer, loving the way our bodies felt against each other, and took the soap in my hands, rubbing it across his chest, his arms, and his back. The rain washed away the bubbles as quickly as I could lather them. Westry pulled me close, and I felt the intensity in his kiss, the hunger. He lifted me in his arms, and the soap, what was left of it, slipped out of my grasp and fell to the sand as he carried me to the bungalow, setting me down on the bed.

I liked the feel of the bungalow's quilt on my bare skin, and an hour later, when the storm had passed, I lay there tracing Westry's face with my finger as he gazed out the window facing the beach. The stubble on his jaw was thick. I counted the scrapes on his face. Four—well, five if you counted the gash on his ear.

"What was it like out there?" I whispered.

"It was a living hell," he said, sitting up against the pillows on the bed.

I sensed his hesitation. "You don't want to talk about it, do you?"

"I'd rather enjoy this perfect moment," he said before planting a soft kiss on my lips.

I thought of Kitty, and realized that hours could have passed. *Is she all right?* I felt guilty for being gone so long.

"Our clothes," I said, a little panicked. "They must be soaked."

Westry stood up, letting the blanket fall to the bed. I giggled shyly, studying his strong, beautiful unclothed body.

"I'll go grab them," he said.

He returned a moment later with my damp, wrinkled dress. I fit it over my head, as he slid into his trousers.

"Can you stay for a while?" he asked, combing my hair with his fingers.

"I wish I could, but I need to get back." I wanted to tell him about Kitty, but I decided against it. "I told Kitty I'd be back hours ago."

Westry nodded, kissing my hand.

We both turned to the window when we heard a rustling sound in the brush, followed by a faint knocking sound on the door.

Westry opened the door cautiously, and I peered over his shoulder to see Kitty standing outside. She clutched her belly in agony. "Anne!" she screamed. "It's *time*."

I didn't stop to think about how she found us. There wasn't time for questions. "We need to get you to the infirmary," I said, running to her side.

"No. I can't bear to have the other nurses see me like this. Besides, it's too late for that," she said. "The baby's coming *now*."

Westry's mouth flung open as I helped Kitty up the stairs into the bungalow, where she rested on the bed, moaning in such pain, it was heartbreaking to witness. *Lance should be punished for leaving her this way.* I shook my head, wiping the perspiration from Kitty's forehead with the edge of the blanket, and began to pray silently. *Please, God, let Kitty be comforted. Give me the strength I lack.*

Kitty moaned louder now. Something was wrong; I felt it. I remembered Tita's eerie warning and shuddered, forcing the thought from my mind, and tried to stay focused. I carefully positioned myself below Kitty's legs, helping her lean farther back on the bed. My hands trembled as I lifted her dress and tried to recall an ounce of what I had learned about childbirth in my nursing courses. Hot water. Forceps. Ether. Blankets. I shuddered. I had nothing but my two hands.

She was bleeding, that much was clear. "Kitty," I said as she screamed. "Kitty, you need to push *now*."

She seemed alone with her pain, unable to hear my voice. I squeezed her hand. "Kitty," I continued, "stay with me. This baby is coming and you need to help me. Please, push. You must be strong."

"Anne, let me help you," Westry said once he finally found his voice.

He knelt down beside me. The bungalow's lantern illuminated his skin, darker from months in the sun. I could only imagine what he'd gone through, and now he returned to this.

Westry soaked his handkerchief with water from his canteen and dabbed Kitty's forehead as I talked her through her next contraction. "I can see the baby's head," I said. "It won't be long now."

Kitty looked up at Westry with eyes full of gratitude. He held her hand and stroked her hair. One more push and the baby slid into my arms.

"A girl!" I cried. "Kitty, it's a girl."

Westry helped me sever the cord with his pocketknife, then placed the baby in Kitty's arms. She clutched the newborn to her chest.

"We need blankets," I said when I noticed that Kitty was shivering.

Westry tucked Kitty's limp body under the quilt, and then unbuttoned his shirt. "Here," he said. "Let's wrap the baby in this." Carefully, he swaddled the child in his green army shirt, ragged and a little bloodied from weeks of fighting.

Once Kitty and the baby were settled, we walked outside together and sat down on the sand. I could no longer repress the emotion I felt.

"Don't cry," Westry said softly. "She's fine. You delivered that baby better than any doctor could have."

I nodded, blotting my tears with the edge of my sleeve. "It's just not what I wanted for her. Lance should be court-martialed for leaving her in a position like this."

Westry looked confused, but nodded. "And the baby? What will become of her?"

"A missionary couple here on the island is taking her," I said. "Kitty agreed to it, but"—I gestured inside the bungalow—"I know how hard this will be for her."

"When she's well enough to stand, I'll carry her back to camp," he said. "If you can take the baby."

I nodded. "We should probably get her home before sunrise to avoid spectators."

Westry paused and stroked my hair softly. "Anne," he said, "I hated being away from you."

My eyes filled with tears. "I worried about you every hour of every day."

"It was misery," he said. "And the only thing that got me through it was knowing I'd return to you."

I nestled my face into his bare chest, smooth and warm. "I don't know what I would have done if you didn't make it home," I said. "I don't know how I could have gone on."

He held my hands in his, lifting up my left hand and touching the ring on my finger. "I can't share you with him anymore," he whispered.

"I know," I said, breathing in his breath. I slid the ring off my finger and let it drop into the pocket of my dress. "You don't have to anymore. I am yours. Completely yours."

Westry kissed me with such passion, it erased the familiar guilt I'd felt about Gerard. We might have stayed like that, locked in an embrace, until dawn if I hadn't heard the baby's cry from inside the bungalow, reminding us of the task at hand.

"We better get them home," I said to Westry, kissing his cheek and then his nose, and then the back of his hand softly.

I had never felt such true and unfaltering love.

Westry carried Kitty, wrapped in the quilt from the bungalow, along the beach back to the base. It was no small feat, even for a man of his strength, and when we returned to camp, beads of perspiration dripped from his sun-kissed skin. The baby slept in my arms while we walked. She looked just like her mother, even swathed in army green. She had Kitty's nose, for sure, and those high cheekbones. I wondered if she'd one day grow a headful of curls. I hoped so.

"We'll get you settled in the infirmary now," I said to Kitty.

"But Anne, no, I—"

"Shh," I whispered. "Don't you worry. You have nothing to be ashamed of."

It was five a.m., and while there may have been a few nurses tending to patients in the far wing, it wasn't likely we'd run into any of them, except Nurse Hildebrand.

Westry carried Kitty inside. I directed him toward a small private room to the right, where he set her down gently on the bed. I nestled the baby girl in her arms.

The child fit like a puzzle piece. Kitty looked at me, and then at Westry, before running her hand along the stubble of his chin. "How can I ever thank you?"

"No thanks necessary," he said, smiling. "But you might help a fellow find a new shirt."

"Oh," Kitty said, smiling, "but doesn't my baby look lovely in this shade of green?"

Westry grinned, helping himself to a white medical coat, probably one of Dr. Livingston's, hanging on a hook beside the bed.

"It suits you," I said, winking.

We all looked toward the door when we heard the knob turn. Nurse Hildebrand walked in, startled at the sight of Westry in a white coat.

"And you are?"

"Westry Green, ma'am," he said. "I was just getting these two—I mean, these three—settled, before going on my way."

"I can take it from here, solider," she said briskly. "And you can return the coat once you've washed and pressed it."

Westry nodded, and walked toward the door. "Good night, ladies," he said, sending a final grin my way.

"Good night," I said. I couldn't help but notice something unsettled in Kitty's eyes as Westry walked out.

"Anne, Kitty, are you all right?"

"Yes," I said. "The baby is healthy. She needs to be cleaned up, though. They both do."

Nurse Hildebrand nodded and pulled a basin from the closet. "Anne, you'll give the child her first bath."

"Of course," I said, taking the baby from Kitty's arms.

"I will phone the Mayhews and ask them to come," Nurse Hildebrand continued. "You can swaddle her in this spare sheet when you're finished. They'll have clothes and blankets for her at their home."

Kitty shook her head. "The Mayhews?"

"The couple who is taking your child," she replied.

Terror appeared on Kitty's face. "But it's so soon," she said. "I—I . . ."

"It's what you wanted, Kitty. And it's what has to be done," Nurse Hildebrand said without emotion. "You can't keep a child here. This is the right choice for her, for you. The sooner you let go, the easier it will be."

Kitty watched despondently as I bathed her little girl, lathering her tiny head with soap and gently wiping the suds away with a washcloth.

"Her name is Adella," Kitty muttered.

"You can't name her, dear," Nurse Hildebrand retorted. "The Mayhews will have their own name."

"I don't care!" Kitty snapped, looking away. "To me she will always be Adella."

I rinsed the remaining soap bubbles off the child's delicate skin before lifting her out of the basin and into a towel. Once she was dry, I carefully swaddled her in a sheet, as Nurse Hildebrand had instructed, then tucked the tiny package into Kitty's arms.

"No," she said, turning away, choking back tears. "I can't hold her. If I hold her, I won't be able to let her go. Can't you see that, Anne?" Kitty began to cry, but it wasn't the same sort of cry I'd heard from her in years past. This was sorrow that emanated from someplace very deep.

I swallowed hard, trying to stay strong for Kitty's sake, and walked the baby outside the room. I waited there for some time, until a couple, maybe in their early thirties, appeared in the hallway. Kitty's muffled sobbing seeped through the closed door.

Nurse Hildebrand indicated the couple and nodded. "John and Evelyn Mayhew," she said, forcing a smile. "They'll take the baby now."

The couple looked kind, and I could see by the woman's eager smile that she would welcome the child with love. She stroked the baby's head. "She must be hungry," she said, retrieving her from my arms. "We have a bottle waiting in the car." Nurse Hildebrand watched quietly, perhaps even proudly, as the new mother bonded with "her" child.

"Adella is her name," I said quietly, on Kitty's behalf.

"It's a beautiful name," she said, "but we've chosen another. I will put it in her birth records, though, so it will always be a part of her history."

I nodded and stepped back as the couple thanked Nurse Hildebrand and left, an instant family of three.

"I'm going to go to Kitty now," I said, reaching for the doorknob.

"Anne, wait," Nurse Hildebrand said, "not

yet. Please, I'd like to have a word with her first."

I wasn't sure what she had in mind, but the seriousness in her face told me to oblige. I waited outside the door for what felt like an eternity. *What is she doing in there? What's she saying to Kitty?*

I pressed my ear against the door, and heard Nurse Hildebrand say something startling. "I was in your situation once." The words shocked me, and I jumped back when the doorknob began to turn.

When the door opened, Kitty emerged with dry eyes and a blank, emotionless expression I'd never seen on her face before.

# Chapter 11

Nurse Hildebrand excused me from my duties at the infirmary so I could care for Kitty in the days that followed. I stayed in the room and kept her company, though I think she would have preferred to be alone.

"How about a game of cards?" I suggested, reaching for the deck in my bedside table.

"No," Kitty said. "Thanks, but I'd rather not."

I brought her meals and tried to interest her in magazines. Liz, believing that Kitty was still recovering from an illness, stopped by to deliver the two latest issues of *Vogue*, but Kitty just set them on her bed, preferring to stare at the wall ahead rather than the latest fashions.

I knew I couldn't fix things for her. She had to wade through this on her own, which is why I excused myself two days after the birth for a beach walk and a visit to the bungalow. I craved a change of scenery, and Kitty needed to be alone.

Westry was there, just as I'd hoped he'd be, napping on the bed as the afternoon sun streamed in.

"Hi," I whispered, nestling my body on the bed beside him. He opened his eyes and smiled warmly at me, pulling me closer.

"I bet you didn't know that you were sleeping in the presence of a masterpiece," I said, grinning.

Westry ran his finger along my face and marveled. "I've known it since the day you stepped foot in this place. You are the world's greatest work of art."

I smiled and shook my head. "No, silly. Not me, the painting." I reached for the painting under the bed. "It's a *Gauguin*."

Westry sat up quickly, looking at the canvas with fresh eyes. "You're serious?"

I nodded.

He shook his head in disbelief. "I always thought it had to be done by one of the Postimpressionists, but more likely by a younger, lesser-known painter, or maybe the apprentice of one. But God, Gauguin? How can you be sure?"

"An old woman on the island told me," I said, smiling proudly.

Westry sat down on the bed next to me for a closer look. "It's not signed," he said.

"Maybe he didn't sign his work early on."

"You could be right about that," he conceded. "Monet did the same."

I nodded. "And look at those brush strokes."

"You could get lost in this painting," Westry said, still marveling at the treasure in his hands.

"What will we do with it?" I asked, smoothing Westry's rumpled shirt.

"I don't know."

"We can't leave it here," I said, "when the war's over, when we're gone. I couldn't bear to think of the painting swallowed up by a tidal wave."

Westry agreed. "Or deteriorating in the humid air. I'm surprised it's lasted this long out here in the elements."

I hung the painting back up on the little hook, and sighed. "Or maybe it's meant to stay right here." I looked at the canvas for a moment before turning back to Westry. "There's something else I need to tell you. Something about this bungalow."

"What is it?"

"The old woman, Tita, she warned me about this place. She said that all who step foot inside live with some sort of curse."

Westry grinned. "And you believed her voodoo?"

"Well, it frightened me, I will admit."

"Anne, remember what we talked about, the first day we met? You told me you believed that life is about free will." He stroked my hair lightly. "Your life will be rich and blessed and filled with love because of what you make it."

I tucked my hand in his. "You're right."

"Besides," he continued, "look at all the good that has come from these four walls. Our love has grown. A baby has been born. And we may have discovered one of the greatest artistic finds in our century. Is that what the old woman calls a *curse*?"

As we sat together listening to the waves

roll onto the shore, I said a silent prayer.
*God, please let him be right.*

Time was growing scarce now; we all knew
that. May had blown through like a fierce
storm, and Kitty and I would be leaving
the island in mid-June, at the same time
that Westry and the other men would ship
off for another tour of duty—this time in Europe. As a result, I could almost hear the
ticktock of a clock in the distance, a constant reminder that the world we'd come to
know was hurtling toward an abrupt end.

I'd have to face Gerard. Kitty would have
to leave her daughter's birthplace. How
could we return to Seattle such changed
women? How could we even pretend to
resume our old roles in that foreign place
we once called home?

"I think I'm going to stay," Kitty announced one morning in the mess hall in
early June. "Nurse Hildebrand could use
the help. Besides, no one's waiting for me
in Seattle."

She hadn't meant it as a jab, but her
words, and the long pause that followed,
pierced. It was true. Gerard would be waiting. He was due home in June.

I wondered about Kitty's motivation to stay. So unlike the woman who had stepped off the plane the very first day on the island, she had become a shell of her former self. Vacant. Distant. Lost. She devoted herself to work, and spent every spare minute in the infirmary.

"I just don't understand," I said to her between bites of boiled egg. "Don't you miss home? Don't you want to leave this island after . . . after everything?"

She glanced out the window toward the lush, emerald hillside in the distance. Just as memories would forever anchor my heart to this place, I suspected that Kitty would always feel that a piece of her was here too.

She forced a smile. "I thought I'd want to leave when the time came," she said. "But now, well, I'm just not ready."

I nodded.

"These past months have sure turned out differently for us," she said, her voice thick with regret. "But you've met the most marvelous man. To think that you found him out here in the middle of a war."

As if on cue, Westry waved from the other side of the mess hall. Then, in a breach of protocol, he approached our table. "Well if it isn't the two most lovely women on the island," he said, a cloth napkin still dangling from his collar. "How are you, darling?" he said to me, as I pulled the napkin free and handed it to him.

"Wonderful," I replied. "I missed you in the bungalow this morning." It felt strange to speak openly about our secret, but it didn't matter now that Kitty had been there herself, and besides, there weren't any other diners at the table.

"Westry," Kitty said, perking up. I didn't like how she batted her eyelashes at him. "I found some stray floorboards in a closet in the infirmary. I thought they might work to fix that creak in the bungalow's floor."

My cheeks burned. *How could Kitty think it's her place to talk to Westry about the bungalow? And how in heaven's name does she know, or remember, that the floorboards creak?*

"Thanks, Kitty," Westry said, unfazed. "I'll stop by today and take a look at them."

"But—" I opened my mouth and then shut it again.

"What is it?" Westry asked.

"Nothing," I muttered. "I was just going to suggest that we meet at the bungalow later this evening." I made sure to look directly at Westry, making clear that he was the sole recipient of the invitation.

"I'd love nothing more," he said. "I'm off at five thirty. Just in time for the sunset."

"Good," I said, instantly feeling better.

As Westry turned to leave, Kitty stood up. "If you'd like to come by this afternoon, I'll be working until eight." She looked at me awkwardly. "I mean, if you want to see those floorboards."

Westry nodded noncommittally and walked out of the building.

We ate in silence for a few minutes, until Kitty spoke again. "So, as I was saying, I'll probably stay on for a few more months, and then who knows?" Her gaze drifted toward the window again. "There's plenty of opportunity for nurses these days. Maybe I'll sign up for a post in Europe."

I watched her mouth open and close and the words pass her lips. *Who is this woman before me?* I searched her eyes, but she looked away. "It's just that I—"

"I told Nurse Hildebrand I'd help her with

the immunizations today," she said, cutting me off. "I'd better be going."

"Yes, right, you'd better be going," I said, but she'd already made her way through the door.

"There's something wrong with Kitty," I said that evening, kicking my shoes off as I walked into the bungalow and collapsed on the bed.

"Well hello to you, too," Westry said, grinning, tucking a bouquet of hibiscus in my hand.

"Sorry," I said, marveling at the blossoms, vibrant yellow—a stark contrast to the more common red hibiscus that grew like weeds all around the base. These were not typical. As far I as I knew, they were the only yellow hibiscus on the island, and they grew right here, mere feet from the bungalow. I set the flowers down on the chair and sighed, thinking of Kitty.

"It's just that I had a strange encounter with her at breakfast, and I'm worried about her. She's changed so much in these past few months. I hardly know her anymore."

Westry pulled out his pocketknife and carefully sliced a red apple on the mahogany desk. "She *has* changed," he said. "Anyone who's gone through what she's gone through would have to. Do you think you might be being too hard on her?"

I nodded. "You're probably right," I said, reaching for the slice of apple he held out to me. Its crunchy sweetness dulled my worries, for a moment.

"You're not upset about the comment she made about the floorboards, are you?"

"No," I lied. "Well, maybe a little." I sighed. "Is it wrong that I feel possessive of this place?"

He grinned, sitting down next to me on the bed. "No, but I'd rather you feel possessive of me."

I gave him a playful shove. "I do, which is why my next question is, did you go to see her at the infirmary today?"

"Yes," he said, reveling in the discovery of my jealousy.

"And?"

He shook his head. "The floorboards she had in mind were all wrong."

"Good," I said. "I like our floorboards."

He ran his finger along the nape of my neck. "Me too."

"And besides," I continued, "new floorboards would mean we'd lose our mailbox."

"It's unanimous, then," he said, striking an imaginary gavel. "The creaky floorboards stay."

He took the gold locket into his hands and carefully opened it. "Still empty?"

"I know," I said. "I've been trying to think of the perfect thing to put inside, but I haven't been struck with inspiration just yet."

Westry's eyes darted. "It needs to be something that reminds you of here, of us—something that will warm your heart with the memories of our love."

I frowned, snatching the locket from his hands. "Memories of our love? You talk as if our days are numbered, as if this is just a—"

"No," he said, putting his hand to my lips. "I intend to love you for the rest of my life, but I have another tour of duty ahead; you know that. While I'm in Europe, however long this war lasts, I want to know that you can find me, and this place, in your memories. It will help sustain you while we're apart."

Westry stood up and searched the room, running his hands along the desk, the woven walls, the curtains, before crouching down to the floor. "I've got it," he said, prying a tiny piece of wood from an edge of a warped floorboard. "A piece of the bungalow. You can carry it with you always, and with it, there I will be."

My eyes welled up with tears as he opened the locket and placed the piece of floorboard, just a mere splinter, inside. It was *perfect*. "There," he said, patting the locket against my chest. "You will always have me with you."

My kiss told him how much I appreciated the gesture.

Shortly after the sun set, Westry lit a candle on the desk, and we huddled together just listening to the breeze and the crickets chirping in the moonlight, until a startling sound caught our attention.

A man's voice, angry and determined, followed by a woman's desperate scream rang out in the distance. The voices sounded far away at first, perhaps deep in the thick jungle brush—far enough away to ignore, but when the screaming grew nearer, I instinctively clutched Westry's arm. "What do you think that is?"

"I don't know," he said, standing up and quickly slipping his arms into his shirt. "But I think she's in trouble. Stay here," he directed me.

"Be careful," I whispered. I didn't know what worried me more—Westry going out there by himself, or me staying in the bungalow alone.

He slipped through the door quietly, listening as he pushed his way toward the brush outside. We heard another scream, and then more footsteps. *Someone is running.*

I stood up and put on my shoes, wishing I had some sort of weapon in the bungalow. *Did Westry bring his gun?* It wasn't likely. The men didn't normally take their weapons out beyond the base. I swallowed hard. *Westry is out there all alone. What if I need to protect him?* I couldn't just stay in the bungalow and wait, I decided.

Quietly, I stepped outside, and when I

noticed a two-by-four propped up against the bungalow, I picked it up. *Just in case.*

I crept toward the beach, but turned around suddenly when I heard a branch breaking nearby. *Was it behind me?* My heart pounded in my chest. I sensed danger lurking. Something evil was in our presence.

Then, another scream rang out, this one near the beach.

"No, no, please, please no hurt me, please!"

I gasped. I knew that voice. *Dear God. Atea. Was she trying to make her way here, to the bungalow, as I instructed her to?* Lance must have followed her. *Where is Westry?* I pushed through the brush to the clearing on the beach and saw the scene that would be burned in my memory forever.

In the shroud of darkness, it was difficult to make out faces, but as my eyes adjusted, the horror came into view. He held her by a clump of her hair; I could see that. Then a flash of steel shone in the moonlight. *God, no.* A knife. He sliced the blade along her neck, and I watched, mute, as her small, limp body fell to the sand.

"No," I muttered, unable to find the strength of my voice. *No, this can't be.*

The shadowy figure tossed the knife like a football deep into the jungle, before pitching a jog down the beach.

I ran to Atea, choking back tears. "Atea, I'm so sorry, I'm so sorry." I lifted her blood-soaked head onto my lap. She gurgled and choked for breath.

"He, he," she sputtered.

"No, honey," I whispered. "Don't try to talk. Don't say anything."

Blood pooled in her mouth. She was dying. If we could get her to the infirmary in time, Doc Livingston might be able to save her. *We have to save her.*

Atea gestured to her belly, swollen, round. *She's pregnant. Oh my God.*

"Westry!" I screamed. "Westry!"

I heard footsteps approach from the direction in which Lance had left, and I prayed he wasn't coming to finish the job. "Westry!" I called out again.

"I'm here," he said. "It's me."

"Oh, Westry!" I cried. "Look at her. Just look at what he's done to her." I gasped. "And to her baby."

Atea lifted her hand in the air, as if to reach for something or someone.

"She's not going to make it," he said.

"What are you saying?" I screamed desperately. "Of course she's going to make it. She has to. I promised I'd protect her from that monster."

Atea's breathing was reduced to a sporadic gurgle and gasp. "She will pull through," I sobbed. "We have to save her."

Westry put his hand on my arm. "Anne," he whispered. "Her neck is half-severed. The best we can do for her is ease her pain, end her misery."

I knew what he was referring to, but could I actually go through with it? It went against everything I'd learned in nursing school, and yet holding Atea's dying body in my arms, I knew it was not only the right choice, but the only choice.

"Go grab my bag under the desk," I said. "Hurry!"

He returned with my knapsack and pulled out the supply of morphine that every nurse kept on hand in wartime. There was enough inside to sedate a 280-pound man, or to send a hundred-pound woman to the gates of heaven.

I kissed Atea's forehead, and injected the first dose in her arm, rubbing the spot where the needle had pricked. "There now," I said, trying to hold back my tears and keep my voice calm and steady for her sake. "The pain will be over soon. Let yourself relax."

Her breathing slowed from choking gasps to shallow gurgles. When I injected the second dose, her eyes turned to the stars, then fluttered and shut. I checked her pulse, and then pressed my ear to her heart.

"She's gone," I said to Westry, tears streaming down my face. "*They're* gone. How could he do this?" I screamed. "How could he?"

Westry slid Atea's limp body onto the soft sand, and helped me to my feet, holding my trembling body in his. "I should have saved her," I cried into his chest. "I promised I'd protect her. I promised I would."

Westry shook his head. "You did the best you could. She went peacefully."

"How could he?" I said, feeling overcome with anger. "How could he do this to her?" I turned to the beach where, just minutes before, the man, presumably Lance, had fled. I pried myself out of Westry's arms and started to run in the direction the man had left in.

Westry ran after me, however, and held me back with a firm grasp on my waist, which made me buckle over, planting my hands on the cold sand. I tried to break free, to stand again, but Westry's strength prevented further movement. "Anne, stop," he pleaded. "You can't."

"What do you mean I can't?" I screamed, throwing a clump of sand toward the lonely stretch of beach where the killer had escaped. "We just watched him murder a woman and her child. We have to find him, Westry. We have to take him to the colonel. He needs to pay for what he did."

Westry knelt beside me, stroking my face. I felt tears on my cheeks, and he wiped them away. "Listen to me," he said softly. "What we saw here tonight was tragic. But I need you to believe me when I tell you that we can never speak of what we saw—not to anyone."

I shook my head. "No, this makes no sense," I said. "A murder was committed;

we must report it. We can bring him to justice."

"We can't," Westry muttered. His voice sounded strange, thick with defeat. "For one, an assault was committed." He paused. "We committed the murder."

"No, that's not true."

"But it's how it would be viewed," he said. "And there's something else, something far worse that could become of us, of those we love, if this secret gets out."

**What does he know? What is he hiding?**

I stood up, brushing the sand off my dress. "This makes no sense," I said. "How can I go back to the base knowing there's a murderer on the loose?"

He searched my eyes. "Tonight," he said, pointing to the bungalow, "you said you loved me; you said you wanted to spend forever with me."

I nodded.

"Then will you trust me?"

I held up my hands in confusion. "Westry, I just, I—"

"Just promise me you won't say anything," he said. "One day you'll understand. I promise."

We both turned to look at Atea. Even in death, she exuded beauty and gentleness. I exhaled deeply and looked at Westry's strong, steady face. No matter how uncertain his plan seemed, I trusted him. If he said this was the right course of action, I had to believe it would be.

"I won't say anything," I whispered.

"Good," he said, stroking my cheek. "We'll have her buried by sunrise."

# Chapter 12

It wasn't a grave worthy of her short, beautiful life, but we laid Atea to rest forty feet behind the bungalow in a makeshift plot under a plumeria tree. Fortunately, we had a shovel; Westry had brought one over a week prior in hopes of resetting one of the bungalow's foundation beams. It took him an hour to dig the grave. I watched him for a long while, then slipped away to the beach when I could no longer stomach the gritty sound of the shovel hitting the dirt again and again.

Once my feet hit the sand, I collapsed to my knees. Never in my life had I seen such horror. And while I had agreed to trust Westry, I couldn't deny the longing in my heart for justice. I replayed the scene in my mind over and over again, hoping to find some clue, some frame I'd missed, which is when I remembered the knife.

Lance had thrown it into the brush before exiting the scene. I remembered the flash of steel in the moonlight, and my heart began beating louder in my chest. *If I could find the knife, I could at least secure proof that he did it.*

I ran back to the bungalow and retrieved the lantern, then cautiously walked to the edge of the jungle. Animals howled and snickered in the distance. The wind rustled the bushes. What used to seem like a place of beauty and serenity now felt like a safe haven for evil. I considered turning back, but I found my strength. *Atea. Remember Atea.* I nodded to myself and took one step forward, and then another. The crunch of my feet on the earth below me seemed to amplify with each step.

I shone the lantern farther down the path. *It has to be close. Just a few more steps, perhaps.* A snake slithered by, too near for my liking, and I gasped, taking an exaggerated step back, before continuing on. *Keep going, Anne.* I looked back toward the beach and tried to mentally calculate the distance the knife may have traveled. I eyed a large palm to my left, moving my search there. It had to be near.

But after several more minutes I wondered if the jungle may have swallowed up the knife, a coconspirator in the gruesome crime. I leaned against the palm and set my lantern down, and when I did, it made a little clinking sound.

I knelt down and immediately noticed a familiar shimmer of metal. My hands trembled as I pulled the bloodied knife from its hideaway in the soil. I inched the lantern closer to read the inscription on the army green handle: *Unit #432; Issue #098.*

"Anne? Anne, where are you?"

Westry's voice filtered through the thicket. *How long have I been gone? What would he think of me searching for the knife like this, especially after I promised to trust him?*

"Anne?" His voice was nearer now. I reached down to the edge of my dress and ripped off a piece of the light blue linen fabric. Quickly, I wrapped the knife inside, then dug a little crevice with my bare hands, deep enough for adequate protection, tucking the blade inside. I covered it with dirt and a pile of leaves before standing up, just as Westry approached.

"Oh, there you are," he said. "What are you doing out here? I was worried."

"Just thinking," I said, brushing off my dirt-stained hands on the back of my dress.

"Come on," he said. "I know this has been a hard night, but we need to"—he paused to find the right words—"see this through."

I nodded and followed him back toward the makeshift grave, where I waited while Westry went to get Atea. He returned with her in his arms, and tears streamed down my face again at the sight.

He set her body inside the hole, and we both stared in silence. After a few minutes, Westry reached for the shovel, but I pulled his arm back. "Not yet," I said.

I picked three pink plumeria blossoms from the nearby tree, then knelt at Atea's grave. "She deserves flowers," I said, without looking away from her face.

I scattered the blooms across her body, then looked away as Westry began shoveling the earth over her. I couldn't watch, but I forced myself to stay until he finished. We walked back to camp in silence, for our world had changed—forever, perhaps.

It was close to three when I snuck into the room that morning. Kitty didn't stir, and with a ripped, blood-and-dirt-stained dress, I was glad of that. I slipped off my clothes, tucking them into the wastebasket, then pulled a nightgown over my head and crawled into bed. Sleep didn't come, though. I knew we hadn't committed a crime, but I was plagued with the horrible and yet very real fear that we were guilty.

The next morning, I awoke to the sound of a fist pounding on my door. I sat up in bed, disoriented, and glanced over at Kitty's bed, which was neatly made. I covered my face when the bright light from the window hit my eyes. *What time is it?*

The pounding at the door persisted. "Yes, I'll be there in a minute," I muttered, stepping one foot out of bed and then the other, stumbling to the door. Stella stood outside, with a disapproving frown.

"Anne, look at you," she said. "Asleep at half past eleven? Nurse Hildebrand is fuming. She sent me up to find you. Your shift started at eight."

I peered at the little alarm clock on my bedside table. "Oh my," I said. "I can't believe I slept this late."

Stella smirked. "Must have been some night." She gave me the once-over, and her eyes paused at my hands. "What were you doing—making mud pies?"

I looked down at my dirt-caked nails and hid them self-consciously in the folds of my nightgown. As I did, the memories of the night before came swirling back. The murder. The knife. The cover-up. Westry's words of caution. I hoped Stella couldn't see the goose bumps that had broken out on my arms.

"Please tell Nurse Hildebrand that I'll be over just as soon as I can dress," I said.

"And wash," added Stella, grinning accusatorily before walking away.

I nodded. "Stell!" I called out to the hallway after her.

"Yes?" she said, turning back to the door.

"Why didn't Kitty come wake me?"

"I wondered that too," she said, her

voice free from sarcasm, rare for Stella. "Something's not quite right about her. It's like she's—"

"Like she's not my friend anymore?" I said. The words felt like grenades hitting my tired heart.

Stella put her hand on my arm. "Don't worry, hon," she said. "I'm sure whatever it is will blow over soon."

I hoped she was right.

Ever since Kitty had given birth, she and Nurse Hildebrand had struck up an unlikely friendship. Kitty would often stay late in the infirmary to help our superior with special projects, and her name was always first on the list when a special assignment or patient needed tending to.

It was good to see Kitty excelling in her work. It was what she'd wanted for her life, after all. And here, she could do something of meaning. Yet the more she poured herself into nursing, the more distant she became.

Such a division would have felt more pronounced at home, in Seattle, but in a war zone, we could push it aside and let the fighting, the news, the misery muffle our personal problems.

"Liz heard from a corporal down at the docks that things are heating up again out in the Pacific," I said to Kitty that night at dinner. We talked about little else besides the war.

"Oh?" she replied, without looking up from the book in her hands.

"Do you think we'll have a few busy shifts ahead?" I asked, hating the formality of our exchange.

"I suppose," Kitty said, yawning. "Well, I better be off. I'm working on a project for Nurse Hildebrand. I'll be in the infirmary."

I spotted Westry on the other side of the mess hall, laughing with Ted and a few other men. *How can he be so calm, so jovial, after what we went through just hours before?*

I carried my tray to the kitchen, and waited for him outside on the path.

"Hi," he said when his eyes met mine. We walked a few paces together, toward the marina. "How are you doing?" he whispered when the other men were out of earshot.

"Not good," I said. "I keep having memories from last night and praying that it was only a nightmare. Westry, tell me it was all a nightmare."

He pulled my head close to his. "I wish I could."

"Have you seen Lance?" I whispered.

"No," he said, looking around uncomfortably. "Didn't you hear?"

"Hear what?"

"He shipped out this morning, on a special mission with a dozen others."

"Sounds to me like he's running away," I huffed.

Westry looked uncomfortable. "We can't talk about this anymore," he said. "It's too dangerous."

I nodded, remembering Liz's paranoia. Convinced that the base could be littered with hidden recording devices, she chose to share secrets only in the barracks, and usually only in the bathrooms. "Will I see you tonight at the bungalow?"

Westry rubbed his forehead. "I wish I could, but I'm working later tonight, and after last night . . . I guess I could use the solitude."

*Solitude?* The word pierced me like an arrow.

"Oh," I said, visibly hurt.

Westry tried to lighten the moment with a smile. "I only mean that we're both operating on such little sleep, it would make sense to turn in early."

"You're right," I said, still smarting.

"Besides," he said, "are you really ready to go back there, after—after all that's happened?"

Yes, horror had infiltrated our private world, but I couldn't shake the feeling that Westry was giving up on the bungalow, on us.

"I don't know," I muttered. "I know that what we had there was beautiful, and I don't want to lose it."

"Neither do I," he said.

It was a week before I stepped foot in the bungalow, and I did so alone. Westry had joined some of the men on a construction project on the other side of the island. He'd been vague about when he'd return. But as the days ebbed on, I felt the bungalow calling me, drawing me back, and after a particularly long shift in the infirmary, where the women spent most of it huddled over a tiny radio listening to the latest on the fight in the Pacific, I succumbed to its call.

It was dusk when I set out for the beach, and I clutched my locket as I made my way up the shore. I pushed past the brush, but took a step back when my eyes detected a figure sitting on the steps of the bungalow.

"Who's there?" I called out.

Someone stood and began to walk toward me. With each step forward, I took a step back.

"Who is it?" I cried, wishing I'd brought a lantern. But as the figure moved out into the open, the moonlight shone down. It was Tita.

"Anne," she said.

*What is she doing here? Looking for Atea, no doubt.* My heart pounded. *What will I tell her?*

The old woman's face looked tired and anguished.

"Would you like to come in?" I said, gesturing to the bungalow.

She looked at the hut with eyes that told me she'd been inside, perhaps a long time ago. She shook her head. "Maybe you don't remember what I told you about this place," she muttered. "It's cursed." She pointed to the beach ahead and began walking out of the thicket. I followed, unsure of what was in store.

"Sit," she said, gesturing at a spot not far from where Atea had clung to life. I was grateful that the waves had washed away the bloodstained sand.

We sat in silence for a few minutes until Tita finally spoke. "I know she is gone," she said.

Unsure of how to respond, I kept looking out at the surf, letting the soothing ebb and flow of the waves numb my heartache.

"I warned you," she said, scowling. "This place is evil. It's no good. And now it took my Atea, our Atea. She was special, you know."

I tried in vain to stop the tears from coming, but they seeped from my lids of their own accord. "Oh, Tita," I cried. "I'm so sorry."

"Hush," the old woman said, standing. "What's done is done. Now it is your duty to make justice."

**What does she know? Or worse, what**

**does she think she knows? Did she see the disturbed ground where Westry dug the grave?**

I watched, bewildered, as she made her way toward the jungle.

"Tita," I said. "Please, Tita, wait. You're wrong. If you think that I, that we—"

"Justice," she said, turning toward me a final time, "is the only way you will ever break the curse."

I watched her walk into the thicket until the jungle seemed to swallow her whole. I sighed and collapsed onto the sand, wrapping my arms around my knees the way I'd done as a girl after a scolding from Mother. Lance wasn't on the island, at least for now, and there hadn't been any Japanese flyovers in months. So why did I sense evil lurking? I thought about the knife, stained with Atea's blood, buried a few hundred feet away, safely wrapped in the swatch of fabric from my dress. No one knew it was there but me. I could retrieve it as evidence. I could seek justice, just as Tita had urged me to. But how could I ignore Westry's convictions?

I rose to my feet and walked to the bungalow, unlocking its door with the familiar motions and then stowing the key back inside the book. The air inside felt thick and suffocating. I thought about the painting under the bed and knelt down to retrieve it. *Who are the subjects in it, and were they in this very bungalow? Did they meet misfortune in the way Tita spoke of? Or were they lucky enough to escape the "curse"?*

I reached for a piece of paper and pen on the desk, and sat to write Westry a letter, my heart racing at what I was about to record:

My dear Grayson,

I wish you were here now, to take me into your arms, to erase my memory of the horrors I have seen. I worry that, after what we've witnessed, I may never view these walls in the same way again, and that frightens me.

I have an idea, a plan. We've only spoken of the future in vague terms, but after the war, after this is all over, perhaps we can go to the military superiors and report the crime. Perhaps the hesitation you feel will be remedied by time. I have evidence, something that will clear our names from any wrongdoing when the time is right. My dear, please tell me when the time is right.

But, there is something else. By now you know of my love for you, and I want you to know that there is nothing else I'd rather do than share my life, share eternity, with you—right here on this island if that's what you want. What I'm saying, my love, is that I am yours, if you ask me to be.

Love, forever and always,

Cleo

I folded the page in half and tucked it under the floorboard, exhaling deeply as I reached for the doorknob.

Two days later, Kitty, seated on her bed, looked up from a magazine, startled. "Did you hear something hit the window?"

It was half past three, but instead of working in the infirmary, we'd all been ordered to the barracks after a Japanese warship was detected two miles off shore. Kitty clutched her rosary as she thumbed through the pages of *McCall's*; I pulled out a novel I'd started the first month on the island, but I found myself unable to read. The fear in the air had a paralyzing effect.

I shook my head. "I didn't hear anything."

No one knew what was going to happen next. One of the nurses said the ship was en route to another destination. Another said that a soldier had confirmed by the ship's coordinates that it was heading dead on to Bora-Bora. War here? On our island? Clinging to disbelief was a comforting defense, but we all knew an attack was a possibility. Our only option was to watch and wait.

"There's a cellar," I said, "below the barracks. Stella thinks we'll be moved down there in the event of—"

Kitty flinched. "There," she said, "that sound. I heard it again. Something keeps knocking at our window."

I forced a smile. "I know you're worried, Kitty, but the Japanese aren't outside our window—yet."

Kitty didn't return my smile. Instead, she stood up and walked to the window. "See?" she said, grinning victoriously. "It's Westry. He must have been trying to get our attention."

*Our attention?* I watched Kitty at the window, waving down at Westry. I didn't like how her spirits lifted instantly in his presence.

"I'll go see him," I said possessively, walking out the door and briskly down the stairs to the entrance.

"Hi," I whispered once outside.

Westry grinned. "Why the whisper?"

"Don't you know? The island may be under attack."

Westry put his hands in his pockets and tilted his head to the right, looking at me with an amused grin. "I love your spirit, you know that? Come here, let me see you."

I lingered in his embrace for longer than was proper for the base, but somehow decorum seemed insignificant now.

"You seem overly confident," I sparred back.

He shrugged. "After you've been through a fight like I've been through, a battleship on the horizon doesn't ruffle your feathers, I guess."

"But what if they're coming?" I said. "What if they're on their way to our island?"

"They may be," he said. "It's too early to tell, though."

I sighed. "And to think we've been here for so many months, and with so little time before our departure, this happens. Some luck."

Westry caressed my chin, tracing my profile with his finger until tingles ran down my back. "Let's go to the bungalow," he whispered into my neck.

"In the middle of all of this?"

"Why not?" he said, hypnotizing me with his caress.

"Because we've been given orders to stay in the barracks," I protested weakly.

Westry looked at me with his big, hazel eyes. "But it may be our last time in the bungalow together before . . . before . . ."

Neither of us knew what would happen next, and in my heart, I knew what mattered was now. I squeezed his hand. "OK."

"If we're lucky," he said, "we can slip through the jungle and not run into a soul."

I nodded. "Do you think we'll be safe out there?"

"We'll be able to see the ship from the beach, and if it gets close enough, we'll head back and I'll join the ranks."

I frowned, remembering the beating Colonel Donahue had unleashed on Westry in the barracks, then hesitated. "Will you get in trouble for this?"

"Probably," he said, his eyes sparkling in the late-afternoon sun. "But I don't care."

He reached for my hand and I glanced up to the second floor, where Kitty lingered at the window. When our eyes met, I gestured toward the beach and then waved, hoping she'd understand. But she turned quickly to the bed without so much as a smile.

Westry unlocked the door to the bungalow, and we exhaled deeply once inside. "I feel like we're fugitives," I said.

"I suppose we are," he replied, resting his hands on my waist.

"Westry?"

"What, dear?"

"I was here a few days ago, and, well, I'm frightened," I said.

"About what?"

"Tita was here."

"Tita?"

"The old woman who Atea lived with. She's some kind of shaman or spiritual leader. I'm not entirely sure, but she seems to know about Atea."

"How could she know?"

"I don't know," I said. "But she warned me again about the bungalow's curse. She said justice was the only way to break the cycle of the curse."

Westry frowned. "Don't believe it for a minute."

"Why shouldn't I believe her? She knows this place better than you or I."

"What she, and you, don't realize is that with justice comes something else, something far worse than the guilt we may carry with us." Westry sat down on the old mahogany chair. For the first time, I detected the weight of the secret in his eyes. He didn't want to keep it any more than I did; yet he was holding to his convictions. "How can I make you understand that we can't seek justice? Not the kind you want, anyway. It's the way it must be."

I nodded, reaching for his hand. It felt wrong to argue on what could be our final night together. I poked my head out the front window and could make out the battleship in the distance. "It's still there," I said.

He pulled me closer, and I remembered the letter I'd left for him, with my heartfelt confessions about the future. *Has he read it? Does he want to spend a lifetime with me, too?* I sighed nervously.

"Westry," I whispered.

"Yes, my love."

"Did you get my letter?"

"No," he said. "I haven't been here in days." He began walking to the floorboard to retrieve his mail, but I pulled his arm back.

"Not yet," I said a little shyly. "Tuck it in your pocket when we leave. I want you to read it alone."

"Is it bad news?"

"No, no," I said. "Just wait. You'll see."

He nodded, pulling my body tight against his. He flipped on the little radio on the desk, and the French station came through again, crystal clear.

"Let's not think about anything else but our love," he said as we swayed to the music.

"OK," I whispered. His suggestion worked like magic, blocking the war, worries of Kitty, and the lingering darkness from the murder on the beach. For a moment, the bungalow was ours again, ours alone.

Westry kissed my cheek shortly after the sun went down. "It's probably time that we started back," he said. I could sense his anxiety building, and it worried me. I didn't know whether it was the enemy in our midst that gave him pause or what we both knew and dreaded—that our time together was coming to an end.

"We probably should," I agreed, considering the prospect of just holding out in the bungalow when the Japanese appeared on the shore. *Would the bungalow's "curse" protect us?*

I smoothed my dress and refastened a pin in my hair. "Don't forget your letter," I said as Westry opened the door.

"Of course," he replied, kneeling down to the floorboard and reaching inside. "Wait, what letter?" He shook his head. "There's no letter here."

"Silly," I said, kneeling down next to him. "Of course there is. Maybe I pushed it back too far." I wedged my hand deeper behind the joists, but was horrified to find the space empty.

"My God, Westry," I said. "It's gone."

"What do you mean? No one knows

about our hiding place. Unless you told someone."

"Of course I didn't," I said, confused.

A light flashed in the ocean ahead, diverting Westry's worries to a bigger concern. "We'll have to figure this out later," he said. "I need to get you back."

The door creaked to a close, and Westry locked it ceremoniously. "We'll head back through the trail in the jungle," he said. "It'll be safer."

I nodded, taking his hand. As we walked through the thicket, I thought about the letter. *Who could have taken it, and why?* Now, with so little time left, I needed Westry to know my true feelings, about him, and about what I hoped for after the war. *Will I have the chance to tell him? Does he feel the same?*

By the time we made it back to base, however, I wasn't thinking about the letter anymore. Instead, something else haunted me.

"Westry," I whispered, in a panic, as he walked me to the entrance of the women's barracks. "We have to go back!"

He looked confused. "Why?"

"The painting," I said. "We left the painting there."

He shrugged. "We can get it later."

"No, no," I said. "Whoever took the letter I wrote could take the painting."

Westry looked momentarily concerned, then shook his head. "No. Whoever may have taken the letter could have taken the painting already, but they didn't."

I shook my head. "I have a bad feeling about this," I said. "I can't bear to think that the painting could fall into thieves' hands. It belongs in a museum somewhere, a gallery, where it can be admired and treasured."

"And we'll make sure it gets there," Westry reassured me. "Just as soon as this ship passes. I promise. I'll bring it back for you."

"You promise?"

"Yes," he said, kissing my nose.

I turned to the barracks. "Be careful," I said.

"You too."

❦

"There you are!" Nurse Hildebrand whispered in the hallway. Even her whispers sounded like shouts. "I don't have time to hear your explanation, nor do I have time to discipline you, so I will just say that you are the last of the nurses to make it to the cellar. The Japanese are coming. The colonel gave orders for the women to go under. We must hurry."

My heart raced as I followed Nurse Hildebrand down a set of stairs. I patted the place on the collar of my dress where I'd fastened the blue rose pin, the one Kitty gave to me in Seattle. I'd worn it on a whim that morning and gasped when I realized it was *gone*. I stopped suddenly.

"What are you waiting for?" Nurse Hildebrand snapped.

Distraught, I looked down at the stairs, then back toward the door. "It's just that"—I fumbled, patting my dress pockets frantically—"I lost something. Something very important to me."

"Your life is important to you, isn't it?"

I nodded meekly.

"Then let's go. We have to get to the cellar."

*How could I be so careless to lose the pin?* I imagined it lying on the beach, buried in a clump of sand as a wave carried it out to sea. I shuddered, thinking of Kitty. *Is it a sign of the end of our friendship?*

I followed Nurse Hildebrand farther down the stairs, through a locked door, and then watched as she pulled up a rug and pried open a hinge in the floor. "You first," she said, pointing to a dark cavern below.

I descended a ladder into a shadowy space where a few lanterns flickered. When my feet hit the floor, I could make out Liz and Stella, and some of the others in the distance.

"Kitty?" I called out. "Are you here?"

Only silence answered back. I turned to Nurse Hildebrand with concern.

"She's over there," she said, pointing to the light of a single lantern in the far right corner.

"Kitty," I said, walking toward her until I could make out her small, frightened face, wayward curls springing out in disarray. She sat against the wall, looking despondent.

"I was worried you weren't coming," she said, wiping away a tear.

I sat down beside her and squeezed her hand. "I'm here now."

No one knew what was happening above. After two hours, or what felt like twelve, Nurse Hildebrand enlisted Stella to help pass out rations, water, and beans in tin cans. Enough to last days, even weeks. I thought about the prospect of living in the dark, eating canned Spam, and I shuddered.

"Here," said Stella, offering me a canteen. I took a swig and swallowed hard. It tasted of rust.

We all froze when we heard footsteps on the floor above.

"Nurses," Nurse Hildebrand whispered, reaching for a rifle on the wall, "put out your lanterns."

We obeyed, and listened in the darkness, as the footsteps grew closer, louder. There was a thud, and then the creak of the trapdoor opening. I squeezed Kitty's hand harder. *Dear Lord. The Japanese are here.*

But instead of a foreign accent, a familiar voice rang out in the cellar. "Nurses, it's all clear. The ship's turned west. You can come out now."

The women let out a cheer—all but Kitty,

who just stared ahead. I reached for her hand. "Come on, dear," I said. "It's over. We can go now."

She looked startled, as though I'd roused her from a dream. When she turned on her lantern, I could detect the familiar cloudiness in her eyes. The distance. "Yes, of course," she said, standing up and walking ahead of me.

❧

"Can you believe we ship out tomorrow?" Liz marveled at breakfast the next day.

*Tomorrow.* I'd been dreading this day since the moment I fell in love with Westry. Leaving the island meant the end of our reality, and the beginning of a new one— one, I feared, that would be more complicated than we might know.

"The men ship out in the morning," Stella added. She didn't like that Will was joining the fight in Europe any more than I liked that Westry was.

"I was thinking," she continued. "If I went to serve in Europe, I'd at least be closer to him. In case—"

I shook my head. The war had taken its toll on Stella, who was now shockingly thin. She needed leave more than any of us. "Going to Europe won't protect him," I said. "Go home. Wait for him there."

She nodded. "Can you believe Kitty? I hear she's heading to France, right in the middle of the action. She's joining a group headed for Normandy."

My cheeks flushed. France? *Why didn't she tell me the extent of her plans? Does she think I don't care?*

"Well, speaking of the devil," Stella said, pointing to the door.

Kitty walked into the mess hall, smiling. Her cheeks looked rosy, the way they once had. As she approached our table, I could see that she was holding a cluster of yellow hibiscus, and my cheeks burned at the sight.

"Morning, ladies," she said. "How are the rations today?"

I felt Stella's eyes boring into the side of my head.

"Fine," Liz, said, oblivious to the tension in the air, "if you like rubberized eggs."

Kitty giggled, setting the flowers, tied in a single white ribbon, on the table. "Aren't they beautiful?" she said, admiring their yellow petals against the contrasting sterile beige tabletop. I knew them instantly, of course—the hibiscus that grew near the bungalow. They had to be.

"Well, well, well," Stella said. "It looks like someone has an admirer.

"Oh, Stell," Kitty said, playing coy.

"Then where did you get them?" she said relentlessly. I wished she'd stop. I didn't want to know.

Kitty grinned and twirled around toward the buffet line, leaving us to our imaginations.

Stella cleared her throat and smirked. "What did I warn you about the first day on this island?"

I stood up abruptly and began walking to the door.

"Anne," Stella called out. "Wait. I didn't mean anything by it. Come back."

Outside on the path back to the barracks, my heart pounded as I retraced the past few weeks. I thought of the way Kitty lit up whenever Westry appeared, and the way she had pulled back from me. *Of course Kitty feels something for Westry.*

I froze for a moment. *Could he possibly share her attraction?* Every man in our past—well, except Gerard—had favored

Kitty over me. She was asked first to dance. She had received a half dozen invitations to the Homecoming banquet, when I'd had one. My mind raced. *The letter. My God. Westry didn't seem at all concerned about the prospect of someone taking it. Did he pretend it had been stolen so he wouldn't have to face my declaration of love, my hope for the future—of a future together?*

I kicked a rock on the path and shook my head, dismissing the disturbing train of thought. *No, I won't think of it a moment longer, not when we are leaving tomorrow. Not when we have mere hours left together. There isn't time for nonsense.*

❦

"That's it," Kitty said the next morning after breakfast, sighing. She bent over to zip up the side of her bag, which looked, strangely, smaller than the enormous duffel I'd lugged into this room ten months prior. Like the bag, Kitty had lost some of herself on the island.

"My flight leaves in an hour," she said in a distant voice, her gaze turned to the hillside outside the window, a scene that often captured her attention. I wondered what she was looking for up in those hills.

"Nurse Hildebrand and I will meet up with a squadron flying into France tomorrow. And then . . ." Her voice trailed off.

*Kitty in France. All by herself.* I hated the thought of it, just like I had hated the thought of her coming here, to the South Pacific, alone. It didn't matter what I thought of her feelings for Westry. I knew that somewhere beyond the layers of emotional scars draped over her like armor, my best friend resided. But this time I wouldn't insist on going with her.

"Oh, Kitty!" I cried, leaping to my feet. *If I could only get through to her.* "Why did things turn out the way they did for us?"

Kitty shrugged, reaching for her bag. She looked at me for a long moment. "The island had its way, I guess," she finally muttered.

"No, Kitty, you have it wrong," I said, hearing the panic in my voice—panic at what seemed like the end of a friendship, the end of an era. I thought about my transgressions as a friend. *I could have spent more time with her. I might have been more supportive through her final weeks of pregnancy—but wasn't I? Most important, I should have been honest with her about the bungalow, about everything.* I had let too many secrets creep in between us. Secrets I had promised never to keep. "Kitty," I pleaded. "I haven't changed. I'm still the same old Anne. And I'd wager that you're still the same old Kitty in your heart. I want nothing more than to go on being Anne and Kitty."

She looked at me with eyes I didn't recognize. They were tired and older, hardened. "I wish that too," she said softly, turning away from me. "But I don't think we can now."

I nodded, feeling tears rise from a place deep inside. They welled up in my eyes before spilling out unbidden on my cheeks.

"Good-bye, Anne," Kitty said without turning around. Her tone was businesslike, the way I'd witnessed her speak to the servants in her home growing up, or the clerk at the drugstore. I felt the urge to scream, *"Kitty, stop this right now! Let's end this charade."* But I could only stand there, mute, too stunned, too sad to open my mouth. "I wish you the best of luck," she said, reaching for the door handle. "With everything."

The door clicked closed and the silence

in the room pulsed. I fell to the floor, sobbing into my hands for what felt like hours. *What right does she have to leave like this, to declare our friendship over? How could she behave so coldly?*

When the clock told me it was eleven, I willed myself to stand, prying my tired limbs off the floor. I'd promised Westry a farewell on the tarmac, and his flight left in a half hour, just after mine.

I set my bag by the door and glanced in the mirror at my red, swollen eyes. I hardly recognized myself.

For a moment, I feared I wouldn't find him. I squinted as I looked out at the thick and frenzied crowd of men, awash in army green. A small cohort would stay on the island, but the majority, Westry included, had been tapped for new assignments. France. Great Britain. And a lucky few, like me, would go home.

I squinted, scanning faces, and then toward the edge of the crowd, our eyes met.

Ignoring the orders over the loudspeaker for the nurses to begin boarding, I set my bag down by Stella and Liz and ran to Westry. He lifted me into his arms and we kissed.

"Don't cry, my love," he said, wiping a tear from my cheek. "This isn't good-bye."

"But it is," I said, running my hand along his freshly shaven face. "We don't know what will happen out there." I realized the statement was as much about him as it was about me.

Westry nodded, pulling a nosegay of yellow hibiscus from his bag and tucking it into my hand. A white ribbon loosely tied the blooms in place. *Kitty.* "These flowers," I stammered. "You gave the same ones to Kitty yesterday, didn't you?"

Westry looked confused, then nodded. "Well, yes," he said. "I was—"

Another voice piped through the loud-speaker. "All men proceed to board."

"Westry," I said, feeling panicked. "Is there something you need to tell me? Something about Kitty?"

He looked to his feet momentarily and then back at me. "It's nothing," he said, "but I still should have told you. A few weeks ago, I found her weeping on the beach. I was on the way to the bungalow, and I invited her to join me."

My cheeks burned. *Westry brought her to our bungalow—alone, without me?*

I shook my head in disbelief. "Why didn't you tell me? Why didn't *she* tell me?"

"I'm sorry, Anne," he said. "I really didn't think anything of it."

I turned to glance at the plane that would take me home. Stella was standing beside it waving her arms frantically at me.

"Anne!" she screamed. "It's time to go!"

I took a final look at Westry. The wind had tousled his hair. I longed to run my hands through the sandy blond strands the way I'd done a hundred times in the bungalow, to take in the scent of his skin, to surrender myself to him. But this time, something told me no.

"Good-bye," I whispered in his ear, letting my cheek brush his a final time. I reached for his hand and placed the flowers in his palm before running toward the plane.

"Anne, wait!" Westry shouted. "Wait, the painting. Did you get it?"

I froze. "What do you mean, did I get it? I thought you were going to get it."

Westry threw his hands in the air. "I'm sorry, Anne," he said, looking panic-stricken. "I intended to go back, but there just wasn't time. I . . ." His unit had already boarded the plane, and I could see his commanding officer walking toward him. I turned toward the beach and wondered—if I ran fast—could I make it back to the bungalow to retrieve the canvas before the plane departed?

"Please," I pleaded with Stella, who was standing at the base of the stairway that ascended to the plane's cabin. "Please tell the pilot I just need fifteen minutes. I left something on base. I promise, I'll be quick."

The pilot appeared behind her. "I'm sorry, ma'am, there simply isn't time," he said firmly. "You need to board now."

My legs felt as though they'd been strapped with lead as I climbed the steps. Before the pilot's assistant pulled the hatch shut, my eyes met Westry's. I couldn't hear him over the airplane's engine, which was roaring like a monster, but I could read his lips.

"I'm so sorry," he said. "I'll come back. Please don't you worry, Anne. I—"

The door slammed shut before I could interpret his last words. What did it matter, I reasoned, blotting my tears with a handkerchief. It was over. The magic we'd found in the bungalow was gone, and I could feel its spell lifting as the plane gained speed and altitude. I watched as the island grew smaller, until it appeared a mere dot on a map. A dot where so much had happened, and so much had been left behind.

Stella leaned over to me. "Will you miss it?"

I nodded. "Yes," I said honestly.

"Do you think you'll ever come back?" she asked cautiously. "Will and I have talked about returning for a visit. When the war's over, of course."

I looked out the window again before responding, unable to take my eyes off the speck of emerald floating in the turquoise sea. "No," I assured her. "I don't think I ever will."

I squeezed the locket resting on my chest, grateful for the scrap of wood from the bungalow nestled safe inside. With it, I could always return—in my heart, at least.

# Chapter 13

"We missed you, kid," Papa said as I climbed into the car, grateful not to see Maxine in the backseat. Even with months to process their affair, the revelation that had destroyed the family unit I belonged to, I still couldn't make sense of it.

I sighed, leaning back into the soft leather of the Buick as Papa started the engine and began to back away. Here there would be no jeeps, no gravel roads or potholes.

"It's good to be home," I said, taking in a deep breath of the temperate Seattle air. The return trip had been a harrowing one, with multiple flights and a four-day sea passage. It gave me time to think, to get a grip on the loose ends that plagued my mind, and yet when I stepped out of the airplane onto the airstrip in Seattle, my body trembled with uncertainty.

"Gerard's home," Papa said a little cautiously, as if to test the waters.

I looked at my hands in my lap, hands that had loved Westry, still loved Westry. Hands of betrayal.

"Does he want to see me?" I asked.

"Of course he does, sweetheart," Papa said. "Perhaps the real question is *do you want to see him*?"

He could read my heart. He always could. "I don't know, Papa," I muttered, beginning to weep. "I don't know what I want anymore."

"Come here, honey," he said. I inched closer to him in the front seat, and he draped a firm arm around me, one that told me that despite everything, I would be fine. I only wished I could believe it.

Windermere looked untouched by time, by war. As we passed the familiar estates, however, I knew that appearances were deceiving. The Larson home, for instance,

still had its beautiful lawn and exquisite garden with the elaborate urns and the cherub
fountain in the center of the circle drive,
and yet I knew that heartache clung to every wall, every surface. The twins weren't
coming home. Terry had died in a fight near
Marseilles; Larry in a plane crash two
days later—on the way home to comfort
his mother.

The Godfrey mansion also kept up appearances, even though I knew there was
a bigger story lingering behind the gates.
As we drove past, I held my breath, remembering the night of the engagement
party, Kitty's face, and how we'd sat on the
curb outside making plans for the future. *If
we'd known the way things would turn out,
would we have gone anyway?*

The memories pierced, and I looked
away quickly.

"He came home Friday," Papa said. "Got
sent home a bit early on medical leave."

I stiffened. "*Medical* leave?"

"Yes," he said. "He took a bullet to the
arm and shoulder. He may never regain
functionality in his left arm, but in the scheme
of war wounds, that's no tragedy."

Waves of emotion rolled through my

body. Papa was right. Boys were getting maimed, dying. Gerard's injury hardly compared, but for some reason the news made me grieve in a way I hadn't expected.

"Don't cry, dear," Papa said, stroking my hair. "He's going to be fine."

"I know," I cried. "I know he is. It's just that—"

"It's hard to take," he said. "I know."

"This war," I cried, "it's changed everything, all of us."

"It's true," Papa said solemnly, pulling the car into the familiar driveway. Everything was the same, of course, just as I'd left it. But it wasn't; I knew that. And I could never get it back to the way it had been.

I heard a muffled knock on my bedroom door. *Where am I?* I sat up and tried to get my bearings. The old lace curtains. The big trundle bed. Yes, I was home. *But what time is it? What* day *is it?* The darkness outside the window told me it was late. *How late? How long have I been asleep?* The rain pelted the roof overhead, and I closed my eyes, remembering the rainstorms in the tropics, particularly the way Westry and I had showered together in that downpour on the beach. I could still feel his embrace, smell his soapy skin. I blinked hard. *Was it only a dream?*

I pulled the blanket tighter around my body and ignored the knock that sounded again at the door, this one a bit louder. I couldn't face Maxine. Not yet. *Go away. Please go away. Leave me to my memories.*

Moments later, a slip of paper slid under the door along the wood floor. I stared at it for a while, trying to ignore its presence, but it seemed to pulse, to flash like a bright light I could not block from my view. So I sat up, forced my feet to the floor, and retrieved it.

I held the square of beige stationery in my hands and took a deep breath as I took in the familiar handwriting.

My dear Antoinette,

I know you are hurting. So am I. Please let me comfort you.

Maxine

I wrapped my fingers around the cold doorknob and turned it slowly, opening the door far enough to see Maxine standing in the hallway outside, her hair pulled back in the usual fashion. An apron, pressed neatly, encircled her slim waist. She held a tray of sandwiches. A single pink rose rested inside a glass bud vase, and puffs of steam seeped from an ivory mug. I could smell the Earl Grey.

I released my grasp on the doorknob. "Oh, Maxine!" I cried.

She set the tray down on my bedside table and took me into her arms. The tears erupted with volcanic power, first in little spurts, then in great big heaves, pouring out of my heart, my soul, with such ferocity, I wondered if they'd ever stop.

"Let it all out," she whispered. "Don't hold back."

When the tears had subsided, Maxine handed me a handkerchief and the cup of tea, and I leaned against the headboard, tucking my knees to my chest under my pink cotton nightgown.

"You don't have to talk," she said softly, "if you don't want to."

I looked into her eyes for the first time and could see anguish residing there.

"I'm so sorry," she said, "about the letter I sent. I should never have sent it. I should have let your father tell you. It wasn't my place."

I reached for Maxine's hand. Her fingers felt cold. "You have always been honest with me," I said. "You were right to send it."

"Will you ever forgive me?" Her thick accent made her sound meeker, more vulnerable somehow. "Will you ever love me the way you once did?"

I took a deep breath. "I never stopped loving you, Maxine."

Her eyes sparkled as if it was the only response she needed. "Now," she said, "eat your sandwiches and tell me about the South Pacific. I sense that there is a story that needs telling."

I reached for a *croque monsieur* and nodded, eager to tell her the whole story. Well, parts of it, at least.

⁂

The rain cleared the next day, and as the clouds parted to reveal the June Seattle sun, my heart felt lighter.

"Morning, Antoinette," Maxine chirped from the kitchen. "Breakfast is on the table."

I smiled and joined Papa at the table, surveying my plate: fresh fruit, buttered toast, and an omelet—a veritable feast compared with the rations on the island.

Maxine hung up her apron and joined us at the table. Papa gave her cheek a nuzzle when she did, and I realized that while I may have accepted their love, it would still take some getting used to. *How is Mother taking the news?*

"Papa," I said cautiously, "have you heard from Mother?"

Maxine set down her fork. The air felt thick and uncomfortable. "Yes," he said. "She's in New York now, dear. Of course you know that. She's written you, I gather." He produced a scrap of paper from his pocket. "She asked that I have you call her at this number. She'd like you to come out to see her." He paused. "When you're ready."

I folded the crumpled paper and set it down near my plate. She was shopping, attending fashion shows, no doubt. *But is she happy?*

"Gerard phoned this morning," Papa said, eager to change the subject.

"Oh?"

"He'd like to stop by this afternoon."

My hands instinctively reached for my locket. For a sign.

"Yes," I said, looking to Maxine for approval. "I'll see him."

Maxine's smile told me I'd made the right decision. The first step in making sense of this new reality was facing Gerard and acknowledging the life we'd planned together. I rubbed my hand along the place where my engagement ring had once resided and sighed.

"Good," Papa said from behind his newspaper. "I told him to come by around two."

I heard Gerard's car pull into the driveway, followed by the sound of his footsteps on the porch. I froze. *What will I say to him? How will I act?*

Maxine peeked into my room and gestured toward the stairs. "He's here, Antoinette," she said softly. "Are you ready?"

I smoothed my hair and walked to the top of the stairs. "Yes," I said, composing myself.

*One step, and then two.* I could hear Gerard's voice in the parlor talking to Papa. His nearness caused my heart to flutter in a way I hadn't expected it to. *Three steps. Four.* The voices stopped. *Five steps, six.* And there he was, standing at the base of the stairs, looking up at me with such love, such intensity, that I could not unlock my gaze from his.

"Anne!" he said.

"Gerard!" My voice cracked a little. His left arm rested in a beige sling.

"Well are you going to just stand there or are you going to kiss this wounded soldier?"

I grinned, and sailed down the final steps, welcoming his embrace before planting a light kiss on his cheek, operating on instincts, or muscle memory.

Papa cleared his throat and nodded at Maxine. "We'll leave you two," he said, grinning. "You have some catching up to do."

Gerard took my hand and led me to the sofa in the living room before closing the double doors behind us with his good arm. "I can't tell you how much I've missed you," he said, sitting down beside me.

I'd forgotten how handsome he was, shockingly so. "I'm sorry I didn't write often," I said, frowning.

"It's all right," he replied lovingly. "I knew you were busy."

**But if he really understood the reason, would he be so forgiving?**

"Your arm," I said, touching his shoulder gently, then retracting my hand in haste. "Oh, Gerard. Papa says you may never use it again."

He shrugged. "I should have died out there," he said, looking at his lap. "All the men around me were shot down. All but me. I can't make any sense out of why I was spared."

I could see that, like me, Gerard carried a great burden in his heart, his a nobler one.

He reached for my hands, and then paused, holding up my left hand, bare without the engagement ring.

"Gerard, I—"

He shook his head. "You don't need to explain," he said. "Just having you here, having you back is good enough for now."

I let my head rest on his shoulder.

September 1944

"Can you believe I'm getting married?" I said to Maxine, admiring the white silk gown Mother had shipped from France before the war broke out.

"You look beautiful, Antoinette," she said, tucking a pin in the bodice. "We'll just have the seamstress take it in a bit here. Have you been losing weight?"

I shrugged. "It's nerves, that's all."

"Is something bothering you, my dear? You know you can tell me."

The phone rang before I could answer the question. "I'll get that," I said bolting down the stairs to the kitchen. "It's probably Gerard."

"Hello," I said cheerfully, a little out of breath. "You'll never guess what I'm wearing."

Static crackled over the line. "Anne?" a familiar female voice spoke. "Anne, is that you?"

"Yes, this is she," I said. "Who is this?"

"It's me, Mary."

I gasped. "Mary! My God, how are you?"

"I'm fine," she said. "I don't have much time, so I'll have to keep this short. I'm calling with some bad news, I'm afraid."

I could feel the blood leave my face. *Mary. Bad news.* "What is it?"

"I'm in Paris," she said. "I'm here on account of Edward, but that's for another conversation. You've probably heard about the liberation of the city."

"Yes," I said, still shocked to be speaking to my old friend.

"It's a dream, Anne. The Allies are here. For a while we didn't think it would happen." She paused. "What you need to know is that today at the army hospital I saw Kitty, and . . ."

I had thought of Kitty often, especially now that my wedding date neared. And now the mention of her inflamed the familiar wound in my heart.

"Mary, is she OK?"

"Yes," she said. "She's fine. But, Anne . . . Anne, it's Westry."

I sat down as the room began to spin, feeling a stray pin from the wedding dress jab my side.

"Anne, are you still there?"

"Yes," I said weakly. "I'm still here."

"He's been hurt," she continued. "He got hit. He was part of the Fourth Infantry Division, the men who stormed the city. But his battalion was struck in the fight. Most died. He somehow held on."

"My God, Mary, how bad is it?"

"I don't know for sure," she said, "but by the look of things . . . well, Anne, it isn't good."

"Is he conscious?"

The line began to crackle again. "Mary, are you still there?"

"Yes," she said. "I'm here." Her voice sounded garbled and more distant than it had a moment ago. I knew the connection could be severed in an instant. "You need to come. You need to see him, before—"

"But how?" I cried, panicked. "Travel is restricted, especially to Europe."

"I know a way," Mary said. "Do you have a pen and paper?"

I fumbled in the kitchen drawer and pulled out a notepad. It had Mother's handwriting on it, which made me realize how much I missed her. After more than a year at home, I had yet to visit her in New York. "I'm ready," I said.

"Take down this code," she said. "A5691G9NQ."

"What does this mean?"

"It's a Foreign Service travel code," she said. "You can use it to board a ship leaving from New York to Paris in four days. And when you arrive, come to my apartment: three forty-nine Saint Germaine."

I scrawled the address on the pad and then shook my head. "You really think this will work?"

"Yes," she said. "And if you run into any trouble, mention the name Edward Naughton."

I clutched the receiver tightly, trying to hold on to the connection, to her. "Thank you, Mary." But the line had been swallowed up by static. She was gone.

"Gerard, I need to tell you something," I said that night at dinner. I pushed my plate aside. The dinner, even broiled salmon with new potatoes, hadn't interested me.

"You've hardly touched your food," he said, frowning.

He looked dapper seated across the table from me in a gray suit. The war had rendered the Cabaña Club a ghost town without the buzz of people and the familiar fog of cigarette smoke. A lone saxophonist played on the stage. In some ways, it felt like a betrayal to be there, a betrayal to those who had lost their lives, or who were in agony in hospitals. I swallowed hard.

"What is it, my love?" he continued, dabbing the corners of his mouth with a white cloth napkin.

I took a deep breath. "While I was in the South Pacific, there was a man. I—I . . ."

Gerard closed his eyes tightly. "Don't tell me," he said, shaking his head. "Please don't."

I nodded. "I understand. But there's something I need to do, before the wedding."

"What?"

"I need to go away," I said. "Just for a while."

Gerard looked pained, but he didn't protest. "And when you return, will you be yourself again?"

I looked deep into his eyes. "It's why I need to go," I said. "I need to find out."

He looked away. My words had hurt him, and I hated that. His left arm, the bad one, hung from his torso, limp, lifeless. He didn't like wearing the sling when we went out. "Anne," he said, clearing his throat.

His voice faltered a little, and he paused to regain his strength. Gerard never cried. "If this is what it takes. If there's a chance I can have your whole heart again, I will wait."

# Chapter 14

Papa took me to the train station the next morning. It would be a long journey to New York, but it was the only way. I'd stay with Mother for a day before boarding the ship Mary spoke of. I prayed that Westry could hold on until I arrived. There was so much I needed to say to him, and so much I needed to hear him say. *Does the grain of love that still lingers in my heart remain in his?*

"Your mother will be overjoyed to see you," Papa said, looking sheepish, the way he always did when he spoke of Mother. It didn't seem fair for him to use the words "overjoyed" and "mother" in the same sentence, given the state of their relationship, but I chose to overlook those details.

"You have the address, right?" he asked.

"Yes," I said, indicating my pocketbook, where my ticket and Mother's address were tucked inside.

"Good," he said. "Take a cab from the train station directly to her apartment. Be careful, kid."

I smiled. "Papa, you've forgotten that I lived in a war zone for almost a year. I think I'll be fine in the city."

He returned my smile. "Of course you will, dear. Ring me with your return details, and I'll be here to pick you up."

I kissed his cheek before stepping onto the train. The conductor took my ticket and showed me to the small drawing room where I'd spend the next two days traveling across the country, alone.

❧

It was late when the train pulled into Grand Central Terminal, and as it glided along the tracks, the city lights glistened. It was hard to imagine Mother making her home in this big, bold place so unlike Seattle.

I stepped off the train, and lugged my

bag through the maze of people, pushing past a woman with far too many children, a man with a monkey holding a set of miniature cymbals, and a gray-haired transient extending his cap and muttering something I couldn't understand.

Outside on the street, a sea of taxis waited. I raised my hand and caught the attention of a dark-skinned driver, who nodded and gestured toward the back seat.

I opened the door and stuffed my bag inside before sitting down. The air smelled of cigarettes and must. "I'm going to"—I paused to glance at the slip of paper in my hand—"560 East Fifty-seventh Street."

He nodded absently.

My eyes blurred as I gazed out the window. The lights flashed—green, red, pink, yellow. Sailors on leave in stark white uniforms clung to women—blondes, brunettes, tall ones, short ones. The war hadn't ended, but the tide had turned. You could feel it—from the little suburbs of Seattle to the vibrant streets of New York.

The buildings outside flicked by like frames of a film, one after the next, composing a picture that was both foreign and lonely. The cab finally stopped abruptly on a tree-lined street.

"Here we are, miss," said the cabbie. I paid the fare, and he set my bag on the street, pointing up to a brick townhouse with a shiny red door.

"Thank you," I said, turning toward the steps. I rang the doorbell, and moments later Mother appeared. It was almost eleven, but she stood in the doorway in full makeup and a red off-the-shoulder dress. A poorly balanced martini glass sloshed in her hand.

"Anne!" Mother cried, pulling me toward her with a freshly manicured hand. An olive bobbled out of the glass and fell to floor.

She took a rocky step back, and I dropped my bag and reached out to steady her. "Let me look at you," she said in an unnaturally cheerful tone. Her eyes pored over me, then she nodded in approval. "The South Pacific was kind to you, dear. Why, you must have lost ten pounds."

I smiled. "Well, I—"

"Come in! Come in!" She turned away from the door, and her red dress swished ahead.

I followed her, lugging my bag into the foyer, where a crystal chandelier, too large and gaudy for the small space, loomed overhead. "It's not Windermere," she said, shrugging, "but it's home for me now. I've grown to love city life."

She led me into a small front room with parquet floors and a Victorian sofa. "Of course," she said, "I'm having it all redone. Leon is helping me with that." She said his name as though I was expected to know him.

"Leon?"

"My interior decorator," she said, taking another long sip from her glass. I didn't remember Mother liking martinis in Seattle, nor did I remember her collarbones protruding from her chest. "He's insisted on mauve for this room, but I'm not sure. I rather fancy a shade of teal. What do you think, dear?"

"Teal might be a little bold for this room," I said honestly.

"That's just the look I'm going for, dear," she said, running her hand along a nearby wall. "Bold. Your father was so traditional." She gulped down the last of her drink, then giggled. "I don't have to be traditional anymore."

I nodded, preferring not to discuss Papa with her in this state.

She shook her head. "Listen to me going on like this," she said, reaching for a bell on a side table. "You must be exhausted, dear. I'll ring for Minnie."

She sounded the bell, and a small woman, no older than me, materialized moments later. "Minnie, be a dear and show Anne to her room."

"Yes, ma'am," she said in a squeak, reaching for my bag.

"Good night, my dearest," Mother said, caressing my cheek. "I know you can't stay long, but I have the morning packed with fun before your departure tomorrow. Go get some rest, sweetheart."

"Good night," I said, following Minnie up the stairs as Mother made her way back to the bar and reached for a bottle of gin.

The sound of a horn outside my third-floor window woke me the next morning. I pulled a pillow over my face, hoping to fall back into slumber, but with no luck. I glanced at the clock; it was barely 6:40, but I got up and dressed anyway. Mother would be waiting, and I wanted to spend as much time with her as possible before I boarded the ship.

The light shone through the windows downstairs, revealing a lonelier space than I'd seen the night before. There were no photos on the walls, or paintings. Mother loved paintings.

"Good morning, miss," Minnie said shyly from the entrance to the kitchen. "May I make you coffee or tea?"

"Tea would be lovely, Minnie, thank you," I said, smiling.

Moments later she appeared with a cup of tea on a tray with a plate with fruit, a croissant, and a boiled egg.

I eyed the tray. "Shouldn't I wait for Mother?"

Minnie looked conflicted. "About that," she said. "Well, it's just that, well—"

"Minnie, what is it?"

"Mr. Schwartz was here last night," she said nervously, searching for my under-standing, or approval.

"Do you mean Leon?"

"Yes, ma'am," she said. "He arrived af-ter you turned in."

"Oh," I replied. "And Mother's still asleep?"

"Yes."

"Minnie, is he still here?"

She looked at her feet before gnawing at her thumbnail.

"He is, isn't he?"

Minnie looked relieved to share the secret with someone. "When he comes to stay, I often don't see her until after twelve, sometimes one."

I nodded, trying my best not to show the disappointment I felt. "Then I'll take my breakfast right here," I said, reaching for the tray. "Thank you."

"Oh, Miss—Miss Anne," Minnie stammered nervously. "You won't tell Mrs. Calloway that I—that I told you anything, will you?"

I patted her plump hand reassuringly. "Of course not," I said. "It will be our secret."

❧

An hour later, I stepped outside the apartment and onto the street. I had five hours before I needed to make my way to the dock to board the ship. I hailed a cab, unsure of my destination.

"Where to, miss?" the driver asked.

"I don't know," I said. "I only have a few hours left in the city. Do you have any suggestions?"

The driver smiled, revealing a gold tooth. "That's funny. Everyone around here seems to know exactly where they're going."

I shrugged, looking up at Mother's apartment. The shades in her bedroom window were still drawn. "I used to think I knew where I was going. I thought I had everything figured out, but . . ."

The driver's face grew worried. "Listen, miss," he said, "I didn't mean to hurt your feelings."

I shook my head. "You didn't."

"Hey," he said, producing a folded brochure from his jacket pocket. "You like art?"

I thought of the painting I'd left in the bungalow. How I longed to have it in my possession just then. "Yes," I said. "I do."

"Then I'll take you to the Met."

"The Met?"

He looked at me in the way one looks at a child. "The Metropolitan Museum of Art."

"Yes," I said, smiling. "Perfect."

"I hope you find what you're looking for," the driver said with a wink.

"Me too," I said, handing him three crisp bills from my pocketbook.

Minutes later, I stood before the great stone building, with its enormous ivory columns flanking the entrance. I climbed the steps to the double doors, walking inside to an information booth straight ahead.

"Excuse me, ma'am," I asked. "You don't, by chance, have any paintings by French artists here, do you?"

The woman, about Mother's age, nodded without looking up from her book. "Of course we do, miss. They're all up on the east wing of the third floor."

"Thank you," I said, heading to a nearby elevator. It was foolish, I knew, to think that I'd find any of Gauguin's paintings here. Yet, I longed to know if the small canvas in the bungalow bore any similarity to his other work. *Could Tita have been right about the true owner of the bungalow? And its curse?*

I exited the elevator on the third floor. Aside from a little boy with a red balloon clutching his mother's hand, and a security guard standing near the west wall, the floor was empty.

I moved from painting to painting, reading the placards underneath: Monet, Cezanne, and others whose names I didn't recognize. When I'd scoured the entire room, I sat down, defeated, on a bench by the elevator.

"Excuse me, miss." I looked up to see the security guard walking toward me. He pulled his spectacles lower on his nose. "May I help you find something?"

I smiled. "Oh, it's nothing. I had a silly idea that I'd find the work of a certain artist here. But I was wrong."

He tilted his head to the right. "What artist?"

"Oh, a French painter, one who did the majority of his work in the South Pacific. I'd have better luck searching in France."

"What's his name?"

"Paul Gauguin," I said, standing up and pressing the Down button for the elevator.

"Well, yes," the man said, "we do have some of his work."

"You do?" The elevator's chime sounded and the door opened. I stepped back and let it close.

"Indeed," he said, pointing to a door a few paces away. A gold padlock hung from its handle. "The wing is closed for maintenance now, but, seeing how much you're interested, I might be able to open it up— for a special occasion."

I beamed. "Could you?"

"I have the key right here," he said, patting the pocket of his pants.

I followed him to the door, where he slipped a brass key into the lock and held the door open for me. "Take all the time you need," he said proudly. "I'll be right outside."

"Thank you," I said. "Thank you ever so much."

I slipped inside the door, letting it close with a click behind me. The room was small compared to the wing outside, but the walls were crowded with paintings. At first I didn't know where to begin—with the landscapes on the right or the portraits to my left—but then a canvas caught my eye, a beach scene on the far wall. It looked *familiar*, somehow. It would be too much to hope that the artist who had once lived in the bungalow could have painted this same stretch of beach, but as I walked closer, the idea didn't seem too far-fetched.

The canvas revealed a yellow hibiscus bush near a thatched-roof bungalow. *Our bungalow.* The silhouette of an island woman lingered on the shore. It looked like a companion to the scene on the canvas in the bungalow—like a photograph of a scene shot right before the other.

I took a step back, searching for a placard with identifying details—anything to hint at its origin, its date, and especially its painter. But the wall was blank.

I opened the door and leaned out into the hallway, trying to capture the attention of the guard. "Excuse me, sir," I whispered.

He nodded and walked toward me. "Yes?"

"I'm sorry to bother you, but you mentioned this room was closed for maintenance. Do you know if some of the placards near the paintings have been removed? There's one in particular I'd like to know about."

The man smiled. "Let me see if I can help."

Inside, I pointed to the canvas. "This is the one."

"I know this painting," he said. "It's very special."

"Whose is it?"

"Why, Mr. Paul Gauguin," he said, grinning. "Surely you could tell by the depiction of the island woman in the foreground, and the signature."

I shook my head in awe. "Signature?"

"Right here," he said, pointing to a spot on the lower left. The yellow paint he'd used to sign his name blended in with the hibiscus.

**Of course it was Gauguin. If only Westry were here.**

"And here's another," he said, pointing to a larger canvas a few feet away featuring a bare-breasted woman with a plumeria in her hair. I gasped when I realized there was a resemblance. *Atea. She's the spitting image of Atea.*

I walked back to the beach scene that had captured me so. "Do you happen to know when he painted this?"

"It would have been during his time in Tahiti," he said, "in the early 1890s."

"Tahiti?"

"Yes, or thereabouts," he said. "It's rumored that he spent time all over the nearby islands. In fact, occasionally some of his work turns up from a ship captain who barters with a local. A priceless painting in exchange for a pack of cigarettes." He shook his head. "Can you even imagine?"

I nodded, feeling the same panic I'd felt the day I left the island, knowing the painting might be lost forever. "Do you know anything more about his life on the islands?"

"Just that he was reclusive," he said. "He lived in little hideaways, mingling with women half his age and often coming into misfortune. He died alone of a syphilitic heart attack. Not a very happy life, if you ask me."

I nodded. *It all adds up. The bungalow. The painting. Tita's warning. The curse.*

I looked at the security guard with new appreciation. "How is it that you know so much about Gauguin?" I asked.

"There aren't many art thieves trolling these halls," he said with a wink. "I have a lot of time on my hands here. Besides, he's my favorite. He doesn't deserve to be sequestered away in this room. He should be out with the Monets, the Van Goghs."

I nodded, wishing I could transport myself back to the island and retrieve the painting Westry and I had left behind. I'd bring it to the museum and request that it be hung right here, right by the other, completing the story one canvas began to tell and the other could finish.

"I'm so sorry I overslept this morning, dear," Mother said from the couch when I returned to the apartment. An ice pack rested on her forehead. "I have a terrible headache."

I wanted to say, *Because you stayed up all night drinking with a certain Mr. Schwartz*, but instead I smiled sweetly. "I kept busy, Mother."

"Good," she said. "I'm afraid I'm much too ill to take you to the dock today. I've arranged for a driver to pick you up in a half hour. You'll get there in plenty of time."

I nodded. "Mother." I paused, considering my words carefully before I spoke them. "We haven't talked about what happened, about Maxine and Papa."

She looked away, unwilling to let her eyes meet mine.

"Mother," I continued, "are you all right? I know it must have been so painful."

I could sense her sadness, even when she tried to stifle it by offering me a scone from a tray Minnie had set on a side table.

"Mother?"

She sighed. "I will be, in time," she said. "I fill my days with as much as I can. And there's no shortage of men now."

I looked away, embarrassed.

"The failure of my marriage was the greatest of my life."

"Oh, Mother—"

"No," she said, silencing me. "I want you to hear this."

I nodded, though I wasn't entirely certain I wanted to listen.

"I loved your father; I always did," she went on. "But I realized, a long time ago, that he did not love me. He never had, in fact. Well, not in the way a husband *should* love a wife." She sighed, and held her empty hands out before her. "So," she continued, changing the tone of her voice from regret-filled to practical. "Let that be a lesson to you, dear. When you marry"— she paused to look deep into my eyes— "make sure he loves you, *really* loves you."

"I will."

She leaned back against a pillow. "You

didn't mention the purpose of your trip to France, dear."

I looked at her with a new understanding. "What you said about love, Mother—that's exactly why I'm going. I need to be certain."

# Chapter 15

The Foreign Services travel code worked just like Mary said. My hands had trembled at the dock, and a skeptical young soldier had looked me over suspiciously, but at the mention of Edward Naughton, he'd handed me a slip of paper containing my cabin assignment and waved me on.

On the final day of the grueling voyage, green from seasickness, I began to wonder whether I was making the trip in vain. Even if I did get to see Westry, would he want to see me? It had been more than a year since our strained good-bye on Bora-Bora, and he hadn't called or written. Sure, it would have been difficult, given the intensity of fighting in Europe, but he might have tried. He didn't even try.

"Coming ashore," the cabin steward called out from the hallway outside my room. "All passengers secure your belongings."

I looked out the tiny window. Through the foggy mist, the sleepy port of Le Havre waited in the distance, with Paris just a short train ride away. Doubt seeped into my heart. *What am I doing here? It's been a year.* A very long year. *Am I merely chasing a dream that has long since died?* I reached for my bag and shook off the thought. *I've come this far; I will see this through.*

I stood on Mary's street, Saint Germaine, looking up at the stone building above— stately, with little terraces adorned with potted flowers and plants. Candlelight flickered inside. I wondered what kind of life Mary had been living here during the city's occupation, and I wondered about Edward and how their story had unfolded. *Did the letter change everything? Did he take her back? Was it a happy ending?* It was late, nearly ten, but it warmed me to see city dwellers crowding in cafes and restaurants, lovers strolling arm in arm. And yet, reminders of the horror that the city had endured were ever present. A Nazi flag lay near a Dumpster, partially burned and ripped at the center. The green awning of a bakery across the street was blackened from fire. One of its windows had been boarded up. A yellow Star of David dangled from the door.

I proceeded inside Mary's building, checking the apartment number again before knocking quietly. Moments later, I heard footsteps approaching and then the sound of a latch opening.

"Anne!" Mary cried. "You came!"

My eyes filled with tears as I embraced my old friend. "I have to pinch myself," I said. "It hardly seems possible that I *am* here."

"You must be exhausted," she said.

I took a deep breath. "Mary, I have to know. How's Westry? Have you seen him recently? Is he . . . ?"

Mary looked at her feet. "I haven't been to the hospital in a few days," she said quietly. "But, Anne, I can tell you his injuries are serious. He was shot. Multiple times."

The air suddenly felt thick, toxic. The tears stung. "I can't bear to lose him, Mary."

My old friend wrapped her arm around me. "Come, we'll get you comfortable," she said. "Save your tears for tomorrow."

I followed Mary inside, where she turned on two lamps and motioned for me to sit with her on a sofa with gold-plated trim. All around were walls decorated in toile panels.

"It's a beautiful home," I muttered, still thinking of Westry.

Mary shrugged. She looked out of place in the apartment, like a schoolgirl dressed in her mother's evening gown. "I won't be here much longer," she said, offering no further details. "Care for a sandwich? A croissant?" I looked at her left hand and noticed that her ring finger was bare. Instinctively, I covered the diamond solitaire on mine with my right hand, remembering how I'd hidden it away on the island.

"I'm fine," I said, "thank you." *What's different about Mary?* She wore her hair, the color of tawny hay, in the same fashion. Her smile still hid the crooked teeth. But her eyes . . . yes, her eyes had changed. Deep sadness had taken up residence, and I longed to know the story.

"And Edward?" The name echoed in the night air, and the second it escaped my lips, I wished I could retract the question.

"There is no Edward," she said blankly, turning her gaze out the window to the sparkling lights of Paris and the great river Seine in the distance. "Not anymore." She paused again, before turning to me. "Listen, I'd rather not talk about any of that, if it's all the same to you."

I nodded quickly. "I can't imagine what you've been through here—I mean, during the occupation."

Mary ran her hand through her thin hair. "It was simply terrible, Anne," she said. "I'm lucky to still be here, being American and all. Fortunately, my college French got me through. The papers Edward—" She paused, as if the mere mention of his name jarred her. "The papers he had drawn up protected my identity. It's a miracle I wasn't found out, given my help with the Resistance."

"Mary, how frightening. You're very brave."

Her eyes looked sad, distant. "The Nazis making their sweeps," she continued, "the fear that if you said the wrong thing, sneezed the wrong way, you'd be taken in for questioning. And the poor Jewish families, removed from their homes." She paused, pointing toward the door. "There were three in this building. A family of four just down the hall. We tried to save them"— she held up her hands—"but, we were too late. God knows if they'll ever return."

I blinked hard. "Oh, Mary."

She shook her head as if to repress another memory, one that might have been too painful to recount, then pulled a handkerchief from the pocket of her dress. "I'm sorry," she said. "I thought I could talk about this with you, but I'm afraid—I'm afraid it's all too painful."

I took her hand in mine, noticing the tiny pink scar on her wrist. Memories of Bora-Bora came rushing back. "Please," I said, "let's not speak of the past."

Mary sighed. "I'm afraid it will be with me always."

"But the city was spared," I said, searching for a positive note.

"Yes," Mary replied. "A miracle. For a while we thought it all might go up in flames, and us with it."

"Mary," I said cautiously, "how is it that you ended up here? Did you come because of . . . the letter I gave you before you left Bora-Bora?"

She rubbed her hands together in her lap. "If only the answer was that simple," she said nostalgically. "No, I was a fool to come here."

I wished, for a moment, that I'd kept the letter in my possession, to save Mary from the heartache she felt then. And yet without that letter, Mary wouldn't have been in Paris. She wouldn't have found Westry. She couldn't have called. I marveled at how our stories intertwined, and I longed for hers to have a happy ending, just as I hoped mine would.

"Where will you go next?" I asked, searching her face for a sign that she would be all right—a glimmer in her eye, a half smile, anything.

But instead, she looked gravely out the window. "I haven't decided yet."

The lights of Paris sparkled, and my heart lightened when I thought of Westry. He was out there, somewhere.

"Will you go with me to the hospital tomorrow? I'm terribly nervous about seeing him, after . . . all this time."

For a moment, the haze in Mary's eyes

vanished. "Of course I will," she said. "You know, Stella's here too."

"She is?"

"Yes," she continued. "She's been here since last month."

"And Will?"

"He's here too. They're getting married in a month or so."

"That's wonderful," I said, grinning. "I'd love to see her."

"She and Will took a train down south for a few days," she said. "She'll be disappointed to have missed you."

"What time should we leave for the hospital in the morning?"

Mary glanced out the window again. "Visiting hours begin at nine. We can catch a cab over first thing. Now, your room is down the hall—second door on the left. You must be exhausted. Go get some rest." She tried her best to smile, but the corners of her mouth seemed stiff and heavy, paralyzed with grief.

"Thank you, Mary," I said, gathering my bags.

I took a final look into the living room before turning down the mahogany-paneled hall toward the bedroom. Mary sat on the sofa, motionless, hands folded in her lap, looking out at the Seine and the shimmer of a liberated Paris.

Something had happened here, inside these walls. Yes, something unspeakable. I could feel it.

The First U.S. General Hospital loomed in the distance, and I squeezed Mary's hand tightly as we stood gazing up at its enormous facade. The sun shone in the sky, but all around the building were shadows.

I gulped. "Why does it look so . . ."

"Evil?"

"Yes," I said, squinting up at the highest story.

"Because it was a place of evil," she said, "before the Allies arrived."

Mary explained that the twelve-story gray building, formerly the Beaujon Hospital, the largest in Paris, had once been a Nazi stronghold. After the takeover, Major General Paul Hawley, a surgeon, transformed the building, clearing out rooms of medical equipment the Germans had used for gruesome medical experiments, mostly on Jews and Poles. Now it had a red cross painted on the highest story, a cross that rather looked like a bomber airplane, I thought.

Mary pointed to a window a few stories up in the distance. "See right up there? The open window on the seventh floor?"

I nodded.

"That's where I found a Polish woman and her infant," she said quietly, "starved to death. Nazi doctors used them for a research experiment. They watched through a window, documenting the whole thing. I read the paperwork. It took her nine days to die. Her baby, eleven."

I shivered.

"But the horror has ended," Mary said solemnly. "General Pawley turned this place around. There's been nearly a thousand admits in the last two weeks, and we expect many more."

I couldn't take my eyes off of the seventh floor.

"Anne?"

"Yes," I muttered weakly.

"Are you ready for this?"

"I hope so," I said.

Together we walked up the stairs and into the building. Darkness lingered palpably in the stiff and heavy air. A structure could not endure such evil without absorbing some of it. Walls could be scrubbed, floors waxed, but the scent of evil remained.

Mary pressed the elevator's ninth-floor button and we began our ascent. As the lights on the panel shifted, my mind reeled. First floor, second. *Will he be conscious enough to recognize me?* Third floor. *Does he still love me?* Fourth floor. *What might be next for us?*

"Oh, Mary," I said, clutching her arm. "I'm so frightened."

She neither comforted me nor acknowledged my fear. "It's the right thing to do, coming here," she said. "No matter what, you'll have closure."

I sighed. "Have you been in touch with Kitty?"

Mary looked uncomfortable for a moment, and I knew by her expression that she'd gotten wind of our history, our troubles on the island.

"About that," she said nervously. "There's something I need to tell you. Since I called you, there's been—"

The elevator stopped suddenly on the

fifth floor, and a doctor and two nurses entered the car, silencing our conversation.

We stepped off on the ninth floor, and I gasped at the sight. Perhaps three hundred, maybe more, wounded men lay on cots with dark green wool blankets pulled over their limp bodies.

"This is a tough floor," Mary said. "A lot of serious cases here."

My heart pounded loudly inside my chest. "Where is he?" I said, looking around frantically. "Mary, take me to him."

A nurse about my age approached us and nodded at Mary without a smile. "I thought you were off today."

"I am," Mary said. "I'm here on my friend's behalf. She'd like to visit Mr. Green."

The nurse looked at me and then back at Mary. "*Westry* Green?"

The sound of his name on another woman's breath sent a shiver through my body.

"Yes," Mary said, "*Westry* Green."

The nurse turned to me. Her eyes narrowed. "And you are?"

"Anne," I muttered. "Anne Calloway."

"Well," she said, giving Mary a knowing look, then glancing back toward the room of men behind her, "I'm not sure that . . ." She sighed. "I'll check."

When she was out of earshot, I turned to Mary. "I don't understand. Why did she act so strange?"

Mary looked around the room, out the window—anywhere but at my face.

"Mary," I pleaded. "What happened?"

"Let's sit down," she said, leading me by the arm to a bench a few feet behind us. A clock ticked overhead, taunting me with each movement of its hand.

"When I called you," she said, "I didn't have all the information. I didn't know that Westry—"

We both looked up when we heard footsteps approaching, clicking on the wood floors. My eyes widened when I saw a familiar face approaching. "Kitty!" I cried, leaping to my feet. Despite the past, I found myself unable to resist the urge to run into the arms of my old friend, to embrace her with the love and forgiveness we both owed one another.

But I stopped quickly when my eyes met Kitty's, the eyes of a stranger. "Hello," she said stiffly.

Mary rose and stood by my side. "Kitty,"

she said, "Anne has traveled a great distance to see Westry. I'm hoping we can take her to him."

Kitty frowned. "I'm afraid that won't be possible."

I shook my head, blinking hard as my eyes began to sting. "Why, Kitty?" I cried. "Is he hurt badly? Is he unconscious?"

Kitty looked down at my engagement ring, and I wished I'd thought to take it off. The nurse who greeted us moments ago reappeared and stood in solidarity next to Kitty. *What are they hiding from me?*

"Kitty," I pleaded, "what is it?"

"I'm sorry, Anne," she said coldly. "I'm afraid the fact of the matter is that Westry doesn't want to see you."

The room began to spin, and I clutched Mary's arm for support. *My God. I traveled all the way from Seattle, and now I stand mere feet away from him and he doesn't want to see me?*

"I don't understand," I stammered, feeling waves of nausea churn in my stomach. "I only want to—"

Kitty clasped her hands together and turned back to the floor. "Again, I'm very sorry, Anne," she said as she walked away. "I wish you all the best."

I watched her proceed into the room, turning right, where she disappeared behind a curtain.

"Let's go, Anne," Mary whispered, reaching for my hand. "I'm so sorry, dear. It was wrong of me to bring you here. I should have explained—"

"Explained what?" I cried. "That I would be barred from seeing the only man I've ever loved by . . . my best friend?" I listened to my own words echoing in the air, surprised by their raw honesty. Gerard may have had my hand, but Westry would always have my heart. I broke free from Mary's grasp. "No," I said firmly.

I pushed past Mary and into the room of injured men. The sounds that had been muffled near the elevator now amplified to reveal moaning, babbling, crying, laughing. The range of human emotion on the floor was maddening.

I walked faster through the aisles of beds, scanning face after face. Some looked up at me longingly; others just stared ahead. *Where is he? Surely if I find him, if I look into his eyes, he'll have a change of heart? Surely he still loves me? I won't let Kitty stand between us. I won't let her speak for Westry.* My heart fluttered as I weaved through the rows of men, praying that just around the corner I'd see the familiar hazel eyes that had captured my heart on the island.

Minutes later, however, I had combed through every aisle without finding a trace of Westry. I looked around the floor frantically, then remembered Kitty slipping behind a curtained area in the distance. *Could he be inside?* Clutching my locket, I walked across the room, stopping in front of the gray-and-white-striped curtain. *Could this swath of fabric be all that separates Westry from me?*

My hands trembled as I lifted the edge of the curtain, just far enough to peer inside. Four hospital beds, all occupied by soldiers, lay inside. I gasped when I made out the face of the man in the bed farthest away.

**Westry.**

My legs weakened when I saw his face—thinner now, with a shadow of stubble around his chin, but just as handsome, just as perfect as I'd memorized in my heart. I pulled the curtain back farther, but stopped quickly when I saw Kitty approaching his bed. She pulled up a chair, and I watched as she ran a wet towel over his face, lightly, lovingly, before caressing his forehead. He gazed up at her with a smile that made my cheeks burn.

I felt a tug at my waist, and then heard Mary's voice. "Anne," she said, "don't do this to yourself. Let him go."

I shook my head. "But, Westry, my Westry!" I cried, releasing my grasp on the curtain and burying my head against Mary's shoulder. "How could she? How could she, Mary?"

Mary lifted my chin, and dabbed my cheeks with a rose-colored handkerchief. "I'm so sorry, honey," she said. "Let's go."

I followed her to the elevator, then stopped, reaching into my purse for a scrap of paper and pen.

Mary looked confused when I sat down on the bench. "What are you doing?"

Moments later, I stood and handed her a folded slip of paper. "Tomorrow," I said, "after I'm gone, will you give this to Westry?"

Mary took the paper in her hands and looked at it skeptically.

"Kitty will intercept any letter I try to send here," I continued. "My only hope is you."

Mary eyed the paper cautiously. "Are you sure you want to say anything more to him?"

I nodded. "I need him to read this."

"Then I'll make sure he gets it," she said, but I could hear a strain in her voice that worried me. "I work the morning shift tomorrow. I can try to give it to him then."

"Promise?" I said, searching her face for the assurance I needed.

"Yes," she said softly. Exhaustion permeated her voice. "I'll do my best."

Seattle did little to take my mind off of Westry. More than a month had passed since that dark day in Paris, and even with the familiar distractions of life at home and a wedding just weeks away, I couldn't get him out of my mind, or my heart. I jumped every time the phone rang, and sat by the window each morning, eagerly awaiting the mail. Surely after he read the note Mary had delivered, he'd write, or call? *Why hasn't he written?*

Then, on a quiet Tuesday morning when

Maxine and I were getting ready to go into town, the doorbell rang. I dropped my purse, and a tube of lipstick fell to the floor, rolling underneath the sofa.

"I'll get that," I called to Maxine. I opened the front door to find a postman standing outside.

"Good morning, ma'am," he said. "Miss Calloway?"

"Yes," I said. "I am she."

He handed me a small envelope. "A telegraph for you," he said, grinning. "From Paris. If I can just get you to sign right here."

My heart lightened as I scrawled my signature on his clipboard and ran up the stairs to my bedroom. Safe behind the closed door, I ripped open the envelope. A yellow slip of paper with five typewritten lines nestled inside. I held it up to the light and took a deep breath:

Came home early from trip STOP
Mary is dead STOP
Hung herself the morning of September
 18 STOP
Edward broke her heart, irreparably STOP
Sending love and well wishes from
 Europe, Stella STOP

I stared at the paper for a long time, letting the words sink in until the haze of shock lifted. *"No!"* I screamed. *Not Mary. Not you, Mary.* I remembered the sadness in her eyes, the hesitation. She'd endured more heartache than any woman should, but to end things like *that*? *How could she?* Tears trickled down my cheeks as I crumpled the paper and threw it to the floor.

Moments later, my pulse raced faster. *Dear God, when did Stella say she hung herself?* I retrieved the scrap of paper. *September 18. No. No, this can't be.*

I stared at the wall in horror. Mary never made it to her shift the day after we'd visited the hospital. She died before she had a chance to deliver my note to Westry.

⁂

"Are you ready?" Gerard stood in the doorway on the morning of our wedding, two weeks later. Spurning tradition, he had insisted upon picking me up and taking me to the church before the ceremony, maybe because he was worried I wouldn't come any other way.

I looked at him in the doorway, dashing in a tux, with a perfect white rose pinned proudly to his lapel. Mother's words rang in my ears: *When you marry, make sure he loves you, really loves you.*

I thought of Westry and Kitty's tender moment in the Paris hospital. *How naive I was to assume he'd wait for me, to assume he still loved me. And what does it matter now if he got the note or not?* I looked at Gerard with new appreciation. *He loves me. He will always love me. That will be enough for a lifetime.*

"Yes," I said, gulping back the hurt, the pain, the ghosts of my past and weaving my hand in his. "I'm ready."

As I stood, my gold locket dangled from my neck, before settling itself once again over my heart.

# Chapter 16

"So you married Grandpa," Jennifer said, her voice pulling me back to the present. The sun had set, leaving just a line of pink on the horizon outside the window.

I smiled, wiping away a tear with the handkerchief in my hand. "Of course I married Grandpa. And aren't you glad I did? After all, you wouldn't have been here any other way."

Jennifer looked dissatisfied with the answer. "So I owe my existence to your heartache?"

"Nonsense," I said reassuringly. "I loved your grandfather."

"But not in the same way you loved Westry."

I nodded. "There are all sorts of love. I've come to realize this in my life." I thought of Gerard—strong, sure Gerard. I missed the way he'd nuzzle my cheek or greet me with the morning paper and a poached egg on a plate with golden brown toast. He'd devoted his life to me, giving me his whole heart freely, when I let him have only a piece of mine. For in my heart, I'd kept a room locked, where a candle burned for someone else.

"Oh, Grandma," Jennifer said, leaning her head against my shoulder. "Why didn't you tell me this story sooner? How lonely to keep it to yourself all these years."

I patted my locket. "No, dear," I said. "I have never been alone. You see, when you share love with someone, even for a time, it always remains in your heart." I unclasped the locket and let the tiny bit of wood from the bungalow's floor fall into my palm. Jennifer hovered over it, marveling at the sight.

"No," I said again, "I have never been alone."

Jennifer frowned. "But what about Kitty?

What about Westry? Didn't you ever try to find them?"

"No," I said. "The day I married your grandfather, I vowed to let it all go, each of them. I had to. It was only fair to him."

"But what about the bungalow, the painting? And what about your promise to Tita? Remember what she said about finding justice?"

I felt a deep exhaustion setting in. "And I haven't forgotten," I said honestly.

"I'm coming with you," Jennifer said, nodding with determination.

"Coming with me?"

"To Bora-Bora."

I smiled. "Oh, honey, you're very sweet, but I really don't think—"

"Yes," she said, ignoring my apprehension. Her eyes looked wild with excitement. "We'll go together."

I shook my head. The retelling of the story had opened up old wounds that felt raw again, as painful as the day they were inflicted. "I don't think I can."

Jennifer looked deep into my eyes. "Don't you understand, Grandma? Don't you see? You have to."

The airplane rattled and shook as it made its descent over the Tahitian islands. "We're experiencing a little more turbulence than normal, folks," a male flight attendant with an Australian accent chirped over the intercom. "Sit tight. The captain will have us safely landed in no time."

I closed my eyes, recalling the flight into Bora-Bora so many years ago, with Kitty by my side and a cabin full of eager nurses listening, with bated breath, as old Nurse Hildebrand warned us of an island full of danger. I sighed, remembering the way Kitty had softly touched my arm, thanking me for coming and promising me that I'd be glad I did. *Would I take it all back if I could?*

The plane jolted violently, and Jennifer turned to me. "Don't worry, Grandma," she said lovingly.

I squeezed her hand tighter as I looked around the cabin filled with young couples, presumably honeymooners. A young man in a seat to our right gently smoothed his bride's hair, kissing her hand as the two looked out the window to the island below. I couldn't help but feel envious. *How lucky they are to have found the island this way, without the complications of war or time.* I longed to be twenty-one again. To start over again from this point forward, with Westry seated beside me.

"Ready?" Jennifer asked, rousing me from my thoughts. The plane had landed, and I stood up quickly, following my granddaughter to the open door, where passengers were already making their way down the steps.

A flight attendant pinned a purple orchid to my shirt, so deeply colored I wondered if it had been spray-painted. "Welcome to Bora-Bora, ma'am," she said. "You will love this island."

"I have always loved this island," I said, smiling, taking in a breath of the warm, humid air. A bustling airport stood where a single runway had seventy years prior. The emerald hillside was now dotted with homes. Everything had changed, and yet the familiar floral scent lingered in the air, and the turquoise water sparkled in the distance, beckoning me to its shore. I knew it then: My heart was home.

"Take my hand, Grandma," Jennifer said, reaching out to steady me.

I shook my head, feeling stronger, steadier than I had in years. "I can do this," I said, making my way down the steps. *Yes*, I said to myself, *I can do this.*

A shuttle deposited us at our hotel, the Outrigger Suites, just a mile from the airport. Jennifer pushed the key card into the door, and we set our bags down in the air-conditioned room.

"Look at that view!" Jennifer exclaimed, pointing to the window ahead. A set of French doors framed a stunning picture of sand and surf, which is when something familiar caught my eye.

"My God," I said, walking closer to the window. "The formation of the sand . . . it's remarkable."

"What is it?" Jennifer asked, running to my side. "What do you see?"

"Well, I may be mistaken, but I think this hotel was built on the old base!" I cried. "I know that beach, the way it hooks up at the shore. The reef below the sparkling water." I shook my head, expecting to see Nurse Hildebrand or Kitty, or—I sighed—Westry walking toward me from the sea.

"To be here again, it's just . . ." I opened the doors and walked outside onto the balcony. Jennifer didn't follow.

"Take all the time you need, Grandma," she said quietly. "I'll be inside."

I sat down in a wicker chair on the balcony and let my mind, my heart become mesmerized by the familiar waves.

I ventured back inside the room an hour later, and found Jennifer asleep on one of the beds. I took a spare blanket from the hall closet and spread it over her softly before reaching for a pad of paper on the desk nearby. I knew where I had to go.

My dear,

I've gone out walking. I didn't want to wake you. I'll be back before dinner.

Love,

Grandma

I reached for my straw hat and made my way outside the hotel, beyond the pool, where women in bikinis lay baking in the hot sun; past the bar by the beach, where couples sipped fruity cocktails; and out to the open shore, which, aside from an occasional home nestled along the edge of the sand, was just as quiet, just as pristine as it had been the day I left.

At once, I was twenty-one again, in nurse's garb, sneaking off to the beach after a long shift in the infirmary, head peeking over my shoulder to make sure I wasn't being followed, heart pounding in anticipation of seeing *him*.

I trudged along. The sand felt heavier around my soles now. I wiped a bead of sweat from my brow and pulled my hat down lower, protecting my weathered face from the sun's unrelenting rays. I searched the palm-lined shore. *Where is it? Surely just a few paces farther?*

Birds called overhead as I pressed on, scanning the thicket with every step. *It has to be here. Somewhere.*

Twenty minutes later, I stopped, out of breath, and sank into a shady spot on the sand, freeing a deep sigh from the depths of my heart. *Of course the bungalow is gone. How could I be so foolish to think it would still be here waiting for me?*

"Excuse me, ma'am?"

I looked up when I heard a male voice nearby.

"Ma'am, are you all right?"

A man, perhaps in his sixties, not much older than my eldest son, was approaching, with a woman of about the same age. She wore a blue sundress, and her dark hair was pulled back loosely in a clip.

"Why yes," I said, collecting myself.

"I'm Greg, and this is my wife Loraine," he said. "We live right here on the hillside."

"I'm Anne," I replied. "Anne Call—" I stopped myself, marveling at the slipup. I'd been Anne Godfrey the majority of my life, and yet here on the island, the name felt wrong.

"Anne Calloway," I finished.

Loraine looked at her husband, then back at me. "Anne *Calloway*?"

"Yes," I said, confused by the recognition in her voice. "I'm sorry, have we met before?"

The woman shook her head, and then gave her husband a look of astonishment. "No," she said, kneeling down next to me. "But we have hoped to meet you for a very long time."

"I don't understand," I said, searching her face.

"Can you believe this?" Loraine marveled, shaking her head at Greg before turning back to me. "You lived on this island during the war, didn't you?"

I nodded.

"There's an old beach bungalow near here," she continued cautiously. "You've seen it, haven't you?"

"Yes," I said. "But how do you know this?"

She turned to her husband and then back to me. "He always said you'd come."

"He?"

"Mr. Green," she said.

I shook my head, feeling my heart rate quicken. I folded my hands in my lap. "I don't understand. You know of the bungalow? And"—I gulped—"Westry?"

The woman nodded, and her husband stood up, pointing to the stretch of shore behind me.

"It's just back this way, near our home," he said. "The brush has grown quite a bit since you've been here. You must have missed it."

I rose quickly. The stiffness in my legs

reminded me that I wasn't twenty-one any-more. "Will you take me there?"

"Yes," he said, smiling.

We walked for a few minutes in silence. Occasionally the couple glanced at me with concern, but I did not return their gaze, instead preferring to let the sound of the surf absorb my thoughts. *Do I want to know the secrets they've kept, about the bungalow, about Westry?*

Greg stopped suddenly, pointing toward the jungle, thick with palms. "Right through there," he said.

"Thank you," I replied, pushing through the brush until I came to a little clearing ahead.

"Wait, Ms. Calloway," he called out from the beach.

I turned around.

"You should know that it isn't what it once was."

I nodded and walked on, pushing past aggressive vines, some reaching out as if they intended to wrap their tendrils around my frail arms. I looked right, then left. *Where is it?* Then, an overgrown hibiscus caught my eye. Not yet in bloom, tiny yellow buds pushed up from its leaves. My heart pounded. *It has to be near.*

I pushed another vine out of my way, and there it was—still standing, but barely. The thatched roof had weakened and collapsed in places. The woven walls were thinning, completely gone on one side, and the front door was missing. I took a deep breath, remembering the way Westry and I had discovered the little hut so many years ago. Now look at it.

The front step had eroded, so I had to raise my body up three feet to the entrance, not an easy task at my age. My arms ached as I hoisted myself inside, the sound of which startled a bird that squawked and flew quickly out an open-air window.

I stood up, brushed the dust off my pants, and looked around the room with awe. The bed with its rumpled bedspread, the mahogany desk and chair, the curtains I'd made, though ragged and falling from the hooks—everything was still there, in its place. I looked up at the wall where the painting had once hung. *Will it be under the bed, wrapped in burlap the way Westry and I left it?*

I took a deep breath and knelt down, patting my hand under the bed. A lizard ran out, and I jumped back. Moments later I regained my composure and pulled up the bedspread to let more light under the bed. There, a few feet back, lay a lonely scrap of burlap. But the painting was gone.

I stood and collapsed into the chair, feeling the weight of seventy years of emotion. Of course it was gone. *How naive I've been to think it might still be here.*

When I stood up again, the floors creaked below my feet, and I smiled as I thought of the makeshift mailbox Westry and I had once shared. It would be silly to think there might be a letter waiting inside. And yet I crouched down anyway, fighting back tears as I ceremoniously lifted the old floorboard and peered inside. I pushed my hand into the little dark space below, feeling around until my fingertips hit something soft, solid.

A book. No, a journal of some kind. I pulled out the leather-bound notebook, fanning its pages to release years of dust.

The light was growing dim, and I knew the sun would be setting soon. I squinted as I opened the cover to read the first page:

Letters to Anne, from Westry . . .

**My God. He returned. Just like he promised.**

I fumbled to the second page, my eyes desperate to read the words and my heart eager to soak them up, when I heard a voice outside.

"Ms. Calloway?"

Greg's voice echoed through the air outside. I closed the journal reluctantly and tucked it into my bag. "Yes," I said, rising, "I'm here."

I stood in the doorway as he and his wife approached. "Oh, good," he said. "We didn't want to leave you out here all alone too long. Let me help you down."

He reached two strong arms up and clasped them gently around my waist, lowering me to the ground.

Loraine looked at the bungalow, and then at me. "Did you find what you were looking for here?"

I glanced back at the little hut. "No," I said, "but I found something else, something better."

She smiled cautiously, as if she knew more than I did about this place, about my story. "Would you like to come back to our terrace, for some tea? Our home is just up the beach."

I nodded. "Thank you. I would like that very much."

Loraine poured black tea from a blue and white kettle. "Cream and sugar?"

"Yes, thank you," I said.

The home was quaint. Just a simple two-bedroom structure nestled near the beach with an ample deck outside. It suited them.

"We've lived here for thirty-five years," Greg said. "Loraine and I used to work in New York City, but after a trip here in the late sixties, we knew we couldn't go back to city life."

"So we stayed," Loraine chimed in. "We opened a restaurant a few miles away."

I envied them, of course. For this was the life that Westry and I might have had, the life I had longed for in my heart.

I took a sip of tea, and then set the white china cup down on its saucer. "You mentioned that you know Westry," I said quietly, afraid of where the sentence might lead.

Greg looked at Loraine and then back at

me. "Yes," he said. "We knew him for many years."

*My God. They're speaking in past tense.* "*Knew* him?" I asked.

"Yes," Loraine continued. "He came here every year. His yearly pilgrimage, he called it."

"Pilgrimage?"

Greg smiled. "Pilgrimage in hopes of finding you."

I watched the cream swirl in my tea, spiraling around in confusion, just as I felt. I let Greg's words sink in for a few moments, then shook my head, remembering Kitty, remembering the way I'd left Westry that day in the hospital in Paris.

"I don't understand," I said, trying to reconcile the story I believed to be true with the story they were telling me.

Greg took a sip of his tea. "He told us your story," he said. "How you'd fallen in love on this island during the war, and how war had separated you."

I shook my head. "But why didn't he try to find me in Seattle? Why didn't he ever write?"

"He didn't feel it was his place," Loraine

explained. "He knew you had a life, a family there. And yet, somewhere in his heart, he believed that you might return, that one day you might be waiting for him in the bungalow, just the way you did in his memories."

I reached down to my feet for my bag, pulling out the brown leather notebook. It pulsed with emotion as I held it in my hands. "I found this," I said. "Letters he wrote me."

"Yes," Loraine continued. "Every year he left you a new one. He left it inside the bungalow, hoping you'd find it." She clasped her hands together and shook her head wistfully. "It was the most romantic thing. Greg and I felt for him, watching him make such a strenuous journey year after year for a man in his condition." She reached for her husband's hand and patted it lovingly. "It was moving to see."

I sat up straighter in my chair. "What do you mean, 'a man in his condition'?"

Greg's eyes narrowed. "You don't know?"

"Know what?"

Loraine gave Greg a disapproving look before leaning in closer to me, as if she was about to reveal something horrifying. "Dear," she said, "Mr. Green was in a wheel-chair. He was paralyzed in the war."

I held my hand to my heart to muffle the ache inside. *Paralyzed.* I closed my eyes, remembering the scene in the Paris hospital, where he lay gazing up at Kitty. Had he refused to see me not because of a budding relationship with Kitty, but because of his pride?

"I know this all must be very hard to hear," Loraine said. "I'm sorry if we've said too much; it's just that all these years we've watched this dear man's story unfold, and we hoped that one day we'd see the conclusion. To have you here, Anne, it's truly amazing. Greg and I had hoped you'd come, for Westry's sake, but after so many years, we'd given up hope."

I looked down at the notebook in my hands, trying to make sense of it all. "What about Westry? Where is he now?"

Loraine looked troubled. "We don't know, exactly," she said. "He stopped coming about five years ago. We were terribly afraid that he might have—"

Greg put his hand on Loraine's arm, as

if to urge her to be silent. "The notebook you have," he said, "why don't you read it? Perhaps you'll find a clue."

I stood up. "Thank you," I said. "Thank you ever so much, for everything. I should be getting back now. My granddaughter is expecting me."

Loraine stood up beside me. "Let us walk you to your hotel, Ms. Calloway."

I shook my head. "I'll be fine. But thank you." I made my way down the steps to the trail back to the beach. I walked quickly, moving my aching legs along the sand as fast as they'd go, praying I wasn't too late.

# Chapter 17

The early morning light shone on the balcony as I made myself comfortable in a wicker chair. Jennifer, out for a jog, would be back in an hour. I opened Westry's journal, turning past the water-stained first page, and let my eyes take in his familiar handwriting:

August 23, 1959

My dearest Cleo,

This is the first letter I have written you since we last saw each other on the island, that final day as the airplanes roared in the distance, taking you one place and me another. I've come back to the bungalow on this day—August 23, the very day we met so long ago—in hopes of finding you, or some memory of you, here, for nearly 20 years have passed and you have not escaped my mind or my heart. You'll be happy to know that the old place has held up well over the years. Everything is as we left it. The curtains, still swinging in the breeze. The desk and chair. The bed. Everything but you.

How I wish you were here, my love. How I wish I could take you in my arms the way I used to. I know you are out there somewhere, living your life, and I do not want to disturb that life. But my heart yearns for you. It always will. And so I will return each year on this day, in hopes that our paths may cross again. I will leave this journal here in our mailbox. I will eagerly anticipate your letter, and you.

Yours,

Grayson

I set the journal down in my lap and marveled at the letter that had taken some fifty years to reach my hands. *He still loves me. God, he still loves me. Just as I love him, as I did in 1959, and as I do today.* And the bungalow—he said it was just as we had left it. *Yet why didn't he mention the painting?* I turned to the next page and continued reading:

August 23, 1960

My dearest Cleo,

I admit, my heart leapt with anticipation as I opened the mailbox and retrieved this journal. I had hoped to see an entry from you, or better yet, to find you here waiting for me. But I've waited all these years, what's one more? I will be patient. I promise, my love.

As time has passed, I've had an opportunity to think. I often wonder why you didn't respond to the letters I sent from the hospital in Paris, or why you didn't come to see me there. Kitty said you had married, but I didn't believe it, not at first. How could you marry after the love we shared?

In any case, I've come to terms with that now, though I still hold out hope that you will return, that we will be reunited. I know that life must go on, but a part of me will never fully live until I am with you again.

Until next year, my love,

Grayson

I closed the journal tightly, too disturbed, too tormented by the unfolding story to read further. Kitty had lied to me at the hospital. She had intercepted his letters. *Why did she do it? If I'd gotten Westry's letters, might things be different?*

I turned to the hotel room when I heard Jennifer at the door. "It's a beautiful morning, Grandma," she said. "You should get out for a walk."

I stood up and nestled the journal in my suitcase, before pulling out Genevieve Thorpe's letter.

"I think we should call her now," I said, more sure of myself than I'd been in years.

Jennifer sat beside me on the bed as I punched the numbers into the phone and then listened to the ringing. One, then two, then three.

A woman's voice answered, speaking a French phrase I didn't understand. "Hello," I said, "this is Anne Call—Anne Godfrey. I'm trying to reach a Ms. Genevieve Thorpe."

The woman's voice switched from perfect French to perfect English. "Why yes, hello, Anne, this is Genevieve speaking."

"I'm here," I said, a little more hesitantly than I'd expected. "I'm here in Bora-Bora."

"My goodness," she said. "What a wonderful surprise! I'd mailed the letter unsure if I'd ever hear from you, much less see you in person. Would it be possible to schedule a meeting before you go?"

"Yes," I said. "It's why I came."

"Is today too soon?"

"No," I said, "it's perfect. We're staying at the Outrigger Suites. Would you like to meet us for a drink?"

"I'd love to," she said. "I've been waiting many years for this visit."

"I suppose I have too," I said. "See you this evening."

I hung up the phone, hoping I hadn't made a mistake.

❧

"Just two tonight?" the hostess asked as Jennifer and I walked into the restaurant.

"No," I said. "We're expecting another guest." Just then, a woman at the bar stood up and waved from across the room. She was striking, petite, with rosy cheeks and light brown curly hair fastened in a gold clip.

"Hello," she said, walking toward Jennifer and me. She couldn't have been much older than my sons, maybe in her sixties. "You must be Anne."

"Yes," I said, trying to place the familiar feeling I sensed when I shook her hand. "And this is my granddaughter, Jennifer."

"Hello to you both," she greeted us warmly. "I'm Genevieve."

"It's so nice to meet you," I said. "Shall we sit down?" She carried a large canvas bag with navy stripes. I wondered what was inside.

"That would be lovely," she replied.

The hostess directed us to a table by the window. When the waiter appeared, I ordered a bottle of white wine.

Genevieve smiled. "I can hardly believe you're here," she said, shaking her head. "You seemed like such a mythical figure. I mean, your name was in the registry of nurses during the war, but you still seemed like such a figment."

A hush fell on the table as the waitress filled our glasses with wine. I took a sip and it warmed me as it traveled down my throat. "So I take it you know of the bungalow about a half mile from here," she said, turning to Jennifer. "Just a little hut. You'd miss it if you blinked."

I nodded. "I know the place."

"It's funny," she said, taking a sip of wine and leaning back in her chair thoughtfully. "The locals won't go near the place. They say it's cursed. I avoided it all my life, especially as a girl. On a picnic with our parents down on that very beach, my brother and I stumbled upon it, but neither of us would dare step inside." She shrugged. "But at some point I suppose my curiosity got the better of me. About twenty-five years ago, I climbed through one of the windows, took a look around. Wouldn't you know it, a week later I found out my husband was having an affair and my mother was dying of breast cancer."

"I'm so sorry," Jennifer said, topping off each of our glasses with more wine.

"So you believe in its curse, then?" I asked.

Genevieve swirled the wine in her glass for a moment. "I don't know," she said. "Part of me does, and yet part of me feels there is so much good that resides there too. I felt it when I was there." She scrunched her nose. "Does that even make sense?

"It does," I said. "It's how I've come to feel about the bungalow myself. I spent a great deal of time there alone."

She reached into her bag and pulled out a small white envelope.

"Here," she said, smiling. "I found this on the floor in a corner of the bungalow. I believe it belongs to you."

I took a deep breath before lifting the flap of the envelope. My fingers felt around inside and met something hard and cold. The sparkle of the blue jewels refracted the setting sun. My pin. The one Kitty had given me. I gasped, reading the inscription on the back, an inscription lost in time. Thick tears welled up in my eyes and the room blurred.

"Surely there were a dozen Annes on the island at one time or another," I said, puzzled. "How did you know this belonged to me?"

"I did my research," she replied, smiling.

"And in your research," I said, pausing, "did you happen to come across a Westry?" I looked at Jennifer. "Westry Green?"

Genevieve nodded. "Yes, I found a book of his, in fact—in the drawer of the desk in the bungalow."

"A book?"

"Yeah," she continued. "Just an old novel from the nineteen thirties. His name was written on the inside cover."

I grinned, remembering Westry's hope to keep our ties to the bungalow hidden.

"It took me a great deal of time," Genevieve continued, "but I found him. We spoke many years ago, before I'd taken on the project I wrote about. I've tried reaching out to him since, with no luck." She sighed. "The phone number's been changed, and no one seems to know what became of him."

I looked at my lap, folding the ivory napkin there in half, and then in half again.

"I'm sorry," she said. "I don't mean to imply that he—"

"What did he say?" Jennifer asked, swooping in to lighten the moment. "When you spoke?"

Genevieve smiled and gazed up at the ceiling as if to recall the exact details. "It was out of the pages of a novel," she replied. "He said that he once loved you a great deal, and that he still did."

"Why didn't he just call or write?" I said, shaking my head.

Genevieve shrugged. "I suppose he had his reasons. He was eccentric, Mr. Green. I suppose all artists are, though."

I frowned in confusion. "*Artists*?"

"Why yes," Genevieve replied. "Of course, I haven't seen any of his work, but I know that he has, or rather had, quite an impressive collection to his name. Paintings, sculpture. He studied art in Europe after the war, and settled down somewhere in the Midwest, where he taught art at the university level."

"Genevieve," I said, "you said he *had* an impressive collection. What do you mean?"

"He donated it all to various galleries," she said. "I recall him saying that art was meant to be shared, to be seen, not cloistered."

I smiled. "That sounds like the Westry I knew."

Jennifer cleared her throat. "Genevieve, you mentioned that Westry did sculpture," she said, looking at me for approval. "Do you know the medium? Clay? *Bronze*?"

I knew where her mind was going. The island had a way of drawing connections that weren't real.

"I'm not sure," Genevieve said, shrugging. "He was very brief about his work. And I could be wrong entirely. It was so long ago. My memory has faded some."

Jennifer and I watched as she pulled a yellow notebook out of her bag and set it on the table.

"Do you mind if I ask you some questions?" she asked cautiously.

"Of course not," I said, using my right hand to steady the clinking water glass in my left.

"As I said in my letter, a young woman was murdered on this island long ago," she began. "I'm trying to put the story to rest, to find justice."

Jennifer and I exchanged a knowing look.

"I understand that you were a nurse here and that you were off duty the night of the tragedy." She leaned in closer. "Anne, did you see or hear anything of significance? There's been such a shroud of secrecy around the circumstances of the murder. It's like the island swallowed her up without a single clue. You may be my last hope for justice."

"Yes," I said, "I do know something."

Genevieve opened her notebook. "You do?"

I clasped my hands in my lap, thinking of Westry's convictions about keeping the secret. Even after years of analysis, turning the story over and over again in my brain, I'd never understood his intentions, or whom he'd been protecting. Perhaps bringing the secret to light would give me the answers I'd longed for.

"Atea," I said. "Atea was her name."

Genevieve's eyes widened. "Yes," she said.

Jennifer squeezed my hand under the table.

"She was a beautiful woman," I continued. "I knew her only briefly, but she exuded the goodness of the island."

Genevieve nodded and set her pen down. "Many of the islanders never came to terms with her death," she said. "Even today. The ones who are old enough to remember still speak of it as a great evil that occurred on their shores. It's why I've made it my mission to find justice, for her, for all of them."

"I can help you," I said. "But I'll need to take you somewhere. I know of a clue that may bring you the justice you're seeking."

The sunset, orange with violet hues, caught my eye outside the window. "It's too late tonight," I said. "But can you meet us near the shore in front of the hotel tomorrow morning?"

"Yes," Genevieve said, smiling gratefully. "I can be there as early as you like."

"How about nine thirty?"

"Perfect," she said. "I can hardly wait."

That evening, Jennifer's cell phone rang inside her purse on the balcony, where I sat watching the waves roll softly onto the shore. The sea sparkled in the light of the crescent moon overhead. "Honey," I called out to her through the French doors, "your phone's ringing."

She bounded out to the terrace in a pair of green pajama pants and fumbled through her bag. "That's funny," she said. "I didn't think I'd get any reception out here."

"Hello?" she said into the phone. I listened halfheartedly to the one-sided conversation. "You're kidding." She listened for what seemed like an eternity. "Oh." She paused, disturbed by something, then smiled. "Well, I'm very grateful. Thank you. Thank you so much. I'll ring you when I'm back in Seattle."

Jennifer ended the call and sat down in the wicker chair next to mine. "It was the woman from the archives," she said, stunned. "They found him. They found the artist."

I blinked hard, remembering her exchange with Genevieve earlier. *Can it be possible?* "He's not . . . is he?" I hated to admit it, but Jennifer's imagination had me hopeful.

"I'm sorry, Grandma," she said. "No. It's not Westry."

I nodded. "Of course," I said, feeling childish for linking the stories the way I had.

She watched a seabird fly overhead, following it with her eyes until it was out of sight. "The artist died four years ago," she continued.

"Sorry, honey," I said, patting her hand.

"It's OK," she replied, forcing a smile. "At least the mystery's solved now—well, sort of. Now that I know who he is, I might be able to talk to his family."

"That's right," I said. "Wish we had a bottle of champagne around."

"Why?"

"To toast the occasion."

Jennifer gave me a confused look.

"Honey," I said, "you finally found your guy."

Jennifer leaned her head against my shoulder. "You'll find yours, too," she said. "I have a feeling that it will all work out."

"Maybe," I said, hoping she couldn't hear the doubt in my voice, because my heart told me I was too late.

❧

Just as we had planned, Genevieve met us on the beach the next day after breakfast. "Morning," she said, approaching with a cheerful smile. She carried a backpack, and her curly hair pushed out of her white floppy sun hat.

"Thank you so much for meeting me

today," she said once we were a good distance away from the hotel. "I can't tell you how exciting it is to be closer to the answers."

"I hope I have the right ones," I said quietly, preparing myself for what lay ahead. "Tell me what you know about the crime already."

"Well," she said, adjusting her backpack, "I know only what the islanders know, or believe they know—that the man who committed the murder was responsible for a series of pregnancies on the island, several native women and an American nurse."

**Kitty.**

I nodded. "I didn't see him," I said quietly, looking out at the stretch of white sand before us. "It was too dark. But the only man it could have been was Lance."

"Lance?"

"Yes," I said. "He was the man my best friend, at the time, was seeing. He left her in a terrible predicament—pregnant and alone, while he continued his philandering with the native women."

Genevieve stopped suddenly and turned to me. "Anne," she said, "I don't understand.

If you knew all of this, why didn't you tell? Why didn't you report it?"

I sighed, clasping my hands tightly together. "I know how it must sound, but it's more complicated than that." The bungalow was close, so I gestured to a bit of driftwood near the shore. "Let's sit for a moment. I'll tell you what I know."

We sat down on a beam that had washed up on the shore, gray and smooth from years of battling with the surf. I pointed behind us. "That," I said, "is where I watched him put a knife to her throat."

Genevieve covered her mouth.

"I hovered in the shadows until he was gone, then ran to her. I held her in my arms as she fought for life, for air." I shook my head. "There was nothing I could do for her. She was dying. Westry appeared moments later. He and I remembered the stash of morphine in my bag. The nurses always kept supplies of it in their medical cases. It could end her pain; we both knew that. I was reluctant at first, but as I watched her labored breathing and heard the way her lungs gurgled, I knew it was the only way. The morphine was more than enough to end her suffering, and end her life. She died in my arms."

Genevieve patted my arm. "You did the right thing," she said. "It's what any of us would have done in the same situation."

I wiped away a tear. "It's what I've told myself all these years, but in my heart, I knew I could have done more."

"Like report the crime?" Genevieve asked.

"Yes."

"Tell me why you didn't."

I nodded. "It was Westry's idea to keep quiet. He told me it was for our own good, that we would be charged for the murder. But I don't think that was the real reason. Westry would never run from justice unless there was an important reason." I looked out to the shore, remembering him on that night, so sure, so strong. He had known something I hadn't. "He spoke of protecting someone," I continued. "If we went to the authorities on base, he feared that something terrible might happen. I trusted him."

"Do you have any inkling of what he may have meant by that?"

"I don't," I said, throwing my hands in the air. "Believe me, I've thought about that night for seventy years now, and I'm no closer to understanding his concerns than I was seventy years ago."

Genevieve sighed.

"But," I continued, "as I mentioned last night, I do have something to show you. A clue. I tucked it away the night of the murder, hoping it may be of use one day years from then, when the truth was ready to be told. That time may be now."

I stood up, and Genevieve and Jennifer followed my lead.

"Would you like me to take you to it?"

"Yes," Genevieve said eagerly.

Jennifer steadied me as we pushed through the brush and made our way farther into the jungle. *Look at me, schlepping through the jungle at my age.* But age didn't matter now. Nothing mattered but truth, and I was intent on finding it.

I stared ahead, attempting to get my bearings. "Yes," I nodded to myself. "It should be right over here."

The landscape looked different, of course, but I knew when I saw the large palm in the distance that we were close. I pushed ahead of Jennifer and Genevieve and hastened my pace until I reached the base of the old palm. I knelt down and sank my hands into the moist soil, excavating as much dirt as I could. *It has to be here.*

"Can I help?" Genevieve asked, hovering over the pile of dirt I'd amassed with my bare hands.

I shook my head. "Just a few minutes longer, and I should have it." Soil caked my hands and arms. It got under my nails in a way that may have bothered me years ago, but I didn't care now. I'd never been so close to justice. I could smell it. And a moment later I could feel it.

My hand hit something hard about a foot below the surface, and I worked harder to secure an opening to retrieve it. I gasped.

"Grandma, are you OK?" Jennifer whispered, kneeling beside me.

"Yes," I said, producing the package I'd hidden so long ago. I unwrapped the ragged fabric, formerly the hem of my dress, which was now in shreds from moisture and insects, and produced the knife.

"The murder weapon," I said to Genevieve. "I searched for it after he threw it into the jungle, then I buried it hoping to find it again when the time was right."

Like a forensic expert, Genevieve pulled a ziplock bag from her backpack and carefully placed the knife inside. Then she handed me a wet wipe for my hands. "The time is right," she said quietly. "Thank you."

"Don't thank me," I said solemnly. "Just bring Atea the justice she deserves."

"I will," Genevieve replied, examining the knife through the bag. "These inscriptions— the unit and issue numbers—they have to mean something."

"They do," I said. "They'll lead you to Lance."

"Good," she replied, tucking it into her bag. "I can look this up with help from the army's historical society. They keep records of everything from the war. It's how I found you, after all."

I smiled to myself as we walked in silence back to the beach. It felt good to set the truth free, and I felt lighter for it.

Genevieve's cell phone rang inside her backpack, and Jennifer and I excused ourselves to the shore, where I submerged my hands in the salty water, cleansing them of any residual dirt—and evil—that had clung to the knife.

"I'm proud of you, Grandma," Jennifer said, kneeling down next to me. "That took a lot of courage, what you did."

"Thank you, dear," I said, patting my hands dry on my pants. "I should have done it years ago."

We walked back up the beach to where Genevieve stood, still talking on her cell phone. "Yes, honey," she said. "I promise, I'll be home later and we can have that dinner together we talked about." She paused. "Love you too, Adella."

The hair on my arms stood on end. *That name. I haven't heard it uttered since, since . . .* I looked at Jennifer and the expression on her face told me she'd made the connection too.

"Excuse me," I said to Genevieve moments later. The hotel was in sight now, and I could hear the splashing and laughter of swimmers echoing up the shore. "I couldn't help but overhear you say the name Adella."

"Oh," she said, "yes, my daughter."

"It's such a beautiful name," I said. "You don't hear it often."

"You don't," she said. "I've never met another Adella in my life, actually. It's my middle name. I was adopted, you know, and it was supposedly the name my birth mother had chosen for me."

I looked away, unable to hide the emotion rising in my heart.

"My parents felt compelled to keep it," she said, looking thoughtful for a moment. "When my own daughter was born, it was the only name that felt right."

"Anne," she said, concerned, "is something wrong?"

"No," I said, collecting myself. "I'm fine. I was just wondering if you ever met your birth mother or tried to find her."

"Believe me," she said, "I've tried. My parents would tell me nothing of her." She looked lost in thought for a moment, then her mouth formed a smile. "A schoolteacher once told me my mother had to be French because I had a perfect French nose. But, I'll never know. The records were destroyed long ago."

**Kitty's daughter. Right here before my eyes. The very baby I helped deliver in the bungalow.**

"Well," Genevieve said, clasping her hands together. Now that I'd put the pieces together, I could see that her eyes were the eyes of Kitty in her youth. "Here I am, going on about myself and keeping you out in the hot sun. It's been an emotional morning. I should let you rest. Why don't I come by tomorrow when I have some news about the serial numbers on this knife? I should know something by the afternoon."

I nodded. "That would be lovely," I said, my head spinning.

"We'll have a lot to talk about, then."

"We will," I replied, tucking a stray curl behind her ear, the way I might have done if Kitty had been standing in front of me just then.

# Chapter 18

"I'm going to run down to the beach for a while," Jennifer said the next morning. I could smell coconut shampoo in her freshly washed hair as she leaned in close. "Want anything? A croissant? A latte?"

I smiled. "I'm fine, dear."

As the door clicked shut behind her, I pulled out Westry's journal and continued reading his letters. I pored over the yellowed pages, learning about the life he'd led without me, and the love he'd harbored, a love that seemed to grow stronger and clearer by the year. When I reached the final page, dated five years ago, my heart seized:

August 23, 2006

My dearest Cleo,

Here I am again—another year, another August—too old now, to be here, to be here without you. This year hasn't been kind to me. I only hope it was kinder to you, wherever you are.

Do you remember the song we heard transmitted over the radio that night in the bungalow, "La Vie en Rose"? The verse went, "Give your heart and soul to me and life will always be la vie en rose." I suppose this is true of my life. For even without your presence, without your touch, I have still had you with me, always. You gave your heart and soul to me once, and I have never let it go.

Whether we meet again or not, that's all that matters.

La Vie en Rose, my dearest.

Yours, always,

Grayson

❧

Genevieve arrived at our hotel room at three o'clock. Jennifer let her in, and she set her bag down on the desk. "You're never going to believe what I found."

"What?" I said eagerly.

Genevieve sat down on the bed beside me. "The inscription on the knife," she said. "I looked it up." She shook her head in amazement. "It doesn't belong to Lance, Anne."

"My God," I said, shaking my head. "Then who?"

She retrieved her notebook from her bag and opened it to the first page. "It may come as a frightening surprise," she said. "The knife was issued to Colonel Matthew Donahue, the commanding officer of the entire base." She looked at me for an explanation. "There must be some mistake."

*I got it all wrong.* "No mistake," I said, sitting up straighter. Images from the past ran through my mind—of Kitty, crying on her bed; of Atea, confused and distraught the night of the Christmas service; of Westry's bloodied face in the men's barracks. *Of course it wasn't Lance.* I could see that now. The colonel had been behind it all, every bit of it.

Genevieve looked confused. "No one will ever believe that a commanding officer, a respected one, at that, could have committed such a brutal crime." She paused to retrieve her notebook from her bag. "The only way we can know for sure, the only way we can get our proof, is if we find the American nurse he was involved with and talk to her. Maybe she's the missing piece in all of this. The knife is much too corroded for fingerprints, and the islanders who are old enough to remember won't talk. Believe me, I've tried." She shrugged in defeat. "What are the chances that we could get that nurse on the phone? Not likely, huh?"

"Maybe," I said quietly, pausing to consider what I was about to say. "I happen to know the woman."

Genevieve's eyes widened. "You do?"

"Yes," I said. "Well, I did, anyway. She was a very old friend of mine. My *best* friend, actually. We traveled to the island together, in fact." I paused to survey her face, so like Kitty's. Would it be too late for them?

"What's her name?"

"Kitty. Kitty Morgan." I sighed. "Of course, I don't know what became of her. We haven't spoken since, well, it's been a very long time."

Genevieve's eyes lit up. "I know that name, Kitty. Yes. I believe I took down her information from the staff roster records for the infirmary. At one point I looked up her phone number, though I never called—didn't see any reason to at the time." She thumbed through her notebook, then paused on a page. "Yes, here it is," she continued. "Kitty Morgan Hampton. She lives in California now—well, at least she did two years ago. Anne, would you call her?"

I felt weak all over. "Me?"

"Yes," she said, looking at me expectantly.

"But this is your project," I said. "You should be the one."

Genevieve shook her head. "She's more likely to talk to you than . . . a stranger."

**If you only knew.**

I thought of Kitty's coldness to me in our final month on the island, the way she'd acted toward Westry—the way she'd put herself between us, severing our love forever. No, I couldn't speak to her.

I felt Jennifer's chin on my shoulder. "Time changes people," she whispered. "You loved her once—don't you want to hear her side of the story?"

I did love her, yes. And maybe still. Her memory still affected me, still moved me, after all these years. "All right," I conceded. "I'll make the call."

Jennifer handed me the phone and I hesitantly punched in the numbers written in Genevieve's notebook.

"Hello?" Kitty's voice was raspier now, but the tone was still the same. I froze, unable to find my voice.

"Hello?" she said again. "If this is a telemarketer—"

"Kitty?" I finally said in a squeak.

"Yes?"

"Kitty," my voice cracked, and tears began streaming down my cheeks. "Kitty, it's Anne."

"Anne?"

"Yes!" I cried. "Anne Calloway, Godfrey."

"My God, Anne," she said. "Is it really you?"

"Yes, it's really me."

Jennifer handed me a tissue, and I blew

my nose quietly, just as I heard Kitty do on the other end of the line.

"Anne, I—I—" Her voice faltered. "I don't know where to begin. How are you?"

"It's funny," I said. "I'm not sure how to answer that question after all these years. Where do I start?"

"Well," Kitty said softly. The edge in her voice, the one that had shaken me so in Paris, was gone now. The years had softened her tone, and perhaps her heart. "I can start by saying I'm sorry."

"Kitty, I—"

"No, let me finish," she said. "I am not well, Anne. I may not be able to say this to you again, so I must say it now." She paused, as if to collect her thoughts. "I should have reached out to you years ago. I don't know why I didn't. I'm ashamed."

"Oh, Kitty," I said, wiping another tissue under my eyes to sop up the tears seeping out.

"I regret everything about the way I behaved on the island, and in Paris," she continued. "I froze after the birth. I sank into a dark place I didn't understand. I know now it was depression—what they call postpartum depression, my daughter tells me. But I—"

I looked at Genevieve watching quietly from the chair near the desk, so like Kitty in more ways than I could count: beautiful, vibrant, impulsive. "Kitty, you have a daughter?"

"Well, yes, I have three—well, four. . . ." Her voice trailed off. "I married a good man, you'll be happy to know. I met him in Paris after the war, a Marine. We moved to California. It's been a nice life." The line went quiet for a moment. "Has your life been nice, Anne? I've often thought of you."

"It has," I said quietly. "In almost every way."

Kitty sighed. "Anne, there's something I need to tell you, about Westry."

*How can his name still stir up such emotion in me? Such pain?* I closed my eyes tightly.

"He talked about you incessantly in Paris," she said. "He was always asking about you and hoping you'd come."

"I did come," I said. "You remember, of course."

"Yes." I could hear Kitty's shame, feel it

ricocheting across the Pacific. "I was jealous of what you had," she said.

"So you intercepted his letters to me?"
Kitty gasped. "You know?"

"I only recently found out," I said.

"Anne, I'm ashamed of myself," she said tearfully. "To think I may have changed the course of your life by my actions. I can hardly bear it."

In an instant, the anger that had churned in my heart lost its steam. "You have my forgiveness," I said. "What you said earlier about time running out—I feel that too."

"I still have my pin," she said after a pause. "The one I gave you at the Cabaña Club. It's in my jewelry box. Anne, I look at it often and think of you."

I remembered the exact moment she'd given me the piece, her gesture of enduring friendship. I closed my eyes and could immediately picture the little box wrapped in crisp blue paper and tied with a gold ribbon. The smoke of the Cabaña Club swirled around us. If only that pin could have held our bond. Or maybe it had. I retrieved it from my pocket and turned it over in my hand, eyeing the engraving.

"I still have mine, too, Kitty," I said. "I have it right here."

"How I'd love to see you again," Kitty said. "Where are you? Seattle?"

"No," I said. "I'm in Bora-Bora."

**"Bora-Bora?"**

"Yes, I'm here with a woman who's researching a crime that was committed on the island, a murder."

Kitty was quiet for a moment. "You're referring to Atea, aren't you?"

"Yes," I said. "You remember."

"Of course I remember."

I decided not to ask her how she knew of the story. That didn't matter now. "I wanted to ask you some questions," I said cautiously, "if you don't mind."

"Go ahead."

"We never spoke of who the father of your baby was," I continued. "I'd always assumed it was Lance, but now we have evidence linking the murder of Atea to—"

"To the colonel?"

"Yes," I said. "You know?"

"I do," she explained. "And so did Westry."

"I don't understand."

"He was protecting me, Anne," she said,

"by not telling. Before the murder, he'd gotten wind of my situation, even before you. He saw us together and overheard a conversation on the beach. Westry also knew the colonel had had similar encounters with island women. I was headstrong and naive. Westry warned me about him, but I wouldn't listen."

I recalled the brutal beating in the barracks. "He threatened Westry, didn't he?"

"Yes," Kitty continued. "The colonel warned him that if he tried to intervene or report any of it to his superiors on the mainland, he'd do something terrible to me."

"My God, Kitty!" I exclaimed. "So by keeping quiet about Atea's murder, Westry was protecting *you*?"

"Yes," she said. "Looking back, I think I was in more danger than I ever knew. Westry spared me from all of that."

I sighed. "It's why you began to develop feelings for him, isn't it?"

"I suppose," Kitty said honestly. "After being treated so terribly by men all my life, here was a man, an honest man, who cared, who wanted to protect me. And yet, he was already in love with my best friend."

I gazed out the window to the shore, remembering the way Kitty had looked at Westry. I couldn't blame her for loving him.

"Anyway," she continued, "Atea was murdered because he got her pregnant, and she refused to keep quiet, just like the other women."

"The other women?"

"Yes," she said. "There were at least two others, one barely fourteen." She paused in the wake of such a disturbing revelation. "I should have come forward about this long ago, but I've had to move on. And after I heard of his death, I decided that he would burn in hell anyway."

"When did he die?"

"Nineteen sixty-three," she said. "A heart attack, alone in a San Francisco hotel room."

I sat up straighter, looking at Jennifer, then at Genevieve. "It doesn't mean justice can't still be served," I said. "He's a decorated war veteran. We'll have the military revoke his status posthumously. I'll see to that."

Genevieve nodded in agreement. *How will she feel when she realizes the man at the center of this evil was her own father?* I took a deep breath, for what I was about to say would change everything, for both of them.

"Kitty," I said, gesturing for Genevieve to come over to the phone. "There's someone I'd like you to speak to. Her name is Genevieve. I think you two have more in common than you know. Her daughter, for instance . . . well, I think you two should talk."

Genevieve gave me a confused look, but reached for the phone and smiled. "Ms. Hampton?"

I walked away from the bed, and gestured for Jennifer to follow. She nodded knowingly, and we closed the door quietly behind us.

"That may have been the best thing that could have come from all of this," Jennifer said, smiling at me in the hallway.

We walked arm in arm down the stairs to the open-air lobby, where we sat together watching the waves crash fiercely on the shore, catching sunbathers off guard and scattering them with sea-soaked towels up to the higher bank. I marveled at the sight.

It was as if the island knew that justice had come and was cleansing its shores of the evil.

I ran my finger along the chain of my locket, wondering if what Tita had said could be true. *The curse she spoke of, will it now be broken?* Only time would tell.

# Chapter 19

The phone rang in the living room, and I groaned. Answering it meant standing up, leaving my bed, and feeling my bones ache with every step. But the persistent ringing enticed me to make the journey. One step, and then another. My legs ached, but they moved, and I reached the phone in time to pick it up and utter an out-of-breath hello into the receiver.

"Grandma, it's me," chirped Jennifer. "Today's the day."

More than three months had passed since we'd returned from the island. The trip had been satisfying in more ways than I'd expected, and yet I wasn't prepared for the emotional exhaustion that persisted upon our return. While I'd made peace for Genevieve, Atea, Kitty, and perhaps even for the island, I had left with a tsunami in my own heart, with only whispers of Westry and a book of old letters to cling to.

"Grandma?"

"I'm here, dear," I said into the phone. "I'm just not feeling like myself today."

"But you're still coming, right?"

"Oh, honey," I said, sinking into the sofa before pulling a blanket over my icy feet. "I don't think I can."

Jennifer's silence pierced my heart. *She accompanied me on my journey and stood by me with such compassion—how can I abandon her on this day?*

"You can do without me, can't you, dear?" I asked, rubbing my aching back. Jennifer had turned in her final article a week prior, and the newspaper had gotten wind of the project, as did the university's public relations team.

"Oh, Grandma," she said. "I know it's a lot to ask, especially since you haven't been feeling well, but I would love it if you came. So many people will be there, and I can hardly stand to face them alone. I'm so nervous. It would be comforting to have you there. I can pick you up in an hour. We'll park close so you won't have to walk far."

I forced my legs out in front of me and stood up. *I can do this. For Jennifer.* "Well," I said, taking a deep breath, "then I will come. For you, dear."

"Oh Grandma, thank you!" she exclaimed. "I'll be over soon."

I set the phone down and reached for the letter from Genevieve on the coffee table. It had arrived yesterday, and I'd already read it a dozen times.

Dear Anne,

I wanted to thank you for coming to Bora-Bora. Your visit was transformative—for the island, for me, for Atea. I hope it was for you, too.

I write with good news: I have been in touch with the army and they have all the details. They've agreed to put a case together against Colonel Donahue. It all feels very strange, knowing my relation to this man, but it doesn't stop me from seeking justice for Atea, for my unborn sister or brother.

While the army can't prosecute him in death, my contact tells me they are working with officials here on the island to assemble the facts of the case. He will likely be stripped of his honors and distinctions, at least in all military records.

The island officials are talking about erecting a monument, a memorial for Atea somewhere in town. Isn't that just wonderful, Anne? Of course, we'd love to have you here, when the time comes, for the ceremony. None of this would have happened without your courage.

Oh, and I almost forgot—I am meeting Kitty for the first time in California next month. She's invited me to stay with her. I'm bringing Adella. I have to pinch myself, as I can hardly believe any of this is real. But it is, wonderfully real.

I will always think of you with warmth, fondness, and appreciation.

With love,

Genevieve

Quiet lingered on campus, and my heels clicked loudly on the brick path, shiny from a recent rain shower. A clock chimed in the distance: noon.

"Just a little farther," Jennifer said, gauging my face for signs of strain.

"I'm all right, dear," I reassured her. The crisp fall air felt good on my skin. It energized me in a way I hadn't anticipated. "You lead the way."

We walked past a row of maples, their leaves tinged orange and red. A stately brick building stood at attention nearby. I recognized it instantly, of course. Gerard had taught finance here after he retired from the bank. How I'd loved taking walks with him through campus, especially in the fall.

"Right through here," Jennifer said, taking my arm in hers as we approached a narrow path that curved around the ivy-covered building. She held up a tree branch so I could duck underneath. Of all the times I'd been on campus with Gerard, I'd never thought to walk behind the building. Not even once.

"There it is," she said, pointing ahead proudly.

I squinted, letting the sculpture come into focus. I could see why it captivated Jennifer so. It told a story. I walked closer, intrigued, and eyed the bronze couple huddled in a crude doorway. *Why is my heart racing?* The man looked at the woman with longing, while her gaze drifted out to the left somewhere in the distance.

"It's beautiful," I said, looking closer. The man held in his hands a large box with a lock, and at his feet a few possessions lay scattered: a painter's canvas, a shattered bottle, and a book. My hands trembled as I knelt down. In that moment, my heart *knew*.

Jennifer stood quietly a few steps behind me. *Where are all the people, the fanfare she spoke of?* I ran my hand along the bronze book at the base of the sculpture, cold, wet from the rain, until I secured the corner of its cover. *Could it be?* I lifted the heavy edge and stared at the tarnished steel key inside, my heart beating faster by the second.

I gestured for Jennifer to come closer. "I can't do this alone," I said, wiping a tear from my cheek.

She steadied me as I slid the key into the lock on the box, its edges sealed tightly to protect its contents. *A perfect match.* I turned it to the right but it jammed.

"The weather must have corroded it," I said. "I'll try it again."

I pulled the key out and inserted it in the lock a second time, giving it a light shake. A faint click sounded as the lock released its stubborn grip.

Jennifer hovered as I lifted the lid and peered inside to find a blue velvet case. I removed it from its bronze crypt and walked to a nearby bench, where Jennifer and I sat down.

"Are you going to open it?" she whispered.

I turned to her with heavy, moist eyes. "You knew, didn't you?"

Jennifer smiled quietly, nodding. "When the woman from the archives called in Bora-Bora, she told me the artist's name, Grayson Hodge, but I didn't recognize it. I should have remembered, but the name didn't click until a few weeks after we were home." She paused, searching my face for approval. "He used the pseudonym in his work. I didn't want to keep it from you, but I wanted you to see this for yourself."

I carefully opened the case and peeled back the brown paper wrapping inside.

Jennifer gasped. "The painting? The one from the bungalow?"

I nodded in awe. The old Gauguin warmed my hands as I held it, as if the Bora-Bora sun had lingered in the canvas all these years. The colors, just as vibrant; the composition, just as moving as the day I first laid eyes on it. And for a moment, I was there again, on the island, feeling the warm air on my cheeks, the sand on my feet, the love of Westry all around me.

"He found it!" I cried. "Just as he promised." *Of course he kept his promise.* "And to think it was here, waiting for me, all these years—right under my nose—and I didn't even look." I turned to Jennifer with eyes of gratitude. "Thank you, dear," I said, looking at the statue and then back at the painting. "This is a gift."

She eyed the nearby building anxiously before turning back to me. "Grandma," she whispered, "are you ready?"

"Ready for what?"

"To see *him*."

My heart swelled. "But you said, you said he was . . ."

"Dead?" She shook her head. "Yes, Grayson Hodge, a ninety-year-old man from Barkley, Utah, died. But not Westry Green."

**Westry. Here? Can it be true?**

"I don't know," I said, choking back tears. "But your project?"

Jennifer smiled. "It's concluded beautifully."

I felt weak, unsure. "I've been dreaming about this day for as long as I can remember, and now that it's here I'm . . ."

"Scared?"

"Yes," I muttered, smoothing my wispy hair—what was left of it, anyway. *Why didn't I put on a dress? And some lipstick?*

Jennifer shook her head, sensing my insecurity. "Westry will only see what I see: your true *beauty*."

She handed me a handkerchief to dry my eyes. "Now, you wait here. I'll go around front and tell them we're ready."

"You mean," I said, fumbling, "he's here already?"

"Yes," she said, smiling proudly. "His son brought him over this morning. They traveled all the way from New York."

Jennifer gave me a passing smile as she turned toward the path, disappearing around the front of the old building. Alone, I looked up at the sculpture, gazing at the man's eyes. Even cast in bronze, they did look like Westry's, very much so. All those times I'd walked this stretch of campus—I exhaled deeply—if I had only stopped once to notice, to see the clue he'd placed in my path, I might have found him.

I heard the crunch of gravel in the distance and I turned my eyes back to the pathway. When a man appeared, a flock of sparrows startled, fluttering away to a nearby tree. Even in a wheelchair, he had a familiar presence—the way he held himself, the outline of his chin. When our eyes met, he waved away the middle-aged man behind him and took the wheels in his hands, pushing the chair with a strength that didn't match the white of his hair, the wrinkles on his face. His eyes remained fixed on my face, holding me in his gaze.

He stopped in front of the bench where I sat, reaching his hands out to me, cradling my icy fingers in his strong, warm palms. "Hello, Cleo," he said, extending a hand to my face. He stroked my cheek lightly, before his fingers found my locket.

"Hello, Grayson," I said, wiping the tears from my cheek.

"You're a little late, my dear," he said with the same mischievous grin I'd been so charmed by on the day we met.

I searched his face. "How can you ever forgive me? For not knowing, for not looking. . . . I was—"

Westry brushed his finger against my lips and smiled in a way that calmed me. *He could always calm me.* "Just a little late," he said softly, "but not too late." In an instant, he was twenty-five again, and I, twenty-one. Age disappeared. Time faded into the distance.

He buttoned his brown corduroy jacket and set the brakes of the wheelchair, then inched closer to the edge of the seat before pushing his body to a standing position.

I gasped. "But I thought . . ."

He grinned. "That you'd like to take an autumn stroll?" He retrieved a gray cane from the side of the chair, securing it in his left hand and holding his right out to me. "Ready?"

"Yes," I said, beaming, marveling at him standing next to me, so tall, so sure. I tucked the painting under my arm before taking his hand in mine, blinking hard to make sure I wasn't dreaming.

We started down the path through campus, unsure of our destination. But none of that mattered, not now. For our story had an ending that suited me. I loved him, and he loved me, up until the very end. This is the story that would whistle in the winds of Bora-Bora, haunt the weathered remains of the bungalow, and live on in my heart forever.

Westry came. The curse ended. Together, we walked slowly, but surely. I nestled closer to him, wrapping my arm around his just as two wine-colored leaves fell from a nearby tree branch, dancing in the autumn breeze on separate paths before falling softly to the ground, where they settled on the damp earth, side by side.

# Acknowledgments

A big, heartfelt thanks goes to my extraordinary literary agent, Elisabeth Weed, for teaming up with me on another book and offering encouragement and guidance (and sometimes free therapy sessions) along the way. It's a joy and a privilege to work with you. Also, much gratitude to Stephanie Sun, who, along with Elisabeth, was the very first reader of this book. Your kind comments cheered me on and your suggestions made the book better. (I also love that you found Westry to be as dreamy as I still do!)

It is not advisable to write a book when

one is deep into the second trimester of her pregnancy and also on the heels of the debut of another book. But I wrote one anyway. And I thank my lovely editor, Denise Roy, for sticking by me as I juggled the baby and the book revisions while prepping for the launch of my first novel. Denise, your sharp editorial eye and creative ideas continually amaze me. In you, I've found a great editorial partner. (Thank you, too, for being so understanding when the baby screamed sometimes during our phone conversations—because he did scream, quite loudly.)

I have much appreciation to Jenny Meyer of Meyer Literary Agency for sharing my story with foreign editors and for being so enthusiastic about my stories. To Nadia Kashper, Liz Keenan, Milena Brown, Kym Surridge, and everyone at Plume, you're the best. Dear friends, Sally Farhat Kassab, Wendi Parriera, Camille Noe Pagan, Lisa Bach, Natalie Quick, and many more all cheered me on along the way—thank you, lovelies. And to my editors at *Glamour*, *Health*, *Redbook*, and other magazines, who gave me a deadline extension or two so I could get book stuff done—I'm ever grateful.

I am thankful in more ways than I can count to my parents, Terry and Karen Mitchell—for loving me, for putting up with me, for encouraging me, and especially for sharing Great Uncle Michael Handgraaf's journal from wartime in the South Pacific. To my brothers, Josh Mitchell and Josiah Mitchell, and my sister and closest friend, Jessica Campbell—I love you so much, but you're still no match for me at Tile Rummy. I also remember my late grandfather James Robert Mitchell, whose stories of wartime in the South Pacific remain etched in my memory.

I have three sons, Carson, Russell, and Colby, all who were under the age of four when I wrote this book. There's only one thing I love more than writing, and it's being their mother.

Last but not least, Jason—my best friend, partner in child wrangling, and loving husband, this story wouldn't have been born had it not been for our 2011 journey to Moorea and Tahiti. For in that rustic little beach bungalow we shared (complete with geckos and lots of tropical ants!) was the first glimmer of this story. You are my inspiration and my rock. I write for you, and because of you.

# THE CATHOLIC WAY

# The Catholic Way

BY

*Theodore Maynard*

APPLETON-CENTURY-CROFTS, INC.

*New York*

Copyright, 1952, By

THEODORE MAYNARD

Nihil obstat:

JOHN M. A. FEARNS, S.T.D., Censor Librorum

Imprimatur:

✠FRANCIS CARDINAL SPELLMAN, Archbishop of New York
September 16, 1952

*To Gertrude and Mary Keefe*

*"I have placed you in the midst of your fellows that you may do to them what you cannot do to Me, that is that you may love your neighbor of free grace without expecting any return from him, and what you do to him I count as done to Me."*

—St. Catherine of Siena, *Dialogues*

# Explanation in Lieu of a Preface

I would avoid anything like a preface altogether were it not called for in justice to the reader and also myself. In the first place, though I have in mind the kind of life lived by an "average" Catholic, I cannot but feel with some dismay that this person is a great deal better upon the whole than—I will not say than I hope to be but than I actually am. All I can claim is that I probably grasp the implications of Catholic living better than do most Catholics, which is why I venture to set them forth.

It will be seen that I begin with a personal note, and my readers should be warned now that this will be struck again—not, I think, in an egotistic spirit, or because I expect anybody to be interested in me, but because my personal experience may be sometimes illuminating. As I have said this, I venture to go on to remark that, if I am correct in my assumption that I grasp the implications of Catholicism better than most, this obviously only increases the danger of my loss of salvation. Though I make bold to say that my faith is sound—"Lord I believe, help Thou my unbelief!"—my hope sometimes wavers, and I often wonder whether I have any charity at all, whether for God or man. Yet I suppose I do, though it is not nearly enough. So I do hope to be saved; but whether or not that happens, I may still help in the salvation of others through the writing of this book.

I have written from the layman's point of view, for which reason the one sacrament that I do not deal with is that of Holy Orders. Yet of course the priesthood is necessary to the Church, because all Catholic life centers around the Mass. While it is true that in the seventeenth century the Church in Japan had to "go underground" for two hundred and fifty years, remaining bereft of all the sacraments except that of baptism, it was during even that heroic time to be considered a Church only in an imperfect and attenuated form. Yet I say this not as that strange hybrid, an "ecclesiastical layman," for though I once nearly decided in my youth to become a priest myself, I came to recognize that mine was a lay vocation. What I write here is an account of what the Catholic Church means to a layman, or should mean to a layman.

Mine is not an apologetic purpose; at all events this is not an exercise in polemics, for which I have neither taste nor talent. While the great majority who remain outside the Church are where they are because they have never bothered to think about the matter, there are also a large number of people who have thought about it a good deal and reject the Catholic claims for what they honestly consider cogent reasons. With these I can sympathize, as I can even sympathize with the agnostic frame of mind. But though it will be found that now and then I offer some arguments in favor of this or that point, my deep conviction is that, as Dryden put it:

> Truth has such a face and such a mien
> As to be loved, needs only to be seen.

At least it was so with me, for nobody argued me into the Catholic Church. The moment I saw what it really was I joined it.

My primary purpose is not to present Catholic doctrine. A number of books, some of the most recent and best by laymen, have done this so well that another from me is not called for, even supposing that I had the competence to produce one. I have something different in mind, something which, so far as I am aware, has not been attempted before. This is a book on the Catholic way of life, and Catholic doctrine will figure in it only incidentally or when it can help to show why Catholic living takes the pattern that it does.

I do not propose merely to indicate Catholic obligations but Catholic privileges and opportunities as well—in short, the way the Catholic outlook colors all aspects of life. It was not a Catholic who said, "In a crust of bread one may taste the stars," but the sentiment is Catholic. Similarly in Hinduism, so I gather from the great book written about it by the eighteenth-century Abbé Dubois, not only the marital act but physical excretions are provided with a prayer. This is closely paralleled by the Christian, "Whatever you do, whether you eat or drink, do all to the glory of God." The religious man should be religious at every moment, which means that for him there are few, if any, deliberately "indifferent" acts. He will not, it is to be hoped, parade his piety, and it would be hardly possible for him to be continuously thinking of the divine; nevertheless the supernatural will permeate the natural, even when he is not aware of it.

If anything I have written should happen to give offence, I ask people to be charitable enough to bear with me. I am obliged to make explanations, not all of which I expect to be accepted; and in these explanations I may find myself compelled to draw what may seem to be invidious comparisons. So let me make this explanation at once: while I believe that Catholicism is something unique, there are large tracts which it holds in common with other faiths, and I shall try to indicate these. My aim is to be charitable in my turn and, perhaps what is still more important, fair. This is an Irenicon.

My book has been written not only for Catholics—or even for dissident Christians—but for everybody who is conscious of God, and even for those who are not. To Catholics I hope to render some service in pointing out implications that may have escaped their attention; to those who are not Catholics I also hope to render a service by telling of the practical nature of Catholic life. Too often in such books there is an acrid and acrimonious note. I think I can promise that here there will be no invective.

I must be understood as writing primarily for an American audience, for though Catholic belief is everywhere the same—as are most Catholic practices—the atmosphere in which the Church maintains itself sometimes varies considerably from country to country. To indicate my personal experience: my first ten years were passed in India, among people so intensely Protestant that, for them, the Catholic Church hardly could be said to exist. This continued for me in England (with a short period in the United States) until I was twenty-two, when I became a Catholic. But though I scrambled into the barque of Peter there, I left England more than thirty years ago, and I know little about English Catholicism, except what I can infer from my knowledge of England. It is American Catholic life that I know best and am writing about.

Even in the United States there are minor divergencies of which most Catholics are unaware. Here, for example, Mass is said in sixteen of the seventeen liturgical languages of the various forms of the Eastern Rite, all of which are in communion with Rome and most of which still have a married clergy. These exceptions are mentioned, not so much for the sake of Latin Catholics—most of whom have never heard of them and would, I fear, be confused and perhaps scandalized to hear of them—but to assure non-Catholics that the Church is not so rigid in its uniformity as they may imagine. Catholic doctrine, whatever the liturgy used, is the same universally, and so is Catholic obedience to the Holy See. But Catholic discipline varies and may change in some ways, as it has already changed several times during the course of the Christian centuries.

Although I have the deepest possible respect and sympathy for other branches of the Church, I shall take the Latin Rite and discipline as the norm, disregarding for much the same reason the exceptional dispensation enjoyed until 1949 by such parts of the country as were once Spanish possessions from the rule of Friday abstinence. It is the Catholic life with which most people come into contact that I shall attempt to depict. The "Way" indicated is the ordinary way.

# Acknowledgments

The quotations from the following books and magazines are reprinted by the kind permission of the publishers and the copyright owners:

*Spirit of Catholicism* by Karl Adam. New York: 1941, The Macmillan Company.

"American Protestantism at the Mid-Century Mark" by Paul Hutchinson, in *Religion in Life*, Spring Number, 1951. Nashville: Abingdon-Cokesbury Press.

*One And Holy* by Karl Adam. Copyright Sheed and Ward, Inc., New York, 1951.

*Christian Perfection and Contemplation* by Père Garrigou-Lagrange, translated by Sister M. Timothea Doyle. Saint Louis: 1937, B. Herder Book Company.

*Four Mysteries of the Faith* by Monsignor F. C. Kolbe. London: 1926, Longmans Green & Company, Ltd.

Letter from G. K. Chesterton quoted in *Return to Chesterton* by Maisie Ward. Copyright 1952, Sheed and Ward, Inc., New York. Used by permission of Miss D. C. Collins.

"The Obscure Night of the Soul" by Saint John of the Cross, as translated by Arthur Symons in his *Poems*. London: 1901, William Heinemann, Ltd. New York: Dodd, Mead & Co.

"On No Longer Being a Rationalist" by C. E. M. Joad, M.A., D. Lit., Reader in Philosophy, University of London, in *The Rationalist Annual*. London: 1946. By permission of the author.

*The Poems of Alice Meynell*. By permission of Sir Francis Meynell and the Publishers, Burns, Oates & Washbourne, Ltd., London, and Charles Scribner's Sons, New York.

*The Idea of a Christian Society,* by T. S. Eliot. Copyright, 1940, by T. S. Eliot. Reprinted by permission of Harcourt, Brace and Company, Inc.

*The Everlasting Man* by G. K. Chesterton. Reprinted by permission of Dodd, Mead & Co. Copyright 1925 by Dodd, Mead & Co., Inc. Used by permission of Miss D. C. Collins, and of Hodder & Stoughton, Ltd., London.

*The Happy Ending* by Louise Imogene Guiney. Boston: 1909, Houghton Mifflin Company.

*Book of Divine Consolation* by Angela da Foligno, translated by Mary G. Steegmann. New York: 1922, Oxford University Press, Inc.

*Introduction to the Devout Life* by Saint Francis de Sales, translated by Alan Ross. Westminster, Maryland: 1948, The Newman Press.

*The Sacramental Way* by Monsignor Martin Hellriegel, edited by Mary Perkins. Copyright Sheed and Ward, Inc., New York, 1948.

*The American Churches* by William Warren Sweet. Used by permission of Abingdon-Cokesbury Press, Nashville.

*Christ, the Life of the Soul* by Abbott Columba Marmion. Used by permission of B. Herder Book Company, Saint Louis, Missouri, and Sands & Co., Ltd., London.

*Texts and Pretexts* by Aldous Huxley. Copyright 1932 by Aldous Huxley. Used by permission of Harper & Brothers, New York, and Chatto & Windus, London.

"Reply to a Parish Priest" in *Stages on the Road* by Sigrid Undset. New York: 1934, Alfred A. Knopf, Inc.

*Alice Meynell: A Memoir* by Viola Meynell. New York: 1929, Charles Scribner's Sons.

*Poems of Gerard Manley Hopkins.* Copyright 1948 by Oxford University Press, Inc.

*Centuries of Meditation* by Thomas Traherne. London: 1908. By permission of the copyright owners, P. J. & A. E. Dobell.

"Fragment from Dante," in *The Collected Poems of G. K. Chesterton.* Reprinted by permission of Dodd, Mead & Co., Copyright 1932 by Dodd, Mead & Co., Inc. Also with the permission of Miss D. C. Collins.

# Contents

## PART III

### SOCIAL LIFE

## PART IV

### THE REWARD

# PART I
# THE DIVERGENCE

# CHAPTER ONE

## What Is This Strange Thing?

The difference that exists between Catholics and non-Catholics is probably one of which non-Catholics are more conscious than are Catholics themselves. For Catholics, while well aware that they stand apart, and that the Church is something unique, often take themselves and the Church for granted. As a rule they are not very curious about the various shades of belief or unbelief of those around them. This may be a shortcoming on the Catholic's part, for he should be concerned about the salvation of his neighbors. His seeming indifference is partly the result of indolence, and again, strange though this may sound, of his habit of tolerance. Then, too, Catholicism has so often been under attack in the United States that only now are Catholics beginning to free themselves from an inferiority complex. Whereas in some European countries the Church is looked upon as being almost a club of the aristocratic and well-to-do, with the result that the working classes have largely turned against it, the opposite is true in the United States. American Catholics do not eat their hearts out about it, but they realize that they are not considered as belonging to the best social circles.

Catholic tolerance, which to some may sound like a contradiction in terms, is sometimes actually carried too far. Thus one now and then hears a Catholic say—and I have said it myself—that those who are not Catholics have a better chance of salvation than other people, on the principle that to whom much has been given much will be asked. That principle is sound, but its application is often faulty. The gravest responsibility indeed rests on those who have been given most grace, for which reason Catholics well might tremble. But the grace given them is so immense as to much more than counterbalance their inade-

3

quacies. All those who are saved will be saved as Catholics, even those who are not Christians in profession; but in view of all the riches that a Catholic has at his command in the sacraments, he certainly has much the best chance of getting to heaven. When I look at myself, I feel sure that I shall be among the lost; when I look at the Church, I wonder how it is possible for me to be lost—short of a final impenitence which my will is firmly set to avoid.

There is an all-too-common assumption that what is a duty for Catholics is not a duty for others. This is perfectly true to this extent: merely disciplinary regulations, such as the Friday abstinence, do not bind any except those to whom the law of the Church has made it apply. But the Ten Commandments bind all men. Similarly it is not true that non-Catholics are free to get divorced and marry again, or to practice contraception, for these are contrary to the law of God. Such violations are not "all right," as is sometimes unthinkingly said, for those outside the Church. The most that may be granted is that nobody is subjectively obligated except by the dictates of his conscience. Therefore, while committing what is objectively a sin, one who is not fully aware of its guilt may be partially exculpated on the ground of his ignorance.

So also with regard to the worship of God. All have an inescapable obligation here, but only according to their lights. The non-Catholic does not sin by not attending Mass, but he is obliged to remember the Sabbath Day to keep it holy, though the Christian's Sunday observance and the Moslem's Friday equate the Jew's Saturday. And as God must be worshiped in spirit *and in truth*, erroneous worship remains error, even when the error is pardonable. It goes without saying that for the creature not to adore his Creator is monstrous.

False belief has no rights, and no more than sin can it ever be justified. Yet he who believes erroneously may have, and in fact does have, rights. Catholics make a clear distinction between sin and the sinner. In practice the Church is much more indulgent towards human frailty than towards false doctrine, knowing that erroneous belief usually leads to the undermining of morals. Nevertheless, it will make every possible allowance for good faith; hell is *not* paved with good intentions. For this reason the Church, while inflexible in principle, applies its principles with careful consideration for the strange workings of the human heart. This is the meaning of casuistry, which in spite of its bad popular connotation is never an excuse for what cannot be excused, but a delicately just weighing of what may be mitigating circumstances. Catholicism is at once the most tolerant and the most intolerant of systems.

Catholics themselves may be, in many instances, rather disdainful in their tolerance. If so, the less Catholic in spirit they. There is not the slightest occasion for their being smug about their faith—whether it is due to their upbringing or to their conversion—for they know, or ought to know, that faith is always a gift, the greatest gift that God can bestow. Those born into a Catholic family should not take this for granted but should be profoundly grateful. Those who are converts should never cease to wonder why *they* should have been given the faith, when many better men have not received it, including some who hover on the brink of the Church for many years and yet die outside.

All Catholics know this in theory, of course, but they cannot always be expected to keep it steadily in mind. They sometimes take their own faith too much as a matter of course, until they need to call upon it for consolation or are faced with some crisis in which they need to summon it to sustain them. Negligent though a Catholic may be, his faith is always there and, consciously or unconsciously, it permeates his thought, however superficial and intermittent thought may be in many cases. Precisely because he is so sure of his own faith he is not likely to bother his head much about what others may or may not believe. His tolerance, like most of the tolerance shown to him, is largely compounded of indifference.

Certainly Catholics have not always been charitable in controversy and cannot escape their share of the blame for the misunderstandings that have arisen between the two main divisions of Christendom. Today, however, this applies only to a small group of rather truculent Catholic writers and editors. There are some who do even worse by studiously avoiding saying anything whatever about Protestantism—not because they wish to give no offense, but because they feel that since it is not worth enquiring about, it is not worth talking about either. Catholics, moreover, because of their history in America, are extremely disinclined to stir up strife. They know that Protestantism is a historical accident for which Protestants of today are in no way responsible; so they are willing to make large allowances for them on the ground of their "invincible ignorance." From the pulpit, when some allusion to Protestants cannot be escaped, they are alluded to in some such vaguely courteous term as "our separated brethren."

This lack of interest, and the ignorance that springs from it, is not at all a good thing; but it is at least preferable to the somewhat morbid interest that many Protestants take in the Church, for this, even in the case of otherwise well-informed people, is often based on grotesque misconceptions. Although the grosser forms of calumny are now circulated only in some benighted sections, even those who disdain anything approaching the Maria Monk line of attack and who are accurate about the main external facts, usually miss all the important implications. The theologian Harnack was not thinking of crude bigots but of those educated in the best German Protestant seminaries when he said: "Some of them know something about Gnosticism, or about other curious and for them worthless details. But of the Catholic Church, the greatest religious and political creation known to history, they know absolutely nothing, and they indulge in its regard in wholly trivial, vague and often directly nonsensical notions. How her greatest institutions originated, what they mean in the life of the Church, how easily they may be misconceived, and why they function so surely and impressively; all this, according to my experience, is for them, apart from a few exceptions, a *terra incognita*."

The purpose of this book is not to supply what Harnack postulated as generally absent but only to give some idea of what Catholicism means to the ordinary Catholic. It is because there is now in this country, perhaps more than ever before, a sympathetic interest in what Catholicism is, that an attempt will be made to indicate the main lines of Catholic life. This is bound to be done inadequately, for a volume or a series of volumes could be produced about almost every point, but it is my hope that it will be done well enough to serve a useful purpose, especially that of helping to increase, on both sides, a friendlier understanding than has often prevailed.

One sometimes hears priests urging their flocks to familiarize themselves with their religion, so that they may be able to answer intelligently when they are asked questions about it by the non-Catholic. This advice is never given, I believe, by Protestant ministers, for Catholics rarely if ever ask questions, partly because they are incurious, but also because there is little that Protestant bodies have to explain. Even within one denomination there is no uniformity of doctrine or of practice. Protestantism is, in Catholic eyes, in so far as it is positive in its teaching, a kind of attenuated Catholicism, and in so far as it is negative (which it mostly is), a faith whose principles, when boiled down, reject not only the Catholic Church but any Church. The lack of logic in the Protestant position was pointed out in 1879 by W. H. Mallock in his book *Is Life Worth Living?* over forty years before he became a Catholic on his deathbed. Mr. Mallock noted that "Any supernatural religion that renounces its claim [to infallibility], it is clear can profess to be a semi-revelation only. It is a hybrid thing, partly natural and partly supernatural, and it thus practically has all the qualities of a religion that is wholly natural...." I have sometimes wondered whether it is not because Protestants have flinched before that remorseless logic that, in order to escape making a claim to infallibility, which they knew would make them cut somewhat absurd figures, they have tended to reduce revelation to something that Catholics would hardly recognize as such.

Apart from certain small groups, Protestants, therefore, have no definite position to maintain. Even were Catholics not sure of their own ground, it would hardly be worth the while of most of them to go beyond it. As for explaining their religion, most of them are not very good at it, not so much because they are inarticulate as because they fear that their terminology might be inexact, or might be misconstrued. Because they are often unduly sensitive to Protestant criticism, they refer such questioners as seem to be in earnest to a priest rather than accept the responsibility of giving answers which might not be perfectly correct.

Catholics are well aware that they are often regarded as peculiar—sensible enough people in all ordinary matters but incomprehensible when it comes to religion. Their difference from others is the occasion of much resentment and distrust and, sometimes, of attack, though such attacks are upon the whole diminishing or taking another form than they had in the past. That Catholics are attacked should be no worry to them; rather they should worry when they are *not* attacked. The criticism they most often hear today is something at which they can only smile broadly; it is that they are plotting to obtain political control of the country and to reduce other Americans to "second-class" citizens. While it is perfectly true that the aim of the Church is to make the whole world Catholic, the progress towards such a goal is scarcely perceptible. In the United States, where Catholics are the largest of all religious bodies—perhaps thirty millions out of a hundred and fifty—the Church hardly does more than, with difficulty, hold her own. The enormous strides during the days of the influx of immigration ended with the imposition of stricter immigration laws. Moreover, the natural increase in population is not so great as it should be, for the simple reason that the birth rate in cities, where the Church has its strongholds, tends to diminish to such an extent that replenishment has to come from the overwhelmingly Protestant rural districts.

It does not help matters that many of these Protestant arrivals, or at least their children, drop any but a very tenuous denominational connection and often become, in effect, pagan. For they commonly retain their anti-Catholic prejudices—the last vestiges of their Protestantism. These are understandably acerbated when they encounter political machines which in many instances are dominated by Catholics, some of whom are more astute as politicians than edifying in the practice of their religion. Although one may heartily sympathize with the irritation and disgust such men create, the Church cannot be held accountable. The Rock of Peter has never formed part of the foundations of Tammany Hall.

Good Catholics deplore political exploitation as strongly as anybody else. Not by such means or through such allies is the Catholic cause to be advanced. Politicians who play their church connections for all they are worth among their Catholic constituents do incalculable harm to Catholicism. While it may be true that now and then a politically minded ecclesiastic has tried to obtain favors on this basis, the vast majority have been most careful to do nothing of the kind but rather have bent backwards even when favors might have been legitimately requested. Unthinking people may take pride in the fact that their mayor attends Mass, just as there are some who seem to think that a victory of the Notre Dame football team is a triumph for the Catholic Church. The silly girls who say their rosary for another touchdown would be much better employed in praying for the conversion to the Faith of the opposing side.

Such things are mentioned only to deny that they are general. When they do exist they obscure the real point, which is that Catholicism, in many respects, is totally different from other religions—and especially from Protestantism, in all its forms. Therefore from the outset it must be insisted upon that Catholicism is not an "opinion"—whether quaint, charming, or terrifying—but divinely revealed truth. One can get nowhere without grasping that fact. Though this seems to be—and in one sense is—the height of intolerance, it nevertheless has to be plainly stated. It has sometimes been suggested—notably by the very brilliant Aldous Huxley—that if only Christianity would consent to be a myth and not demand to be taken as history, everybody would be Christians. It seems to have escaped the attention of Mr. Huxley that this is nothing but the Modernism so completely eradicated by the encyclical *Pascendi* issued in 1907 by Pius X from those small sections of the Church in which it had taken precarious root. But Protestants continue to toy with this idea in various forms, yet do not fill their churches because of it. For who is going to worship a myth, however beautiful? The Catholic Church must hold, however much modernists may wail, what Sir Thomas More wrote in the Tower while awaiting the execution he knew to be inevitable: "The sayings of Our Saviour Jesus Christ were not a poet's fable nor a harper's song but the very holy word of Almighty God Himself."

That much, despite the disintegration that has come to large tracts of Protestantism, will surely be acceptable to most of those who call themselves Christians. It should be remembered that the original attack of the Protestant reformers was not upon Catholic doctrine but upon the power of the priesthood. Such doctrine as came to be abandoned by them—that of the Real Presence, Purgatory, Confession and so forth—were challenged mainly because the priestly power seemed bound up with them. Other things soon followed, as might have been foreseen—when the baby was thrown out with the bath—and the invocation of saints and even the Blessed Virgin was also rejected. Historically, the whole thing was precipitated by the abuse of indulgences, not on the part of the Church but of some injudicious and perhaps unscrupulous traffickers in what was holy. There was a real need of reform, which the Church herself effected at the Council of Trent, and towards which some moves had been made even before Luther's revolt occurred. This, however, came too late to save the situation, which by that time had got out of hand. Even so, Catholics rejoiced at the large elements of Catholicism retained by most of the reformers, and still retained by most dissident Christians.

It is within this framework that the Church should strive to recapture Protestantism. The celebrated Catholic theologian Karl Adam even goes so far as to say that rapprochement between Catholicism and Protestantism must take Luther as its starting point. *There* there would be something solid to rest upon, as a halfway house to the Church. Adam says that Lutheranism was so greatly modified by seventeenth- and eighteenth-century theologians that any attempt to restate it in its original form is always regarded with suspicion as a tendency towards Rome. Now there has emerged a disposition to think of Protestantism as never final but always in a state of becoming, so that many so-called Protestants, even in the eyes of their more "orthodox" coreligionists, are no longer Christians at all. It would help matters immensely if Protestantism returned to its origins so that everybody could make a fresh start from that point.

Amid all this flux and change the Catholic Church has stood unmoved. Its abuses—and there have been serious abuses—have been corrected, but the doctrine of the Church, though always susceptible of clearer and more delicate definition, remains unchanged. Its depths may be more deeply plumbed, but the depths to be explored are only charted more completely. "O Beauty, ever ancient and ever new!"—the cry of St. Augustine still wrings the heart. The most unalterable body of thought is also the one that is perennially fresh.

No person, except for the rare spirit, can be expected to be conscious of his religion all through the day. This, however, does not mean that religion should be something that is dusted off for use on Sunday and immediately afterwards put back on the shelf for another week. Religion, even when one is not thinking about it, can and should be entwined with all that has to be done. Hinduism is probably, upon the whole, the most God-conscious system of thought on earth. Islam must also be commended for its five daily periods of prayer, and there is no doubt that some of its adherents attain a high degree of spirituality. But Christians have been told to "pray without ceasing," and many of all shades of belief attain to the practice of the presence of God. Although for the majority of people this might prove too much of a strain, there are those who acquire a settled habit by which during the day they recollect themselves in their mundane duties to lift their thoughts to heaven. To all Christians, and especially all Catholics, their religion should impart a distinctive cast of mind, a color and atmosphere, an aura that is never quite absent.

Only with charity and compassion should a Catholic regard those who have not reached his firm foundation of belief. For though no other position is possible to him than to deny that men have an inalienable right to choose their religion, he will fully grant that all must choose according to the light granted them and the dictates of conscience. The honest believer in dissenting Christianity and the honest believer in Israel or Islam or even paganism is in a vastly better state of soul than any who, for whatever reason, "go through the motions" of Catholicism without believing it to be true. Indeed, to take an extreme and perhaps impossible case, a Catholic who has lost his faith and finds it irrecoverable must act accordingly. This was what that great poet but extremely muddled philosopher, Tennyson, was trying to say in his famous and fatuous stanza about there being more faith in honest doubt than in half the creeds.

This then is the position of an intolerant Catholicism—an extreme tolerance accorded to the sincere. Knock and it shall be opened unto you, seek and ye shall find, should lead to the discovery of the truth—and would do so, if the seeker were allotted enough time. To honest antagonists of the Church and to honest agnostics—many of whom really wish they could believe—and to others who grasp some parts of the Catholic Faith, yet spend all their lives groping towards it, the promise of the Church still holds good. Even while failing of totality, they may be embracing enough of the faith, hope and charity requisite for their salvation.

# CHAPTER TWO

## *The Protestant Dissatisfaction*

Spiritual dissatisfaction is probably keenest among people who, while they may describe themselves as Protestants and even mention the denomination in which they happened to have been brought up, do not actually participate in their church. Active members of any church, even when they feel that something may be amiss, are usually kept too busy to dwell much upon their sectarian shortcomings. It must be remembered that a very large percentage of Protestants are so hardly more than in name. They do not of course disbelieve, but their beliefs are a bit nebulous, sometimes not going much further than the general idea that the Protestant frame of mind is best. Rarely do they have any intention of ever becoming Catholics, for though many of the more intelligent of those who have drifted away will tell you that if they professed any religion it would be Catholicism, one soon comes to discover that in nearly all cases this amounts to nothing but talk.

Nominal Protestants, even when they are free of any positive prejudice against the Catholic Church, often have a kind of ingrained snobbery. They cannot but recall that there was a time when Protestantism was dominant in America—as, in some ways, it still is—so they are inclined to look upon Catholics as belonging to a lower breed intellectually and socially. They know that this is not true in all European countries; that for instance in England to be a Catholic is sometimes considered "smart." Those who say that they would join the Catholic Church if they joined any church at all, and also some fallen-away Catholics, will explain that if they lived in France, let us say, they would adhere to the Church. They imply that in Europe they would find "intellectual" Catholics of a kind sadly lacking in America. This is

13

conceit of the most arrogant sort. More often, if they happen to be Irish, they shudder at the thought of being anything so commonplace as an Irish *Catholic*. But apart from persons of this stamp, whom it is a little hard to treat with patience, undoubtedly the vast majority of American intellectuals are not Catholics, nor do Catholics, except in isolated instances, enjoy much social prestige. But if the American convert to Catholicism stands to lose something, the question still remains whether it is really any great loss. In any event, there is a hundredfold reward guaranteed by Christ Himself to such as make a sacrifice to follow Him.

It might be remembered, however, that even the more timid and self-effacing Catholics are always certain of their superiority —startling though this will seem to those not of the Faith—not, of course, as individuals but by virtue of their being members of the Church. When bigots and snobs can be brought to realize this—and I assure them that it is perfectly true, however absurd it may seem—they set it down to an arrogance so enormous that they can afford to smile at it good-naturedly. But let them rub the grin off their faces and think again. No arrogance is involved. Catholics are not proud of themselves; they are proud and thankful to be Catholics.

Those who will look closely at Catholics will surely have their equanimity disturbed by noticing that they feel a supreme confidence in their religion and make claims for it that no Protestant would venture to advance. A still closer inspection will make it clear that in this Catholics are not being smug, although no doubt it is possible to set this confidence down to the fact that Catholics are fortified by a unity not to be found elsewhere.

In recognition of the advantages of such unity, Protestants have repeatedly tried in recent years to retrace their steps, wondering whether a centripetal instead of the former centrifugal movement might not effect the trick for them. They seek to obtain spiritual unity for themselves by an amalgamation of denominations, by a greater dignity in their services, and a higher degree of efficiency. Efficiency, by the way, is not, despite Macaulay's famous essay on von Ranke's *History of the Papacy*, very prominent among Catholics. The hierarchic organization is unquestionably a fine thing, yet it has some of the defects of all organizations that are so large as to become slightly unwieldy. Even in the United States, where if the clergy is "efficient," it is rather because they are American than because they are Catholic, the average Catholic parish is usually managed with a good deal less efficiency than the average Protestant church. One must therefore look for the secret elsewhere.

Protestants have to deal with their problems according to the circumstances in which they find themselves. They therefore consider what regrouping might do. Obviously it would do a great deal to achieve efficiency. The presence in one town of half a dozen poorly attended churches of half a dozen different denominations, which are not divided by any very fundamental conflicts in doctrine, cannot be particularly desirable.[1] The ideal of these advocates of union—which in Catholic eyes is very desirable—is a single Protestant body, with a creed accepted by all (if this can be devised), a uniform order of service, and the dropping of sectarian divergences, in order to work towards a common end. This, they contend, would offset what some of them regard as the Catholic menace. But despite all the weight of wealth and respectability and the social and political position they possess, they are steadily losing ground, although there has been (at least on paper) a recent flurry of adhesions. However hard they may contrive to enlarge their membership and increase church attendance, it is hardly contestable that their own membership does not take them as seriously as it did in the past. Therefore, they are hoping to effect a unity—even unity of a somewhat formal and flimsy kind—in the wistful hope that out of this there will eventually emerge what might be described as a Protestant Catholic Church. As Bishop Bromley G. Oxnam puts it in his *Church and Contemporary Change:* [2] "It is only a united, non-Roman Christianity that can hope to save Christianity from its exclusiveness and ecclesiastical totalitarianism, and thereby enable non-Roman and Roman Christianity to work together for the eventual

[1] I cannot resist the story of the man who stopped a stranger on the street one Sunday morning to enquire where the Third Baptist Church was. The man could only answer, "I don't even know where the *First* Baptist Church is."

[2] P. 112. Macmillan, 1950.

unity of all Christianity and the building of Christ's Holy Church." This is a name to which Catholics have no objection, for they even use it as one of the variants or synonyms to their own official title. The bishop does not seem to be very hopeful about the attainment of the ultimate goal, but it is to be commended. However, he might as well give up all hope that the Catholic Church will renounce its exclusiveness or what he calls its "ecclesiastical totalitarianism." The right term, of course, should be "authority," but it must be understood that the Church does not claim an unlimited authority but one that is strictly defined. It is to be feared that the bishop has failed to see what it is that makes the Catholic Church Catholic. In any case, we may all wish him and his friends well in their efforts towards unity.

What is forcibly brought home to everybody who uses his eyes is that, whereas Protestant churches are usually half empty, few Catholic churches are half large enough for those who go there. Since Protestants usually have their services at eleven in the morning, they may not be up in time to see the crowds that go to Masses which may begin as early as five and never later than noon. In a large city parish so many Masses are necessary that the basement and the school auditorium often have to be used in addition to the church proper. It is not unusual to have a dozen Masses on Sunday, and even country parishes will have several. This is absolutely necessary if all the people are to be provided for. The crowds never cease, despite the numbers of lax Catholics who rarely attend Mass and still more rarely receive the sacraments.

Observant Protestants must ask themselves the question: "What do Catholics have that we don't?" Commonly they do not return the right answer, which they might discover if they went to Mass to see what happens, but are likely to suppose that Catholics go to Mass because they are obliged to go. It is perfectly true that their attendance is commanded by the Church under pain of mortal sin, but most Catholics would go even were there no such command. They themselves desire through the Mass to participate in what they consider the supreme act of worship and the heart of the Catholic religion. Protestants would be surprised if they could kneel where they would see the rapt look of adoration that comes over every face at the more solemn moments. This does not mean that some of the children do not fidget and whisper, except at the elevation, and that some of their elders do not yawn and look bored during the sermon and the giving out of the interminable church announcements. Those who are unmannerly elsewhere are only too likely to carry their bad manners into the house of God. But in general there is a profound reverence. These people are not merely attending church; they are pouring out their hearts in worship.

The Protestant who attends Mass will discover that, whatever else it is, it is not the preaching that attracts the people. There are, of course, some eloquent sermons, but the best preaching that I have heard in Catholic churches has been distinguished primarily only by the earnestness of the priest, something that more eloquent preaching may lack because it is so often a bit studied.[3] Nevertheless, connoisseurs of oratory will find it more often in Protestant churches. Priests do not have to be good "performers" in the pulpit, as ministers are obliged to be if they are to hold their jobs or hope to obtain a more lucrative call. While it might be said that much Protestant preaching is often about nothing in particular, if the soul of religion is the criterion, there is no Catholic sermon from which spiritual profit may not be drawn. Even so, it is certainly not for the sermon that Catholics go to Mass.

Nor is the music very good as a rule. While there are extremely well-trained choirs, these are the exception. The average choir generally manages a sung Mass fairly well only because its repertoire is ordinarily limited to two or three settings which, with even a little practice, can hardly be ruined. At children's Masses, where hymns are sung, they are rarely appropriate. It is deplorable the way the stately hymnology of the Church is ignored. Even the better popular hymns are rarely heard, but instead half a dozen of the worst specimens are repeated *ad nauseam*. Efforts at improvement are now being made and welcomed with an

[3] The tradition that subordinated instruction to rhetoric appeared early, judging from what St. Augustine said in his commentary on Psalm cxxxviii: *melius reprehendant nos grammatici quam non intelligant populi* (Better that the grammarians should reprove than that the people should not understand).

eagerness that is very encouraging. Still it must be said that, at least in the United States, Catholic churches make only occasional use of the magnificent music available to them. It is not the music that attracts Catholic congregations. High Mass usually has the smallest congregations, primarily because it is sung at an hour after the more pious members of the flock have already assisted at a low Mass.

The surmise is often made that the stateliness of the Catholic ritual may be the explanation. Stately indeed it is, not to please the people but to honor God. The "dim religious light"—or, as a French nun I knew used to pronounce it, the "damn religious light"—is not always very noticeable. The gingerbread Gothic and the cloissonné stained glass that used to be so common are today found only in older churches which have not yet been rebuilt. But the general architectural and artistic level, while greatly raised, is still below what it ought to be. At any rate it is not there that one can discover the Catholic secret. The products of Barclay Street may have improved a bit, but a plaster statue is still a plaster statue. Catholics are far from being held in the Church by its aesthetic appeal; indeed, converts of the more sensitive type often have their feelings harrowed. Anyone looking for the best specimens of ecclesiastical architecture will find them among the wealthier sects. A rather odd situation has, in fact, come about: the Catholic trend is away from Gothic to structures that give an unimpeded view of the altar, whereas the Protestant trend is towards Gothic and the dim religious light.

In the quarterly *Religion in Life,* Paul Hutchinson, the Methodist editor of the *Christian Century,* after candidly acknowledging Protestant decline as compared to Catholic strength, writes: "In most centers of population today, the 'strong' Protestant churches are typically in the suburbs where they have about the same influence on the city's morals as the commuter has on its politics." He points to the "liturgical" bent of such churches, remarking: " 'Churchmanship' is no longer a monopoly of Episcopalians and Lutherans. Stately liturgy has grown commonplace in communities which, five decades ago, were vigorous in their opposition to anything which smacked of 'Romish' tendencies. I worship in a Methodist church where the service opens today with the entrance of an acolyte to light the altar candles and closes when he reappears to snuff them. There is a Unitarian church in Chicago in which a sanctuary light burns constantly." Obviously Mr. Hutchinson is not very happy about such external trappings, which Catholics must be pardoned for considering somewhat comical. He too hopes for organic union but sees that, however thick the clouds of incense, however many the candles, they are meaningless apart from religion, in particular apart from the center of Catholic worship, the Mass.

Catholics can only offer cordial sympathy to Protestants of Mr. Hutchinson's persuasion, and these we may believe are still the majority. They are doing something to check the deliquescence observable elsewhere, and to that extent are Catholic allies. Few, we may be certain, would think Bernard Shaw's remark, "Never believe in a God you can't improve on" as other than characteristically flip, for it must be one of the most idiotic things ever said by an extremely clever man. But it does indicate the extreme of a process which is going on, its *reductio ad absurdum.* Protestantism is gradually—and not so gradually either—being emptied of its doctrinal content; and all efforts to save it by means of the devices indicated seem doomed to failure. The best that can be hoped is that one section of Protestantism will make its mind clearer and firmer while the other lapses into a vague humanitarianism, embellished with "Romanist" frills.

Karl Adam, the Catholic theologian, has another kind of hope, though it depends upon there remaining something solid in Protestantism upon which to build. He suggests that it is not impossible that the Catholic Church, to further the return to her fold of dissident bodies, might withdraw or restrict the law of celibacy for her ministers. The Church, in this event, might meet outsiders halfway by permitting Protestant ministers, upon their submission to the Holy See, to retain their wives and might create for them a reconstituted diaconate. Dr. Adam notes, correctly enough, that the Protestant denominations, reunited to Rome, would be capable of bringing with them great Catholic values: "If ever a lasting union between the Catholic Church and the Protestant communions were to take place, there would be a giving and receiving of gifts on both sides. It would be quite impossible that one single item of truly Christian value could be lost." This is no doubt true, but although it is not "impossible" that the Holy See would consider some such arrangement as Dr. Adam suggests, it would seem to be very unlikely that concessions of this sort, even though they do not touch essentials, would be made.

But to come back to the immediate question before us—the Protestant discontent—it may finally dawn on the Protestant observer that Catholics go to church solely to worship God. While it would be patently false to suggest that this object does not prevail among Protestants, there may be more than a suspicion that some of them are actuated rather by a desire to do the "correct" thing or, in certain communities, to appear respectable and gain social standing. How are such people to be made to believe in God vividly enough to make them rejoice to worship Him? Again the Protestant must ask, "What is the Catholic secret?"

# CHAPTER THREE

## *The Power of the Priesthood*

Since this is a book by a layman for laymen, the only sacrament that will not be discussed is that of Holy Orders. The priesthood itself, however, is concerned with every phase of Catholic life, and some indication must be given of its essential importance.

It is conceivable that a small, or even a large, group of Catholics might, by some accident, lose the service of priests and be obliged to carry on as best they could alone. As baptized people they would remain an integral part of the Church. But it is obvious that in such a case the Church would be unable to function fully. In the early years of the nineteenth century on the American frontier, several years might often pass before a priest was able to put in an appearance at an isolated settlement to say Mass and to administer the sacraments. During that time the little band of Catholics would appoint one of their number to marry couples by witnessing the ceremony. Such marriages were recognized as valid, and were then blessed by a priest when he arrived. Laymen also read the prayers at burials and even led those who gathered in the prayers of the Mass, though of course without any pretense that there could be celebration of the Mass. People might help their dying friends to make an act of contrition, or even hear their confession, as a reassuring gesture of what would be done were it possible. The arrangement was makeshift but heroic. It may have conferred more merit than is derived from an easy and comfortable practice of religion, but it was precarious and left much to be desired.

A recent movie showed an island off the coast of Brittany that was deserted by its only priest in disgust at his people's addiction to praying for the wrecking of ships. But the people, in spite of their nefarious ways, retained their faith. During this crisis they got the sexton, as the one who knew most about ecclesiastical matters, to perform some of the priest's functions, pushing him on reluctantly to hear confessions and finally persuading him to say Mass. From this he was saved by the return of the wayward priest just in the nick of time. There is some implausibility about all this, for the people, however ignorant, would at least have understood that only a priest can say Mass and that without consecrated Hosts there can be no Holy Communion. But the point is not that they denied the indispensability of the priest but that they were, in their own fashion, asserting it. They remind one of those Crusaders who, unable to receive Holy Communion before an impending battle, knelt down and with all the fervor of their souls put into their mouths a blade of grass. This is doing the best one can under the circumstances, but for the complete exercise of the Catholic religion there have to be priests, and for the continuation of the sacerdotal line there must be bishops. It is this that gives the priest his power.

It may be that this power has sometimes been abused. The power itself cannot be exaggerated, but it may be possible to use that power for improper ends. An individual cleric may be something of a tyrant or a tartar; if so, he exceeds the scope of his office and makes himself liable to severe reprimand by his bishop. In practice, however, the nasty term "priestcraft" has little meaning. The Catholic priesthood does not maintain its power by anything except the need that Catholics have for the Mass that only a priest can say, for the sacraments that only a priest can dispense. Far from resenting that power, Catholics are immensely grateful for it, as they are also for the teaching and disciplinary authority of the Church as exercised by the priesthood under the direction of their Ordinaries.

Here we encounter in Catholicism something quite unique. It is true that some schismatic bodies have a validly ordained priesthood, but this is derived from their former connection with the Apostolic Succession. The case is otherwise with the Church of England (or its American offshoot, the Protestant Episcopal Church), for though they give some of their ministers the title of priest, only the High Anglican faction among them attach the Catholic meaning to the word. At least twice the Anglicans have asked the Holy See to consider the question of the validity of their orders, and this was done, with the decision going against them. Nor is it likely, after the declaration made by Leo XIII on November 5, 1896, that any change in the Catholic attitude will occur. But here and there a few Anglican ministers have reassured themselves by obtaining surreptitious schismatic ordination, as have a handful of nonconformist ministers connected with what was called the Free Catholic Movement in England. Several of these later entered the Catholic Church, and I know of at least one instance where such a priest was allowed, after the death of his wife, to exercise his sacerdotal office, after he received "conditional ordination." In general it must be said that even from the early days of the separation of the Church of England from the Roman unity, extremists (Archbishop Cranmer among them) held that priests were not really necessary, and bishops still less so, convenience though they might be. When Protestant congregations call certain men to the ministry, it is primarily because they have gone through a special course of studies that equip them for the pulpit; they do not, however, differ from the laity in any essential respect.

The Protestant theory looks upon all Christians as priests (as indeed they are, in a sense that will be touched upon later). In the form of Protestantism in which I was brought up—the Plymouth Brethren—no ministers are officially recognized. The communion service with them is the central act of the Sunday morning service, but no person administers the bread and wine to another. A loaf on a plate is passed from hand to hand, and from it each communicant breaks off his own portion; and so with the chalice. The Mass is, among other things, a memorial of Christ. But the Plymouth Brethren communion was *only* a memorial, and all idea of a Sacrifice was strongly repudiated. So also is it repudiated by Protestantism in all its forms, though no other of its forms is so drastic (or so logical) as this.

The Catholic priest on the other hand is one upon whom special powers have been conferred, the chief of which is the sacerdotal function but which also includes the administering of the sacraments. Under the direction of his bishop he is also the teacher and the administrator of his parish. As such, a paternal relationship with his people develops. But priestly tyranny, if it ever existed, would not be tolerated today. Perhaps now and then in former times a "Father O'Flynn," like the man in the excellent song of that name, might be encountered, but even he only "coaxed" the lazy ones on with a stick. In any event, he was vastly preferable to the man in another good song, the Vicar of Bray, the pliant fellow in the seventeenth century who, whatever England's official changes in religion might be, always contrived to hold on to his living. Catholic priests do have great power over their flocks. They stand apart, yet mingle on very intimate terms with their people; and while the laity stand in awe of the priest's office, there is a warm affection for him as a man. He would have to be a most disagreeable person to lose their love, and even should that happen, he would retain their respect; should even respect go, veneration for his priesthood would remain.[1]

This is not to assert that every priest is an amiable human being; most of them are, but some are not. Priesthood, however, is likely to bring out whatever engaging qualities a man may possess. The priest's position is secure. He is not harassed with domestic cares. He does not have to ingratiate himself with his congregation to hold his job, and so does not have to smear himself with the butter and treacle that can be so obnoxious. He takes his people, and they take him, for granted. He is not dependent upon them; rather it is they who are dependent upon him. Priesthood imparts a special and indelible character to the soul, and the exercise of the priesthood should—and it is surely not too much to say that it usually does—give charity and compassion and understanding of his fellow mortals to the priest.

---

[1] I have myself known of several cases of priestly apostasy, but I have never personally known a priest who, while still exercising his priestly functions, lost respect. The two cases I have heard of resulted in conversion. One was of a Protestant who discovered that every Saturday night the parishioners had to post a cordon around the priest's house to make sure that he would be sober on Sunday morning. The other was of a visiting Catholic lady in Mexico whose Protestant husband accompanied her to Mass. She thought this a hopeful sign until, as soon as Mass was over, the priest appeared with a fighting cock under his arm to hurry to the ring. She at once thought that all was lost. Not at all: her logical husband rightly inferred (like Boccaccio's Jew) that only the true Church could survive such things. As for the bibulous cleric, he gave positive proof as to how seriously his people took their religion. Accordingly there was another convert to the Faith.

His priesthood cannot be taken away. Even if his bishop should suspend him and he contumaciously continued to say Mass, it would still be a valid Mass, as it would be even if he were excommunicated or went into apostasy. For such conduct, as for other sins, he might end up in hell, but even should that happen, he would nevertheless be a priest to all eternity. So, for that matter, will any baptized person who comes to be among the damned bear forever a mark upon him. It will be to his greater shame, but it will always be there. The point must be clearly understood: the priest is not simply a man appointed to a position, he is one consecrated to God. Whatever he does, he cannot lose his priesthood; it is this that gives him his power.

A good many Protestants in the past—and this may still be true of some backward people in isolated regions—thought of the priest as being, in some way, rather sinister. He was regarded as a wire-puller, who high-handedly influenced a superstitious and groveling flock, an adept at political chicanery and so forth. Anyone who has ever come into contact with priests will smile at the absurdity of all this. For though priests, being human beings, are not exempt from faults and failings, taken as a class they are kindly and humorous and wise. The sinister notion probably is largely due to the fact that the priest is known to be a special sort of man, and his celibacy makes him a figure of mystery to some, where there is really no mystery at all. It was assumed that, as he belonged to a highly disciplined body, he was probably up to devious craft. Nothing definite was ever heard about this, or about grosser charges, which were always generalized. The only specific accusations were those brought against a particular group of priests, the Jesuits, who were supposed to hold that the end justifies the means—hence the calumnious adjective "jesuitical"—and to be incorrigible politicians.

It is not my intention to defend the Jesuits. They are entirely capable of looking after themselves. I might mention, however, the effect upon my mind when in my youth I encountered a Jesuit villain in a Joseph Hocking novel, a priest named Ritzoom who had the sleek cunning of Satan himself. His main purpose in life seems to have been to convert innocent Protestant girls—he never bothered with any except heiresses—and then pack them off to a convent so that the Church might get its hands on their money.

I am happy to report that his plots were always foiled by the appearance upon the scene of a fine upstanding young man of sound anti-Papist principles, who rescued the girl from the clutches of Rome by marrying her at the last minute. All this was dreadful, yet I noticed that even Father Ritzoom, a man not at all personally ascetic but fond of good wine and cigars, was depicted as a cultured and charming man of the world. I could not help liking him a good deal better than some of the sour-visaged Protestant "saints" of my boyhood.

In his aptitude for intrigue Father Ritzoom reminded me of Father Holt of Thackeray's *Henry Esmond,* and may even have been suggested to Mr. Hocking by that affable character. In both instances I was fascinated, even while I shuddered. They made me want to know more about that strange institution, the Catholic Church, and to that extent may have had some slight share in my conversion. Yet although I became a Catholic at the earliest possible moment, it was not on account of the personal attractiveness of priests. The first priest I ever met happened to be the one whom I later asked to receive me into the Church. I went to him because I was already convinced of the truth of Catholicism. The only priests who had anything to do with the matter were the fictitious priests of anti-Catholic novels! Alas, while since numbering a good many priests among my friends—several of them brilliant and charming men—none of them quite measures up to Father Ritzoom or Father Holt.

I have never caught any of them in the most innocent piece of wire-pulling. Their "priestcraft" (if that odious word must be used) was of a totally different kind. They had authority to teach, and I recognized my need of being taught; they had authority to pardon sins, and I knew myself to be a sinner; and they were ordained to offer Mass. It is around the Mass that Catholicism revolves, for the Mass is Calvary. The priest is among us to offer the Sacrifice for himself and his people. He may have strong political views, but he never vents them in the pulpit, and if he did, even those who agreed with him would resent it. In so far as they are personal opinions, as often as not I disagree with them. The only bond of unity in the Church is that of doctrine— unity in faith, in morals, and in worship.

# CHAPTER FOUR
## *Like and Unlike*

It would not be quite accurate to say that Catholicism is unique among the religions of the world in that it rests upon divine revelation. A strong affirmation of revelation was at the outset true of Protestantism. But today, even those Protestants who believe in divine revelation do not lean upon it as a basic tenet. Those who still consider the Bible to be the inspired word of God—except for those who treat every comma and even the interpolations as inspired—give to the word "inspiration" almost every shade of meaning, including that which a good poet is supposed to have. Christianity to them is indeed hardly more than a moral code (without much sanction) or a set of beautiful stories, not to be taken too seriously. For the most part revelation is ignored.

One and only one of the more recent Protestant bodies, the Mormon Church of the Latter Day Saints, which is presumably to be classified as Christian, steadfastly maintains a new revelation, supplementary to the Bible, in the book which is supposed to have been found in a cave on an upstate New York hill by Joseph Smith. On the other hand, I think it must be said (as some "orthodox" Protestants themselves say) that Unitarians are not really Christians at all. As a corporate body they are in decline, but their ideas have permeated, to a greater or less degree, most of the Protestant sects; and these ideas, in so far as they are Unitarian, are not Christian.

I say this with the greatest respect for the high, if somewhat frosty, distinction of this denomination, to which I once briefly but only nominally belonged. Indeed, it was while preaching at their church at Maidstone in Kent, where Hazlitt's father had been minister and in which William Hazlitt had been baptized, that I discovered that I was a Catholic.[1] But because Unitarianism can mean almost anything, ranging from William Ellery Channing's opposition to Calvinism to a position hardly distinguishable from agnosticism, it is not always possible to regard its followers even as Christian heretics, as is possible with Moslems.

In Islam we do find what purports to be a revealed religion. The Koran has drawn upon several sources, especially the Bible (including the New Testament) and the Talmud. Its strength is enormous, and its spiritual vitality arouses admiration. But because the sole point of unity is the Oneness of God, and because there is no acknowledged center of authority, it inevitably splits into a number of sects.

The Oneness of God has also been steadily affirmed by Israel, though any reader of the Old Testament will discover that the Jews were at first inclined toward "whoring after strange gods," to use the phrase of their prophets, and we have to include the abomination of Baal or Moloch. However, they were eventually cured by chastisement and, like the Moslems, they have been witnesses in the world of a great truth. Their revelation in the Old Testament seems to a great extent to have boiled down among the orthodox to a punctilious insistence upon early dietary laws, and to the preaching of the ethical code formulated in the Ten Commandments. From the Christian point of view, the Jews have rejected the main part of their revelation: the prophetic utterances bearing upon Christ. Yet what they do retain, especially the psalms, is part of the Christian heritage. Although we must regretfully say that the Jews have failed to carry out their great mission, in some ways they remain the Chosen People, even though it is the Church that must now be considered the true Israel. It is noteworthy that a number of distinguished Jews of our time have come within an inch of the Church—Bergson and

---

[1] At that time I had a somewhat vague intention of studying for the Unitarian ministry but never did so. However, as a layman of twenty-one I did now and then "supply" at Unitarian churches while their ministers were on vacation. The minister at Maidstone announced before he left for six weeks that his pulpit was to be filled for the first three Sundays by one whom he described as "a very decent sort of a man, and a scholar— within limits." I did my best to worm out what he said about me, knowing that it must have been something very juicy; but nobody had the courage to tell me.

Werfel, for instance, and Simone Weil, who entirely accepted Christian beliefs, and the identification of Christianity with Catholicism. Nevertheless she, though she might almost be classed as a Christian mystic, died outside the Church. I confess that I cannot fully understand this frame of mind, but it is not for me to offer any criticism. One cannot but be deeply moved by the contemplation of such cases, with their tangled problem in the background, and one must respect those who adhere to the traditions of Israel. I would be astonished that those who profess to be Christians should remain outside the Catholic fold, did I not find a clue in the case of these Jews; this helps one to understand how many are the things that may hold people back from the Church.

Of the religions of the East (except for Islam) I make only cursory mention. Buddhism of course has its sacred books and has produced its mystics. It has had some impact upon the West, and upon the whole this impact, in my opinion, has been good. But it can and does produce a kind of religious eclecticism. When one sees side by side in the house of a rich and fashionable woman, who mistakes her sentimentality for spiritual insight, statues of Buddha, St. Francis and the Goddess of Mercy—with perhaps the gory Siva dancing on her mantelpiece and a Catholic vestment draped over the grand piano—one can only throw up one's hands over such frivolity. Hinduism, from which all the religions of the East stem, has wonderful sacred books, but it is difficult to define Hinduism itself. It accords with the Protestant mind in being amorphous. From one aspect it is the grossest polytheism, with so many gods in its Pantheon that nobody has ever been able to list them. But from another aspect Hinduism is a religion which, in its loftiest moments, seems to be monotheistic. It was for this reason that the seventeenth-century Jesuit Robert de' Nobili and his companions determined to go to the Madura district dressed in the saffron robes of Indian ascetics and, after steeping themselves in the terminology of Hindu philosophy, were able to state Catholicism in such acceptable terms that they made converts wholesale among the Brahmins, who supposed that they were being initiated into deeper mysteries, as indeed they were. This missionary effort was condemned by the Holy See as too great an "accommodation," but now, under due safeguards, the condemnation has been rescinded. I have heard recently of two French priests in the Trichinopoly diocese (which is a part of India as well known to my boyhood as Madura) who dress as *sunyasis* and live in a hut and observe the nonsuperstitious practices of Hinduism, to the tremendous interest of the higher castes.[2]

So much for religion in the forms that it takes in the Orient. As my main concern is nearer home, I must now note the beliefs that we share with Protestants, and also the beliefs that divide us, but I think without any proselytizing intention. Some feelings will probably be hurt, but I trust that my readers will recognize my good will and make suitable allowances. This book will fail in its purpose if it does not contribute to a better understanding among Christians.

For the confines of our discussion, let us say that all Christians to a greater or less degree base their faith upon supernatural revelation. Yet having said as much, immediately one has to point out a difference. I do not remember who it was who said, "The Bible and the Bible alone is the religion of Protestants," but he stated an issue clearly if somewhat crudely. It cannot be precisely what he meant, for it is equivalent to saying that the Pope and the Pope alone is the religion of Catholics; but one catches the drift: Protestants will admit no authority outside of the Bible. If they would only stick to that, the whole question would be relatively simple, for Catholics as fully as Protestants accept the Biblical revelation. Catholics would only like to ask what was happening to the Church before the New Testament was written. There was, it is true, the incomplete revelation of the Old Testa-

[2] Being so proud of the fact, I cannot refrain from telling that more than sixty years ago the Salvation Army, under the prompting of Judge Tucker (later known, because of his marriage to one of General Booth's daughters, as Commissioner Booth-Tucker) asked for volunteers to emulate de' Nobili. The only two who answered the appeal were my father and mother. Others were *sent* out, but none of them had the high degree of education necessary and except for living like Indians, they accomplished little. My mother's health broke down and she would have died had my father not dragged her out of the Salvation Army and married her, in spite of Emma Booth-Tucker's shaking her fist in his face and saying, "You villain! To steal Lily Teague from us!"

ment, which pointed to Christ but needed Christ to fulfill it. But was there no other revelation for Christians?

Obviously the Apostles did not think so. In His last discourse to His disciples Christ told them: "I have yet many things to say unto you, but ye cannot bear them now," to which He at once added: "Howbeit, when He, the Spirit of truth is come, He will guide you into all truth." Yet Christ had already imparted much to them directly, especially the sacrament of the Eucharist. He had even hinted at it long before the meeting in the Upper Room, saying, "Unless ye eat My flesh and drink My blood, ye cannot have life in yourselves"—a doctrine so hard that many, after hearing it, "walked with Him no more." Even so, everything was not written down in the gospels when they appeared. Much was transmitted orally to the disciples and orally by them. Even all the epistles of the Apostles were not preserved, although it may be taken as certain that all those which were inspired and were intended by God for the eventual New Testament were saved by Him from oblivion.

While it might not be quite accurate to suggest that Christ's purpose was only to impart a certain spirit or point of view, this was surely part of His purpose, the essential preliminary. That point of view was acquired with difficulty, as it still is, but it is clear that up to the time of Christ's departure from this earth, not even His disciples were fully informed about specific doctrines.

Naturally enough, this has lent some substance to the supposition that Christ's purpose was not to state definite doctrines but rather to inspire men, lift them to "higher things," indicate a far-off horizon, and teach them to love their fellows. In short, what His disciples had to do was to keep on preaching the Sermon on the Mount. If that were all, Christ would have excited a general hope, and then left His followers to their own devices. Such a method would have been cruel, for that hope would have soon faded away and all that He had stood for would have been forgotten. This was, of course, part of His method, but only a part; He followed up what He had done through the Church He founded.

From the day of Pentecost, that Church was a *teaching* Church,

even though there were a number of points that had to be eluci-
dated by degrees, in an education that is still going on. Yet that
Church for a long time to come had as its scriptures only the Old
Testament, whose main value lay in the fact that it foretold the
Christ whom the disciples had known in the flesh. Had they not
actually known Him, much would have been hopelessly sealed
to their understanding, except for what they knew of events that
had occurred and of the revelation made by the Holy Ghost. An
instance of this is the comparison that Christ Himself drew, before He had died or risen again, between Jonah's three days in
the belly of the whale and His three days in the tomb. On the
other hand He gave them the formula of the consecration at
Mass, as well as authority to bind and loose, and He appointed
Peter their head. Much of His doctrine was not explicitly stated
by Him, nor were some Christian practices (as far as we know)
so much as alluded to. For instance, we do not come across
mention of extreme unction until the epistle of St. James, but we
know that Christ himself instituted this sacrament. We recognize
it at once as part of the Christian revelation.

Facts of this sort have left the door open to those who wish to
question the authenticity of that revelation. And the door might
be permanently open were it not for the commission to the
Church—not clear in every detail at the outset but soon to become clear. Therefore St. Paul could write of the "deposit of
faith" and of "the faith once committed to the saints." The Catholic position is that it does not need to repose every one of its
doctrines upon a specific text—though usually a text can be found
that adumbrates each doctrine and no text can be found that
contradicts any doctrine. Christ left it to the Church, under the
inspiration of the Holy Ghost, to round out His teaching. This
does not mean that the Church has ever added anything to
Christian doctrine but only that it is authorized to preserve those
doctrines intact and to interpret them. We know that not everything was recorded for us, because in the last verse of the gospel
written by Christ's closest personal friend, St. John, we find him
saying: "There are many other things that Jesus did, the which,
if they should be written every one, I suppose the world itself
could not contain the books that should be written." Since the

four gospels in large part cover the same ground, and with the Epistles and the Apocalypse make up only a small book, it is evident that not everything can be there.

Even this did not exist in its entirety until a long time after Christ's departure, and at a period when the Church was spreading rapidly. I suppose that somebody must have pointed it out, but as I do not remember its having been done, I mildly remark that should the higher criticism be correct in assigning later dates to some of the books of the New Testament than those of tradition,[3] the Catholic position is left all the stronger. For then it would have to be granted that the Church was functioning in "high gear" an even longer time before the appearance of the New Testament than the Church itself claims. This would mean that it owed everything to the personal teaching of those commissioned by Christ, or those whom they had in their turn commissioned. In short, this would absolutely demonstrate that what Catholics call "tradition" was an integral part of the divine revelation.

Up to this point I do not believe that many Protestants who hold to the Biblical revelation could seriously object to my statement, if they make allowances for the sketchy way I am obliged to present it. They may, of course, object that none of the books of the New Testament come under the heading of "tradition," and I daresay that they are right, in their sense of the term. But they will not be able to deny that the Church existed a long while before the earliest part of the New Testament was written down, or that its progress was due to other forces. Christ Himself had told His disciples to search the scriptures, but this was that they might discover in the prophecies of the Old Testament the many passages that bear upon Him. Christians continued to search the scriptures for the same reason, but they had the living witness of those who could tell of His resurrection, and this and His dying for them constituted their great theme. Even when the gospels had been written it was, in the nature of things, a long time before they circulated throughout the Christian world. The im-

---

[3] I am not suggesting of course that any of these dates could actually be post-Apostolic; this is merely that common forensic device of supposing "for the sake of the argument."

mediate effect of the epistles, which were pastoral letters such as Catholic bishops still write to their flocks except that the Apostolic epistles were inspired, was limited to those localities to which they were addressed; they too had to be circulated.

But, to indulge in argument for a moment, let us suppose that the entire New Testament had been gathered together and was known to all Christians by the year 60 (of course it was actually later). This would mean that the Church had taken shape without this compendium. It would also mean that during all those thirty years there had been a recognized teaching authority. Finally, is it reasonable to suppose that a reliable interpretation of the writers' meaning would have been intended to cease with the death of the writers themselves? In this connection, St. Peter has an interesting comment on his "beloved brother Paul," which is still more interesting for another reason. Paul, says Peter, writes some things which are hard to understand. He does not say that he (Peter) does not understand them, but he issues the warning that passages such as these "they that are unlearned and unstable wrest, as they do also the other scriptures, unto their own destruction." Peter pronounced that Paul's epistles are scripture, the inspired word of God; but he recognized that scripture must be handled carefully and calls for an interpreter.

Can those who are close friends of the writers serve as adequate interpreters? Our experience should tell us that even the most faithful friend might misunderstand or air his own little crotchets. So important a matter cannot be entrusted to private individuals, however gifted. There can be only one safeguard: there must be an authority to which everything may be referred for judgment. A parallel might be the way the Supreme Court passes upon the constitutionality of laws. Although that court may err, even should it hand down a 9–0 decision, and in the opinion of many has several times erred, its decision has to be accepted by a good citizen until it is reversed. However, the Church does not err, and nowhere except in the Church is an authority of this sort to be found.

Historical Protestantism recognized the authority of the Church, which is logically inescapable, although it limited the jurisdiction to the five great early councils. Protestants of our own time do not show that they are aware of the vagaries they were saved from by the action of the Church, probably because those heresies were so effectually destroyed—with the exception perhaps of Arianism, which may be considered to have been revived as Socinianism or, as we should say, Unitarianism. Protestantism itself would not have been possible had the Catholic Church not preserved the Faith. Protestantism was rather a recoil against the Church, and you cannot push except with some firm ground under your feet; it is hard to see upon what Protestants of our time take their stand.

Old-fashioned Protestantism held that salvation is by faith alone. But although Catholicism makes salvation depend upon faith, it maintains that faith alone is not enough; there must also be hope and charity and the observance of the law of God or repentance for such breaches of it as have been committed. Here the Catholic position today is what it always has been. Protestantism, on the other hand, has wandered away from its original cardinal principle regarding salvation, for nothing is more common than to hear that what a man believes is of slight consequence, that it is what a man does that matters. This is throwing Luther into the ash can, and it also means getting further away from Catholicism than Luther ever did. Although there is a tendency in certain Protestant groups to adopt a closer external resemblance to Catholicism in the order of their services to a degree that would have filled earlier Protestants with horror, these very elements are often the ones that have gone further than any others towards depleting the dogmatic content which gave them a real kinship with Catholicism. As long ago as the seventeenth century, shrewd observers foresaw that this would happen. Then Protestantism, in spite of its antagonism to the Catholic Church, was really making what progress it did on what may be described as the "acquired momentum" derived from Catholicism, something which would inevitably grow less and less until, according to the logical argument, it was finally completely exhausted. This has not happened yet, and perhaps it will never happen if Protestantism finds means of replenishing itself. As matters stand at present, however, the large Catholic element in Protestantism is diminishing. Catholics sometimes too blithely assume that Protestantism is dying. They should never wish that to occur, because then they would be faced with the problem of having to convert a pagan society which would be all the more corrupt because of having turned away from all its traditions. The curious situation today is that Protestantism in general shows greater tolerance than ever before (for why not be tolerant, if beliefs are not of paramount importance?), but along with this there is a smaller amount of understanding. There is more willingness to hear what it is those strange people, Catholics, believe, and in some cases to attain a fair grasp of it. But as Protestants cease to share what they once held in common with Catholics, in most cases there is a lessening grasp of its inner implications.

My purpose here is to stress such points of contact as still exist —they are many—rather than the points of difference. Speaking for myself, I would be better pleased to see more bigotry among Protestants, as long as this was based upon genuine religious conviction, than to watch such conviction evaporate into a vague humanism. I was for instance much entertained at an Ethical Society service I attended in England many years ago, when the hymn "Nearer my God to Thee" was revised into "Nearer mankind to thee." No doubt those present were high-minded people, but one look at them showed them to be desiccated, even further away from mankind than they were from God.

It seems to be a general law that the closer people resemble one another, the more they are puzzled by, and even resent, such dissimilarities as may exist. Thus, we Americans are not in the least troubled that a savage in central Africa should be unlike ourselves in his habits and ways of thought; this is only what we expect. But as we go upwards—to the highly civilized Orientals of India, China and Japan—we are disposed to get impatient that people who have so much in common with us do not have everything in common. Going still further, all the Russians struck us as being slightly, though charmingly, insane, until Communism spread its drabness over them and they became terrifying. The English and Americans, just because they are so close to one another in many ways, are irritated that they are also so different from one another, although on both sides this irritation usually manifests itself in good-humored amusement. However, when it comes to a question of religious differences, where deep feelings are stirred, the irritation is often not very good-humored.

In all religions there is some common factor; the Christian mystic prays, but so does the devotee of Mumbo Jumbo kneeling before his idol. On a higher plane, one finds Buddhist and Moslem monks, Tibetan prayer wheels and Mohammedan rosaries. And it is only natural that the Christian ritual has points of similarity to that of the Jews, in view of the fact that the Church arose within Israel. Yet the first tendency of Protestantism was to sweep away ritual. When this was not done drastically enough by Lutheranism and Anglicanism, the Puritans made their furious protest against anything even faintly reminiscent of Rome that had been retained. Luther went to confession right up to his death and in his sermons was laudatory of the Virgin Mary, and the Anglican Book of Common Prayer was to a large extent a translation from the Missal. In objecting to all this the Puritans were, from their own point of view, quite right. They were very afraid that an overlooked bit of Catholicism might leaven the whole lump. At that, they upheld many elements of Catholic doctrine, even when, as in the case of the excessive emphasis they laid upon predestination (a Catholic doctrine), they made it most un-Catholic.[4]

If it had been merely a question of the rejection of the supremacy of the Pope, schism rather than heresy would have resulted, as it did originally with the Greek Orthodox Church (today the Orthodox Church is also in heresy, since it has rejected certain truths of faith). And as long as Henry VIII lived, Anglicanism was by and large Catholicism without the Pope, although a number of powerfully placed people were only waiting for the old king to die so that they could make the Church of England Protestant. When this happened, some of the forms and ceremonies of the "Old Religion" were retained, but much of essential importance was discarded—the Mass, confession to a priest,

---

[4] I speak of this later. However, I may say here that by predestination we mean that God foreknows from all eternity what is to be; but He does not force men to be saved or otherwise. Each man is free to seek salvation, and each may hope to achieve it. I need not point out how contrary to this is the Calvinist belief in the elect and the damned.

purgatory, the invocation of saints and so forth. Nevertheless, the fundamental doctrines of the Trinity, the Incarnation, heaven and hell, and the Redemption remain unchanged. In Anglicanism there have always been some who insist that they are Catholics, not Protestants, and it must be allowed that, both in doctrine and practice, they are hardly distinguishable from Catholics. Except for those sects that have whittled away Christian beliefs, or misinterpreted them until they have been left with little meaning, it must be conceded that there are still wide areas in which Protestants are at one with Catholics.

It is therefore possible to speak of a "common Christianity," just as there is a sense in which Catholicism may be said to hold what historic Protestantism holds, *plus a good deal more besides.* One would, however, have to supplement this by saying that, even when Protestants maintain Catholic doctrine, every article, however correctly stated by them, is always somewhat attenuated because it lacks the richness imparted to every component detail that shines when it is presented in the truth taken as a whole. Isolated from totality, these Catholic truths, without ceasing to be Catholic, wear a somewhat wintry and arbitrary look. And of course the history of Protestantism is ample evidence that it is scarcely possible to be very confident about its permanent retention of these truths.

We can hope for the best, and at least we must guard ourselves against anything like the Jansenist error of *extra ecclesia nulla conceditur gratia,* or no grace outside the Church. This was among the propositions condemned by Clement XI in 1713. It may look like a corollary of the principle *extra ecclesiam nulla salus,* but it is not. Even this principle may be stated in so extreme a form, as happened recently in the case of a Boston Jesuit who was later suspended by his bishop, that it may be repudiated. Oddly enough, many Protestants have the impression that the Jansenists were the best and most zealous type of Catholics. Zealous they certainly were, and several of their leaders were men of great brilliance, but they were far removed from the Catholic ideal.

Instead of making any examination of specific doctrines, let us take as our starting point the virtues—not the natural virtues

about which everybody is agreed but the supernatural or evangelical virtues of faith, hope and charity. If even here some
differences in tone, as between Catholics and non-Catholics, have
to be noted, these are unimportant as compared to the common
ground upon which both sides build.

Faith is not altogether a matter of the formal acceptance of
this or that article of the creed, or of all the articles, but of a
supernatural attitude, the infused theological virtue. The distinction is made because it may be possible to have complete dogmatic orthodoxy, but to have it in a somewhat arid and sterile
fashion. We have been told that "Without faith it is impossible
to please God," and St. James, in his famous insistence upon the
need for good works, reminds us that "the devils believe—and
tremble," a warning that faith, standing alone, is insufficient. But
even faith should not merely be formal orthodoxy—important as
this is—but a permeation and illumination of everything.

> The angels keep their ancient places;
> Turn but a stone and start a wing!

Lest there be a danger of being misunderstood—and I fear that
some modern Protestants think that a vague and generalized faith
should be cultivated without too close a reference to the basis of
faith, Christian doctrine—a few other considerations should be
added. With regard to the heresies that are contrary to faith,[5] a
distinction must be drawn between what the theologians call
"formal" and "material" heresy. A formal heretic denies or twists
awry some Catholic truth with the full knowledge of what he is
doing; the material heretic is equally in error, but may be excused
because of his good faith. He is one who cannot disentangle himself from the prejudices of his upbringing; he is considered "in-
vincibly ignorant"; no malice is involved. Sincere Protestants
would not be illogical if they adopted the same line towards
Catholics, as a few of the more rigid among them still do. St.

[5] Historically speaking, most of the heresies were not so much a rejection
of truth as the isolation of one particular segment of it and the exaggeration
of it until it became false. This was the case with all the Christological heresies of the early centuries. It was so too with the later Calvinism. Most of
what now passes for heresy is merely crude denial or muddled misunderstanding.

Francis de Sales, in conversation with Theodore Beza, Calvin's successor at Geneva, managed to extract from him the grudging admission that Catholics might be saved, but it was only after he had maneuvered Beza into the position of either conceding this or saying that the true Church had disappeared for several centuries before Calvin restored it. The fact is that Calvinism at that time really did regard itself as the Church and the Roman organization as a cluster of enormous heresies.

Faith is by many attained with difficulty, and only after years of search and struggle. Yet it can become so firmly fixed that it is much easier to believe than disbelieve. I hope it is not presumptuous of me to say that I cannot imagine myself not believing that the Catholic Faith is true. Difficulties may now and then cross the mind, but as Cardinal Newman once said, a thousand difficulties need not create a doubt, and even doubt may be only a momentary temptation over which faith surges back in triumph. One is reminded of the two famous stories that De Joinville relates in his life of his friend King Louis IX, whom the boyish-hearted old man lived to see canonized. One told of a famous cleric who admitted to the Bishop of Paris that he was unable to believe in the Sacrament of the Altar. When the bishop asked him whether he took pleasure in this, he received the answer that it gave unspeakable torture. The bishop continued by asking who would have the greater credit—the commander of the castle at la Rochelle (it was at a time when there was war between England and France, and this was the most exposed of French strongholds) or the commander of the castle at Montlhéri, safe in the heart of the country. Of course the cleric responded that it was the commander at la Rochelle who would most merit praise. Then the bishop said that he himself was like the captain of Montlhéri, for he had never suffered any doubt, adding, "Your conduct is more pleasing to Our Lord than mine." The other story concerns St. Louis himself. One day a courtier ran to the king in great excitement asking him to go at once to the chapel; the altar on which Mass had just been said was stained with blood. Louis refused to go; he said his faith did not require such a proof of the Real Presence.

As this is great faith, one had best not begin the discussion there. Instead let us take the basis of all religion, the existence of God, as even in this some people apparently cannot believe with much confidence. No proofs are going to be adduced here; it is enough for my purpose to say that there are those who think it very ingenious to dodge their difficulty by suggesting that God cannot be omnipotent, or He would not permit the existence of evil. Setting on one side the philosophical explanation that evil has no real existence, but is no more than the privation of good, one can only say that the idea of a circumscribed God is a shameless sophism, as such a God is metaphysically impossible. Nevertheless such sophisms were toyed with by the admirable and beloved Thomas Hardy. Indeed, I sometimes think that he best revealed his really kind heart in the poems which he did not intend to be a final explanation of anything but which displayed his sympathy for suffering mankind. In one of them, "God Forgotten," he has God say:

> Thou shouldst have learnt that *Not to mend*
> For Me could mean but *Not to Know.*

Here God is exculpated on the grounds that He is not omniscient; in other poems He is exculpated because he is not omnipotent. If this is blasphemy, it is blasphemy of the kind that, little credit as it may give to the head, gives much to the heart. But Hardy never ceased to mourn his own lack of faith, writing, for instance, in "The Impercipient":

> O, doth a bird deprived of wings
> Go earth-bound wilfully!

Without attempting to solve what looks like an insoluble problem, this much perhaps may be said here: If the sin and suffering that exist in the world force one to the conclusion that God does not exist, how does one account for an anomaly at least equally as great—the existence of good? We hear people talking about the "problem of evil," but never of the problem of good. Is not this because we postulate good as normal and, in doing so, postulate God? Is not evil inconceivable except in relation to good? Take God out of the world and you take the devil out too. Nothing would be left except chaos, darkness, filth, slime, until God created everything all over again.

On the assumption that God does exist, his distance even from unfallen man was so immense that through the divine grace of revelation alone can man reach any close communication with his Creator. But man, though free to test by reason what purports to be revelation, is simply not in any position to declare, or even guess, what that revelation should contain. However, once he is satisfied that the revelation is genuine, he is inescapably obliged to accept it. The bare fact of the existence of God is within the reach of the unillumined human intelligence; so too is the fact that God is One. Such was the conclusion reached by some of the philosophers of antiquity, living in the midst of a polytheism to which they yielded a kind of assent; and such also seems to be true of much cruder polytheism, which always keeps behind its confused welter of good and evil spirits a conception, however vague and however rarely brought into play, of one supreme God. Yet even among the loftiest Greek philosophers, this truth was reached only in a confused and imperfect manner, because without revelation much would be totally beyond the reach of the unaided intellect. All that the intellect can do is to assent to its need for revelation, and when that revelation comes (and is accepted as authentic) the intellect must proceed to direct actions accordingly, or stultify itself.

The doctrine of the Trinity, that three Persons constitute One God, is of course beyond the sweep of human intelligence. Less difficult than this, but still a great mystery, is faith in the infinite value of Christ's merits, upon which depends our redemption. The fact of original sin as well as actual sin is something observable—the one being within each day's experience, the other, though less obvious, something of which all men, who are conscious of what Newman called some aboriginal calamity, are aware. Paganism and Israel knew that atoning sacrifice to God was necessary, though nobody could ever feel that "the blood of bulls and goats" could be other than a kind of token atonement. It was a good deal to be aware of even this much, but for condign atonement—man's injury being against his Creator, an infinite God—only the reparation of the divine to the divine could be adequate. That much might have been reached by reason (though it is doubtful whether it was), but reason could certainly not have perceived that this could only be effected by the life, death and resurrection of the God-Man.

About this I say no more at the moment. As to the Trinity, it may be suggested that man was perhaps to some extent prepared for the acceptance of this sublime doctrine by noticing the analogies to it that may be found in nature. For example: the three transcendentals—the good, the true, and the beautiful—which make up a single entity, correspond up to a point with the concept of Father, Son and Holy Ghost being One God. So also the immortality of the soul may be divined by intuition, and few (if any) races of mankind have failed to have a deep conviction of this, however absurd are some of the forms that it has taken. Similarly, too, it is natural to venerate holiness, for this accords with conscience, which is implanted in all men. The difficulties that arise are those relating to unmerited suffering. Most people can accept the idea that everything is redressed in the life to come, but some remain resentful that rewards are not always given in this life to the good and that sometimes the wicked flourish. This is why Browning wrote: "We may believe in heaven; we must believe in hell."

Miracles can be rejected only on *a priori* grounds. A vast number of them are supported by irrefutable testimony, though of course this does not prevent some people from concocting an ingenious natural explanation for facts they are unable to deny. This was done even by the Jewish leaders on the day of Christ's resurrection who contended that His disciples had come while the Roman soldiers were asleep and stolen His body.[6] Granted that God exists—and only an infinitely powerful God is meta-

---

[6] This explanation does not bear a moment's examination. Even supposing the guards at the tomb had been asleep, can it be imagined that they would not have been awakened by the noise unavoidable in removing huge slabs of stone? Some of the later explanations have been more ingenious, but none is convincing.

physically conceivable [7]—no physical miracle is beyond His power. As St. Peter said with common sense, "Let it not be thought an incredible thing among you that God should raise the dead." When skeptics postulate an unalterable law, this is because they have no belief in God, or only a very hypothetical belief. In addition to such people there are those who, while having a genuine enough faith, are heard to use the expression "the age of miracles," without explaining why miracles happened in one age and can no longer happen. Yet there are some Protestants who recognize that such a position is logically untenable and pray for miracles, and I have heard of such occurring, without any reason to doubt it. It was to the Syro-Phoenician woman and the Roman centurion that Christ could say, "I have not seen such faith, no, not in all Israel." The Catholic temper of mind—which to many will seem superstitious—expects a constant overlapping or intermingling of the natural and supernatural. Yet as Père Garrigou-Lagrange has said, "The slightest degree of sanctifying grace is superior to a miracle, which is supernatural only by reason of its cause, by its mode of production (*quoad modum*), not by its intimate reality; the life restored to a corpse is only the natural life, low indeed in comparison with that of grace." It is therefore possible to speak of miracles of grace, though as most of these go unobserved, they are not ordinarily classed as miracles.

Before leaving miracles, I should draw attention to the position taken by Canon Bernard Iddings Bell, an Episcopalian sympathetic to Catholics, in his *Religion for Living*. His argument is by no means peculiar to him, but will serve as an example. He ac-

---

[7] Perhaps I should explain the difference between the physically and the metaphysically impossible. It is physically impossible for a man to leap over a mountain, though not for a grasshopper to make an almost correspondingly high leap, allowing for its size. Therefore if a man did leap over a mountain one would know that a miracle had happened, a physical impossibility but something that one can at least conceive as happening. The mountain simile was used by Christ when He talked of Faith great enough to move mountains. All this is something we can picture, something the mind is capable of receiving. But the mind cannot receive the notion of a square circle or of an untrue truth. There we have metaphysical impossibilities. Not even God can perform these, for qualities inherently and by definition unchangeable are involved.

cepts the theory that God Himself is inexorably bound by law, by which the Canon confuses physical and metaphysical impossibility. But as he is well aware that miracles do happen, he offers the supposition that these are due to the operation of laws about which we know little or nothing. This may be true in some instances, but it is surely hard to imagine any unknown "law" by which lepers are cleansed or the dead raised. Against Dr. Bell one might pit another Anglican, Colonel W. H. Turton, who in his *Truth of Christianity*—the best book of its kind that I have seen—makes the interesting point: "We observe that heat is followed by expansion, and we therefore assume that the one is the cause of the other. But calling it a law of nature for heat to expand bodies does not in any way account for its doing so.... And the same is true in other cases, so that a law of nature *explains* nothing, it is merely a summary of the facts to be explained."

Since the horrid word superstition has come up, it must be discussed. Some superstitions are harmless enough, some far from harmless, but, as the very word connotes, all are beyond faith, or in excess of it. While much belongs to faith that is beyond reason, no part of it is contrary to reason. Faith and reason go together, faith and superstition never. Joan of Arc was burned as a witch because it was alleged that as a little girl she frequented the "fairy tree" at Domrémy. This she did not deny, but declared that she never put any stock in it. Irish peasants may say that they believe in fairies; if so, I fear they are liars.[8] Sentimentalists may pretend to believe in fairies, in which case they are silly. But it is better to believe in fairies than to think that going under a ladder or seeing a black cat will bring "bad luck." Worst of all is it to believe in ouija boards and spiritualistic séances, as these *may* have a certain amount of reality about them. The thoroughly religious person is also the one who is least superstitious. Faith has no use for fooleries.

When we come to hope, the second theological virtue, we must

[8] However, they may *imagine* they do. At any rate their ignorance makes them more excusable than does the affectation of a man like W. B. Yeats. He once took my brother-in-law, the present editor of the London *Times,* to a pool on Lady Gregory's estate and pointed out where the fairies were dancing. "Look, Casey!" he said. "There they are." Casey, being an honest man, could see nothing.

first understand that it means a great deal more than a state of general hopefulness or cheerfulness of disposition. That kind of hope, of course, is good to have, but it is at best a natural virtue and, if it is part of one's make-up, hardly to be called a virtue at all. Supernatural hope may to some extent repose on it, but goes far beyond it. What is involved is primarily hope of salvation, and of the means to salvation. "We are saved by hope; but hope that is seen is not hope, for what a man seeth why doth he hope for?" It is akin to faith and charity, as Dante indicates in his *Purgatorio* (XXIX, 121–129) where he shows us the three theological virtues as ladies dancing in a round, as part of the pageant of the Earthly Paradise. They are dressed in the appropriate colors of red, white and green, and now faith seemed to lead, and now charity, but never hope, as in the theological sense this must spring from one of the other virtues:

> *ed or parevan dalla bianca tratte*
> *or dalla rossa, e dal canto di questa*
> *l'altre togliean l'andare e tarde e ratte.*[9]

Hope is not merely a confidence that we shall obtain our deserts but the anticipation of receiving much more than we merit through the mercy and grace of God. It is therefore at once audacious and humble: "O holy hope and high humility!" But as Henry Vaughan concludes his stanza, they are "To kindle my cold love."

This hope is not solely for our soul's salvation but looks to the salvation in which the body will partake, for not until the resurrection will salvation be crowned. To turn again to Dante, he quotes Aristotle as explaining that the more a thing is perfect the more it has of pleasure but the more also of pain. So for the damned, the resurrection of the body can only bring greater agony. Christ completed the process of redemption by arising again from the tomb, and St. Paul declares: "If Christ be not risen, your faith is vain; ye are still in your sins"—thus staking the whole of Christianity upon the resurrection of Christ, but mak-

[9] Later in the *Paradiso* Dante treats formally in several cantos of the same virtues, about which he is put through a searching examination by Beatrice, who symbolizes theology.

ing it also the "sure and certain hope" of our own bodily resurrection. This last is something that not a few Protestants regard themselves as too spiritual to believe. With my own ears I heard one of the greatest Protestant pulpit orators of our day exclaim vehemently: "I *am* a soul; I *have* a body," as though the whole man were not made up of both.

Perhaps this will help to explain why the Church has recently defined as a doctrine of faith, what has throughout the Christian centuries been part of its tradition, the Assumption of Our Lady into heaven. (This doctrine must not be thought of as reposing solely on tradition, for it is a further unfolding of the Church's teaching regarding the Immaculate Conception.) The present Archbishop of York, Dr. Cyril Garbett, said in a most "sub-acid" tone when the Assumption was promulgated that it was very "un-English," until a *Time Magazine* correspondent drew attention to the seal of Eton (the school, if I am not mistaken, attended by the Archbishop); on that seal, made at the time of Eton's founding by King Henry VI, was depicted Mary's Assumption. Apparently nobody in Protestant England had the least suspicion as to what was signified.

Two sins of almost equal seriousness may be committed against hope: that of presumption and that of despair, but with despair the deadlier. In the Old Testament hope is frequently mentioned in the sense of a general trust in God; in the New Testament its objects are more specific—ultimately God Himself, the inspirer of our hope and its foundation, but also the hope of our bodily resurrection. For those who think that heaven is not likely to be opened to such as they, there is the hope of purgatory. This is not a subject of dread, though it will be no light matter to undergo, but rather the assurance, while its pangs are being endured, that the joys of heaven are certain. Even in this respect we may hope for what greatly exceeds our merit.

A final word about hope, as a kind of postscript. Although the main object of hope is our salvation, it is not limited to that. At least once every day we pray, "Thy kingdom come, Thy will be done *on earth* as it is in heaven"—and that hope often seems more remote than anything else. Hope is not restricted to eternity but has some bearing upon time, as in the hope for the kingdom but also in our trust in God for our daily bread. Events that are happening in time have a considerable effect upon our souls. So we may have a temporal hope, even a political hope, for these are not unconnected with our heavenly destiny. "Thy kingdom come on earth"—that is an immensely important part of Christian hope.

And now for charity. Tyndale, the sixteenth-century translator of the New Testament, rendered the word "charity" as "love"— one of his many deliberate falsifications.[10] For charity is much more than love, love hardly implying more than the natural virtue. Yet even in earthly love—that of a mother for her children or a husband for his wife—love may be supernaturalized, passion transformed to compassion or rather fused with it, so that natural love may take on something of the character of charity. On the other hand, charity has too often had the restricted connotation of almsgiving, which should have merciful loving-kindness in it and be an expression of our love of God, but sometimes is so far from that as to have occasioned the expression "as cold as charity." It will be used here in the sense of being the love of God above all things and the love of all things (including enemies) in God. The man of charity should, of course, show himself kindly and amiable, for these are the natural fruits of the supernatural virtue, if they are not also its natural basis. But they are not charity itself. Charity, like faith and hope, is essential to salvation. The burning passage in St. Paul sets it as the greatest of the three related virtues, which unless a man have, nothing profiteth him. It is above the tongues of men and angels, above prophecy and the knowledge of all mysteries, above giving one's goods to the poor, above giving one's body to be burned. Faith, hope and charity are all three necessary, "but the greatest of these is charity."

10 The "Revised Version" of the Bible, which is much used by Protestants, changes the "charity" of the King James version to "love," and it is hard to see what is gained. Rather such a passage as that in St. Paul's First Epistle to the Corinthians on charity, loses immeasurably, even from the literary point of view, by substituting the word "love." And I have just looked up this passage in another well-known Protestant version, that edited by Dr. Scofield, and find it titled "The ministry gifts must be governed by love." That strikes me as appallingly flat. However, in the text itself "charity" is retained.

In this matter it is possible to accord to Protestants, and some-times even to those who are not professedly Christian, high ap-preciation. It is not a question of Abou ben Adhem's name leading all the rest, for Leigh Hunt's celebrated poem is about as loath-some a piece of sentimentality as one can find, but the love of God, and *that* Abou specifically admitted he did not have. Catho-lics must be permitted to consider the faith of their separated brethren defective, for this is something that may be gauged without undue unfairness. In view of the uncertainty that pre-vails among many Protestants about the resurrection of the body, it would seem that their hope is far from perfect. When it comes to charity, it may be admitted that many of them surpass us, or to put it still more plainly, it is undoubtedly true that many Protestants have a deeper love of God than have many Catholics. If the Protestant spirit does not often tend towards mysticism, this may be due to the emphasis they place upon practical aims. However, the average of Christian devotedness among Protes-tants of the best type is undoubtedly high. They may rightly ask how one can love God whom one has not seen, unless one also loves one's brother whom one has seen, but after all the true love for one's fellows depends upon love of God, or in other words, the minor upon the major charity. In both respects many who are outside the Church put to shame those who are within. It is through this charity that their faith and hope, in so far as they are defective, may be restored to perfection.

Mystical considerations are not likely to weigh much with those cut off from the sacramental channels of grace, which enable all practicing Catholics to be in communion with God in a very real sense. Listening to sermons and reading the Bible and singing hymns may all be means of grace, but they can never be an ade-quate substitute for what Protestants have renounced. On the other hand, a great many Protestants do seem always to bear in mind Christ's injunction: "If ye love Me, keep My command-ments," and their goodness is touchingly beautiful. The keeping of the commandments may, it is true, degenerate into primness and phariseeism, and respectability may be mistaken for virtue; but this is true of Catholics as well as Protestants, so we have little here upon which to base any claim to superiority. In addition to the code of the Ten Commandments, there is the more general enumeration of the four cardinal virtues, so called because all the virtues hinge upon them. This classification was taken over by Christianity from the philosophers of ancient Greece, and admirably summarized by St. Thomas in his prayer: "Give me justice, to submit to Thee; prudence, to avoid the snares of the enemy; temperance, to keep the just mean; fortitude to bear adversities with patience."

Dr. Johnson, himself a rather notable Christian philosopher, has made the penetrating observation that unless a man have courage, none of his virtues are safe; and a still greater Christian philosopher, who was also a great theologian, has given to the courageous, in canto after canto of his *Paradiso*, a high place in heaven. As for prudence, it is sometimes confused with a somewhat ignoble caution, a determination to avoid every possible risk. When Lascelles Abercrombie in his poem "The Sale of St. Thomas," goes so far as to warn the fleeing Apostle, "Prudence, Thomas, is the deadly sin," he has this false prudence in mind. Real prudence is often daring: "Out of this nettle, danger, we pluck this flower safety," or as Christ actually said, and not in the imaginary words attributed to Him by any poet, "He that would save his life must lose it."

Still another poet, Hilaire Belloc, has sung:

> Of courtesy, though it is much less
> Than courage of heart or holiness—

but that courtesy, as he shows by the examples he takes, is the fruit of charity. It is witty but untrue to define a gentleman as one who never says a word to wound another—except deliberately. Good manners which do not come from a kind heart are of this sort. And since we have come to notice what some of the poets have said, Coventry Patmore might be quoted in conclusion: "All grace is the grace of God."

# PART II

# BRANCHED IN THE VINE

# CHAPTER ONE

## *The Incarnation*

In this book there is little if any need to say anything formally about the divinity of Jesus Christ, for my theme flows from that divinity. As Browning's "A Death in the Desert" puts it:

> That Jesus Christ is God
> Solves all things in this world and out of it.

The denial of this doctrine makes him who denies cease to be a Christian. He may be able, learned and noble-minded; he may carry along some of the shreds of Christianity, as many agnostics do; he may even very powerfully affirm such Christian truths as he has salvaged from his lost faith, but when he does not believe in the godhead of Christ, he no longer has the distinguishing mark of the Christian. By implication this doctrine is in that of the Incarnation, which would be meaningless without it. To put that doctrine in its classical terms, I quote from the Nicene Creed, as said at Mass every Sunday, and at many of the weekday Masses as well: "I believe ... in one Lord Jesus Christ, the only-begotten son of God. Born of the Father before all ages. God of God, light of light, true God of true God. Begotten not made; being of one substance with the Father; by whom all things were made. Who for us men, and for our salvation, came down from heaven. And was incarnate by the Holy Ghost of the Virgin Mary: and was made Man."

This doctrine was as completely accepted by historic Protestantism as it was, and is, by Catholics. Although the majority of Protestants still profess to believe it, many so dilute it or qualify it, that the position of some of them is hardly distinguishable from that of Israel or Islam. To these Protestants Jesus was a great teacher, a prophet worthy of all honor, and perhaps in some vague sense "divine"—for that term can be blown like a cloud of vapor to cover all men—but not God incarnate. Yet it is hard to see how in that case such people can reasonably revere Jesus at all, for this would indicate that Christ was a madman or an impostor in making the claims He did, or that the evangelists and apostles more or less consciously "invented" His godhead. Of course a man such as they envisage might be a very engaging figure, but at best he would be a charming lunatic who managed now and then to throw out some striking remarks.

The notion that the writers of the gospels wished to deceive simply will not hold water, even for a moment. The point seems to me too obvious to waste time discussing. When Jesus said of Himself, "Before Abraham was, I am," it is clear that the full import of His words only by degrees dawned on His disciples. Some of those who did understand were scandalized and "walked no more with Him." It was not until late in His ministry that Jesus asked the direct question, "Who do men say that I am?" to get the rather halting answer, "Some say"—with John the Baptist and Elias and Jeremiah and other prophets suggested, until Peter blurted out, "Thou are the Christ, the Son of the living God." It was immediately upon this that Peter was told that he was the Rock upon which the Church (never openly mentioned until then) was to be built.

Even before this, however, we can see that several of the disciples were all but sure of the astounding truth, and when they looked back upon some of the things He had said and done, all must have wondered why they had not been sure from the beginning—as Mary the Mother of Jesus had always been sure, but kept it all in her heart. Christ's method was not to rush on too fast, lest too early a revelation be overwhelming; first the disciples must know Him as man, their friend and companion. So while flashes of insight came, these often faded in the light of the common day they spent with Jesus. Only bit by bit were they prepared for the full truth, which did not dawn in certainty upon them until after they had known and loved Him as a human master. They had to be sure that He was man before they were made sure that He was the God-Man. But that they were all eventually unshakably convinced (except perhaps Judas) is beyond all question. Without such an absolute conviction on their part, their subsequent history makes no sense. Even allowing the supposition that Jesus of Nazareth was Himself insane, it is past all credibility—almost past imagining—that all the disciples could have been insane too.

The Incarnation is the foundation of everything in the Christian religion. It is true that some theologians entertain the speculative idea (though without advancing it as more than that) that God might have wiped clean the slate of man's sinfulness and offered forgiveness by mere indulgence, saying in effect, "I am willing to forget all that; now make a new start." Here, however, we at once meet the objection that such a solution would not have been consonant with the justice of God. As for His love, it was manifested both by the Incarnation and all that followed. "God so loved the world, that He gave His only begotten Son, that whosoever believeth in Him should not perish but have everlasting life." As the great cry of the Holy Week Liturgy has it, *O felix culpa!* Man had indeed fallen, but he might rejoice in his fall because it had resulted in the richness of his redemption. One can go still further and say that even had Adam and Eve not fallen and been expelled from Eden, the Incarnation would have taken place, for it is through Christ as man that the human race is absorbed into the divine. To quote St. Augustine, "God became man in order that man might become God."

Man's transgression against an infinite God was so outrageous that it could be adequately pardoned only if the Son became man and so offered the Father the satisfaction that sin demanded. Nevertheless it was not, strictly speaking, necessary that Christ should die on the cross. This was because the Incarnation itself, being an infinite humiliation, would have been abundantly sufficient. Add to this Christ's life of suffering and poverty and obloquy, and the reparation offered is still greater. But by the cross the extravagance of God's love for man was manifested. Nails would not have held Christ to the cross, says St. Catherine of Siena, had love not held Him there. His shameful death was to demonstrate his love beyond all question; redemption had already begun from the moment that Mary accepted her role on the day of Annunciation. As Robert Stephen Hawker, the Parson of Morwenstowe, put it:

> So linked, so blent, that when, with pulse fulfilled,
> Moved but that infant Hand,
> Far, far away His conscious Godhead thrilled,
> And stars might understand.

Even the cross did not quite complete the process of love. "It is finished" marked only Christ's giving up of the ghost. The Resurrection had to follow, and that too was a manifestation of love. For while Christ died as man, because His manhood and divinity—His two natures—constituted one Person, the grave could hold His body for no longer than a symbolical period, a period to be determined by Him. It would have been possible for Christ to have risen from the dead and for nobody to have known it. The huge slab of stone over the entrance to His tomb could have been left where it was, and the tomb itself left empty. But Christ wished the disciples to see Him after He had risen from the dead, with Thomas to touch His wounds and all of them to eat with Him on the lakeside, to be assured that this was no apparition but the Jesus they had known before Calvary. The "first-fruit from the dead" was needed to prove beyond all question that He was also God, and to be the assurance of their own eventual resurrection from the dead. It was upon this, as ascertained fact, that they were willing to stake everything. Had He not risen from the dead, and shown Himself as risen, they would have had to think of Him as being, after all, only a man; and faith in a man, though he be honored as the greatest of heroes, and reverenced as the most sublime of teachers, is not Christianity.

In all this Mary was an indispensable means. She had been given the unique privilege of being conceived free from original sin, for no less was fitting to one who was to be the Mother of God. For the same reason she had to bear her Son as an intact virgin. That was the difficulty which she at once presented to the angel Gabriel: "How shall this thing be, since I know not man?" —meaning not merely that she was a virgin then but that she had vowed her virginity to God, as she preserved a lifelong virginity. How then could she bear a son? Since the Triune God knew from all eternity what her answer would be, it is only a pious fashion of speaking to say that all heaven waited with bated breath for her answer. But she was not *compelled* to answer as she did; her will was perfectly free. She could have set her virginity above obedience. Instead her instant compliance, "Be it done to me according to Thy word," ensured that she would be Mary ever virgin. As St. Bernard in one of his sermons on the Mother of God pointed out, virginity, though glorious, is not necessary to salvation, whereas humility is. It was upon Mary's humility, and the obedience that sprang from it, that the Incarnation depended. She may therefore be called our co-Redemptrix.

Judas's betrayal, on the other hand, though also foreknown and used as a means, was not necessary. His will, like Mary's, was free. But had he not sold his Master for thirty pieces of silver, one of several other ways could have been found for the apprehending of Christ. Nor was it necessary that Judas should give his traitor's kiss; Christ was a familiar figure and hundreds of people could have been found to identify Him. Indeed, at the moment of His arrest, Jesus reminded the mob of this—"I was daily with you teaching in the temple and ye took me not." Judas's betrayal merely inflicted further pain, especially as it was a betrayal for such a trifling reward, possibly a means of making up an embezzlement on the part of the carrier of the common purse, and perhaps also because he counted upon Jesus' being able to extricate Himself, as had happened before. Whatever the motive in the traitor's mind, he took no part in Christ's prosecution, though obviously he would have been a valuable witness had he consented to appear. Instead there was immediate grief, leading to despair and suicide. To this he was not compelled; he could have sought and obtained pardon, but, as Christ said when He was taken, "The scriptures must be fulfilled." Judas gave back the money he had received for his treason, but he would not ask Christ's forgiveness, which, available to all men, was especially available to His disciples.

What Judas actually would do was not only foreknown—as in the mind of God every happening to the end of time is distinct—but Christ Himself foretold it at the Last Supper. Yet at the last minute Judas could have changed his mind, for he was not bound by predetermined necessity. He must have loved Christ to have become one of His followers, but because his was a love without humility, while he remorsefully returned the reward he had been paid for his treason, he would not ask forgiveness and so cast himself, the son of perdition, into hell. It is a story that should come to every Christian with terrible impact, for we have all of us betrayed Christ—and sometimes for much less than thirty pieces of silver.

Christ's cup was filled to overflowing with the sins and ingratitude of millions of Judases. His disciples fled. The Rock upon which the Church was to be built quivered before a pert servant girl, and Peter swore that he had never seen his Master. Maltreatment was suffered by Christ before He was crucified, both in the hall of the High Priest and in the guardroom of the Roman legionaries. Here there was an inescapable concurrence, according to Dante, between the Chosen People and the Imperial Race (which he seems to have regarded as having its own kind of sanctity): Only in this way could sentence and execution be a total rejection. The crowd, instigated by their religious leaders, howled for Christ's blood. And there was a crowning series of insults: the preference for the notorious murderer and bandit Barabbas, the snarls of one of the criminals executed beside Him on Golgotha, and even the placard that was put over His head, which the cynical secular governor also intended as an insult to the people whom he ruled and despised.

In considering the Incarnation, it may be dimly perceived how God, though not obliged to adopt this particular method of redemption, may well have been under a constraint of His love to have sought the redemption of His creatures, His children, through means that made His love for them more staggeringly manifest than any other could have. To have simply deserted them and left them to suffer what they had brought upon themselves would not have been consonant with even our poor concept of what He is. God was in no way constrained to make man at all. For though some men have contributed to His glory, they have done so only accidentally. Nor was He in any need of the angels themselves. The Godhead might have dwelt in solitary loneliness (to use the word analogically, as the Trinity constituted a kind of society) blissfully satisfied, and needing nothing but His Own infinite perfections. It was in love that He created all things visible and invisible, giving to each species what that species required, but to man alone the means of consciously communicating with Him during his earthly pilgrimage and the promise of a consummated union in heaven.

Man cut himself off from God by deliberate act and had to wait for the "fullness of time" when his redemption, long promised, could come. Yet during the centuries of darkness there was some light. Man never lost all possibility of contact with God and to the Chosen People was committed an incomplete revelation. Even pagans had some intuition of this. As the great sequence of the *Dies Irae* expresses it, *Teste David cum Sibylla.* However, with redemption came man's divine adoption. This is vastly more than a mere figure of speech, for human paternity is no more than co-operation with God, the real Creator even of the body, and altogether of the soul. Where human adoption is only a legal fiction, God's adoption of man makes him a partaker of the divine nature. Here too an astounding generosity is shown, for having created man, God might have been willing to accept from him a merely figurative sonship, based upon obedience to His law, though without the same degree of the supernatural element such as is known under the New Covenant. But Christ came as the "first-born of many brethren" to make us "coheirs with Christ." While He is God's son according to the very constitution of the Triune Godhead ("begotten not made"), we, His creatures, are sons only by adoption, but sons none the less, becoming such through our relationship with our Redeemer. Some kinship with the divine existed before, as is true of all of God's creatures of whatever order; but this was an adoption of a kind of which man could have had no conception and, even now that he knows it, can hardly grasp.

Consequently, as sons of God, we share in some sense in the Incarnation itself, not only the benefits of our redemption but a participation in the redemptive process. St. Paul spoke of "making up that which is lacking in the sufferings of Christ." This does not mean that any supplementary contribution on our part is called for but that, forming part of Christ's Mystical Body, we have our role to play—an astounding privilege. Everything before the Incarnation points towards Him; everything after the Incarnation is linked with Him. The whole creation is bathed in this light, or, as I wrote in one of my own poems which I beg indulgence for quoting; it now lives in

> The radiance incarnational
> That makes the star and sparrow rest
> With Seraphs on the Father's breast.

The Incarnation was God's means for bringing about our redemption. It may be that another means of redemption could have been found, but it cannot be imagined that so abundant a redemption could have been given. Whether or not the crucifixion was absolutely necessary—unless because men everywhere had been prepared for that Sacrifice by the idea of offering to God of such sacrifices as were within their power—the crucifixion itself would have conferred nothing on mankind except the uplifting spectacle of a noble death if the sufferer had not been the God-Man. It was an abandoned outpouring of love, as was the Incarnation itself, and it culminated in the death offered as a sacrifice of atonement for the sins of mankind. All that we know is that He "bore our sins in His own body on the tree," and that "He who knew no sin was *made* sin for us."

The night before His death Christ said the first Mass, using the words still used by the priest at the consecration of the sacred species. As St. Thomas Aquinas's great hymn for Maunday Thursday puts it:

> *Se dat suis manibus;*

He gave Himself with His own hands. The cross awaited Him on the morrow, as He knew, but Calvary was already in the Upper Room. He was "the Lamb slain before the foundation of the world." This is why we see Him pressing towards what He called "My hour" with what might be almost described as impatience. It was for this that He had come: "Ought not Christ to suffer and so to enter into His glory?" If we are to share that glory, we must be prepared, to the extent that is possible to us, to share also in

His sufferings. All Christians, and not only priests (to whom usage generally reserves the term), are "other Christs."

Yet even after the Last Supper He had to undergo the final temptation to which His human weakness was subjected. In the bloody sweat of Gethsemane He cried out, "If it be Thy will, let this cup pass from me"—only to add at once, "Nevertheless not my will but Thine be done." He dragged Himself to the last step of the *Via dolorosa*, falling because of weariness and loss of blood several times under the weight of His cross, so that the burly Simon of Cyrene had to be summoned to help Him carry it. And there between the two thieves executed with Him was love made visible, a love so astonishing as to remain largely incomprehensible. Perhaps the best statement of it is in Newman's *Dream of Gerontius:*

> O generous love! That He who smote
>    In man for man the foe,
> The double agony in man
>    For man should undergo.

> And in the garden secretly,
>    And on the cross on high,
> Should teach His brethren and inspire
>    To suffer and to die.

# CHAPTER TWO

## The Church

Only recently I was reading the Methodist Bishop Fred P. Corson's *Your Church and You*. It did not seem to me a very rewarding book, possibly because the good bishop is so mild in his approach to every subject. But his chapter "Your Church and its Beginnings" (and he means any church, not merely his own) is a clear statement of what might be called the "middle" Protestant position. He does not maintain, as the early Calvinists did, that theirs was the only true Church or, as many Protestants now do, that the Church is invisible, with those who make it up known only to God. He says rather that it is institutional and that it is one in spite of all denominational differences. Moreover, in his view (which is of course the Catholic view) it was founded by Christ Himself and the words recorded in Matthew xvi.18 mark its inauguration, but he sidesteps the idea that Peter was the Rock, except to say that some have claimed too much (obviously meaning Catholics) while others (meaning most Protestants) have allowed the words too little weight. He attaches slight importance to sectarian divergences, apparently seeing in every sect a true church, but presumably holding that only the two hundred (or whatever the number is) denominations in the aggregate constitute the organism he postulates.

Without entering into argument with Bishop Corson—much of whose book is true, as far as it goes, and all of it admirable in spirit—we may start by saying that all the baptized (even when they are not members of the Catholic Church because of some accidental schism or material heresy), may have a relationship to it if they are in a state of grace. As Pius XII in his encyclical *Mystici corporis* says clearly: "Those who are divided in faith or government cannot be living in one body such as this, and cannot be living the life of its one Divine Spirit." The expression sometimes heard from this or that good man who says that he belongs to the "Soul of the Church" but not to its body is inaccurate, though one understands what is meant. The Soul of the Church is the Holy Ghost. As for its Body, as Christ said to His disciples: "I am the true Vine and my Father is the husbandman. . . . Abide in Me and I in you. As the branch cannot bear fruit of itself unless it abide in the vine, so neither can you unless you abide in Me. . . . If anyone abide not in Me, he shall be cast forth as a branch, and shall wither, and they shall gather him up, and cast him into the fire, and he burneth." This does not mean that those not actually Catholics are all destined to hell, but that by remaining outside the Church they have deprived themselves of much life-giving grace, though outside of the sacraments they may receive more than enough for their salvation.

Other figures of speech are sometimes used for the Church. It is not only the Vine and the Body of Christ but is sometimes spoken of as His Bride. And Catholics often speak of it as their Mother, in the sense that St. Cyprian said that no man can have God for his Father who does not have the Church for his Mother. The contemporary German Protestant theologian Heiler admits: "So far as Catholicism is genuinely universal and represents fully all religious values, it must be exclusive. But this exclusiveness is not the exclusiveness of narrowness, but of inexhaustible wealth." That wealth, it might be added, is something that will increase, for although Christ Himself has always been consummate in perfection, in the sense that He, with his Church, forms a Mystical Body, full growth has not yet been reached.

I have said that Christ is the Head of the Church. But on earth He has a Vicar, the Pope, whose jurisdiction begins with his election and ends only with his death or resignation.[1] It is the Church itself which is the repository of revealed truth, and its guardian is the dispenser of the sacraments which are the main channels of grace, the holder of the keys (though there is a spe-

---

[1] Theoretically too he would cease to be Pope if he became a lunatic or a heretic, though God has preserved the Church from these calamities. That there have been a handful of popes of evil life has no bearing upon any *ex cathedra* statements on faith or morals.

cial sense in which their holder is Peter), the representative of God among mortal men. It was not only to Peter but to the Church, already fully constituted but still awaiting the promise of the descent of the Holy Ghost, that the commission was given: "As the Father hath sent Me, I also send you; he that heareth you heareth Me, and He that despiseth you, despiseth Him that sent Me." Just as none goes to the Father except through Christ, so none goes to Christ except through the Church. Only in that unity, whether in actual membership of the Church or an implicit desire to belong to it, can there be any spiritual life, any salvation.

The Catholic principle of *Extra ecclesiam nulla salus* has been so often misunderstood, though explained so many times to apparently totally deaf ears, that rather than try again in my own words, I quote from a distinguished theologian and philosopher of our time, Monsignor F. C. Kolbe of South Africa.[2] After affirming the absolute necessity of baptism, he goes on: "Even into the heathen world the possibility extends of the baptism of desire, at least as far as the possibility of divine faith. And among Christians separated from us, valid baptism is very general. Most . . . children therefore are (though they do not know it and their parents will not admit it) Catholics;[3] for there is only one baptism and only one Church. And Catholics they remain until they *sinfully* cut themselves off from the Faith.[4] They may thus, and many do, remain organically connected with the Visible Church though neither they nor those around them recognize the union." If this point were grasped, it would remove all misunderstanding regarding *Extra ecclesiam nulla salus*.

Thus all baptized persons may be saved, unless they knowingly and willingly reject the Catholic Church as the only true Church established by Christ. The unbaptized adult may be saved where

[2] I believe he was made a bishop before he died. His father, whom he held in great reverence, had been a minister of the Dutch Reformed Church.

[3] It will be noted that the writer restricts this to children, as they are too young to have made any choice of schism or heresy; adult non-Catholics cannot be said to belong to the Church, however close they may be to it, or however admirable their lives.

[4] The Monsignor means not until they commit one of the ordinary sins but until they deliberately reject the Church. But in most cases this is probably only a *material* sin, not one of the deadlier *formal* kind.

there is an implicit desire for baptism. But what about children whether of Christian parents or not, who die before they are baptized? Some people imagine that the Church teaches that they inevitably undergo the tortures of hell. Not at all: they are indeed excluded from heaven, but the "hell" they go to is the Limbo of infants, where the unbaptized remain excluded from the beatific vision but do not suffer any positive punishment for actual sins, since they have none.

Logic here is inescapable: the children who died unbaptized were never Christians and therefore cannot share in the supernatural life. But the life they do live knows nothing of earth's ill but only of its joys. As it is impossible for an infant, or for any child who has not reached the age of reason (usually considered seven) to have committed a mortal sin, it follows that it is impossible for such children to go to the hell of those who are damned for personal mortal sins. It is even possible that some of the heathen (whether or not they are among what Dante would consider the loftiest pagan intellects) never incur the guilt of mortal sin because they have never understood sufficiently clearly that any of their acts were, in themselves, contrary to the law of God. If among the unbaptized there are any such adults in age who are only infants in moral life, having never obtained the use of reason, it is possible that God will deal with them not as adults but as infants, so that they too would upon death enter the Limbo of infants. We leave, however, to God the final judgment in this matter.

Recently Mr. Paul Blanshard has once again given wide publicity to the old charge in his best-selling *American Freedom and Catholic Power*. Most of his documentation is drawn from secondary or not very reliable sources, and in this instance he cites a pamphlet published by the Catholic Truth Society of Brooklyn. He might have found a weightier authority for his statement, but he says correctly enough that those who remain outside the Church through their own fault—"such as through pride or willful ignorance, or through fear of loss of goods or friends, or gross neglect and indifference"—will be lost if they remain obdurate in this state to their dying day. What is this but sinning against the light, a sin against the Holy Ghost, calculated to lead to final impenitence? Nobody can say how many, or how few, commit it. What the Church does is to indicate certain conditions, but without pretending to say whether, in this or that particular instance, the conditions have been met.

The importance of adhesion to the Church can hardly be overstated. But it must always be remembered that any member of the Church—up to and including the Pope—is capable of losing his soul because of dying in the state of mortal sin. The Church does all it can to save souls but it can guarantee salvation to nobody, not even to its most highly respected members. There are those to whom the deathbed repentance of lifelong notorious sinners seems a scandal, for they forget that the very first person to whom heaven was promised by Christ Himself was one of the thieves who was crucified by His side. More scandal may be derived from what is an unlikely but quite possible case—that of a man who has lived blamelessly for most of his years but who dies impenitent. He would unquestionably go to hell.

As for doctrinal belief, the Vatican Council of 1870 pronounced: "The divine mysteries by their own nature so far transcend the created intelligence that, even when delivered by revelation and received by faith, they remain covered with the veil of faith itself and shrouded in a certain degree of darkness, so long as we are pilgrims in this mortal life, not yet with God." They are not very intelligent people who talk, as some Protestants do, about a "simple gospel." The disciples themselves did not find it simple. Only this is true: There should be simplicity of faith and a knowledge that not even the most sublime intelligence can penetrate all mysteries. Not even those in heaven enjoying the Beatific Vision—not the angels themselves—can ever know God as God is known to Himself. But one does not have to be learned or clever to be saved, and it is not by dialectics that God has chosen to save His people. Yet having said as much, and allowing that the full import of the doctrine of the Mystical Body is beyond us, we can nevertheless belong to it fully as Catholics, and even the tenuous connection with it of those not formally Catholics, will suffice. For all there must be "Christ in you, the hope of glory."

Those outside the Church, in the way of professed adhesion,

are yet at least potentially of it, in every instance, even those who declare that they do not wish any membership. In their case, and even more in the case of those of "the household of the faith," there can be no distinction on the ground of race or color or social rank. St. Paul was speaking, however, of the members of the Church when he said that all were one, Jew and Gentile, bond or free. All are members of one another; all are priests by virtue of their baptism, of the "royal priesthood," though they lack the sacerdotal powers conferred only on those dedicated to the service of the altar. All are builded together as the temple of God in the Spirit. All have, or may have, the same magnificent destiny. The life of all is the life of Christ.

The authority of the Catholic Church is divine, because it is derived from Christ and exercised in His name. That authority is centered in the See of Rome, though Peter's see was at first in Jerusalem. Non-Catholics think that Rome was selected for geographical, historical and political reasons, and this is a possible opinion for Catholics, but most Catholic authorities incline to believe that it was selected *instinctu divino*. For three quarters of a century during the fourteenth century, the Popes were absent at Avignon, without ceasing to be Bishops of Rome. This would also be true if Rome were threatened and they migrated to Nome, Alaska. The supremacy of the Pope was exercised from the beginning; but though it was usually acknowledged, its implications were not always clearly understood. Even St. Thomas More, who died for that supremacy, acknowledged that, like many others of his time, he once regarded it as reposing upon historical necessity and practical convenience rather than on divine sanction. More said humorously that it was Henry VIII's book on the Seven Sacraments, written in confutation of Luther, that had converted him. What probably really happened was that the king's strong "papalism" of 1521, which More at the time thought a bit excessive, started him on years of study of the question, which eventually led to an iron conviction that it was the papal supremacy that upheld everything else. This must be stated again, for it is still what upholds everything. The reformers of the sixteenth century, in so far as they protested against abuses, have much to be said for them, and it may well be that they were not always handled very wisely by ecclesiastical authority. In any event, whatever tactical mistakes were made on either side, the principle stands: "Thou art Peter and upon this Rock I will build My Church."

All churches, all religious bodies of whatever sort, have as their professed object the bringing of men to God. Some social and political organizations, without professedly making this their object, may actually do something in that direction. A noble and selfless cause is always of benefit to him who advances it, if to nobody else. But although some part of the Catholic purpose may, consciously or unconsciously, be achieved in other than Catholic ways, the Church is alone in knowing just how to achieve it. By its guardianship of revealed truth, by the sacraments which are the divinely ordained means of grace, by the juridical system by which it exercises control, and by its wide wisdom, garnered in two thousand years of experience of humankind, it is enabled to apply its methods to the best possible advantage.

Among the means employed, but one calling for the utmost discretion, is that of fear—in particular the salutary fear of hell. I do not mean, of course, that the Church has devised this as a means to an end. Christ Himself several times issued the clearest possible warnings. Indeed, that He was so very explicit about the fire of hell, may be taken as a gauge of His mercy. Many of the coarser-grained might merrily tread the broad way that leadeth to destruction, careless as to whether or not they would be forever separated from God, were it not for the bottomless pit, the worm that dieth not, and the fearful fire. Yet a very injudicious use of this fear is exemplified by the effect on James Joyce's mind of the sermon he reports at length, and it is to be feared with the utmost fidelity, in his *Portrait of the Artist as a Young Man.* Nevertheless people must be plainly told that hell is a possibility to be borne in mind.

Periodically each believer should be reminded of the Four Last Things—Death, Judgment, Hell and Heaven—not in such a way as to paralyze him with terror but to recall to his attention what should never be lost sight of. Bernard Shaw is hardly among the prophets or the theologians, but he did, I believe, speak the truth when he flippantly remarked that nobody goes to hell unless he wants to go there. One does not wind up in hell by accident but because one has, so to speak, forced one's way in. The final decision is what counts, the state of the will at the time of death. After that has come, God no longer can be ignored. Then there emerges the buried hatred for Him that has long existed, and that hate is fixed beyond any possibility of change. Sins can be expiated in purgatory, but in hell the damned furiously hold to their breasts for all eternity the sins they have chosen instead of God, and God Himself cannot help them. For every human soul a heavenly destiny has been prepared; but the very nature of the will is such that if it obdurately refuses what God has designed, it remains frozen in the flame.

As it is only the believer who is really able to blaspheme, one might quote here the famous passage from *Aucassin and Nicolette:* "To paradise go none but the old priests and the palsied and the cripples who crouch day and night before the altars and in the ancient crypts, folk who are naked and barefoot and full of sores, folk who are dying of cold and hunger and misery. To hell go the handsome clerics and the goodly knights who meet their death in tourneys and in the sport of war. And thither go the fair and courteous ladies who besides their husbands have two or three friends, and thither go the gold and silver and rich furs and miniver and the harpers and minstrels and all the kings of this world. With them will I go." This is a kind of perverted Catholicism. It is not true that only the pleasant people are lost, but it may well be true that in hell there is a redressing of the former fortunes of the hale and the well-to-do with those of the poor and the unfortunate and the suffering. One can see the connection between this idea and the fierce Dante's concept of an Inferno where the adulterous are tossed on a never-ceasing wind. There he sees Paolo and Francesca damned because of unlawful love but still always together. The sowers of schism are cloven: one exclaims in a kind of exultation, drawing his wounds apart so that his entrails gape, "See how I dilacerate myself!" They are where they want to be. Whatever the pains of hell, they prefer to be there rather than in heaven.

O. S. Lewis in his brilliant *Screwtape Papers* presents his chief devil as a highly astute and polished personage, reminding us of somebody in the British Foreign Office. I incline, however, to the view that the satanic intelligence is now much enfeebled and is little more than low cunning, though it may be more than a match for most people. But as for hell, where is there a more heart-shattering passage than this from one of John Donne's sermons? "When all is done, the hell of hells, the torment of torments, is the everlasting absence of God, the everlasting impossibility of returning to his presence: *Horrendum est*, says the Apostle, 'It is a fearful thing to fall into the hands of God,' ... but to fall out of the hands of the living God is a horror beyond our expression, beyond our imagination.

"That God should let my soul fall out of his hand, into a bottomless pit and roll an unremovable stone upon it, and leave it to that which it shall find there (and it shall find there, which it never imagined, till it came thither) and never think more of that soul, never have more to do with it; that of that providence of God, that studies the life of every weed, and worm, and ant, and spider, and toad, and viper, there should never, never any beam flow out upon me; that that God, who looked upon me when I was nothing, and called me when I was not, as though I had been, out of the womb and depth of darkness, and will not look upon me now, when though a miserable and banished and damned creature, yet I am his creature still, and contribute something to his glory, even in my damnation; that that God, who had so often looked upon me in my foulest uncleanness and when I had shut out the eye of the day, the Sun, and the eye of the night, the taper, and the eyes of the world, with curtains and windows and doors, did yet see me, and see me in mercy, by making me see that he saw me, and (for that time) to a forebearing of that sin, should so turn himself from me to his glorious Saints and Angels, so that no Saint or Angel, nor Christ Jesus himself should ever pray him to look towards me, never remember him that such a soul there is; that that God, who hath so often said to my soul, *Quare morieris?* Why wilt thou die? and so often sworn to my soul *Vivat Dominus*, as the Lord liveth I would not have thee die but live, will neither let me die, nor let me live, but die an everlasting life, and live an everlasting death; that that God, who when he could not get into me by standing and knocking, by his ordinary means of entering, by his word, his mercies, hath applied his judgments, and hath shaked this house, this body, with agues and palsies, and set this house on fire with fevers and calentures, and frightened the master of the house, my soul, with horrors and heavy apprehensions, and so made an entrance into me; that that God should frustrate all his own purposes and practices upon me, and leave me, and cast me away as though I had cost him nothing; that this God at last should let this soul go away as a smoke, as a vapour, as a bubble, and that then this soul cannot be a smoke, a vapour, nor a bubble, but must lie in darkness as long as the Lord of light is light itself, and never spark of that light reach to my soul—what Tophet is not Paradise, what brimstone is not amber, what gnashing is not a comfort, what gnawing of the worm is not a tickling, what torment is not a marriage bed to this damnation, to be secluded eternally, eternally, eternally from the sight of God?" Although John Donne, the greatnephew of St. Thomas More, was an apostate, his complex nature retained much of his early Catholicism, interwoven with High Church and Calvinistic strands. Even so, I quote this passage from him not for its theology, which is sometimes questionable, but because it can never be forgotten by anybody who ever reads it. As such, in a sentence almost as unending as eternity itself, it depicts the state of those separated from God.

The Catholic attitude is far removed from that of the cruder sort of hell-fire preachers, still sometimes encountered among Protestants, who have no more subtle concept than that souls are lost because of failing to conform to what is often a faulty moral standard advanced by a particular sect. A man thus becomes damned not because of his hatred of God but because of his human frailty, sometimes one gathers because of what is not really a mortal sin at all. In dealing with sin such people have no finesse nor a particle of psychological understanding. It is largely on this account that the modern world has concluded that the devil must be, to use a Scotch phrase, a bogey to scare bairns.

On a higher intellectual level are the Calvinists, who still exist, with their emphasis upon predestination. This is a truth but a mystery: God leaves the will free, but His foreknowledge—a foreknowledge that has reference only to ourselves—confirms that what He has seen from all eternity will be done by the free will. He does not say to one arbitrarily, "You are for hell" and to another, "But you, my lucky fellow, are for heaven." The concept of Calvinism works havoc because it tends to induce despair among those—often the finer and more sensitive people (the poet Cowper was one of them)—who cannot believe that they have been selected for bliss; on the other hand, it also induces pride among those—usually the coarser grained—who have been able to persuade themselves that they are among the elect. This frame of mind has been described in a quatrain which has been attributed to Dean Swift but which bears all the marks of having been produced by a wit of a later age. Whoever its author, it is worth quoting:

> We are the chosen few,
> All others will be damned;
> There'll be no place for you—
> We can't have heaven crammed.

As a recoil against Calvinism, there arose the Unitarian and Universalist protests, which in New England in their inception were hardly more than a recoil against the doctrine officially held at that time by the entrenched Congregationalism. Universalism has been said to have maintained that man was inherently too good to be damned, whereas Unitarianism maintained that God was too good to damn anybody. Or as the *Rubaiyat* puts it, "He's a good fellow, and 'twill all be well." [5] The result comes to the same thing, so that Universalism has no longer any reason to exist as a separate body, and Unitarianism has gone further and further along the path of ridding itself of such vestiges of Chris-

---

[5] The bibulous Omar Khayyám produced several neat bits of blasphemy, as where he says to God, "Man's forgiveness give and take." In a letter by G.K.C. quoted in Maisie Ward's *Return to Chesterton* (pp. 285-286), he writes, "Though Omar's position was a helpless, useless one, and he knew it himself, he was not a bad man. In his poetry there is no inhuman note, no touch of coarseness, of cruelty, of arrogance, of selfishness, of coldness of heart, or any uncharitableness. He felt gently, even beautifully, towards the race for which he could do nothing: for whom he had no gospel except resignation and wine.... That drunken, disreputable old wine-bibber, his 'robe of honor' in tatters, the flagon in his hand, sitting on the ground was a profoundly religious man. He was one of those who cannot get out of the Presence."

tianity as it once possessed. I am sorry to speak so harshly of people so eminently respectable and so distinguished, but I am afraid that their denial (or any denial) of the reality of hell is vulgar in a way that would shock them if they realized it. The Catholic Church for its part does not declare that many people go to hell, for it admits that it simply does not know. The story is of course mythical that an urbane Cardinal once explained, "Yes, hell does exist—but there is nobody there." A true story is that of the poet John Banister Tabb preaching at a children's Mass at Richmond. He told them: "My dear children, of all of God's creatures the only one we positively know to be damned is the devil. But let me remind you, that though the devil is damned, he is no damned fool." One of the devil's most serviceable devices is, as Baudelaire remarked, to get people to believe that there is no devil, that there is no hell. For he is not only the enemy of God but the enemy of what is most like God—man.

Its conviction that hell exists may be the most dreadful of the Church's doctrines, but it must be accepted as an integral part of its teaching. Catholicism will have no dainty eclecticism; one must take revelation in its entirety. It is simply foolish to reject any article of the Faith on the ground that it is unappealing or rather harrowing to the feelings. If one cannot believe, one is a heretic, but perhaps with the extenuation that has been mentioned—that the soul is unenlightened. For those who say they accept the Christian revelation, there is no excuse, for an unequivocal belief in hell was advanced by Christ. This much, however, might be added: it is only those who love God—whether in the sense of *amor* or *delectio*—who really fear hell; they fear it not so much because of its pangs as because it means the eternal loss of God.

> The goad is pressed
> To make me seek—because I seek—
> His breast.

Later on, we will discuss confession, the means by which the sinner may be restored to God. Here it is enough to say that provided the penitence is perfect, confession can be a virtual guarantee against the loss of one's soul, if it comes just before death.

Christ told His disciples that the sins they forgave would be forgiven by God, and the sins that they retained would also be
retained. It stands to reason that this was not intended to apply
to the handful to whom He gave this commission but to the
Church which He was at that moment instituting as something
against which the gates of hell would never prevail.[6] Except for
schismatics and perhaps the High Anglicans, no such authority is
so much as claimed by non-Catholic bodies, and certainly not
by any of the Protestant denominations with whom we come into
contact. Even if any of them suddenly decided to exercise it,
they would be at a loss as to how to proceed for lack of experience. Gross and obvious breaches of the Ten Commandments
they would of course reprehend, without recognizing that such
sins are usually due to frailty rather than malice; but the spiritual
sins of pride and envy and avarice and the like, they often con-
done.

In addition the Catholic Church has to deal with breaches of
its own law—such as the deliberate failure to attend Mass on
Sundays and holy days of obligation or the observance of the
prescribed days of fasting and abstinence. Canon Law is for the
greater part a means of implementing God's word, but it also
contains a good many disciplinary regulations that could be
changed at any time and which, even now, do not universally
apply. This is not merely a question of administration; the laws
the Church itself imposes are made binding under pain of grave
sin. In this it acts by the authority conferred by Christ.

In general it may be said that the Church, without deviating a
hair's breadth from its principles, has during the course of history
become much more lenient, in some ways, than it was at first
when the penances imposed were severe beyond modern comprehension. A hundred-days public penance, or even one of a
lifetime, could be imposed; and there were some (of whom
Tertullian is an instance, but by no means the last of them) who
took the extreme position that some grave sins committed after
baptism could not be remitted by the Church but only by God.

[6] This does not mean that the Church cannot in this or that country be
exterminated, for this happened in Scandinavia, and may happen elsewhere,
but that the Church throughout the world can never fail.

The result was that many people postponed baptism until they were on the point of death. There can be no doubt that the early Christians would consider Catholics of recent centuries as rather lax.

All this may help to explain the misunderstandings surrounding indulgences. That indulgences came to be abused—not by the Church itself, but by individual preachers of indulgences (of whom Tetzel was the most notorious example) cannot be denied. Most non-Catholics now recognize that an indulgence has never been thought of as a permission to commit sin, or even as a pardon from sin, but indulgences are still not always fully understood, even by Catholics. The theory behind them must therefore be explained.

The doctrine briefly is this: the treasury of merits—primarily the work of Christ but added to by countless saints—is infinite, and, with so much available, the Church is very free-handed, as it can well afford to be. Why have so incalculably large a reserve and not draw upon it, especially as it is being augmented daily more than it can be depleted? An indulgence has a judicial nature, for the Church has attached to relatively insignificant acts or prayers a much wider degree of satisfaction than might be expected. The latest edition of the *Raccolta*, which was issued in 1950 and has not yet been translated into English, gives (to pick almost at random) a three years' indulgence for the sign of the cross, and seven when it is made with holy water. For the silent ejaculation of "My Lord and my God!" at the elevation or during exposition of the Blessed Sacrament, there are also seven years, with a plenary indulgence once a week if it is said daily and one confesses, communicates and prays for the intentions of the Pope. Many ejaculations, which may be said of course as often as one pleases, give from three hundred to five hundred days. The daily reading of scripture for fifteen minutes is evaluated at three years; mental prayer for the same length of time, five years; and the teaching of catechism for twenty minutes, three years. There are so many indulgences—for the saying of the rosary, for making the stations of the cross, for the wearing of certain specified medals and scapulars and for the performance of what are for most Catholics ordinary acts, that even those of very moderate piety are bound to receive a great many—more, if reckoned by their time value, than such people have time to live. To gain them, it is not necessary to remember just what the indulgences are but to have a general intention of obtaining them. But once again, it *is* necessary that one be in a state of grace.

Does this mean that he who wins such indulgences for himself will have his period in purgatory shortened by the total amount of the indulgences credited to him? That is not the point; what is meant is that, thanks to the satisfactional value attached to indulgences by the Church, he has performed the equivalent of what had to be done in the old days of severe and often public penance. And a plenary indulgence, which completely remits *up to that moment* all that might have been formerly exacted, may be obtained in a single hour—indeed sometimes in five minutes—if all the conditions are fulfilled. While one can transfer the satisfactional value of none of this to the living, who are able to obtain their own indulgences, one can transfer some of the indulgences one obtains (or all of them) to the souls in purgatory, sure that this generosity to them will be equaled by their thankfulness. Some people may think that it is rather a small mind that fastens upon this one privilege and goes about intent on scooping up indulgences all the time, but the privilege is so immense that for this alone it would be worth being a Catholic. Actually, however, nobody ever thinks of indulgences as more than an "extra dividend." Yet it is about this relatively minor corollary of the Christian mysteries that there has been perhaps the greatest amount of non-Catholic misapprehension.

The early severity of the Church, as compared with its increasing mildness, may be to some extent accounted for on the ground that most of the first Christians were Jewish, and the Jews had always been a "stiff-necked" people. As for the pagan converts, the world they had lived in was so corrupt, and they had themselves grown up to take its licentiousness so for granted, that discipline had to be all the more stringent to keep them under control. Yet this cannot be the whole explanation, as the severity continued long past the apostolic age and was maintained into the early middle ages, when Christendom was united in its faith. Even then the treasury of indulgences that could have been

drawn upon was vast; yet a plenary indulgence was given only
for some such toilsome and expensive deed as a pilgrimage to the
Holy Land or one of the great shrines. It was considered un-
precedented when the Pope acceded to the request of St. Francis
of Assisi for the Portiuncula indulgence. Yet at that time the rigor
of fasts was already much softened and the penances exacted for
positive sins were relatively light.[7] The temper of Catholic government, so far as these externals are concerned, has grown
progressively mild. What must be understood, however, is that
it is as strict as ever when it is a question of defending matters
of faith, but that it deals gently with sins, so long as they are
sincerely repented.

We are concerned here with the Church as the Christian knows
it upon earth, the Mother who teaches and protects and guides
him towards his salvation, or what is called the Church Militant.
When anyone speaks of the Church, it is this division of it that
ordinarily comes to mind. He is aware of the other two divisions,
but they are invisible and may be even to his mind a little in-
distinct. These other sections, which together with the Church
Militant constitute the *Una Sancta,* are the Church Suffering, or
the souls in purgatory, and the Church Glorified or Triumphant,
those in the bliss of paradise. Those in purgatory can be assisted
by those on earth, and may be able to do much for those who
pray for them, although the main help of this nature comes from
the saints and angels. But they being pure spirits and never
having needed Christ's redemption, do not form part of the
Church, closely concerned though they are with its good.

More will be said about these divisions of the One Holy Church
in the proper place. The Church as it is on earth, in all its perils,
its struggles and achievements and the all too common human
failings of its members, is quite as much a part of the Mystical
Body of Christ as are the other divisions. The good of all its
members is, at least to some extent, dependent upon the rest of
its members. "When one member suffers all suffer with it," for it

[7] Yet public penances were still sometimes imposed in the case of notorious public crimes—as when Henry II, King of England, had to submit to a
scourging in Canterbury Cathedral for the murder of Thomas à Becket. And
penances for private sins were still stiff, even though they were getting less
severe.

constitutes a living entity in which every Christian plays a vital part.

One section of the Church Militant is the *ecclesia docens,* those with authority to teach. For several centuries this authority was virtually restricted to the bishops. We learn from the stern decree of the Fourth Lateran Council of 1215 that the bishops were often unable to carry out this duty effectively and sometimes neglected it, which was why the friars were so actively encouraged by the Holy See.[8] St. Jerome had said, "The duty of a monk is to weep, not to teach," though it must be said that subsequently monks did magnificent missionary work and that Benedictines were the apostles of England and Germany. This, however, was only because of special circumstances; when the need had been met they withdrew to their cloisters. Many of the diocesan clergy in medieval times did not have the requisite learning to do more than read homilies to their flocks, though we can see from the specimens that have come down to us that these were usually excellent and almost always full of scripture. It was really not until the devastation of the Black Death, which hit the clergy with special force, that many poorly qualified men had to be ordained, any priest being regarded as better than none. Yet Milton did not have in mind the Catholic clergy of sixteenth-century England—who compared very favorably in learning and morals with the clergy of any other country in Europe—but the Protestant clergy of his own time, when he called them "blind mouths" and said, "The hungry sheep look up and are not fed." In our own time the press has become almost as important a teaching instrument as is the pulpit; but it will always be true that, whatever the medium, the instruction of the faithful rests upon the bishop and those whom the bishop appoints for the purpose.

Even so, the chief obligation of the priesthood is the saying of Mass and the administering of the sacraments. And here the aids to the spiritual life are so infinite that one is almost tempted to think that preaching is of little importance, which is far from being true. Faith comes from hearing, and hearing from the word

[8] The bishops are still the chief teachers, but they are now able to delegate most of this work to their diocesan clergy.

of God—not merely the written scriptures but the oral exposition of doctrine, which was what the Apostle had in mind. While faith may also be furthered by the written word, this is in large part an extension of the word that is spoken. The Church remains the teaching Church.

The aids to salvation, some of which have already been indicated, with more still to be touched on, are so varied and so vast, that one might suppose that it would be rather difficult for any soul to be lost. So in fact it would be, if each person gave even a fair amount of attention to his salvation. To reach heaven one must belong to the Church, but one must also be in a state of grace at the time of death. The Church can do a great deal to help this be attained, but it cannot carry its members skywards willy-nilly without some degree of co-operation. In the last analysis the matter rests upon each individual; that is why we are warned that we must work out our salvation with fear and trembling.

There are a few Protestants of the old-fashioned school who sometimes accuse the Church of making Catholics overscrupulous by teaching that no man can be sure of his salvation but must pray for the grace of final perseverance. One may say in reply to this, that while Catholics may occasionally be too conscientious and worry themselves to a shadow over trifles, at least they trust in God, knowing the riches at their disposal. Faith cannot be exactly equated with this trust, but it can be said that the trust springs from faith. While the *opera salvifica* of charity is also necessary, it is more true of Catholics than of Protestants that they may be said to be saved by their faith. As St. Francis Xavier, dying on Sancian Island within sight of the China he was never to enter, murmured with his last breath the last lines of the *Te Deum*, we too may say, "In Thee, O Lord, have I confided; may I never be confounded."

# CHAPTER THREE

## *The Sacraments*

A sacrament is an outward and visible sign and cause of an inward and invisible grace. In other words, the "sign" indicates something more important: the operation of the grace imparted by it. There are seven sacraments of the Church—Baptism, Confirmation, the Holy Eucharist, Penance (or as it is commonly known, Confession), Extreme Unction, Matrimony and Holy Orders. As I have previously indicated, I shall omit Holy Orders, and Matrimony will be treated in a separate chapter.

The dissident churches of the East assert all seven sacraments, and confer them all validly. The sacraments of non-Catholic bodies—such as the High Anglicans, who cling to Catholic sacramental ideas at variance with the official doctrine of the Protestant Episcopalianism of which they form a section—may be occasions of grace, even though they have no objective validity. Baptism and Matrimony are, of course, exceptions. Baptism may be administered by anybody, clerical or lay, man or woman, including unbelievers, as long as the intention is present of doing what the Church prescribes. As for Matrimony, though Protestantism has reduced it to a "rite," it remains in the eyes of the Catholic Church a sacrament even for Protestants, if both parties to the marriage are validly baptized. The ministers of the sacrament in this case are the contracting parties.[1]

Another point to bear in mind from the outset is that all of the sacraments confer grace *ex opere operato* and not *ex opere operantis*. This means that they do not depend for validity upon the

---

[1] The idea seems to prevail that the Church does not recognize non-Catholic marriages. So far from that, it recognizes as valid any kind of legal marriage, with the exception of a marriage at which a priest does not officiate, when those being married (or one of them) belong to the Church.

interior dispositions of the one who administers them. Wycliffe revived the Donatist heresy of the fourth century in maintaining that, unless a priest was in the state of grace, the sacraments he dispensed were of no avail. Obviously such a doctrine completely undermines all confidence in the sacraments that are received. To take what may be an extreme case, the penitent, before he could be assured of the worth of the absolution he hoped to obtain, would first have to get the confessor to make a confession to him! But as Father Martindale puts its, the sacraments, in addition to being signs of spiritual grace, "cause and confer what they signify." [2]

Christ could, of course, have chosen some other means of sanctification than the sacraments, but this happens to be the means He did choose. It is clearly the one best suited to human needs, because it makes evident by some material medium or some spoken words (or both) the immense good imparted. Since the sacraments have a very real relation to His own Incarnation, there is nothing of a "magical" nature about them, as is sometimes alleged by the more coarse-grained critics of Christianity and even, as in the change that occurs in the bread and wine of Mass, by some Protestants. One may mildly point out that if the officiating priest uses magic at the Consecration, then it inescapably follows that Christ Himself was performing magic when, at the Last Supper, He said, "This is My body," "This is My blood." That He meant this quite literally is evident from the fact that He had previously given great scandal to some who had formerly been among His followers by telling them, "Unless you eat My flesh and drink My blood, you cannot have life in your souls."

Nevertheless, it must be said that, incalculably conducive though this is to salvation, it is not, strictly speaking, in every instance absolutely essential to that end. The same is true of the rest of the sacraments, with the exception of Baptism, for obviously a person may be saved without having received Holy Orders or Matrimony; so also with regard to Confirmation and Extreme Unction, and even Penance, though for those who have reached the age of reason at least private repentance of sin is a requisite to admission to heaven.

[2] *The Sacramental System*, p. 25.

Baptism is the greatest day in the Christian's life, not only because it has the effect of cleansing the soul from sin—original sin, in the case of children, and actual sin as well, in the case of adults—but because it is an incorporation into the Mystical Body, the conferring of sonship and the making of the baptized coheirs with Christ. One can receive none of the other sacraments unless one has first received baptism. This, like Holy Orders and Confirmation, sets an indelible mark upon the soul. These sacraments therefore can never be repeated, though the grace which they confer may be lost.

One might go a little further. Nuns are sometimes called the "brides of Christ"; but this is no more than a fashion of speaking, for this marriage is only analogous, unless it be in the case of a few saints, such as Catherine of Siena and Rose of Lima, whom we hear of as having had a "mystical" marriage and of wearing thereafter a ring, given by Christ, invisible to all except themselves. But the souls of all the baptized may have a bridal relation to Christ, along with the sonship to God which can be claimed with less presumption, as it is a plain and solid fact and not a mere figure of speech. The imagery that the great mystic St. John of the Cross used in his famous poem "The Obscure Night of the Soul," while primarily applying to exalted mystical experience, has at least a secondary meaning that falls within the experience of many Christians. If St. John could say that they have not only the relationship of a bride to Christ but that Christ can also have the relationship of a bride to them, that too gives a further application of the nuptial imagery of this poem as translated from the Spanish by Arthur Symons. From it I quote two stanzas.

> Upon my flowery breast
> Wholly for Him, and save Himself for none,
> There did I give sweet rest
> To my belovèd one;
> The fanning of the cedars breathed thereon. . . .
>
> All things I then forgot,
> My cheek on Him who for my coming came;
> All ceased, and I was not—
> Leaving my cares and shame
> Among the lilies, and forgetting them.

Baptism requires for its valid administration the pouring of water over the head, and other liquids, even when water is not available, are not permissible. Moreover the correct formula is necessary, the one given by Christ, by which baptism is given in the name of the Father and the Son and the Holy Ghost. Ordinarily the water is poured while the words are spoken, but immersion was fairly general during the early days of the Church and is still the mode employed by some of the Eastern Rites in communion with the Holy See.

In addition to the baptism by water, two other forms must be mentioned—that by blood and that by desire. The first of these is probably now rather infrequent, but it may be presumed that, as during the persecution in the Roman Empire, so now in China some catechumens are sent to martyrdom before baptism can be conferred. Of more immediate concern to those living in civilized countries is baptism by desire, which is the sincere wish to conform to God's will and to do all that the Church (as they understand it) ordains. Nobody knows how many such baptisms occur, but it can be said positively that they can remit sin, actual or original, if the person who receives baptism by desire corresponds with the actual grace of God, makes an act of supernatural faith, and is truly repentant for any sins he may have committed. Moreover, the Church allows that such a baptism may be by a desire which is implicit as well as by a desire that is explicit. It ventures no opinion on a particular case, as this is something known only to God, but we may be sure that, great as is the hope the Church holds out, the mercy of God is even greater.

If a convert has not been baptized before he is received into the Church, he is baptized with the full solemnity of the rite. But if he can be sure that there was no possible flaw in his baptism,[3] as was true of the late Robert Hugh Benson, whose baptism had been administered by his father, the Archbishop of Canterbury, in this instance in perfect conformity with that of Catho-

[3] Anybody may baptize in an emergency, and nurses in a hospital are taught how to do this correctly, but should the person recover, he is not baptized again, except conditionally, if any doubt remains concerning the validity of his baptism. When in an emergency a person is baptized outside the church, the ceremonies that were omitted are later supplied in the church.

lics, baptism is not administered again. When there is any question of some defect in the validity of an earlier baptism, it is administered conditionally with the preliminary formula, "If you have not been already baptized..."

It was in this way that I myself was baptized when I was received into the Church. Upon the whole I wish that I had been what is called a "born" or a "cradle" Catholic. Yet I would be an ingrate did I not fully acknowledge the imprint that the form of Protestantism in which I was brought up left upon my mind. For some people it would probably have erected a barrier never to be surmounted; in my case it made me curious to climb the barrier to see what was on the other side—and when I did...! Although the convert misses a good deal—for a Catholic childhood with its simplicity and tenderness has been cut out of his life—he may have the compensation of seeing the Catholic Church more sharply and in a clearer light than many who have never known anything else.

A final word about baptism. Although it remits the guilt of original sin, some part of the propensities of original sin remain, as most of us are only too well aware. Yet there are those who deny original sin. This does not mean that Catholicism asserts that the natural appetites—not merely sexual concupiscence but all concupiscence—themselves constitute original sin, for they are only a consequence of the disorder it has introduced into what are, in themselves, good. But original sin does implant in every human being a propensity towards satisfying these desires in a way contrary to the law of God. It is strange that so many of our moderns should reject an observable fact which ought to be as plain as the nose on the face. If logic, in the hands of some of its more desiccated practitioners, may seem a bit inhuman, it serves humanity by saving it from human absurdity. Dr. C. E. M. Joad, the well-known English philosopher, in his article "On No Longer Being a Rationalist," says: [4] "The Christian doctrine of original sin expresses a deep and essential insight into human nature. Reject it and you fall victim, as so many of us whose minds have developed in an atmosphere of Left-Wing politics and Rationalist philosophy have fallen victim, to a shallow op-

[4] *The Rationalist Annual* for 1946 (London), p. 74.

timism in regard to human nature which causes you to think that the millennium is just around the corner waiting to be introduced by perfectly psycho-analysed, prosperous Communists." Even without bringing psycho-analysts and Communists into the picture, man is only to be understood in relation to what Newman called "the aboriginal calamity" which I cannot but believe that every man, at the bottom of his heart, knows has occurred.

A few words will have to suffice for Confirmation. This sacrament is considered as the completion of baptism, though of course baptism is essential to salvation, whereas confirmation is but contributory to the same end. It makes those who receive it the soldiers of Christ, arming them for the warfare they have to endure. Among Catholics of the Eastern Rite it follows immediately after baptism and may be administered by any priest, whereas in the Latin Church its administration is normally restricted to bishops.[5] Because it is a kind of knighthood, the bishop strikes those who are receiving the sacrament lightly on the cheek. By confirmation the seven gifts of the Holy Ghost—wisdom, understanding, counsel, knowledge, fortitude, piety and the fear of the Lord—are increased in the soul. Of these gifts the first four dispose the intellect to receive and act upon the light and assistance of the Holy Ghost; while the other three do the same for the will. In the Western Church the sacrament is deferred until after the child has made both his first confession and First Communion.

Confession calls for fuller treatment. Children begin to make it when they are judged to have reached the age of reason. Before then mortal sin is impossible, and it may be that many people live a long life without incurring its guilt because the conditions from which it might stem are not present. If so, they can do no more than confess the faults and failings that nobody is without, but venial sins are not of the kind that one is obliged to confess.

What is called confession, but whose more correct name is penance, has several parts: The examination of conscience, contrition (about which more in a moment), the resolution of amendment, confession or self-accusation itself, and satisfaction or the

[5] Junipero Serra, the first missionary (and really the founder) of California, was given special permission to confirm, but this was something very unusual in his day. Since 1947 all pastors may administer confirmation, if a bishop is not available, but under certain restrictions.

performance of the penance imposed by the confessor. Further, the making of restitution may be involved—the restoration of material goods obtained by theft or fraud, but also the rectification of damage done to the reputation of another by talk. This, however, is demanded only in so far as it is possible.

The priest, who sits as Christ's representative, has to judge whether the confession made is "good." If he suspects that something is being held back, he may question the penitent. However, it is hard to see how any properly instructed Catholic would deliberately conceal sins that he had committed, as he knows that under such circumstances even the sins he had confessed would remain on his soul (with the sin of sacrilege added) even if the confessor pronounced the formula of absolution. Priests have so much experience that they are not easily imposed upon; they can tell pretty accurately from the demeanor of the penitent whether he is being open and whether he has the necessary disposition for the confessional. Far more often than he is questioned, the penitent is told to mention some sin of his past life, if no real matter for absolution can be found in what he has just said.

This does not mean that few mortal sins are committed, for such is notoriously not the case. Yet moral theologians hold that many acts which are in themselves materially sinful do not have the weight of mortal sin because of a lack of full deliberation and malice. We might remember Pascal's comment that, "There are only two kinds of men: the righteous, who believe themselves sinners; the rest, sinners, who believe themselves righteous." For both classes the sacrament of penance exists; if the righteous receive it more often than others, this is because they wish to be pardoned immediately of even their venial sins; and great sinners, when they can be brought to repentance, find in the sacrament a cleansing not otherwise to be obtained.

Mr. Leslie D. Weatherhead, the present minister of the City Temple in London, argues that the commission of Christ to the Apostles was rather to an indeterminate number of disciples (we hear of Jesus sending out seventy of them to preach on one occasion). According to Mr. Weatherhead the commission to bind and loose means no more than that any Christian (male or female, clerical or lay) is simply to judge whether the repentance is "sincere." Are such fanciful notions, even when tossed out by such a charming man as Mr. Weatherhead manifestly is, to be taken seriously? Who would submit himself to the judgment of such a tribunal? Who except the censorious would undertake to judge? It is true that the Blessed Virgin and other women are mentioned as having been present when the Holy Ghost descended. But not even Mary possessed any sacerdotal powers, although the great service of women in the building up of the early Church has been several times acknowledged.

Nobody, of course, enjoys going to confession, any more than people enjoy going to the dentist. Nevertheless, one may thank God for dentists as well as for priests. It was only as part of their program for reducing the power of the clergy that Protestantism rejected confession. It was open to them to have retained it for their ministers, though it goes without saying that no absolution except that given by a priest would have any value. Yet even without this absolution Protestants have often tried to reintroduce confession in disguise, for it is at least a great relief to the mind—a fact which to some extent accounts for the vogue of psychoanalysis.

An example of what I have in mind occurs in a letter that Charlotte Brontë wrote to her sister Emily while she was living in Brussels. One day when she was in Sainte Gudule's Church, as she watched the penitents going into the box, she felt impelled to do the same. As she did not know the formula, she explained to the priest that she was a foreigner and a Protestant, upon which he told her that as such she could not go to confession. However, at her insistence he let her make her confession, but of course said that he could give her no absolution. Charlotte supposed that he hoped that this would prove the first step in her conversion, but more probably he was merely willing that she should have the subjective good that might be derived from unburdening her soul. Charlotte tried to pass off the incident to Emily as a "freak," but it is evident from the tone of her words that it was a good deal more than that.

The case of the Buchmanites, or as they now prefer to style themselves, the Oxford Groups or Moral Rearmament, is another illustration of the point. Their practice of making public confessions of their sins—and in gatherings of both sexes—smacks of exhibitionism. But though healthy-minded people cannot approve, here too may be seen a desire for getting rid of sin by the process of confessing it. It is different with the confessions made, so I understand, among Alcoholics Anonymous, for these are not so much a confession of sin as the admission of a pathological condition, which their experience has led them to believe necessary as a preliminary to rehabilitation. If they aim at anonymity, they will find it in the Catholic confessional, where absolute secrecy is the rule; without it the penitent would have no confidence that his sins (some of which might be punishable under secular law) would not become known. As the words of the *Confiteor* make perfectly plain, it is primarily to God that the confession is made.

It is Catholic teaching that even mortal sins are remitted by a private act of perfect contrition, though the obligation remains of making confession to a priest as soon as opportunity serves. In Catholic hospitals Protestants are often helped to make a perfect act of contrition, usually by being given a card which directs them what to do. Even the humble cry, "My Jesus, mercy!" will suffice; so for that matter would the unspoken sentiment of the heart. As Christ has told us, "I did not come to call the righteous but sinners to repentance," further enforced by the parable of the Good Shepherd and the story of the Publican and the Pharisee. De Joinville has related how before an impending battle the Crusaders confessed to one another, a priest not being available. He says that the Count of Eu confessed to him and that when it was over he (De Joinville) did not have the slightest memory of what he had heard. Perhaps this was because De Joinville was a very great gentleman and did not wish to remember, but priests, too, rarely, if ever, can recall what has been said to them. For confessions come one after the other in such rapid succession and are, presumably, most of them so much alike, that no distinguishing feature remains. This is part of the reason why Catholics feel no embarrassment in meeting their confessor afterwards, though what weighs still more is that he has listened to their sins not as a man but as a priest.

Mr. Weatherhead—to come back to him again—is shocked that

the Church teaches that the absolution given by a priest does not depend upon his character and would be valid even if the priest were himself in a state of mortal sin. A moment's thought should remove the scandal: is a judge in a secular court empowered to pass sentence by virtue of his personal merits or by the authority that has been conferred upon him? Nobody will deny that a judge—whether in a secular or spiritual court—should be a good man, but whether he is or not has no bearing upon his official acts.

The confessor, while he always hopes for the perfect act of contrition—where sorrow is not because of fear of hell or the material consequences that might follow in this world but only because of having offended an infinitely good God—nevertheless will accept the imperfect act of contrition, known as attrition, in lieu of anything better. In neither case is any external exhibition of sorrow necessary; Catholicism is an unsentimental religion and looks to the will rather than to the emotions. In that tribunal the only witness is the penitent himself, and the priest is the judge. Pardon is won by the seeking of pardon, though a purpose of amendment (even if it is feeble) is looked for, and in all cases a penance is imposed. If absolution should be refused, after the priest has decided that the conditions for absolution have not been fully met, the penitent is free to go to another priest. Ordinarily, of course, there is not much sense in doing so, since another priest would be almost certain to take the same attitude. If absolution is given, it is incumbent to perform the prescribed act of penitence. Since it is ordinarily the saying of a few short prayers, these can be, and usually are, said before the penitent leaves the church.

One condition is always present. It is stated in the Lord's Prayer: "Forgive us our trespasses, as we forgive those who trespass against us." To retain an unforgiving spirit in ourselves is virtually to ask God not to forgive us. But as this is an interior disposition, the priest may not discover it, unless some chance phrase were used that led him to suspect it, in which event he would be bound to probe a little deeper. While it may be reasonable to expect an apology from those who have offended us, even when this is not forthcoming, the Christian must not bear resentment. Whatever injuries we have received, they are as nothing compared to the sins we have committed against God.

The confessor has to decide whether the sin being confessed is mortal or venial. Protestants have sometimes tended to obliterate this distinction, thus making all sins mortal in theory but, in practice, leading people to regard even mortal sins as venial. It should be obvious that there is a vast difference between, let us say, telling a "fib" that injures nobody and committing theft or murder. A large part of the confessor's duty is to weigh the gravity of the sins brought before him. A mortal sin must, in the first place, be a grave matter, and there also must be full knowledge of its gravity and yet a deliberate intention of committing it. This is the "malice" without which, even when the other two factors are present, the full guilt of mortal sin cannot exist. Though a well-instructed Catholic may have a fairly good idea about his degree of guilt, he must not indulge in self-exculpation: the sin must be presented to the confessor for his decision.

Another consideration should be borne in mind. A soul sincerely desirous of pleasing God may commit a very serious sin out of human weakness. If he repents that sin, it may have less serious effects than the habitual commission of deliberate venial sins, for which there is no real remorse. For these harden the heart and thwart the operation of grace, so that in the end mortal sins may be fallen into and left unrepented, like the venial sins that led to them. There is therefore no safety in dismissing venial sins as trifles that do not matter. What should be remembered is that temptation, however grievous, is not sin. "Count it all joy when ye fall into divers temptations," St. James tells us. And Christ Himself reassured St. Catherine of Siena about her temptations to impure imaginings; that these distressed her as much as they did was a sign that they were occasions of merit.

Catholics are advised to go to confession frequently, and many do so every week. St. Philip Neri belonged to an age when daily communion was not at all common, but he urged his disciples to make a daily confession, and this he heard himself. Most Catholics go to confession before receiving Holy Communion, but it is not obligatory. In fact the reception of either sacrament is under the strict command of the Church only during the Easter season, and priests will tell penitents who are doubtful as to their fitness for the Eucharist to follow what amounts almost to a rule-of-thumb: Go, unless you can take an oath that you have committed a mortal sin.

Despite the fact that venial sins need not be confessed, good Catholics usually do confess them and probably in many instances never have anything worse to bring before the tribunal. The act of confession is an exercise in humility, which is always beneficial. Even more important, the sacrament not only cleanses from sin but strengthens the soul against it. The priest, like his penitent, is aware that, sincere though the purpose of amendment may be, human nature is such that the kind of sins that spring from natural weakness will in all probability be committed again. Yet these may be gradually overcome. Most of us may be unable to notice any improvement in ourselves, and may even think we are getting worse with each successive year, but there may be an improvement of which we are unaware. In any event, the struggle to do better is itself meritorious.

Protestants say that they confess their sins not to a priest but to God. Very good, if this is really done. But one suspects that such a confession in almost all instances is no more than a generalized admission of sinfulness, as it is also in the act of contrition that many Catholics make just before going to sleep. In their case a daily examination of conscience is also recommended, mainly with a view to noticing progress (or regression). While nobody has to search to discover his mortal sins, his motive may be so complicated, and so many venial sins may be glossed over, that it is well to make sure that these are acknowledged. They are later mentioned in the confessional by those who wish to eradicate them.

Dante, who flinched from nothing, shows us in the *Inferno* (Canto XXVII) Guido Count of Montefeltro among the Evil Counselors. After a political career he became a Franciscan in 1296, shortly before his death, but again gave evil counsel to Dante's favorite enemy, Pope Boniface VIII, whom the poet had earlier pictured in hell. On Guido's death St. Francis came for his soul, but this was literally snatched out of his hands by a devil who cried, "Maybe thou didst not think I was a logician!" His son, however, was in purgatory, saved by a brief act of contrition made at the very instant of death. His was a salvation like that of the man in Sir Walter Scott's poem:

> Between the saddle and the ground
> I mercy sought, and mercy found.

Nobody can possibly say how many such cases there are. But though the Church declares that one little word may suffice, it would be the utmost rashness to count upon being able to make it.

While holding out this hope—even to those who do not have the chance of making a deathbed confession to a priest—there is a warning against complacency. Catholics are not much addicted to hypocrisy or smugness, and if they do happen to be, such a frame of mind will not long survive under the scrutiny of their confessor. It may be that they are somewhat given to detraction and envy; and these, as they often spring from the belief that all souls are equally precious in the sight of God, may perhaps be described as being, in a sense, Catholic vices. Even this, however, may be too much to say, for the same thing may be observed in any democratic society, which postulates the equality of all men. At any rate, though Catholics are by no means immune from human frailty, Pharisaism is not often found among them. But overstrictness may exist and reach the pitch of a serious spiritual malady which is often difficult to deal with. For this the confessional is almost the only cure.

We have a striking instance of this disease of the soul in a pious lady of the seventeenth century who was a penitent of the famous French Oratorian Charles de Condren. Her trouble and the way he was able to remove it are described by himself. He told her: "It is true that you cannot properly express the degree of your sinfulness; but that is because it is impossible, in this life, to represent sins in all their true ugliness; nor shall we ever know them as they really are except in the light of God. God gives to some souls an impression of the enormity of sin, by which He makes them feel that some sin is incomparably greater than it seems. Such souls must conceive their sins as faith represents them (that is, as they are in themselves), but must be content to describe them in such human words as their mouth is able to utter." This kind of scrupulosity is not very common. Still rarer (if it exists at all among Catholics) is the kind of false conscience frequently met with among Protestants of the old-fashioned type. It may, however, occasionally be found among converts who have brought with them into the Church some of their former prepossessions from which they do not easily disburden themselves. What is possible to Catholic and non-Catholic alike is the opposite fault—the stifling of conscience due to repeated acts of sin. Fortunately Catholics possess a corrective to this in the confessional.

There is, nevertheless, a false application of a true principle which is not infrequently encountered. The true principle is that Catholics have a heavier obligation than Protestants, as all Christians have a heavier obligation than pagans. Christ Himself said, "Unto whom much is given, much will be required." The Church is the way to salvation, and though, for this very reason, the sins of Catholics are more serious than the sins of others, the grace of God, coming to them through so many channels, much more than makes up for the deficiencies of the sinner. If they are always liable to suffer from the effects of routine, this, like formalism, is a danger in any religion. Catholicism, it must be admitted, demands a number of prescribed acts, but it can also be trusted to correct anybody who attaches a preponderant importance to a mere external correctness. When adherents of other religions find themselves in the fatal rut, since they lack the confessional it is hard to see where they can find the necessary means of extricating themselves.

There was a stupid accusation once current among Protestants that Catholics "pay" for absolution. It was expressed, with farcical intention, in W. S. Gilbert's "Bab Ballad" about the gentle daughter of good Robber Brown who, after having confessed her little murders, is assessed: "Let's see, five crimes at half a crown—exactly twelve and six." The old charge is now recognized as completely preposterous, yet recently Mr. Blanshard has advanced it in another form. True, he says, Catholics do not pay for the forgiveness of sins directly, nevertheless in a roundabout way they pay. Masses are said for the forgiveness of sins, and Masses are paid for. Here is a new tangle of misunderstanding. In the first place, Masses are not paid for, though a customary offering is usually given—and waived in the case of anyone too poor to give even this small amount. In every Mass, which is primarily an act of worship, there are prayers for the living and dead, the Pope and the local bishop, and for the forgiveness of sins. But even the Mass, though it is Calvary itself, does not automatically pardon sins; to obtain God's pardon it is necessary to make an explicit and detailed confession of sins in the sacrament of penance.

Finally, it should be said that sins of human frailty are leniently dealt with. Spiritual sins are much more serious—in particular the sin of pride, which forms part of every sin. This sin, if it results in final impenitence, brings eternal loss. And it may be induced either by presumption, which in the last analysis is too great a trust in ourselves (though it may parade as a trust in God) or despair, which is a refusal to trust God's mercy. Never must the sinner think himself beyond all hope, in this life or with regard to the world to come. Here the confessor acts not merely as judge but as guide, the pastor of souls, a kind father who offers consolation and encouragement. Even in the decisive moment of death, his ministrations may not come too late.

Often the last of the sacraments to be conferred is Extreme Unction, always administered with the sacrament of penance, if this is possible, and also with Holy Communion which, under these circumstances, is called the Viaticum, the provision for the journey the soul is about to undertake. To one already unconscious, and even to one pronounced dead by a doctor (so long as death has only just occurred) a priest will give conditional absolution, on the ground that nobody knows how long it takes for the soul actually to leave the body. While there is any chance at all of its still being there, absolution may avail, because even after the material senses have ceased to operate, the soul may be eagerly waiting for this. The same rule applies to the giving of Extreme Unction.

This sacrament is administered only when there is a real danger of death, and in many instances it aids in recovery, even in the case of those who were considered almost certain to die. In other words it possesses curative properties for the body as well as those that are spiritual. I myself, at times separated by several years, twice received Extreme Unction, but I am still here.

It may be thought rather strange that this sacrament is never permitted to soldiers before battle, or even to those whose death is absolutely certain, those condemned to be executed. He who receives it must be ill, so ill that he is in danger of death. For others confession, Holy Communion and, if that has not been received, baptism are available. So armed, even a great criminal may have the assurance given by Christ on the cross to the good thief—"This day thou shalt be with Me in paradise." Though Extreme Unction does not guarantee salvation—as does baptism under certain circumstances—this and the other "last sacraments" give to the dying and those he leaves behind very substantial grounds for hope.

For this reason Catholics (or the best of them) are never frightened when the priest arrives to anoint them, but on the contrary are immensely consoled. Should death intervene before this has been completed, the priest will nevertheless go on with what he is doing, for the reason mentioned—that the cessation of the beating of the heart does not necessarily mean the soul has left the body. Moreover, it is a medical fact that, even under such circumstances, resuscitation occasionally takes place. Regarding the primitive existence of Extreme Unction we have the words of St. James: "Is any one among you sick? Let him call the priests of the Church, and let them pray over him, anointing him with oil in the name of the Lord. And the prayer of faith shall save the sick man, and the Lord shall raise him up; and if he have committed sins he shall be forgiven." As the Council of Trent in its decision on the point set no limits to the degree that Extreme Unction forgives sin, it may be held as certain that mortal as well as venial sins are included. There is no wonder that Catholics are always full of joy when they can record on the obituary notices they send out that their dear dead were "fortified by the last rites of the Church."

In view of all this it is somewhat surprising that this sacrament is sometimes so little appreciated. Father H. A. Reinhold, in the paper he read before the Liturgical Conference of 1941, described Extreme Unction as being the "stepchild among the sacraments in practical Catholic life today." He proceeds to cite in defence of a very different position passages from eminent theologians, most of them Jesuits. Among these are Joseph Kern, of the University of Innsbruck, from whose introduction to a Latin treatise on the subject, Father Reinhold quotes: "It is my experience that not only lay people but even priests are very much astonished, when they hear that the Sacrament of the dying was given by Christ to the Church in order that through this sacrament the faithful, after their death, might be spared the pains of purgatory and that they might be transferred to their heavenly abode without delay." Father Kern gives four reasons to account for the present state of affairs: rigorism, ignorance of the ancient Catholic tradition, overzealousness in the insistence on the doctrine of purgatory, as this had been rejected by heretics, and in the field of popular devotion and popular preaching, "a certain kind of private revelation"—by which he probably has in mind too great a reliance on the so-called promises relating to some scapulars or even the making of the Nine First Fridays. From Suarez he quotes further: "This sacrament, unless it finds an impediment, takes away all that might hinder or delay our entry into glory. . . . Nothing else has been instituted to achieve this end." Finally from a liturgical source, the *Pontificale,* he is able to cite: "May all who have been anointed with this heavenly medicine have it as a protection of mind and body, may all pains, all weakness, all sickness of mind and body be turned out through it, with which Thou hast anointed priests, kings, prophets and martyrs." Certainly nothing could be more consoling to the dying Christian who, shriven of his sins, and with the Viaticum, goes forth in his anointing, knowing that whatever else may be lacking is now supplied and that he can throw himself with confident love into the arms of God.

Upon the Sacrament of the Eucharist or Holy Communion I shall touch very briefly, for though I have received this sacrament far more often even than that of Penance, I dare not say much because of my consciousness of my own inadequacy.

Maisie Ward in her recent *Return to Chesterton* says of G. K. C. that when he went to confession he was sorry not only for his sins but for the negligence of the confession he made, for his wild and active mind speculatively wandered far afield regarding every sin upon which he tried to fix his attention. So also with Holy Communion. *Lord I am not worthy* he felt to be a prayer made especially for him. "He had all the longing and wonder, but only humility could give him courage." The Jansenists discouraged frequent communion not through humility but the pride always discernible in them. Who *can* be really worthy of receiving the Lord's Body? But we can begin to be a little less unworthy by daring to welcome Christ in Holy Communion. This is so overwhelming a matter that I do not find words a mortal man can use. In intimate union with Christ we sup with Him and He sups with us, each of us simultaneously both host and guest.

We can see why St. Thomas Aquinas called this the "greatest" of sacraments, for by it Christ, really and truly and not under any symbol or figure, gives Himself to us, and through His coming confers the richest of graces. Well might St. John Chrysostom say: "What is the bread? It is the Body of Christ. What becomes of those who eat thereof? They become the Body of Christ—not many bodies, but one Body. For just as many single grains of wheat are so molded into one mass that the grains can no longer be seen, so are we joined with one another and with Christ to form one Body . . . for we all partake of one and the same Body—the Body of our Lord Jesus Christ." Spiritual goods, when shared, so far from being diminished, are increased. As Alice Meynell has written in one of her poems:

> A thousand single central daisies they,
> A thousand of the one;
> For each, the entire monopoly of day;
> For each, the whole of the devoted sun.

Setting aside for the moment all consideration of the Real Presence, it will surely have to be conceded that, with the possible exception of a few High Anglicans, only Catholics give to Holy

Communion anything that begins to approach its true importance.[6] The dissident Eastern Churches have a validly consecrated priesthood and therefore a genuine Mass, but among them Communion is only rarely administered. For that matter, apart from the early Church, it was administered relatively rarely, even in religious houses, until Pius X (now beatified) so strongly recommended frequent and even daily Communion. Moreover, until his pronouncement, First Communion did not come until after a child's twelfth birthday. Now in practice there is no lengthy separation between confession and first Communion— it follows as soon as reason has been attained. For confirmation he has to wait a few years longer, so that he can be instructed still further. The day of his first Holy Communion is—so the phrase runs—the happiest day of the child's life. So it is, objectively, in most cases; but whether it is so subjectively is a question. A priest would say that his greatest day is that of his ordination. I would be inclined to say that the greatest day in the life of a Christian is that of his baptism, but purely objectively, as by the great majority it is received in infancy.

It must be striking—and should be edifying—to a Protestant who happens to be present at Mass to see how many people crowd to the altar rails after the *Domine non sum dignus*. On any Sunday (except for the few late Masses, and even at these there are usually a few communicants) such crowds press up "to receive" that whenever another priest is available he comes forward to assist the celebrant. And on great feasts the distribution of Holy Communion takes almost as long as the Mass itself. Some people go to Communion every day, or at least now and then during the week, and more would do so were it not that they are prevented by their occupations. Nor do their occupations deter all of these. At the church of the Franciscans on

[6] As I write these words I read in the daily paper of a group of about 300 people of the congregation of the Episcopalian cathedral of Long Island protesting to the bishop that Communion is given each week instead of once a month—which they consider obnoxiously "high." But of course it is not of primary importance as to *how often* this service is celebrated—for some strongly Protestant bodies, among them the Plymouth Brethren, celebrate it every Sunday—but what significance is attached to it.

West Thirty-first Street in New York City, for instance, where a noon Mass is said daily, a surprising number will be found who have gone to their offices fasting in the morning and who use their lunch hour for Mass and Communion, taking a hurried sandwich and a cup of coffee afterwards.

This rule of fasting, by the way, is disciplinary and may be dispensed under certain circumstances. It does not hold for soldiers in the field of battle, nor does it apply to the sick in hospitals. At Christmas, when Mass is said at midnight, the faithful are advised to abstain from all food and drink for several hours before they frequent the Lord's Table, but they are not commanded to do so. If the Church today may sometimes seem to be making many disciplinary concessions, these are all slight and gradual. In any event they are made only for the good of souls.

An organization which is used to attract men to Holy Communion is the Holy Name Society. It was founded in the Middle Ages under Dominican auspices to promote reverence for God, especially by the avoidance of profane language. Now in the United States, where it has by far its strongest membership, it exists as a parochial organization—though I believe with a Dominican as national director. While its original purpose has not been forgotten, it also serves as a means for organizing a monthly Communion, a somewhat similar sodality existing for those who are sometimes called the "pious sex." Yet even without this spur a large number of men and women go to Communion much more frequently than once a month. It is a quite common thing to find those who go at least weekly. Whatever the shortcomings of American Catholics may be—and sometimes those of the Eastern Rite, perhaps smarting under misunderstanding, accuse them of having a "businesslike religion"—so far as my observation extends, they seem to me to compare very well with the Catholics of any other country, with the possible exception of Ireland.

What draws all these people to Holy Communion? Precisely the same thing that draws them to Mass, at which many of those who for some reason or another are unable to approach the altar rail will make what is called a spiritual communion. This means that although they do not actually receive the Host, they will express to Christ their love for Him and their desire to receive Him. It is because Christ is present at Mass, in as completely real a sense as He was present on the cross, God and Man, that they worship Him, consummating that Sacrifice, which is never offered without at least the priest communicating, by making, when they are unable actually to communicate, a spiritual communion.

It is not part of my purpose formally to expound Catholic doctrine, but some explanations are unavoidable, and these may sometimes seem to be of a controversial tone. I therefore merely remark that our Protestant friends might be invited to read again the sixth chapter of St. John's gospel. It is beyond my comprehension how a symbolical meaning can possibly be attached to the words of the Upper Room, "This is My body," "This is My blood," when we hear of Christ's saying some time before this, not only to the disciples but to the "fringe" that so often accompanied the twelve, "Except ye Eat the flesh of the Son of Man, and drink His blood, ye have no life in you." Some of those who heard Him use these words were scandalized and some of them "walked no more with Him." Let me ask a simple question: What would friends who had been startled by such a remark have the right to expect? What else than that the speaker should elaborate on what he had said so that misunderstandings should be removed? Anything less would have been unfair and unkind. It is clear that there was no misunderstanding whatever: "My flesh is meat indeed, and My blood is drink indeed."

One question may reasonably be asked: Why is the Cup refused to the laity? This was a sore point with some of the sixteenth-century reformers. But if the Cup is not given to the laity in the Western Church, this is only as a matter of discipline based on convenience. It is held not to be strictly necessary, as the consecrated Host contains the whole Christ, His divinity as well as His humanity, His Blood as well as His Body. Nevertheless among the Eastern Rite Catholics, there is communion in both kinds, and Catholics of the Western Rite are encouraged to attend an Eastern Rite church now and then, and to receive

Holy Communion as it is given there.[7] This is a means of emphasizing the unity that exists in diversity. In whatever form Holy
Communion is received the words of St. Augustine, put by him
into the mouth of Christ, should be remembered: "I am the food
of the strong; have faith and eat Me. But thou wilt not change
Me into thyself; it is thou who will be transformed into Me."

Where St. Augustine is mystical in his statement (though the
word "mystical" must not be understood as excluding the dogmatic), St. Thomas Aquinas was purely dogmatic in the stanza
of his *Adoro Te*—one of the rare specimens of his massive and
masculine verse—in which he wrote:

> *Visus, tactus, gustus in Te fallitur,*
> *Sed auditu solo tuto creditur:*
> *Credo quidquid dixit Dei Filius:*
> *Nil hoc veritatis Verbo verius.*[8]

The only one of the five senses that St. Thomas does not mention is that of smell, and though some of the saints have declared
that the consecrated Host has sometimes given off an exquisite
odor, this may be merely subjective; in any event it does not
matter as the Host ordinarily gives out no odor at all, and so is
outside the argument. But that the rest of the senses perceive
nothing whatever, makes faith all the stronger. Catholic belief
in the Eucharist depends on nothing but Christ's word. Let God
be true and every man a liar.

[7] This is expressly laid down in Canon Law (canon 866). As Donald
Attwater points out in his *Catholic Churches of the East* (Vol. I, p. 21) the
only limitations that there are restrict the members of each rite to the making
of Easter duties according to the rite to which they belong "if possible" and
also the reception of the last sacraments.

[8] Sight, touch and taste in Thee fall short. By hearing only safely is
believed. I believe whatever the Son of God hath said. Naught can be truer
than the Word.

# CHAPTER FOUR

## *Marriage*

A separate chapter is given to this sacrament not because it is greater than the others (for it is not) but because of its special importance in the lives of most lay persons. It is not for all men and women, although it is for the overwhelming majority.[1] In the Western Church a vow of celibacy has to be taken before the subdiaconate is conferred; among Catholics of the various Eastern Rites marriage can take place before the diaconate is conferred. If a priest's wife dies, however, he is not permitted to marry again, and only celibates are appointed to the episcopate. That some of the Apostles were married is evident from the second Epistle to the Corinthians (ix.5) in which St. Paul asks: "Have we not power to lead about a sister, a wife, as well as other apostles, and as the brethren of the Lord, and Cephas." But gradually clerical celibacy, which, it must be remembered, is only a disciplinary regulation, was enforced over the whole Western Church. There is, however, no necessary connection between priesthood and celibacy, and if the marriage of the higher clergy is now not only illicit but invalid, this is because the Church has made it so.

There is an idea in some quarters (even among poorly instructed Catholics) that the sin of the fall was sexual intercourse between Adam and Eve, which would suppose that the Old Testament author had a sudden attack of squeamishness never shown elsewhere and so used the euphemism of the apple. The fact, of course, is that it was for marriage that Adam and Eve

---

[1] This does not mean that most of those who marry are going to find happiness, for it is common knowledge that a large proportion of them do not. If so, this is almost always their own fault, and even when it is not, marriage may still be their vocation, in the sense that through this state in life they may attain the spiritual good that God intended for them.

had been created. Moreover, gravely sinful as are the relations of the sexes outside of marriage, even in their case the sexual act remains one of the noblest *natural* acts that human beings can perform.[2] But in the brute creation there can be no marriage but only mating, even among such animals who, obeying the law of their creation, keep to the same partners. On the other hand, marriage, which is possible only among human beings, may rise far above the natural order, though always based upon it, to the sublime elevation of a sacrament. Christ's presence turned water into wine, and though the wine of that miracle was of course natural wine, it typified the supernatural element in marriage. God's blessing upon marriage was the only one of the specific privileges not lost at the time of the fall.

Nevertheless, we must remember that the state of virginity, or of celibacy after the loss of virginity, is placed by the Church even higher than that of marriage. Here the Church is not quite alone. Virginity was venerated even among pagans, as witness the Vestal Virgins. Yet G. K. Chesterton, writing his *Orthodoxy* in 1906, when he was not as yet a Catholic though close to the Church, said that virginity was one of the flowers of his Father's garden whose full beauty he was not at that time able to perceive, though he thought he might do so at any moment. Another Anglican, that strange tortured genius John Donne, in his *Paradoxes and Problems* says of virginity that it is to be praised only if it exists before marriage, but that if it is preserved with the intention of keeping it "perpetual," it becomes a "most inhuman vice." Well, even that was something in the corrupt seventeenth century, if it is fair to call one century corrupt when all produce a number of very immoral people. Donne's, it need hardly be said, is not the Catholic view; to begin with, virginity is a positive not a negative virtue and, if preserved from a religious motive, is of the highest excellence. While this is best done under a formal vow, which is also its strongest protection,

---

[2] This of course is also true of animals, who glorify God in all that they do, as they are unable to do anything not in accord with their nature. Tennyson recoiled in sensitive horror from "nature red in tooth and claw." Well, I, like the little boy in Belloc's poem, would detest it were I eaten "bit by bit" by a lion; but the lion could not be justly blamed, any more than I am at fault when I eat an oyster.

it remains a virtue even in the case of those who feel no call to the religious life. In our days, for the first time in the history of the world, a considerable number of women are virgins—or at any rate remain unmarried—by force of circumstances. These need not repine but can make of their condition, though it is involuntary, a cause of merit. Others remain celibate because they prefer that state. Dr. Johnson delivered the massive dictum, "Marriage has some pains, but celibacy has no pleasures"; but the avoidance of pain is itself akin to pleasure. An enforced celibacy should still be looked upon as a vocation, and vocation is what matters.

Sometimes Catholics talk and write in such a way as almost to give the impression that only priests and nuns and brothers have a vocation. As against this it should be remembered, first, that all Christians are called to be saints and, in the second place, that while most of the means of sanctification are available to all, others are very diversified, including the faithfulness of the individual to his vocation. Everybody has a vocation and (even apart from his heavenly destiny) it is only in the one into which he fits that he will be happy in this life. If celibacy is a vocation, so—one might say, still more—is marriage. Even those vowed to celibacy can be dispensed for good reason. On the other hand, the vows taken in a valid marriage are beyond the Church's jurisdiction, except to the extent that it may be asked to pronounce upon that validity. It should therefore be plain that anyone entering the state of marriage should make sure that he is called to it. Once in it, only death can release him.

Mr. Blanshard, an urbane but rather bitter bigot, nevertheless insists that those who become priests or join a religious order do so only because they have a "guilty feeling about sex." Without pressing the question how he can possibly know, one might at least ask why on earth should they have a guilty feeling. It may be true—though I doubt it—that some people are so afraid of committing a sin of this sort that they take refuge in a cloister. But a far more common case is that of Sir Thomas More, who lived in the London Charterhouse for four years while he was studying law, and who seriously considered joining the Carthusians but who gave up the plan because he feared that celibacy would prove too much for him. In later life, after he had married twice, he thought his apprehensions on this score had been exaggerated. Although occasionally—very occasionally—it happens that a celibate breaks his vow, common observation shows that what thousands of people do without any indication of strain, any person who wishes can also perform.

Christ on one occasion said that there were some who were celibates—or "eunuchs" as He termed it—for the kingdom of heaven's sake, and His implied praise was clear. And St. Paul, while praising marriage, added that not to marry was still better. He even used the grim phrase, "It is better to marry than to burn." At the same time he indicated that marriage was for the overwhelming majority of men. From the foundation of Christianity virginity was recommended, but there was no positive law about clerical celibacy until the fourth century, and its general enforcement could not be effected until still later.

The classic expositions of Christian marriage come from the same St. Paul who has sometimes been rather absurdly thought to be opposed to marriage or at least rather scornful of it. He speaks with most force at the close of the fifth chapter of his Epistle to the Ephesians. The relationship, he tells us, between husband and wife is closely analogous to that between Christ and the Church. Indeed, in sacramental marriage the wedded pair may be said to constitute a church within the Church. But lest the subjection of wives to their husbands be misunderstood, Pius XI's encyclical *Casti Connubii* says: "This subjection of wife to husband does not diminish her rights as a human being, nor make her a slave to all her husband's fancies; nor is the wife, as it were, a minor. The husband's requests must be 'in accordance with right reason and with his wife's dignity as a wife.' The rule is intended merely to secure that, in the family, the head be not separated from the heart. . . . If the man is the head and the woman is the heart, [just] as he occupies the chief place in ruling, so she may and ought to claim for herself the chief place in love. And should the husband neglect his duty, it falls to the wife to take his place in directing the family." The essential equality between the married partners comes out most clearly in the Christian doctrine regarding the marital act. Neither husband nor wife has any right to refuse one another,

for with marriage the ownership of the body has been transferred, though it need hardly be said that this should never be
demanded in the spirit of a right that can always be exacted but
rather in a love in which the husband is solicitous of his wife,
the wife solicitous of her husband. The chief pleasure each derives is in giving to the other. But even more than pleasure is
the communion obtained, the serenity, the tenderness. Cana's
water is still capable of being miraculously turned into wine.

It may be confidently said that most people are intended for
marriage and find in it their vocation, that it is for them the way,
the truth and the life, a means mightily conducive to their salvation. In fact, since their salvation may be dependent upon
faithfulness to their vocation, a word or two should be said on
that point. Rarely, in the case of any kind of vocation, does any
indication come from heaven. Except in very exceptional instances, one has to be content to be guided by circumstances
and the wisdom of those more experienced than oneself. Yet the
doctrine on the point should be remembered. St. Alphonsus
Liguori (with a religious vocation in mind) states the case in
an extremely rigorous form. If one enters religion, he says, without a true vocation (about which few people can be absolutely
certain) one loses one's soul, as one also loses it by rejecting
that vocation, if one happens to have it. St. Thomas Aquinas,
however, posits the question more temperately. Should a man,
he says, enter a religious order or the priesthood for a bad motive—let us say ambition or the desire for security—he will obtain
the grace of a vocation upon repentance, as will also one (though
without the grace at the outset) who takes his vows in good
faith. This applies with equal force to marriage. Good will and
an intention to live as one should in that state amply suffice and
are far more important than "being in love," desirable though
this is. We have all seen for ourselves that being in love is no
guarantee of happiness in marriage. On the other hand, a determination to correspond with the grace conferred by marriage
will ensure its success, whatever trials it may have. The Church
in its marriage service insists upon giving the warnings about
poverty, ill-health and the rest while receiving the pledges of
the man and woman who are being married.

It must always be remembered that the priest does not administer the sacrament of matrimony. Catholics are now in increasing numbers being married with a Nuptial Mass and, as their first act, receive Holy Communion together. Yet this excellent practice is in no sense essential to the validity of the marriage. What is necessary for the validity of marriage where a Catholic couple is concerned, or where only one of the couple is a Catholic, is that the ceremony be performed by a priest. The marriage of Catholics by a Protestant minister or a magistrate cannot be recognized, unless it be properly validated afterwards. Nevertheless, it is the husband and the wife who confer the sacrament to one another by the vows they exchange. Coventry Patmore remarks that the consummation of a marriage has a close resemblance to Transubstantiation—the making divine what was not divine before—and it might be added that, like the Sacrifice of the Mass, this can be perpetually renewed.

It may now be more easily understood why Catholics regard such a marriage as of its nature indissoluble. In the first place it is the most solemn of contracts, which nobody with a scrap of honor should think of breaking. However, it is not merely a contract, but a sacrament. One would think that even those who do not recognize the sacrament as such would have enough sensitiveness to realize that the well-nigh incredible physical and psychological intimacy entered into, of itself establishes an unbreakable union. There are, it is true, a number of clearly defined grounds upon which the Church may pronounce a marriage to be invalid. But it is beyond the power of the Church to dissolve a valid sacramental marriage after it has been consummated.

One sometimes hears it said that wealthy and influential Catholics can always obtain a decree of nullity if they wish it. This is not true. Most of the cases are decided by the diocesan matrimonial courts, and these do not issue statistics, but of the cases which are carried to the Rota in Rome, of which there are never more than fifty a year from the entire Catholic world, about a third are those of people too poor to pay any legal fees, or who pay only a nominal sum. The proportion of such people whose suits are successful is very much higher than those able to afford the high legal dues of this court.[3]

A valid sacramental marriage, after consummation, will not be pronounced null and void, even by the Pope. In that sense marriages are made in heaven. The marriage state is, indeed, a great school of sanctification, although on the human plane it may not be at all happy. While in perhaps every instance a reasonable amount of happiness may be obtained if both husband and wife show sincere good will, it cannot be denied that there are times when not only is any patching up apparently impossible, but when a separation of husband and wife becomes advisable, even for the good of their children. The couple who take this into their own hands act very wrongly, but with the bishop's consent they may live apart. Remarriage is under no circumstances permitted until death intervenes. Least of all is falling in love with somebody else sufficient grounds for a divorce. This is an incalculable thing that might happen to anybody—though I find it hard to see how it can occur if the marriage is what I have postulated. If it does, one may legitimately explore the circumstances of one's marriage to discover, if possible, some defect in it that would bring release, but if such a defect cannot be found, there can be no remarriage. I know of one pious Catholic wife who found that she was in love with another man. Theirs may seem a very odd case (and is probably a well-nigh unique one) but for years they have gone together daily to Mass and Holy Communion. While they hope that the time will come when somehow or other they may be free to marry, they must not hope specifically for the death of the man to whom the woman is bound, for this would be a very serious sin.

Another case concerns the sister of a friend of mine. The man she married had announced beforehand that, if things did not

[3] Michael Williams and Julie Kernan in *The Catholic Church in Action,* Macmillan, p. 142, give some statistics. Between October, 1916, and October, 1922, the Rota passed on 117 marriage suits. Of these 69 paid in full, but in 39 cases there was no charge at all, and for the remaining 9 only a small offering was made. Of the rich 69 a third lost their case, whereas of the 48 poor people, 40 were successful.

turn out all right, he intended to get a divorce, which he did. But though his attitude invalidated his marriage, the matrimonial court took eighteen years to reach a decision in his wife's favor. Meanwhile she had fallen in love with a man who had divorced his first wife and married again. In his case annulment was out of the question. Yet they waited for one another, confident that somehow things would come out as they wished. In the end almost simultaneously the ecclesiastical court declared her marriage null and void, and the man's first wife died. As his second marriage in the eyes of the Church was no marriage at all, they were now, in middle age, at last free to marry.

To return to the question of a vocation for marriage, perhaps the wish to be married may be taken as an indication that this vocation exists, just as it may be presumed that those who "in the world" live as celibates have a vocation to celibacy, whether or not this is quite voluntary. Often of course it is celibacy only for a time, until an opportunity for the right kind of marriage occurs. But in some instances women (and also men) bind themselves, either permanently or for a stated period, by vow to a single life. It would be very ill-advised to do so except with the permission of one's spiritual director, and when, as not infrequently happens, those who take such a vow repent later of their rashness, it is not difficult to obtain a dispensation from a vow of this private character. But there is no doubt that there are lay people of both sexes—probably a good many more than one would suppose—who have reached the conclusion that in this state they have special opportunities for serving God and who add to the value of this service by taking a vow. In any event the old-fashioned gibing against an "old maid" was always very unkind and stupid; and one sometimes suspects is most often vented by those who seek in this way to get even with fate for dissatisfaction with their own marriage.

At this point, as a link between what has already been said and what follows, the following passage from T. S. Eliot's *Idea of a Christian Society* might be quoted: "It may be observed," Mr. Eliot writes, "that the natural life and the supernatural life have a conformity to each other which neither has with the mechanistic life: but so far has our notion of what is natural become distorted that people who consider it 'unnatural' and therefore repugnant, that a person of either sex should elect a life of celibacy, consider it perfectly 'natural' that families should be limited to one or two children. It would perhaps be more natural, as well as in better conformity with the Will of God, if there were more celibates and if those who were married had larger families."

That is well said. But I think it will be evident that those who have the concept of marriage that I have tried to sketch will need no admonishing; they will recoil with horror from all the evils in our time connected with marriage, especially from divorce, followed by another marriage, and from what is called birth control.

A non-Catholic marrying a Catholic (which can be done only under a dispensation, after the non-Catholic party has entered into certain definite undertakings) is bound by the general law and his sense of honor, but is not subject to ecclesiastical sanctions, in the event of obtaining a divorce later. Nevertheless, such a person is despicably unfair, for the Catholic wife or husband is bound, whereas the non-Catholic (though he also should consider himself bound) often does not seem to be in the least bothered about his obligations. On the other hand, Canon Law sometimes works to the fullest advantage of those Catholics who take their religion in only a nominal sense. As "once a Catholic, always a Catholic," one who perhaps has never "practiced" since childhood is able to take advantage of the technicalities that are found in any system of law. The Church does its best to administer its code fairly and with due consideration for human needs, but what can it do but grant an annulment to the cold-blooded scoundrel who has concealed the fact of his Catholicism until it suits his purpose? Yet not all such people have acted craftily; there are those who have been simply ignorant of Canon Law and discover to their surprised delight that it provides relief for them. And there are cases I know of when the annulment of a marriage on technical grounds of this sort has meant the reclamation of a fallen-away Catholic. In other cases, if the new marriage is happier than the old, it may be mainly due to this very reason; even a poor Catholic can hardly have a good conscience in flouting the law of God as implemented by the Church's legal code.

The Church's primary mission is to Catholics, but of course she also has ultimately a mission to the whole world, as all human beings are potentially Catholics, highly improbable though it may be that many who are outside the Church will enter it. It is to protect those who are trying to practice their religion that the Church lets it be known that it disapproves of what are called "mixed marriages." In this there is no obscurantism but plain common sense, for few people would bet very heavily upon the success of a marriage between, let us say, an Episcopalian or Presbyterian and one of Jehovah's Witnesses. The non-Catholic partner in such a marriage often resents the conditions imposed by Canon Law. Sometimes an engagement is broken for this very reason. Very well, let it be so. The person who refuses to accept what the Church demands deserves respect for adhesion to principle—far more respect than do those who glibly make the promises tongue in cheek or later get it into their heads that they are not in honor bound to perform what has been promised regarding the upbringing of the children of the marriage. Although mixed marriages make some gains by way of conversions, these are much more than offset by the losses that ensue—either by the Catholic ceasing to practice, or by the neglect of the children's Catholic education. Yet I have a case in mind (which is no doubt typical of others) in which a non-Catholic wife married to an only nominally Catholic husband took it upon herself to see to it that their children fulfilled all their Catholic duties, which, except for her admirable sense of honor, would not have been attended to at all. In general, however, one might almost say that a Catholic who makes a mixed marriage is already on his (or her) way out of the Church. Those who are really permeated by their faith can hardly be imagined as being willing to go into marriage with anyone who does not share it— and this quite apart from the Church's legislation on the matter. Alas, over a third of the marriages contracted by Catholics in this country are of this sort. It is a confusing and disheartening situation.

There is, of course, a great deal more to marriage than sex, though its exercise is an indispensable element. Yet even in a normal marriage, the physical pleasure that accompanies it, though one of God's good gifts, is rather a means than an end—the end being the procreation of children, followed by the obligation of seeing to it that they are brought up as Christians. The child is not merely an addition to its parents' family circle but, to use Pius XI's phrase, "the fellow citizen of the saints and one of God's household." The fact that "Be fruitful and multiply" was said after the fall, has led some to suppose that only afterwards was there intercourse between Adam and Eve, even if this was not, as has been stupidly conjectured, the actual occasion of the fall.

John Milton is not usually a safe guide in theology, but he was quite right in depicting Adam and Eve as effecting their loves on beds of asphodel, and while of course God foreknew that they would prove unfaithful to Him, He reserved a high destiny for the human race. This concept remains unspoiled in spite of the strong suspicion that the poet was trying to justify the ways of Milton to God, with the memory of the first Mrs. Milton still rankling.

It may cause some surprise that Adam and Eve, after eating the apple, tried to cover their nakedness with fig leaves. This was not merely because even the act of love was momentarily spoiled for them by the Serpent, the enemy of man as well as of God. The explanation given by theologians is that the fall, with the original sin that entered in, destroyed the integrity of their nature, so that they became conscious of a war within themselves. One must conclude that the first impact of concupiscence, a disorder in desires which hitherto had been under complete control, so startled them that their first instinctive move was to cover themselves with aprons of leaves.

Once the marriage has been consummated, should congress later become impossible, because of accident, sickness or old age, the union is just what it was before, for it was perfected by the first embrace of love, and all that happens afterwards can only make it firmer. By this embrace a deeper consciousness of the union between husband and wife is established, a greater and fuller understanding. Although on the bridal night the essential part is achieved, it may take as long as several years before husband and wife can discover all the physical joy possible to them, and what is even sweeter, the psychological joy.

Children are the primary end of marriage, and yet there can be a true marriage between a couple who know in advance that there is sterility, though it need hardly be said that should there be impotence from the outset the marriage is *de facto* null and void. Should only sterility exist a number of other ends of marriage may still be attained. One is the mutual help and comfort that husband and wife bring to one another on the natural plane but also (and more important) on the supernatural plane. To those who enter into marriage in the right spirit it can be a vast furtherance of their spiritual life, and in this physical union plays a part that should never be minimized.

The realistic Catholic phrase that marriage is a remedy for concupiscence has offended many. This does not mean merely that marriage is a means for legitimately satisfying desires which otherwise might be criminally satisfied. As Henry VIII (of all people!) put it in his *Defence of the Seven Sacraments*, the book he wrote in 1521 in confutation of Luther, "What should the conjugal act be but concupiscence, if God had not made it the remedy thereof." One may go still further and say that it is possible (and usual) that in marriage physical desire should be so completely concentrated upon a sole object that no room is left for so much as a passing thought upon any other object in this relation. Therefore an absolute chastity is obtainable in marriage, though probably it is not often obtained. Yet perhaps it may be more successfully achieved than is sometimes possible to those vowed to celibacy who remain conscious of the drag of their propensities. Every thought, word and deed can be so consecrated as to result in what might be described as a recovery of innocence, paradise regained. As Patmore says in his essay "Love and Poetry": "What love does in transfiguring life, that religion does in transfiguring love. . . . Love is sure to be something less than human if it is not something more."

In case there be some who think that a mere poet has no authority to speak, I quote again from Monsignor Kolbe. Nothing could be better than his statement: "Every Christian . . . is part of the Incarnational Marriage, and cannot enter into a human marriage without that also becoming incarnational, i.e. sacramental." As Patmore has the Dean say in his "Wedding Sermon":

> Christ's marriage with the Church is more,
> My children, than a metaphor.

Every member of the Mystical Body may be considered under several aspects—as coheir with Christ of the kingdom, as His servant, His soldier. But the most intimate relationship of all, the marriage of the soul to God, and more specifically to Christ, should never be lost sight of. If it is remembered, if there is any serious attempt to lay hold of the wonderful graces God provides for His sons and daughters in marriage, it will be recognized that there is something infinitely more profound than any sentimentalist or romantic can imagine. Fleeting though may be its intensest pleasures, and not to be sustained, they are veritable glimpses of heaven. That they are evanescent is to remind us that earth is not heaven, otherwise we might seek no further than this glory, this ecstasy. But while reminding us to lift up our eyes to the hills whence cometh our salvation, in earth's valley which is for all of us at times a vale of tears, we are strengthened and solaced. For all except those summoned to tread a loftier and lonelier path, marriage is designed to prepare men and women by its joys, but also by its abnegation and discipline, for the Paradise prepared by our Heavenly Father for those who love Him.

# CHAPTER FIVE

## The Life of the Spirit

### THE MASS

There would obviously be no meaning or value in the Mass apart from the incarnation of Christ and His atonement. It may be possible that those who deny these doctrines are quite honestly able to think that the dozens of prophetic passages in the Old Testament which Christians believe were fulfilled by Christ refer to something else, or perhaps were not intended as prophecies at all. I put it in this extreme way only for the sake of argument, for Christ Himself on several occasions claimed that He was making this fulfillment. It is, however, impossible for me to see how anybody who treats as merely figurative what Christ said about eating His flesh and drinking His blood shows judgment or literary sense, though even when these are lacking, of course, honesty may be present.

It has been well said that it is "the Mass that matters." In it the consecrated bread and wine are transubstantiated—converted, in all except appearance, into the flesh and blood of Christ, who in every particle and drop is as really and truly present as God and Man—that is, in the two natures that constitute a single Person—as He was as an infant on His mother's knee or hanging upon the cross or risen from the dead on Easter morning.

First of all it must be said that the Mass is a sacrifice, an unbloody sacrifice indeed but a sacrifice none the less. Those two learned ladies Edith Cooper and Katherine Bradley, aunt and niece who wrote under the name of Michael Field, after producing a number of verse plays on themes taken from the Greek classics, came by chance on a Missal. They read entranced and from time to time exclaimed in surprise—the surprise that even the erudite show when meeting Catholic things for the first time

115

—"Why, here is sacrifice!" To this idea of sacrifice they were already accustomed because of their pagan studies. It was an instance of *Teste David cum Sibylla*, and it ended by their becoming Catholics not long afterwards.

The Mass is an unbloody Calvary, not simply a memorial (though it is that as well) but Calvary itself. It is not quite accurate to speak of that Sacrifice as "repeated," for it stands timeless in time, but rather as renewed and re-presented. It should never be thought of as a service which one attends but a service at which one assists, because it is being offered by all those present along with the priest, and the high priest is Christ Himself. All the baptized, of whatever sex or age, have by virtue of their baptism, a real though not a sacerdotal priesthood. Christ is the Victim offered, but the officiating priest is a victim too, as are all the worshipers by identifying themselves with Christ as members of His Mystical Body. The words of the Mass make this unmistakably clear, as when the priest says, "Brethren, pray that my sacrifice and yours may be acceptable to God the Father Almighty." When Christ died for us, He identified Himself with us, and in baptism we were buried with Him, to rise to newness of life. So at Mass each worshiper undergoes a kind of mystical death by which he is united to the Sacrifice on the altar. It is even possible to effect this union at any hour of the day or night, for there is no moment at which, in some part of the world, Mass is not being offered. Nor is it necessary to be without sin to do this, because the Mass, being Calvary, is offered to cleanse us from sin; sinners as well as saints may reach out towards it. As Pius XII wrote in his encyclical *Mystici Corporis: "In this pure oblation* He offers Himself not only as Head of the Church to the heavenly Father, but in Himself His mystical members as well. He embraces them all, even the weak and ailing ones, in the tenderest love of His heart." The Mass is at once the supreme act of God's justice and of God's love.

Therefore the Church declares that those who willfully neglect to attend Mass on Sundays and holy days of obligation—unless they have some valid excuse—are guilty of mortal sin.[1] It is easy

---

[1] In the United States these holy days are the Feasts of the Circumcision of Our Lord (January 1st); Ascension Thursday, which falls forty days after

to see why this should be, for such neglect is not short of outrageous. Yet it must not be imagined that Catholics go to Mass
merely out of fear of incurring a penalty; rather they go as a
priceless privilege. Many go far more often than they are obliged
—some even daily—and there are few who do not go on at least
a few extra days in the course of the year, if only when Mass is
being offered for their beloved dead. As Christ said to the Samari-
tan woman, "If you but knew the gift of God. . . !" The Mass is the
heart of Catholicism.

To get the full benefit from Mass it is not sufficient to be
merely passively present, though that much complies with the
letter of the ecclesiastical law. Some sort of active participation
is supposed. By far the best way is undoubtedly that of following in a Missal the words spoken by the priest at the altar. This
is very easy to do, because those who do not know Latin can
follow with the translation provided in the parallel column, and
one gets the impression that there are now twice as many people
who use the Missal than who did so thirty years ago. However,
though Pius X urged Catholics to "pray the Mass," other methods
are permissible. Many people say the rosary. It would be more
appropriate to read and meditate on the sixth chapter of St. John's
Gospel, at least from verse 22 to the end, for there is contained
Christ's Eucharistic promises and Peter's great cry, "Lord, to
whom shall we go? Thou hast the words of eternal life." Then
there are those who read from the Fourth Book of the *Imitation*,
or meditate upon one of the phases of the Mass, and others still
use a manual of prayers prepared for the purpose. But whatever
the method used, there should be active participation in the
Sacrifice.

We think of the Mass as being said in Latin, for it is only a
Latin Mass that most of us ever hear. It is, however, said in a
number of other liturgical languages by the 9,000,000 or so Catholics of the various Eastern Rites that are in communion with

Easter Sunday; the Assumption (August 15th); All Saints' Day (November
1st); the Immaculate Conception (December 8th); and Christmas. In
most European countries the Epiphany (January 6th) is also a holy day of
obligation.

Rome.[2] In most of these rites, which are of an ornate and poetical character compared with the terse austerity of the Latin usage, Holy Communion is administered in "both kinds"—that is, the Host is dipped into the chalice of the Precious Blood with a golden spoon and then placed in the mouth of the communicant. During the Reformation there was a good deal of clamor for the chalice to be given to the laity. This in itself presents no principle in the slightest degree opposed to Catholicism—and was in fact the ancient practice in the West, as it still is in the East—but because it was clear that the object of the demand was to cause trouble, it was rejected.

In the Western Church the saying of Mass in Latin is virtually universal, although in Yugoslavia it is permissible to use the Latin ritual translated into Old Slavonic. There are a few places (the archdiocese of Milan, for example) which have their own Latin rite, and the same is true of the liturgical peculiarities permitted locally in Spain and France. Moreover, the Dominicans, Carmelites, Carthusians and Cistercians have their own slight deviations. Yet the Benedictines, whom one might have expected to have had their own rite because of their antiquity, strictly follow the Roman usage. The advantages of having Mass in Latin should be obvious. It is (or was) a universal language and, because it is what is called "dead," the meaning of its words is not subject to gradual change, as always happens to languages that are living. Yet there are advocates for the use of the vernacular up to the Preface, and also for the Paternoster, and they have a case, though it is very questionable whether the advantages would equal what might be lost. At present the priest, after reading the Sunday Gospel in Latin, according to the prescribed liturgy, reads it again in English for the benefit of those who do not know Latin or are

[2] As there may be some of my readers who may never have heard of these rites, or who have heard of them only to associate them with India or China, it should be said that most of their adherents are found in Middle Europe, the Balkans, Asia Minor, or Africa. Mass, it may be remarked, was said for a long time in Greek in Rome itself, and the first use of Latin for the purpose is said to have occurred in North Africa in the third century. All of the sixteen Eastern Rites are to be found in the United States with the exception, so I am told, of the Coptic. They must not be confused with the dissident counterparts that almost every one of them has, for while these are schismatic, the Eastern Rites referred to here are thoroughly Catholic.

not following Mass with a Missal. It sometimes even happens that on Palm Sunday, when there is a very long Gospel, a layman who is a good reader will read it aloud while Mass is being said. In my opinion it is a pity that this is not done more often. If there is any objection to a lay reader, a priest could perform this office. It serves no very useful purpose that the congregation should be kept on their feet during those two long chapters from Matthew (xxvi and xxvii), understanding nothing and, because the Latin Gospel has occupied so much time, not having it read afterwards in the vernacular.

The young John William Walshe, in the novel of that name by Montgomery Carmichael, which was written so convincingly in autobiographical form as to make his bishop wonder how it had happened that he had never met so admirable a person, was first attracted to the Catholic Church by the fact that its prayers were in Latin. Probably few people are so enamored of Latin as all that, but there are a good many (among whom I must be included) who would feel rather nervous should the speech of everyday occupations be substituted. However, there is no immediate likelihood of such a breach with tradition. What is more beneficial is the practice that has come into vogue, under the influence of the Liturgical Movement (and this had its real inception under Pius X) of the congregation's making the responses, instead of leaving everything to the server. This, however, ordinarily is feasible only when there is an exceptionally well-educated and well-disciplined congregation, such as might be found in a college.

There are a number of Masses commemorating special occasions, apart of course from the Masses marking Saints' days. Most of the saints get no more than what is called "the common" for confessors, martyrs, virgins, virgins and martyrs, doctors of the Church, or to whatever category they belong. In most of such Masses there is no more than a mention of the saint whose feast is being kept, usually in the collect. For the rest there are Masses for a Papal Election, for the Consecration of a Bishop, for the Ordination of a Priest, for Peace, for the Forgiveness of Sins, and similar intentions. The Mass appointed for the day may be said for the repose of the faithful departed, but there is a special Mass for the burial of the dead (the stately and very moving Requiem), and for a marriage there is the Nuptial Mass to which reference has been made in the previous chapter. It is not obligatory, and the marriage service has in fact been completed before the Mass begins, but beneath the cross of Christ bride and groom may in this way begin their life together.

Although Mass is the most important part of the Liturgy, priests are not obligated to say it every day, but nearly all of them do. On the other hand, they are bound to say daily after their ordination to the subdiaconite what is called the Office. This consists of Matins and Lauds (the longest part), the four "hours" of Prime, Terce, Sext and None, concluding with Vespers in the late afternoon and Compline as night prayers. A few lay people, out of devotion, say the whole or (more commonly) some part of the Office, and most Sisters say the Little Office of Our Lady, whether in Latin or English. This takes only half an hour as against the full hour for the Office as given in the Breviary. If this is chanted in choir—especially if done with the solemnity that the Trappists and Carthusians give to it—it occupies several hours, and Matins and Lauds are said in the small hours, thus breaking the night's sleep, something to which no monk ever gets accustomed. But the Office is rich and beautiful and full of sweetness, mostly consisting of the psalms but with appropriate lessons from various parts of the Bible and the Fathers of the Church. Its spirit is that of the Mass which is its center.

### THE BLESSED SACRAMENT

Upon one of the altars of every Catholic church—usually the high altar [3]—the Blessed Sacrament is reserved for the adoration of anybody who comes in, if only for a few minutes, during the course of the day. What is reserved, is either a single consecrated Host in a pyx or a quantity of such Hosts in a ciborium. There in the tabernacle is Christ Himself, with His people until the end

---

[3] Really it should be at a side altar, but except in a very large church this is not feasible; therefore the high altar is used as a matter of convenience. However, in some German churches the medieval tabernacles attached to the wall near the altar are still in use.

of the world.[4] Few if any people who go into a Catholic church fail to notice at once the "feel" of something quite different from anything they get in other places of worship. It is true that there are some architectural differences, but many modern Protestant church edifices do not differ markedly from the churches where Catholics worship, except for the statues. It is the atmosphere that is different. There have been non-Catholics who were converted on the spot by this, though of course the majority get no further than a vague wonder that Catholic churches "feel" as they do. Probably many ascribe their sensations to the "dim religious light," though as this is to be found elsewhere it explains nothing. Others again may think that there is something "eerie" about Catholicism, and that it is this of which they are conscious. Mr. Aldous Huxley in his *Perennial Philosophy* says that there are mosques and temples in the Orient "where even the most irreligious and unpsychic tourist cannot fail to be aware of some intensely 'numinous' presence." All I can say is that I have never had such an awareness, though in my youth I was in a good many temples and mosques in India. Mr. Huxley offers the explanation that this is due to the "psychic presence of men's thoughts and feelings" about the divine as it is worshiped there. Well, I have a great respect for his intelligence, but here he strikes me as being a bit superstitious; this seems to be on a par with the theory that would account for ghosts as emanations that sometimes come from the walls of a house saturated with the emotions aroused by some extraordinary happening perhaps centuries before. I think we may safely dismiss such a fancy; of course the Blessed Sacrament does not receive adoration in Catholic churches because it is *felt* to be there, nor does this adoration fill the air with, so to speak, a heavy incense. As for Catholics themselves, many (if not most) enter a church in so matter-of-fact a way as to feel nothing at all, and feelings are of no importance anyway. Rather the Blessed Sacrament is adored because Catholics believe it is there, the Real Presence.

[4] In the Western Church the Host is a flat circular piece of unleavened bread; in the Eastern Rites leavened bread is used. But among Catholics of those rites there is not the same degree of worship paid to the Blessed Sacrament, except during Mass itself.

The Blessed Sacrament, which is now reserved in a tabernacle on the altar, was during the Middle Ages often reserved in a hanging pyx, usually in the form of a dove. Before it an altar light burns perpetually, for Christ is there in His plenitude, God and man, with His two natures united in one Person in what is called hypostatic union. That is, the two distinct natures are inseparably united, each conserving what is proper to each, with two wills and two modes of operation, yet with a single subsistence. It is this God-Man who is adored. As Sister Miriam Teresa, a young American Sister of Charity who died in 1927, wrote: "He has a human heart that dilates with a human love; a human understanding divinely responsive to our every least mood and thought and desire. And He is God."

Not for an instant can a Catholic forget or doubt that Christ is God, the Second Person of the Blessed Trinity. But the humanity we share with Him has been united to His divinity, and this humanity is properly adored (as it is not separable from His Godhead), especially under the aspect of its compassion for the whole human race, under the visualized object of Christ's human heart, or the Sacred Heart. Here is our Redeemer, our Friend, our Brother, our Lover. In the Blessed Sacrament He stays with us in a special and very intimate way.

About Christ, the human being as He appears in the Gospels, the historic Christ, I shall have something to say a little later. First let me touch upon some of the devotions connected with His person that Catholic piety has developed. Not all of these will appeal to everybody, and none of them is obligatory; indeed they have seized upon the imagination of Catholics to such an extent that one sometimes fears that they may tend to obscure more essential things. There is, for example, the Holy Hour, which, as the name implies, is the exposition of the Blessed Sacrament in a monstrance for an hour, so that it may be adored. It is not during that time more truly present than in the tabernacle, but the circumstance that it is set up in a monstrance where it may be seen—that is, where the physical accidents may be seen—makes people more conscious that it is there, and so draws out their faith in the Substance concealed beneath the accidents. To the Blessed Sacrament so exposed, one does not make the ordinary genuflexion but goes down on both knees. The same exposition occurs in the service of Benediction, which has become quasi-liturgical; and again in the Forty Hours Devotion, where exposition takes place for the indicated length of time. It recalls the forty hours (those making up part of three days) when Christ was in the tomb, and originated in the sixteenth century. This is also, strictly speaking, extra-liturgical, but Canon Law ordains that it be carried out once a year in every church in which the Blessed Sacrament is regularly reserved, and the adoration is controlled by a number of regulations laid down by Clement VIII in 1592.

Probably the most popular of all the devotions connected with the Blessed Sacrament is that connected with a Visitation nun of the seventeenth century now canonized as St. Margaret Mary Alacoque. On the Feast of Corpus Christi, 1675, Christ Himself told her that He wished a feast to be instituted in honor of His Sacred Heart in reparation for the sins of the world. About this something needs to be said, especially as there were a number of other private revelations.

First of all, it must be clearly understood that no private revelation is binding on the faith of Catholics. Though the Church has passed favorably upon what Margaret Mary has imparted, and has confirmed this with the seal of canonization, this only means that the Church finds what she said in consonance with its own doctrine, and that the effects that flow from the recommendations she enunciated (if one may put it that way) are beneficial to the spiritual life. But Margaret Mary Alacoque did not originate devotion to the Sacred Heart, though she and Blessed Claude Columbière did much to propagate it. As for the words she records that Christ said to her, I, for one, would be incredulous (if only because of the stilted style she reports Christ's having used) were it not that allowances have to be made for the human instrument. A perfectly straight stick put into the clearest of water will at once appear as refracted; something similar to that phenomenon must have happened here.

The question may be asked why the heart of Christ should be the object of adoration. Actually, of course, the devotion of the Sacred Heart is to Christ in His entirety, but, if one must single out a single aspect of this, to the love of Christ, represented by His heart. Yet it is doubtful whether the fleshly heart is the organ of love, for modern experiments seem to have proved that the organ is the brain. Although in some places in the Bible the heart is mentioned as the instrument of love, as it is in popular speech, the bowels are almost as often designated, St. Paul in his epistle to the Philippians even using the phrase (i. 8): "the bowels of Jesus Christ." Modern sentiment naturally recoils from such an expression. In any event there can be no objection to the heart as the organ of love so long as it is understood that the adoration is of the human love of the God-Man.

One sometimes notices a tendency on the part of those who have written about mysticism to deplore a Christocentric religion and to exalt above it a theocentric approach. This is especially observable among learned and clever people such as Aldous Huxley who, one often suspects, have no experimental knowledge of what they are writing about. Indeed, Mr. Huxley has declared that mysticism is the perfect religion for unbelievers, which provokes the question why he should spend his great gifts upon something about which he has no real conviction. With him mysticism seems hardly more than a technique for the attainment of something that does not exist.

It is of course true that mysticism, which is the experimental as contrasted with the doctrinal knowledge of God, often dispenses with all images in its experiences, including the image of Christ, although it is only through the Son that we can come to the Father. One even finds a mysticism that Christians have to recognize as genuine among Buddhists, Moslems and Hindus. I write this with the hardly necessary disclaimer that I have no personal knowledge of these matters, and even a very imperfect theoretical knowledge of them.[5] But I think I may venture to point out that, after the efflorescence of mysticism in France and Spain during the sixteenth and seventeenth centuries, mysticism came to be regarded as a dangerous field, and though it has regained its threatened position, it still needs to be safeguarded by

[5] Even Abbot Butler in his great book *Western Mysticism* makes the same disclaimer, so far as personal experience is concerned. Obviously he is very learned in the theoretical knowledge of his subject.

dogmatic theology. In any event the matter hardly concerns this book. I have suggested that ordinary forms of Catholic living are mystical in a very valid sense, but that sense is limited. Beyond that it would be ridiculous for me to venture.

Within this sense it cannot be other than that Christianity is Christocentric. Étienne Gilson, most orthodox of Catholics, says that "The Incarnation . . . should be regarded as one of the consequences of man's transgression, so that the love for the person of Christ is, as a matter of fact, bound up with the history of a fall which need not, and should not have happened." Other philosophers and theologians have suggested (and I think rightly) that the Incarnation would have occurred even had man not fallen, but as man *did* fall, how can it be other than that all men should bend their thoughts to the One who declared Himself the Way, the Truth and the Life? I know just enough philosophy to be aware that abstractive, discursive thought is the human way of attaining truth, as contrasted to the intuitive mode of knowledge exercised by the angels. But even in human intellectual processes I am inclined to accord more to intuition than is commonly allowed. At any rate, too severe an "intellectualism" has (or may have), to my way of thinking, for all except "professionals," something so chilly about it as hardly to seem human at all.

To refer to Aldous Huxley again, he says in his *Perennial Philosophy* that he has noticed, when making use of university libraries, that books on mysticism were much less frequently taken out than was the case in public libraries, "patronized in the main by men and women who had not enjoyed the advantages, or suffered under the handicaps, of prolonged academic instruction." The inevitable conclusion is that the kind of education now doled out leaves the impression that God does not much matter, even if He exists. To this extent Abbot Butler corroborates Mr. Huxley when he says in his *Western Mysticism:* "Mysticism is not the privilege of the intellectual, but is within the reach of the poor and unlearned and the little ones of Christ; and without doubt it is most successfully cultivated by those who know not its name." More recently the Trappist Thomas Merton, writing of those whom he calls "masked mystics," says that they would be very much surprised if they were told that they were any sort of mystic. Surely to this group belongs the aged peasant the Curé of Ars tells about. He used to sit for hours in Church before the Blessed Sacrament and could explain what he was doing only by saying, "I look at Him, and He looks at me."

To return for a moment to mysticism, the very word has for many people a somewhat terrifying ring, for even those who have read only cursorily about the subject have come across elaborate expositions of its stages—the purgative, the illuminative and the unitive way. They have naturally supposed that these were definitely marked-off strata, each of which had to be thoroughly explored, and probably for years, before there could be any progress in the next. But as a matter of fact these stages usually overlap, and many mystics never experience the "dark night of the soul" at all. For ordinary people—or shall I say good Christians sincerely anxious to attain some degree of union with God?—it might be helpful to suggest that technical terms are for them of little practical value. While the old distinctions hold for those for whom they were intended, the gates to union with God are not formidably bolted and barred; all may enter, in so far as they are able to do so.

Let us take a concrete instance: the reception of Holy Communion is actually of more spiritual value than what might be called the concomitants of mysticism—visions and locutions (whether interior or exterior), ecstasies, levitations and so forth. These things have happened to some saints, but even they have attached no great value to them but rather to the accompanying grace. Most of these saints have said so plainly, and there is a standing warning that those to whom these phenomena come are always in danger of being deceived, if not by the devil then by their own imagination. St. Philip Neri is a case in point; he could not look at a religious picture for five minutes without going off into an ecstasy, nor did he dare to say Mass until he had brought himself down to earth by reading a few pages of a joke book— yet he never tired of begging others to be on guard against what are commonly supposed to be the indications of mysticism. The love and service of God are what matter, and these are within the reach of all.

One visionary already mentioned, St. Margaret Mary Alacoque, has made very popular what is called the devotion of the Nine First Fridays. As sometimes unfortunately understood, she is supposed to have brought an assurance from Christ Himself that those who go to Holy Communion on the first Friday of the month for nine successive months seal their salvation as certain. It need hardly be said that she made no such declaration, and to believe otherwise would be superstition. The only possible guarantee of salvation is dying in the state of grace, for which reason it is highly advisable to pray for final perseverance and the avoidance of an unprovided death. The famous "promise" rests upon a letter of very doubtful authenticity. Its date is uncertain, and it is a transcript and not an original. Even so nobody knew anything about so momentous a thing until thirty-four years after the Saint's death. The first bishop who came across it renders the "promise" as a leading to the Sacred Heart through the practice of devotion "to hope for the grace of final repentance, and for that of receiving the sacraments of the Church before dying."

At this nobody can possibly cavil, but it may be asked whether the "nine" is not itself superstitious. In an age of numerology Dante attached great significance to this figure, but it would be superstitious to attribute any magical property to it. There is no value in performing a particular act on certain days and for a designated number of times. Friday is certainly no better than Sunday for receiving Holy Communion, if as good. Nevertheless, the Church has approved the devotion, because of the immense good that has flowed from it. Nor is there anything rash in believing that a promise was given in the moderate terms that have been indicated, for this really offers no more than an augmentation of the hope of salvation. Even those who may be skeptical on philosophical or historical grounds as to the authenticity of the promise, will acknowledge that it has been an inducement to people to go to Holy Communion on at least one day in the month when they are not under any obligation even to assist at Mass. Therefore the devotion of the Nine First Fridays has been productive of much spiritual good.

### THE CHRIST OF THE GOSPELS

It should be plainly said at once that the Christ depicted in the Gospels is vastly different from the statues and paintings of Him in our churches. There He is always the meek and gentle Jesus, only too often a figure that is incredible in its insipidity and lack of masculinity. I think I can understand why this has come about, though I think it unfortunate. Christian piety presents to the poor and humble and distressed the meekness and lowliness to which they may make their piteous appeal. "Come unto Me, all ye who labor, for I am meek and humble of heart" is the right note to strike, though it should also be remembered that He told us of a yoke and a burden, while assuring us that they would be light—light only because He carries the weightier part of the load—and that the Christian must "take up his cross and follow Me." The vivid and vigorous and virile Jesus has almost faded out of our recollection, and somebody quite different has come to take His place.

Let us forget the Jesus of Barclay Street and look instead at the Jesus of the Gospels. He is, it is true, a figure often enigmatic. But one thing can hardly be missed—the ringing heartiness He shows, as when he emphatically exclaimed, "I have not found such faith, no not in all Israel," or when He called to Peter in the boat to join Him where He was walking on the water. And when He told the Syro-Phoenician woman that it was not meet to take the children's bread and cast it to the dogs, He was immensely pleased when her woman's wit immediately threw the expression back at Him, "Yea, Lord, but the dogs eat of the crumbs that fall from the children's table." His talk was filled with extravagant hyperboles—mountains being cast into the sea, camels going through the eye of a needle. The other side of His heartiness was His devastating scorn for whited sepulchers, for those who laid on men's shoulders burdens greater than could be borne and who devoured widows' houses. On one occasion, it will be remembered, He took a scourge and in His wrath swept the money-changers out of the temple.

Moreover, He was a very sociable and affable person. The first miracle of His public life was that of Cana. Those who had arranged the wedding party may have been a bit niggardly, though one would suppose that they would have taken care to lay in a sufficient stock of wine. It was after this had been all consumed that Jesus turned the water in six large jars into wine—and as we know how much those jars held, we also know how much additional wine was provided; it was from a hundred to a hundred and fifty gallons. He was by no means disinclined to see people making merry on such an occasion. The comment about the guests having already "well drunken," at which stage they would not have been very critical of wine of an inferior grade, whereas the best wine had been kept until then, suggests food for reflection for Prohibitionists. Jesus was accused by the Pharisees, as He tells us Himself, of being "a gluttonous man and a winebibber." Though this was a malicious exaggeration, He did not bother to deny it. He did not even do what He might have been excused for doing, carefully separate the truth from the falsehood. Whatever else Christ was, He was not in the slightest degree prim or what might be called stuffy. At any rate He dined out often enough to give some substance to the Pharisees' charge.

On the other hand, He once spoke of the foxes having holes and the birds of the air their nests, whereas the Son of Man had nowhere to lay His head. This, however, may be taken as applying to a particular place and occasion, for there were several houses where He was always a welcome guest, especially in the house of Lazarus, the brother of Mary and Martha. Nor did He in the least resent it when, after Lazarus' death, his sisters reproached Him for not having come sooner. Instead He went to the tomb and called the already putrefying Lazarus to come out. He did not much cultivate the rich and powerful. In one houses where He was always a welcome guest, especially in the poor entertainment, which was made up for only by the alabaster box that Mary Magdalene broke in the extravagance of love. But He seems to have exercised some influence over people of the official sort. Nicodemus, a member of the Sanhedrin, went to Him by night, and another member, Joseph of Arimathea, provided for Him the tomb he had prepared for himself. And of course there was the Centurion.

He had made enough of a stir in the world to have become at

least a curiosity to people still more exalted. These He avoided completely, His mission being to the poor and lowly. Instead we find Him sending a scornful message to Herod Antipas, the son of the earlier Herod who had massacred the innocents of Bethlehem thirty years earlier. "Go and tell that fox" was the reverse of being an ingratiating way of talking. And when on the day of His condemnation He was sent to Herod's tribunal, Christ treated him in much the same style, though it is more than likely that the Roman officials would have protected Him had Christ wished their protection.

This is one facet of His character; another is His great power of poetic pathos as shown by what He said about the lilies of the field, the sparrow that could not fall to the ground without the Heavenly Father's knowing. Over Jerusalem He laments: He would have gathered its children as a hen gathers her chicks under her wings. And most of all this comes out in the wonderful parables—all so vivid and full of matters of the most homely sort that everybody knew about—the lost sheep, the woman's lost groat, the wine in new bottles, the uselessness of trying to patch a cloak with new cloth, the man who fell among thieves, the surly son who in the end obeyed his father where his glib brother merely gave fair words, the prodigal son, the sower of seed, the enemy who creeps in at night and throws cockle among the wheat. Looked at merely as literary art, nothing was ever more easy, more natural, more completely in mastery of the desired effect—in short, more perfect.

Yet one of these parables has often been misunderstood. In the story of the fraudulent steward it was not the Lord who commended his shrewdness, but the lord, the man's employer. Christ's sardonic comment was, "Make yourselves friends of the mammon of unrighteousness, that they may receive you into eternal habitations." That, of course, is precisely what the mammon of unrighteousness cannot do. The implication has gone over many people's heads to this day. I heard only recently a priest who agreed with the rest of the interpretation given here suggest that the bit about the mammon of unrighteousness means that one may legitimately make use of donations to good purposes that come from questionable sources. Without in any way challenging the idea that this may be done, I cannot find this idea in the parable, or even implied. Christ's method was always that of making a single point, without going off on any side issues. His pungency was constant: Of those who do good works to be observed by men, He says devastatingly, "They have their reward."

In the performance of His miracles there seems to be what some might consider inconsistency. He could not perform miracles without their "fame" being spread far and wide, and yet He often asked those whom He healed to say nothing about what had happened. His first miracle occurred at a wedding but with so little parade that not even the master of the feast was aware how the new supply of wine had come. Yet on one occasion He miraculously provided food for five thousand men, on another for seven thousand. The paralytic was healed in front of a whole roomful of people; the blind man, by the wayside in view of passers-by; the widow's son at Naim was raised from the dead before the cortege carrying him to the grave; the woman with the issue of blood was healed in a crowd; the daughter of Jairus was brought back to life before the eyes of her parents, with the servants knowing all about it.

But though Christ had a reason for trying to keep His miracles secret, He knew perfectly well that people would talk about them, and once He urged that if people would not believe in Him for His doctrine, they do so at least "for the works' sake." To the disciples of John the Baptist who had been sent to enquire, He said that they should return to their master and tell him what Jesus knew that John knew already but wanted his disciples to witness, listing among His miracles the raising from the dead, as though this was of almost daily occurrence,[6] but including, as of equal importance, that "the poor have the gospel preached to them." Christ did not come primarily to work miracles but rather

---

[6] We are told in the Gospels only of Lazarus and the widow's son at Naim, so one cannot but infer that there were a good many more of such stupendous miracles which went unrecorded. St. John's Gospel, in fact, indicates that it contains only a very little of what Jesus did and said. And this, by the way, is a support to Catholic contention that the faith of the Church rests largely on tradition, by which is meant the oral testimony of those who knew Jesus while He was on earth, or what they had related by word of mouth to those who were to succeed them. I invite Protestants whose religion is the Bible and the Bible alone, to weigh this suggestion.

to form a band of disciples to continue His work after He had departed. His main purpose, however, was to die on the cross. As He Himself said, "It was for this that I have come."

It must be pointed out, moreover, that Christ showed whatever caution He did because He was on guard against two opposing things: first, that the common people would "by force" try to make Him their king and, second, that the ruling classes of the Jews feared such an action because it threatened to deprive them of their privileged position. The Romans, as was their settled policy, supported the Scribes and Pharisees, and these groups knew that in the event of a popular insurrection, the Romans would make their own rule absolute. This motive was put forward at the trial of Jesus before Caiaphas, when, though He was there judged guilty of blasphemy (as He *was* guilty if He was only man), they passed Him on to the Roman governors (as they themselves were not empowered to pass a death sentence) on the charge that He was a seditious person. As a matter of fact, Christ had several times to go into hiding lest He should be made a king—the very last thing He wanted—and similarly He several times hid from the Pharisees, lest they assassinate Him. This they at least twice attempted, and He got away in a more or less miraculous fashion. Their rage was always enkindled by what they considered blasphemy or by the miracles that proved that He was more than man.

One gets the impression that the vast crowds that followed Him, even into the desert, were not especially interested in His teaching—for certainly the majority failed to grasp it—but hoped to be cured themselves or hoped to see somebody else cured. No doubt they were fascinated by the marvelous stories He was always telling, but they did not understand the spiritual significance of His parables,[7] as even the inner circle of disciples usually had to have the meaning explained to them. One of the few

[7] It may be wondered why He did not explain this significance to the crowds, as, upon request, He explained it to His disciples. It may be suggested that He knew that in some cases the inner meaning would dawn upon some of His listeners; upon those who never got His point, there would be that much less culpability for failing to respond to spiritual things. However, it must be said that this was due in large part to the gradual unfolding of the Messianic character as the people were prepared for it.

times that He spoke without a parable was when He delivered the Sermon on the Mount. But it should be noted that this plain teaching was delivered at a time when He was alone with the Twelve. Even so, it was not to tell them about His death and resurrection and the Eucharist, for all that came later, after they had been prepared; the Sermon on the Mount provided only a moral code, though one of a kind that they must have found startling, to say the least. When we hear of His sending out a band of seventy disciples to preach, their doctrine could only have been of the kind that was in the Sermon on the Mount. The rest He reserved for an inner circle. Men being what they are, it was not advisable to throw out profundities before gaping crowds that would have entirely missed the point. Such things could only be told to a small group sitting around Him to whom He could talk in a quiet confidential tone.

He did not want—even less than the Pharisees wanted, had they only understood—to set Himself up as king of Israel. The Romans could have promptly crushed any popular insurrection. But His was the power of greater weight for it lay in the supernatural: His kingdom was not of this world. However, had He been made a King, as He feared, the Pharisees—though they supported the Romans because the Romans supported their privileges—probably would have swung over to Him when they saw that it was useless to do anything else. Then, of course, they would have seen to it that the whole purpose of His mission was refashioned according to their ideas.

Their judgment was in a sense correct: There was enough explosive force in His teaching to shatter the whole social structure, as there still is, which is one reason why the world has always been so careful not to apply His teaching too drastically. But while one must deplore the way it is often overlaid, or used by reactionary forces for their own ends, perhaps upon the whole it is best that this teaching has only gradually molded our civilization—for such a molding *has* occurred, though it has been far from perfect, and the development of the practice of Christianity may take another two thousand years to reach even a decent level.

Such are some of the overlooked features of Jesus of Nazareth, the Son of Man, a thousand times more of a *man* than He is usually represented as being. This manly Christ was the man that His own friends and disciples knew. However, we may and should bear in mind what Chesterton so finely says in his *Everlasting Man:* "The figure in the Gospels does indeed utter in words of almost heart-breaking beauty His pity for our broken hearts. But they are very far from being the only sort of words that He utters. Nevertheless they are almost the only kind of words that the Church in its popular imagery ever represents Him as uttering. That popular imagery is inspired by a perfectly sound popular instinct. The mass of the people are poor, and for the mass of mankind the main thing is to carry the conviction of the incredible compassion of God."

The intimate friendship of Christ remains available to all of us in the Catholic Church, for He is a friend who is always present—physically present in the Blessed Sacrament, but spiritually with us at every hour of the day and night. As Alice Meynell has written:

> Thou art the Way.
> Hadst Thou been nothing but the goal,
> I cannot say
> If Thou hadst ever met my soul.
>
> I cannot see—
> I, child of process—if there lies
> An end for me,
> Full of repose, full of replies.
>
> I'll not reproach
> The road that winds, my feet that err.
> Access, Approach
> Art Thou, Time, Way, and Wayfarer.

### SOME OTHER DEVOTIONS

First of all it might be as well to touch upon *Sacramentals,* as many of these form part of Catholic piety, and all, as their name implies, bear some relation to sacraments, though of course without actually being such. Of these there are a great many and they are usually put in six categories: first prayers, such as the Our

Father and those of the Liturgy; then the use of holy water and similar acts; thirdly the taking of blessed bread—a custom in French churches though not used in America; the saying of the *Confiteor* when going to confession; the blessings given to churches, houses, bells, medals, rosaries, scapulars, of the palms on Palm Sunday and of the ashes on Ash Wednesday; the making of the sign of the cross; the blessing of holy oils and holy water; having one's throat blessed on St. Blaise's Day; these sacramentals are too numerous to mention and most if not all of them have some indulgence attached to them. In fact, it is not always easy to keep perfectly distinct the sacramental and the indulgence.

In matters of this sort it is often supposed that there is a good deal of routine, which gives rise to the common notion that Catholicism is largely formalism. As to that I think it should be said that a routine performance is not necessarily a bad performance. In most human doings—whether the training of an army, or running a household or a business, the observance of a set routine helps a good deal. So one can develop a habit of religion; indeed, unless such a habit is developed, religion is not going to be of much service, since it cannot always depend upon the hour of intense inspiration. Such hours are rare for all people, and some people never experience them at all. One has to recognize that though routine may be dull, an orderly and fruitful life will to a great extent be sustained by routine.

Yet I should totally deny that Catholicism is more deeply tinged with formalism than are other religions, or other forms of Christianity. Rather I should say that it is more free of routine, though depending for its day-to-day functioning upon ordinary processes, in which some routine is unavoidable. The Pharisees were condemned by Christ not for the use of ceremonies, but for behaving as though they constituted the whole substance of religion. There is undoubtedly a "shell" within which Catholicism operates, but this is only the shell and not the heart of the matter. Properly used this shell may be protective of more precious elements. Grace may be at its most powerful when our emotions are most lethargic.

Perhaps an analogy may serve at this point. A young man and woman marry very much in love. But in due course they find out the truth of what is expressed in the somewhat cynical saying, "The honeymoon is over." Of course a honeymoon ends, and though the old rapture may be recaptured from time to time, it tends to grow less. Is one to rush off to the divorce court when this happens? The real satisfactions of marriage come only to those who disregard the fading of the rainbow and who settle down to love, even though the forms of its expression have a good deal of routine. So it is also with regard to religion. No more than in marriage can one live only upon great moments. The acceptance of stretches of tedium is also necessarily involved, and the acceptance of the still more galling fact that we are only human beings.

So it is with many devotional practices. Even Mass may sometimes seem a rather cut-and-dried affair; though if this is so, the fault lies in us and not in what is the most overwhelming and thrilling thing we can encounter. But if this can be true now and then of our feelings at Mass, still more will it be true of many of the minor devotions that make up a considerable part of Catholicism. There are far too many of such devotions to be enumerated, and it would be hardly possible for anybody to practice them all. Some, such as the wearing of a medal or scapular, take up no time, but others take up anything from a minute to an hour. Of these the most common are novenas, often made to a favorite saint and normally lasting nine days. But there are people who, being unable to wait as long as that for something they want, make what is called a "flying novena," which may be as simple as saying a Hail Mary at every hour or every half-hour of the day. The attaching of a magical property to the number nine would be of course superstitious, but, as has been suggested already, the nine days of prayer probably commemorate the period of waiting between the Ascension and the first Pentecost. On the other hand, the *Catholic Dictionary* edited by Donald Attwater says, "At root the custom seems to have been taken over from Roman paganism." The fact that the Church did preserve whatever was worthy of preserving in the paganism amid which it rose is not a sad confession but almost a boast;

never did it uproot what could be allowed to remain. And such elements of paganism as it took over have all been Christianized.

The devotions which Catholics practice—or rather are *free* to practice, for none of them are of obligation—are so numerous that I knew two dear old octogenarian ladies who, in order to find time for their night prayers, had to start them at ten in the morning. The other members of the household used to laugh at this, but the old ladies did not mind, for they well understood that everybody there accepted the Catholic principle of live and let live. There is so wide a diversity of practice in these minor matters, that probably no two Catholics could be found who regarding their favorite devotions were absolutely identical.

The religious obligations of Catholics are few and carefully defined—attendance at Mass on Sundays and holy days, the observance of the prescribed days of fasting and abstinence, and the performance of the Easter Duties, that is, the going to confession and Communion during the Paschal season. Of course most Catholics do a good deal more than that; if so it falls under the category of "works of supererogation." These are not necessarily prayers or devotions in the ordinary sense but may be charitable works; all are conducive to salvation. Nevertheless one is sometimes a little appalled at the way one new devotional practice after another is started, so that the fear arises that, if too much is attempted, there may be an actual hampering of the spiritual life, which should depend primarily upon the Liturgy and the sacraments and meditation and (if possible) some degree of contemplative prayer. It is all too easy to get cluttered up with too many undertakings, to the neglect of what is more important.

Even such devotions as the reception of ashes on Ash Wednesday and the Veneration of the Cross on Good Friday, though they form a part of the Liturgy, are not compulsory. Yet the majority of Catholics make an effort to perform them. On the other hand, the washing of the feet on Maunday Thursday, though fairly general during the Middle Ages—especially on the part of exalted personages, who usually gave an alms to the poor whose feet they washed—has now, except in some religious communities, fallen into desuetude. It is not really less practicable today than formerly, but apparently it seems so—it may be that a good deal of the old Catholic simplicity has been lost because of the Church's having to function in a hostile world.[8]

What is universally popular—so much so that most religious wear beads hanging from the belt—is the *Rosary*. Many lay Catholics carry a rosary in their pocket. It is not necessary to believe that the Blessed Virgin gave the first rosary to St. Dominic, for rosaries of various kinds had existed before his time, and such rosaries continued to be used.[9] The rosary is a very simple form of meditation—into which indeed meditation may, in some instances, hardly enter. But the beads of the *Our Father* and *Hail Mary* can be said anywhere—in bed or walking down the street with one's hand in one's pocket. The saying of the rosary is always indulgenced, and some rosaries that have been specially blessed have extraordinarily generous indulgences attached to them. The beauty of the rosary is that, for those who can manage no more, the mere recitation of the prayers will suffice, whereas scholars and mystics can direct exalted thoughts to the fifteen joyful, sorrowful and glorious mysteries. But lest this give a wrong impression, I hasten to add that it is frequently the semiliterate who have the exalted thoughts, whereas the theologians may have three-quarters of their minds occupied with other considerations and so be only able to say the rosary by rote. There is a hierarchy *of office* in the Church, but "superior" people—or those who

[8] Young Queen Elizabeth last Maunday Thursday gave an alms to twenty-six poor people—one for each year of her life. But this time the washing of the feet was symbolized by a towel the Dean of Westminster Abbey wrapped around his waist; there was no pretense of using it.

[9] Bishop Sheen in his recent *The World's First Love* gives an explanation new to me, that as in the days of the first martyrs of the Church they marched into the Colosseum crowned with roses, these roses were afterwards used to number the prayers. I am afraid that I am not persuaded as to the truth of this, for how many roses would be left intact after the lions had done their mauling? Nor can I believe that Mohammed adopted this practice for his followers; it seems to me more likely that the Crusaders brought back the Moslem rosary to Christendom. The Bishop himself records that St. Bridget of Ireland had a rosary of her own, and we know from the contemporary portrait of the poet Chaucer, in which he was shown with a string of beads in his hands, that he used a rosary. Finally, we do not hear of the Dominican rosary until nearly two hundred years after St. Dominic's time. But while the historical origins are perhaps of little importance, it must be fully granted that the Domnicans propagated the use of the rosary.

consider themselves such—are accorded no spiritual pre-eminence.

The *Stations of the Cross* was a devotion introduced by the Franciscans (who also originated, or their founder did, the charming and touching Christmas Crib). Every church now contains the fourteen crosses which represent Christ's road to Calvary and His death on the cross. These are usually illustrated by plaques or pictures, but it is not to them but to the fourteen crosses that the indulgence is attached. The saying of the Stations led by a priest is most often done during Lent, but at any time the devotion may be made privately in church or, if that is not possible, at home before a special crucifix so blessed.

Somewhat similar to the Stations are the *Wayside Shrines* still to be found in many Catholic countries but rarely in the United States outside the grounds of some religious establishment. In Europe the shrine is usually a crucifix. In this country the shrine most frequently seen is a replica, more or less accurate, of the grotto of Lourdes, with of course the figure of Our Lady—something along the lines of Fabische's famous statue which Bernadette always said was not at all like the Blessed Virgin as seen by her—and Bernadette herself kneeling in prayer. Now the vogue of Fatima seems likely to eclipse that of Lourdes, probably because the children to whom Our Lady appeared there are reported to have given assurances about prayers for the conversion of Russia (significantly this was in 1917 before the worst of the Communist enormities); and naturally we are all terribly scared by the threat of Stalinism.

In Europe, of course, shrines abound, though the attraction of some of them has declined, and others have been obliterated. The most famous in England was that of St. Thomas à Becket at Canterbury, which drew pilgrims from all over the world—pilgrims often of a very mixed sort, as Chaucer's *Canterbury Tales* indicate. It was destroyed and pillaged by Henry VIII. The same king sent commissioners to deal with that other "object of superstition," the shrine of St. Cuthbert at Durham. When they broke his coffin open they found his body perfectly intact, and were so overawed that they wrote to Thomas Cromwell for further instructions. Meanwhile the monks at Durham buried the body in a secret place, and this secret was entrusted to three Benedictine abbots, each of whom was to nominate another abbot to take his place when he died. St. Cuthbert's burial place is therefore still known to three men, but to nobody else will the secret be divulged so long as Durham Cathedral remains in the hands of the Anglicans. The shrine of Our Lady of Walsingham has been restored in our time and has come again into Catholic possession. In Ireland Croagh Patrick, where the saint made his famous Lent, has never ceased to be a great place of pilgrimage, those who visit it going up the rocky mountain on bare feet. Other famous Irish shrines are those called St. Patrick's Purgatory at Lough Derg, St. Kevin's Bed (where the hussy Kathleen met her fate by falling off the cliff) and, more recently, that of Our Lady at Knock.

In North America there are the shrines in Mexico of Our Lady of Guadalupe, St. Rose in Lima, St. Anne de Beaupré near Quebec, and that of Frère André in Montreal. St. Anne's shrine draws nearly a million pilgrims every year, and there, as in the shrine of Brother André, one is impressed by the number of discarded crutches and votive offerings. The sensitive may be distressed at the kind of exploitation that is found, not among the custodians of the shrines but in those who hang around offering pious objects and souvenirs for sale. But such are always the concomitants of a popular devotion; one might as well blame presidential candidates for the people who do a brisk trade selling election buttons. It is worth noting that the shrine of the first citizen of the United States to be canonized—Mother Cabrini, whose remains are exposed for view in a chapel just above the George Washington Bridge in New York—is completely free from this not very edifying feature.

*Relics.* Popular custom but not, so I understand, any official decision, divides these into two classes, the first and the second. First-class relics are in the nature of things rare, as they are parts of a saint's body—usually, but not always, a fragment of bone. A second-class relic is anything that has been touched by a saint, and such relics are commonly a small particle of the clothing worn by the saint. There is a priest in this country who humorously exhibits one of his ears as a relic of this kind. It seems that as a boy he was with a group being received by Pope Pius X, recently beatified, and a Jew in the party, unfamiliar with protocol, grabbed the Pope's hand and shook it, whereupon the boy laughed. But when Blessed Pius came up to him he boxed his ears saying, "Don't be so unkind about an innocent mistake."

The Church does not guarantee the authenticity of any relic, though there is no doubt that most of them are what they purport to be. It used to be said that there were enough fragments of the True Cross to make an eighteenth-century battleship, if they were all assembled. This, however, has been conclusively shown to be a wild exaggeration; as a matter of fact it is doubtful whether there are enough of them to make a single arm of the cross.[10] Even so, some of them may not be genuine. But it would be very hard to impose on people today in a matter of this sort, and it is hard to see why it has to be supposed that those of the Middle Ages were less wide-awake than we are. Chaucer, it is true, suggests that the Pardoner among his Canterbury Pilgrims was doing a fraudulent trade in palming off "pigges' bones" for those of martyrs—but we do not hear of any of the pilgrims rushing forward to buy these spurious articles. In any case, it is a very serious offence to *sell* a relic. Those of the second-class sort are distributed among the laity, but only churches normally possess first-class relics. Indeed churches *must* have these, even if they are of ancient martyrs whose names are unknown, to embed in the altar stone upon which Mass is said. At one point the priest kisses this stone saying: "We beseech Thee, O Lord, by the merits of Thy saints, whose relics are here, and of all the saints, that Thou wouldst vouchsafe to forgive me all my sins. Amen." A good many churches also possess other precious mementos of the saints which are kept in reliquaries. Even if a few of them may not be actually genuine, grace will

[10] In the Middle Ages there may have been some passing around of spurious relics. But it must be remembered that many of these, which are now accepted as genuine, may be accounted for on the ground of honest confusion. For instance, a copy of a nail from the cross could come to be taken to be the original nail, and not even an expert archaeologist could tell the difference.

nevertheless flow to those who venerate them in good faith and devotion.

*Novenas,* which have already been touched on, merit a further word. They are of various kinds, and most of them can be said anywhere, though of course a novena of Masses can be said only in a church. In the case of some of the more popular novenas, the priest makes a point of leading his congregation in the devotion. Among these are the novenas said in honor of St. Francis Xavier, said March 4–12, and called the Novena of Grace, because it is generally accounted specially efficacious. Another is that of the Miraculous Medal, which depicts the occasion on which (November 27, 1830, and at other times) the Blessed Virgin appeared to a young Sister of Charity in Paris named Catherine Labouré, who is now canonized. In many places this is made a perpetual novena, which means that the moment one ends another begins. But again it must be said that none of these devotions are essential to Catholic life, though they are among the many indications of the devotional possibilities open to the faithful, whatever their degree of intelligence and taste. Some may appear to be rather trivial, but for many people a deeper spiritual life may begin at this point, and there are souls not capable of what is very exalted. For them this is a simple and easy way to establish contact with the divine. It goes without saying that devotions never take the place of Mass and the grace derived from the sacraments.

The mention of the Miraculous Medal brings us to a general consideration of *Medals and Scapulars* in general. The Miraculous Medal does not have any necessary connection with the novena associated with it but is worn by thousands, especially the Children of Mary and the members of the Sodality of the Immaculate Conception, merely by way of expressing their devotion to Our Lady. Among other popular medals, there is that of St. Christopher which many people attach to their cars, for this third-century saint has become the patron of travelers; and that of St. Benedict, which is always supposed to be carried by Benedictine Oblates—lay people who have an affiliation with one or other Benedictine abbey similar to that of the tertiaries in other orders. Devotion is the primary object, but a secondary object is that in the event of serious injury in an accident, those who wear these emblems will be at once recognized as Catholics and a priest will be summoned.

Somewhere between medals and scapulars is the Sacred Heart badge that is commonly attached to some part of the clothing, especially that of a sick person. There would undoubtedly be some degree of superstition in regarding this or a medal or scapular as a "charm," but it is doubtful whether there are any Catholics so poorly instructed as not to know that a material object of this sort draws all its value from being a sacramental that excites devotion and has attached to its wearing the special invocative prayer of the Church. Here we meet something similar to the charge that used to be brought against Catholics that they "worshiped" images. It is now recognized that they do nothing of the kind, as that would be idolatry; the statue or picture merely serves to call to mind the saint to whom the prayer is addressed. All this is precisely on a par with the business man who keeps a photograph of his wife and children on his desk; he knows just what they look like but finds it pleasant to let his eyes rest for a moment on their features.

A scapular is a small oblong piece of the cloth from which the religious habit is made, to indicate the order to which a person belongs as a tertiary or, in the case of the Benedictines, as an oblate. It is simply hung around the neck on a tape and symbolizes the religious habit. In addition the Carmelites have a Brown Scapular which is given to the members of the Scapular Confraternity. The famous and truculent Catholic publicist Orestes Brownson was very caustic on the subject, as he feared that many of those who wore it did so because of a promise that Our Lady is said to have given to St. Simon Stock that they would be speedily released from purgatory, especially on the Saturday following their death. This he declared to be rank superstition, and a very dangerous one, as it might lead people to neglect what is really necessary to their salvation. However, it must be said that Paul V and Benedict XIV gave permission to the Carmelite Fathers to preach what are styled the "Sabbatine Privileges," which looks like an indirect sanction of the idea. It was really not quite that, but rather an expression of toleration

on the part of two individual popes. The Church has never pronounced on the subject, nor can one imagine the Church's ever
declaring that there is any act or formula by which salvation is
assured. The most that can be affirmed is that the performance
of certain acts or the saying of certain prayers is so conducive
to the good of the soul as to augment its chances of salvation.
In some instances things of this sort may even be taken as
probable signs of one's predestination. Catholics, of all people,
know that they must work out their salvation in fear and trembling and never delude themselves that there is any short cut to
heaven.

### PRIVATE PRAYER

Most people do not pray—or suppose that they do not pray—
very much. As against this it should be remembered that even
our faintest and feeblest spiritual impulses set up "vibrations,"
so to speak, in heaven. The desire to pray is itself a prayer, and
many of those who regard themselves as rather remiss are so, if
at all, only because they do not quite know how to go about the
matter unless they have a prayer book in front of them. There is
such a thing as taking heaven by storm, but Christ did not seem
to demand any special intensity from His disciples. He told them,
it is true, the parable of the importunate man who got what he
wanted by being importunate, by making a nuisance of himself.
Yet the prayer He taught His disciples, the Lord's Prayer, is very
calm. It is impossible for most people, unless it be during some
period of exceptional stress, to do other than make their needs
quietly known to their Heavenly Father. For ordinary purposes
this is best, for it shows trust in God and submission to His will.
What Christ did tell those who followed Him was that prayer
had a special virtue when "two or three are gathered in My
name"—that is, that communal prayer (better still, liturgical
prayer) is better than any other, though He recommended them
to retire to their room and pray in secret without making any
parade of their piety.

The greatest of all prayers is the Mass, and if a Catholic does
not pray at other times, at least he prays then. Other prayers are
not binding under pain of mortal sin, but it is hard to see how

anybody can advance in the Christian life—or even be very securely a Christian at all—unless he prays. "Pray without ceasing" is less impracticable than might appear, for most good people at the start of every day make an offering of all their thoughts, words and deeds to God, by which everything is sanctified. This does not mean—usually it simply cannot mean—that the mind is consciously fastened upon God throughout all one's waking hours, for the duties of life (even the duties of priests and religious) make it difficult to pray except in brief snatches. But if the heart is set in the direction of heaven, all that happens takes a heavenly tinge. The bricklayer at his work, the housewife at her baking, can retain a filament of connection with the divine; nor is this lost in recreation, which *should be* hearty and joyous to do most good.

Fortunately long prayers, or set prayers, or even prayers that would be recognized as such, are not necessary. Christ said that it was the heathen who thought of prayer as something that had to be "spread out." Ejaculations made at intervals during the day serve to bring the mind back to God. And many manage to live in what is called the practice of the presence of God, not of course always thinking about Him but always in the certainty that He is present and that they abide in Him. Those who can make a habit of this attitude know that they have only to stretch out a hand to obtain His instant help. Even ejaculations are not necessary; prayer is a lifting of the mind and heart to God, and this may be wordless, or done without our even being aware that we are doing it.

Nearly everybody should be able to find time at least for morning and evening prayers—for these, while they are best said kneeling (the posture of prayer is itself a prayer), may be said dressing, or walking to the station, or driving a car, or in the train. It is a comely custom to have grace before and after meals to thank God for His good gifts. In some families there is even the old Irish way of the family gathering in the evening to say the rosary, and this has recently been promoted with considerable success in the United States, Canada and England, in spite of the difficulty of prying children away from the radio or television, or getting early arrived "dates" for the daughters to wait a little while. Modern life is not very conducive to piety, but after all the Church arose in a society much more inimicable to it than our own.

Morning and evening prayers, reduced to their bare bones, should consist of the Apostles Creed, the Our Father and the Hail Mary, with a petition for the repose of the souls of the faithful departed. At night there should also be an act of contrition—for who can say that he will live until morning?—but these prayers may be, and usually are, added to according to the preference of the Christian. It is not necessary to use any set prayers, though for most people these are much easier than offering something "original" to God.[11] That is why prayer books are available as a safe and convenient guide.

I have already spoken of "devotions," and any one of these may be included—or perhaps half a dozen of them. But incomparably the best of devotions is to the Blessed Trinity or to one or other of the Three Divine Persons. It should be remembered that it is to God that one always prays—whether it is to Him directly or through the saints and angels. Only a very poor Christian would forget that Mary is our Mother, or fail to place himself under her kind protection. So also we should address ourselves to the guardian angel who has us in charge, and to the saints we have chosen as our patrons. With regard to the saints we have a free and wide range of choice; all should be honored but not all will have a personal appeal.

The main thing to note is that a Catholic life, lived even in accordance with these not very exacting standards, is capable of becoming strong and beautiful. Catholics hate to appear "unco guid," and so tend to hide their spirituality. But probably many of them are mystics, in however small a way. Père Garigou-Lagrange has said: "All souls receive a general remote call to the mystical life, and if all were faithful in avoiding, as they should,

---

[11] Many Protestants—and I am thinking particularly of the admirable people among whom I had my upbringing—are so much opposed to set prayers as to avoid even the Lord's Prayer. As my father and mother happened to be exceptional people they seemed to be always able to pray spontaneously and with fervor; but how many can do so? The supposedly spontaneous prayers of the ministers in church are usually as carefully prepared as their sermons.

not only mortal but venial sin, if they were each according to his condition, generally docile to the Holy Ghost, and if they lived long enough, a day would come when they would receive the proximate and efficacious vocation to a high perfection and to the mystical life properly so called." Aldous Huxley has in several places made his own illuminating comment on the text, "Many are called but few are chosen": that this is simply because they do not choose themselves. Heaven's treasures are available to all: "Ask and you shall receive, knock and it shall be opened unto you." God is very near to us all, however far away we may be from Him. "Closer is He than breathing, nearer than hands or feet."

It has often puzzled people that their prayers go unanswered. But *are* they unanswered? They may be answered in a different way than we expect, for our foolish and turbulent hearts might ask that an enemy die—which would be not a prayer but a curse—or for something silly or, at any rate, far from being for our good. Mary Austin, who got to know the Indians well, has assured us that *they* never have any trouble about unanswered prayers; they can always get what they want. If that is really the case, they are not praying but practicing magic, something abominable to a Christian. We pray with the proviso, "If it be according to Thy will," sure that God will hear us and give us more than we would dare to ask for, if only we trust Him. While Christ encouraged us to ask for the things we need, He explained, "Your Father knoweth that you have need of all these things."

There are various kinds of prayer—the highest of which is adoration or worship, but praise, thanksgiving, sorrow for sin, reparation and petition are included. Yet St. John Damascene affirms—and St. Thomas Aquinas follows him when he treats of prayer—that there is only one kind of prayer, petition. One hesitates to disagree with such eminent authorities, who may be technically correct in the sense in which they use their terms, but surely the Mass, though it contains petitions, is basically a prayer of thanksgiving. Certainly Christian prayer is quite different from prayer in classical paganism. This is even more true of paganism at some lower levels, since it is to this or that member of the pantheon that pagans appealed to avert impending disaster or to grant favors. Never does one catch in their prayers any note of love or trust.

Nor was there in classical paganism, beautiful as so much of it is, and showing at times a spiritual insight deeper than it could itself understand, any very definite consciousness of the gods as our creators. How could this be, when everything was such a welter, when, for example, Aeneas had the man Anchises for his father but a goddess (Venus) for his mother, or when Pasiphaë, the daughter of Helios the Sun God and the wife of Minos, who was the offspring of Zeus and Europa (a mortal maiden), as a result of intercourse with a bull, bore the monster the Minotaur? As contrasted with this, Christians always pray to the Creator upon whom they depend, but to more than their Creator, to their Heavenly Father, offering Him adoration and love, seeking to know His will but laying their needs before Him, subject always to His infinite wisdom and tenderness. In His praise the human heart feels that alone it is not enough and so summons to join in the chorus the angels, the heavens, the sun and moon and stars, showers and dew, winds and tempests, cold and heat, frost and snow, night and day, light and darkness.

The Practice of the Presence of God is far more common and not nearly so difficult as might be supposed. Possibly it has never been more charmingly expounded than by Brother Lawrence, a seventeenth-century Carmelite, who after having served as a soldier and a valet, became a lay brother among the friars in middle life. Unlike the Fathers of his community, who could withdraw to their cells for quiet contemplation, Lawrence was always occupied with manual tasks, which often took him outside his monastery. Nevertheless his communion with God remained unbroken even when he had to take down the river a consignment of barrels of wine and roll these along the barge. He declared that if he picked up a straw it was for the love of God. However, I turn to a more recent author, the Jesuit Father T. F. Vaubert, who defines the practice as "a simple but affectionate remembrance of God present within us. I say a simple idea or remembrance, for it does not require any representation or image, any reasoning or effort of the mind, or labor of the imagination." He declares that it is, if faithfully practiced, the shortest way to attain perfection. It is, in other words, the recollection of our wandering thoughts, or rather, since nearly all of us are obliged to think about many matters that might seem far removed from the divine, the maintenance of a quiet core within us, of which we may or may not be conscious, except at intervals, but which we know to be always there. Out of the whirlwind of many distractions speaks the still small voice.

It is possible to have even more than this, for as I have already remarked, some degree of mysticism is within the reach of all Catholics—unless the term is to be restricted to "pure contemplatives" (and where are these to be found, unless perhaps in a Carthusian cell?)—in the frequentation of the sacraments, particularly in the reception of Holy Communion. There all achieve a union with God, and a union moreover that is to be preferred to what are too commonly considered the marks of mysticism, visions and ecstasies. So far as we know, the majority of even the greatest saints never had any experience of such things, and many who had, deprecated them, as having little if any value in themselves. We should be thankful that they do not come our way, for we might be deluded, as many others have been.

A final word as to contemplation. The Trappist Thomas Merton says in his *Ascent to Truth:* "The fact that contemplation is actually the lot of very few men does not mean that it has no importance for mankind as a whole." By this I understand him to mean that to those living engrossed by many unavoidable duties, at least the spirit of contemplation is attainable. Even in the silence and settled order of the cloister it is, in its higher reaches, relatively seldom fully won, though everything there is designed to make this possible. For those amid the hurly-burly of the world there are no such aids, and if one wants to find a cell one must withdraw into one's own heart. But precisely because our ordinary lives are so broken into by "business" of one sort or another, we need the contemplative spirit even more than does the monk. And the central part of our being *can* remain in union with God, for such a union is shattered only by sin, and should we be so unfortunate to have committed it, it can be obliterated by a single word of penitence, and reunion instantly restored.

### READING

I shall not be concerned here with spiritual reading, except the most excellent spiritual reading, the Bible, to which I shall come in a moment. My guess is that ordinarily devotional and ascetic works are read by few who are not set aside to the service of religion, and that, even in religious houses or seminaries, books of this type become known largely because a definite period of the day is set apart for them. Some of these books are first-rate and might even be described as thrilling; others are so dull and platitudinous and flaccid that one wonders how they ever got published.[12] It is books of this sort that have discouraged so many people. As they are not much read by lay Catholics I need not bring them into the discussion.

Of books of a more general character I have in mind two main kinds. There are, of course, novels and biographies and collections of poetry that may nourish the soul because of their religious import, whether explicit or implicit; the others are the books that one reads merely for the relaxation that everybody needs. In these the prevailing convention treats religion as though it does not exist, but as long as this is known to be merely a convention no harm is done. Even so much as a parson would be out of place in P. G. Wodehouse, and Angela Thirkell may give us parsons galore, but they are merely part of her social background, not one of them giving a thought to religion. Never mind, such books serve an excellent purpose, and they are, by the way, better written than many with much loftier pretensions. Of course, the best novels of all are about real rather than conventional life, and it is a very meager sort of life that is devoid of religion. Although not so long ago Catholics woefully lagged in this department of literature, it is noteworthy that some of the best novels of our times are by Catholics. At the head of the list of their writers I would place Sigrid Undset, though she is still rather neglected by Catholics; but closer to the world in which we find ourselves are Evelyn Waugh and Graham Greene,

---

12 Few of them get published today. Whether or not we are better Christians than were our fathers, we seem to be more exacting in our literary standards, even as regards religious works.

with Mauriac and Bernanos doing work of comparable value in France.

American Catholics taken as a group are not great readers of books, but I hasten to add that during the past thirty years there has been immense improvement in this respect. Whatever deficiencies there have been in the past, and which still exist to some extent, may be accounted for by complex reasons. The chief of these reasons is probably that a good many American Catholics lack intellectual antecedents and training, or come from a stratum of society where there is such a lack. Another may be that the Irish (the majority of Catholics in the East and prominent everywhere) are generally of a lively and sociable rather than a sedentary disposition. Still another reason may be that there are Catholics who are somewhat inclined to be a bit suspicious of what passes for intellectualism. While in this they are not altogether wrong, they are, upon the whole, wrong rather than right. There are people (often people with good minds, too!) who try to justify their intellectual laziness on the ground that they are striving to preserve their precious souls from "the contagion of the world's slow stain." Certainly there are books—but not a great many of them—that the average person would do well to avoid. Yet I sometimes wonder if there is any book so bad that from it a wise man is unable to learn something good.

The book that all Christians should read a great deal more than they do, if they read nothing else, is of course the Bible. Possibly it is because Catholics have noticed that many Protestants make a superstitious use of the Scriptures that they tend to neglect the sacred writings. What may have even greater weight is the fact that Catholics in their schools and colleges have to give so much time to the study of doctrine (which, naturally, cannot be studied without learning something about the Bible) that they have little leisure to spare for, let us say, the so-called Mosaic books or those that are merely historical chronicles. All these—though not to quite the same extent as the prophets—bear strongly on the promise of our Redeemer Christ, but only a careful study will make this clear; a cursory reading is not likely to be very rewarding.

Most Catholics do not know that the reading of the New

Testament for a specified time is indulgenced. This is a fact that should dispose effectually of the Protestant notion that Catholics are forbidden to read the Bible. Only the reading of Protestant versions is forbidden, first, because all of them omit some books that the Catholic Church places in its canon of scripture, second, because many of the translations are not quite accurate, and third, because some of these versions contain notes which, though in nine cases out of ten may be helpful, are occasionally not in consonance with Catholic teaching. It must be admitted, however, that the Catholic Church has produced in none of its translations of the Bible into English anything of the literary excellence of the King James version.[13] I confess to wishing that this could be adopted by the Church in all English-speaking countries—of course after the necessary revisions had been made. This, however, is not likely to happen.

It must be remembered that a great deal of the Bible is incorporated into the Introit and Gradual at Mass, and a passage from one of the Epistles is always read (the "Epistle" is occasionally taken from the Old Testament), and also another from one of the Gospels. Therefore those who assist at Mass absorb a good deal of scripture, and those who say the Office from the Breviary absorb a good deal more. In one way or another more of the Bible enters into the consciousness of Catholics than is usually supposed.

Protestant controversialists used to make much of the fact that the Bible was chained to a desk in church. This is easily explained: before the invention of printing any version of the Bible—whether in the Latin vulgate or the vernacular—was immensely valuable, and even after printing had come in a Bible was at first costly.

---

[13] Until recently the accepted Catholic version of the Bible was that made during the late sixteenth century by exiles in Douay and Rheims. It therefore antedates the King James version which, in fact, drew fairly heavily upon it. This Catholic translation was revised by Bishop Challoner in the eighteenth century but has now been generally replaced in the United States by the translation sponsored by the Confraternity of Christian Doctrine. Still more recently Monsignor Ronald Knox has come forward with a version, as though no translation had ever been made before. As one might expect from a man of his scholarship and literary distinction, it has special merits, but I must say that I do not like it very much. In the United States it has no official approval.

Bibles were chained to a lectern to prevent their being taken away, just as telephone books are chained. Because of the lack of books few people had any incentive for learning to read; but those who were literate sometimes give the impression that they were more conversant with the Scriptures than are most Catholics (or most Protestants) of our own time.

It must be plainly said that, though the Church fully accepts the Scriptures as a guide to faith, it has never regarded them, as do Protestants, as the *sole* guide. Even for the Bible the Church declares the need of an authoritative interpreter, which of course is the Church itself. There is no obscurantism here, for Christianity had spread all over the Mediterranean basin and was well established there before much of the New Testament was written. We know from two passages in St. Paul's epistles that he wrote a letter to the Corinthians, and another to the Laodiceans that have disappeared.[14] Moreover it took some time to gather together all the extant epistles, not to mention the other books of the New Testament. And because after these had been assembled, some copies proved to be better than others—for errors of transcription, omission and interpolation occasionally occurred—there is a Papal Biblical Commission which has been struggling for years to produce as nearly perfect a text as possible. Yet when (or if) this is produced, the Church will continue to base itself upon tradition as well as the written word.

The position of Protestants regarding the Scriptures is perhaps as well stated as it can be in Karl Adam's *One and Holy*. There he writes: "For a Protestant the word of the Church is not something final and supreme, the word of Christ Himself. To hear that he must go to the Bible. And since even the Bible only reveals the eternal word of the Lord in a form conditioned by the time, thus concealing it as much as revealing it, he must stretch his mind and heart to the utmost in an effort to experience Christ Himself, to penetrate through the letter of the Bible to spiritual understanding, to the reality, the very word of God. Thus the Protestant is in the last analysis thrown back on himself." The theory was once held in some quarters that the Holy Ghost

14 Cf. I Corr. v.9 and Coloss. iv.16.

could always be counted upon to elucidate to the individual believer the real meaning of the difficult and sometimes seemingly contradictory statements abounding in a given book. The trouble is that this theory manifestly does not work, and it has been the main reason for such a multiplicity of sects, each apparently sincerely convinced of its own rectitude. It is a logical impossibility that all of them could have been inspired by the Holy Ghost. The right to "private judgment" claimed by Protestantism can only bring about many vagaries of judgment, until almost the only common factor to be discovered is a rejection of Catholicism.

It is not my intention to be critical of Protestants, and what I am about to say applies only to some of them—possibly only to a few. These have a kind of Scriptural superstition, which tends to make the reading of the Bible something close to a sacrament, though of course this would be denied and should not be pressed too far. When I first went to a boarding school, for example, my mother exacted from me a promise that I would every day read a chapter of the Bible from the very handsome copy of that book she gave me at the time. (She did not, as I recall, make me promise to say my prayers, presumably because she took it for granted that I would not fail in that matter.) What was the outcome? To comply with the letter of my promise I took some pains to pick out the shortest chapters, so as to get the business disposed of as quickly as possible. Yet I must admit that by being brought up on the Bible I was given something for which I cannot be sufficiently thankful. At school, however, prayers were perfunctory, and in chapel I regret to say that we sometimes beguiled the tedium of the sermon by making a search in our Bible for what we considered the "smutty bits" and passing them along to those in the same pew for their delectation. As for our study of the Bible in the classroom—and in this we had, I believe, a lesson almost every day—we generally ploughed through an account of the kings of Israel and Judah, which I will not say was an altogether unprofitable study but which was surely not very rewarding to boys. We liked the bits about Ahab's enormities and Jezebel's being thrown out of the window, but most of these chronicles made slight impression on us. It was quite different with the piety of our Bible-reading household at home. While I would gladly exchange it for a Catholic upbringing, it was definitely of great spiritual benefit. It is no doubt true that Catholics do not as a rule make sufficient use of the treasures of the Bible, but they get something still better—a firm grounding in faith and a moral discipline which Protestantism as it is now constituted seems unable to exercise.

In seminaries the Scriptures are, of course, studied in regular courses, and in religious orders, where the Office is said, the psalms and other biblical passages which constitute most of it come to be known almost by heart. This is true even of some of the laity with regard to certain of the psalms. In such institutions there is always reading aloud during meals, and usually books are chosen that bear upon religion, but out of consideration for divided attention, these, for the most part, are not too formidable. For several of the seven months I spent in England as a Dominican novice, for instance, we had to listen to Josephus during our midday dinner (and how we groaned!) but at supper we were let off lightly with the autobiography of Mrs. Hugh Fraser, the sister of Marion Crawford, a lively and entertaining work that hardly touched upon religion at all.

A few parishes have libraries, but fewer still have a library that is of much service, for the shelves are usually stocked with books that parishioners have donated because they did not want them. Such being the case, slight use is made of these libraries, though I have seen some (and that connected with St. Peter's on Barclay Street, New York City, comes to mind) from which people do borrow with avidity, for while the number of books is not very large they are carefully chosen. However, when priests advocate the reading of Catholic literature, I am afraid that more often than not they are only thinking of the diocesan newspaper sold at the church door on Sunday, and most of these do little more than give diocesan news. One of them, the *Hartford Transcript*, has as good a literary page as one could hope to find, conducted by Father John F. Kennedy. Not all the others follow the policy of the man in *Hudibras:*

> To prove their doctrine orthodox
> By apostolic blows and knocks,

but there are apparently editors of Catholic papers who walk about with a chip on their shoulder and are much admired for doing so.

The pamphlets which are sometimes offered for sale are in many cases ably written but, because they usually discuss some practical problem, they do not accomplish much by way of generally enriching the mind. However, during the last twenty or thirty years there has been an immense improvement all along the line, and further improvement may be expected. What is still lacking is a daily newspaper under Catholic editorship that is at all comparable to the *Christian Science Monitor*. Nearly a century ago Isaac Hecker projected such a paper, and since he had what was, for those days, good financial backing, he might have made a success of it had his health not broken down before he could start publication. The daily paper published for a while at Dubuque, Iowa, had too small a circulation in too narrow an area to accomplish much, and it has now been transformed into a diocesan weekly. The various Catholic foreign-language dailies which are, so I believe, still in existence, fail to do more than meet sectional needs. Catholics are therefore thrown back upon newspapers which may have discovered that it is good policy to be formally respectful towards the Church, but often pander to the lowest instincts of their readers.

Recently there was a valiant attempt to supply the crying need for American Catholics when the *Sun Herald* was founded in Kansas City, Missouri, and began publication on a capital of $10,000 and with a daily circulation of 2,900. It operated from October 10, 1950, until April 28, 1951, by which time it had a circulation of 10,500, 94 per cent of which was national. It then transferred itself to New York City, where it was to have appeared under the name of the *New York Banner*. While financial backing was being sought, a few issues appeared monthly (from September, 1951, to January, 1952). Now the promoters have reached the regretful conclusion that they must abandon their project. Miss Norma Ann Krause, the general manager, has supplied me with information of their doings and with copies of what they did publish. Good as the undertaking was, so far as it went, it was not quite what was needed; in any event adequate support was not forthcoming. Catholics will have to wait for a first-rate daily until the times are more propitious.

A heartening sign of our times was the founding of the *Commonweal* by a group of laymen twenty-six years ago. Included among its original board of trustees were several non-Catholics of general Catholic sympathies, and though these dropped away after a time (a great pity to my mind) the *Commonweal* is not to be classified as a Catholic magazine, but rather as a weekly review edited by laymen, writing as such and without claiming official standing. I imagine they must get vastly annoyed to see themselves constantly referred to as "liberal Catholics," though I do not suppose they would object to the transposition of these terms. The magazine has had a considerable influence and has done much good, but, like most periodicals of its type, it has often found itself in financial difficulties. Several times it seemed on the point of expiring, but quite recently has had an astonishing success in its drive for new members, so that it is assured of continuance if not of permanence. One suspects that some small literary and philosophical magazines, such as the one edited by John Pick of Marquette University, are in a precarious position, but it is good to see that there are people with the courage to undertake these ventures. Their appearance is another sign of the intellectual vitality to be found among American Catholics. *Integrity,* a magazine of a different type, is a brave venture but would be journalistically better if it were less eccentric. In my estimation by far the best of all such periodicals is the *Catholic Worker.* Started on a shoestring and almost by accident twenty years ago by Dorothy Day, it now has a circulation of 150,000.[15] I strongly dissent from the pacifism of its editors, and have told them so plainly, but it would be hard to think of any Catholic publication which offers so moving a presentation of Christian realities, not merely in theory but in the lives of this group. The *Catholic Worker* is not only a peri-

[15] She calls herself an ex-Communist, but probably was never one of the kind with whom we have grown familiar. In any event, she is almost alone in never having tried to cash in by turning informer against her former associates; instead she follows the method of approach of looking for whatever good there may be in them.

odical but a record of various heroic enterprises furthered by Dorothy Day and her friends. It is a wonder that these enterprises can survive at all, but they seem to increase and expand under her direction, even while always hanging on the very edge of the abyss.[16]

Although Catholic books and magazines are now of a much higher quality than they used to be in this country, it is still lamentable that with 30,000,000 members of the household of faith,[17] we should put so small a mark on the intellectual life of America, while English Catholics, though only a tenth of that number, have an influence quite out of statistical proportion. Perhaps the reason may be that in the large centers of population, where Catholics are mostly gathered, they are tempted to throw their weight into local politics, often with unfortunate results. In England, on the other hand, the Catholic flies above the murk and mud to more serene regions, finding it unnecessary to drag out a Communist from under every bed. By dealing instead with the essentials of Catholicism he wins a respectful hearing. The American Catholic, on the other hand, often merely succeeds in antagonizing his fellow countrymen by seeming to claim that opposition to Communism was his own bright little idea. Apart from all this, it must be pointed out that many of the best Catholic brains are drawn into organizations which may provide an invaluable framework for the future, but whose immediate impact upon the mass of the American people is largely lost.

For a final word about Catholic books: Where formerly these stood little chance of publication outside avowedly Catholic firms, now all publishers have suddenly discovered that there is a good general market for them—a market by no means limited to Catholics—and so are anxious to get some Catholic titles on their list. The book I am now writing is a case in point: it is one

[16] As I write this, word comes of a new Catholic magazine to be conducted by lay editors formerly on the *New Yorker, Look* and *Collier's* that is to be financed by its charter members and named *Jubilee*. While wishing it good luck, I would have preferred to see a daily newspaper.

[17] Again I remark that the official figure is 26,000,000 but is manifestly too low. On the other hand a good many Catholics—how many, nobody knows—are not very regular in the practice of their religion.

more indication that there now exists a wide interest in Catholicism. While it is impossible to say that this interest in Catholicism is going to last—for it is without any precedent in the United States—I see no reason why, once started, it should not increase. But as to that, of course, I make no prophecy.

# CHAPTER SIX

## The Life of Discipline

### A WARFARE

All human beings are conscious of a division in themselves; only too often they fail to do the good they desire, and perform the evil they wish to avoid. The world, the flesh and the devil are always with us, so also is our human nature which, even after having been cleansed from original sin in baptism, still suffers from its vitiating effects. Only by dint of great resolution and courage can we so much as hold our ground; indeed, if we do no more than hope for that, we are in danger of collapse: what we must do is never to give up trying to advance, and not be discouraged even when we seem never to go forward an inch. The struggle counts far more than the success that may attend it.

Asceticism, of whatever kind, is intended to subdue the impulses that war against the spirit, though it can have a further purpose—the preparation for the soul's illumination, its union with God. Before that can begin, the Christian has to be ready to subject his whole being to God, which in a few instances is so decisively complete that all is accomplished at a stroke, but which usually is a long process with many discouraging setbacks. "The devil goeth about as a roaring lion seeking whom he may devour." While we have constantly to be on guard against him, even more we have to watch for the fickle or treacherous movements of our own hearts.

There are still cases of diabolical obsession or possession, and though these are now very rare, they were once common, as witness the frequency with which Christ cast out devils.[1] Such

[1] I do not know how to account for this except on the ground that the appearance on earth of the God-Man, being recognized as a challenge to the

possession can occur only because of the yielding of the will, for the devil has no power over God's children. Should that grisly and terrifying shape appear to any of them, he may be put to quick flight by the sign of the cross, by holy water, or even by ridicule. St. Thomas More has assured us that there is nothing the foul fiend more dreads than to be mocked. Yet I do not forget that the Curé of Ars had his brief sleep broken nearly every night for twenty years and that when at last the apparitions ceased, the Curé, who had borne it all with humorous patience, said, "The *grappin* and I had almost become old comrades." The fact that such assaults were made at all would seem to indicate that Lucifer has lost most of the intelligence he once had, and now possesses little but low cunning. However, as this is enough to inform him that our own propensities offer enough for his purpose, he rarely has to put himself to any further trouble. It is most unlikely that we shall be bothered by him except in this way.

As for our human frailties, it is a matter of observation that certain sins, if persisted in, will weaken faith. This is specially true of sins of impurity, which, though not among the worst of sins (for the worst are those of a spiritual nature), are among the most serious in their possible social effect and the coarsening they impart to the character. Robert Burns was a deep psychologist when, prescinding from all moralizing, he cried out, drawing upon his own considerable experience:

> I waive the quantum of the sin,
>  The hazard of concealing;
> But och, it hardens all within
>  And petrifies the feeling.

The effect of other sins may be despair—as with intemperance, for example. Many a person gets drunk in order to escape the necessity of contemplating himself; he is drunk on Wednesday so as not to be under the disgusting necessity of remembering

---

whole kingdom of Satan, brought about a concerted effort on the part of the demoniac powers. Today, however, because of Christ, grace has re-entered the world in abundance and Satan's power to possess has correspondingly diminished.

what he was on Tuesday. It used to be said of priests who left the Church that it was always because of either Punch or Judy. This is witty but by no means invariably true. When it is true, "Punch" and perhaps even "Judy" are due not so much to malice as to human weakness. And these weaknesses, like the weakness of an irascible temper, may be such a grief to the one who has it as to be veritably a cross. The struggle with one's self may actually be more meritorious than an easy and comfortable virtue. Most of us know alcoholics who are basically good people but who have a terrible affliction.

In one way or another we may be sure that a cross is going to be laid upon our shoulders. In this vale of tears it is not necessary to seek out suffering. Sooner or later it is certain to come, and the way it is received can either harden and embitter or make radiant. When we do what Christ told us to do and take up our cross, it instantly becomes lighter. St. Thérèse of Lisieux was able to say that she no longer had any sufferings, because they were all joys to her.

This is obviously entirely different from a grim stoicism, rather noble though that may be. Nor is it a question of grinning and bearing it, or keeping a stiff upper lip, or packing up one's troubles in the old kit bag—good as this somewhat facile advice may be in overcoming life's minor irritations and disappointments. There are three ways of meeting these, and more serious troubles: the cowardly way, the manly way, and the Christian way. Following the cowardly way, one commits suicide or goes insane (for psychiatrists assure us that insanity is a mode of escape, just as alcoholism ordinarily is). The manly way is admirable but, if relied on solely, insufficient; and it has its limits. The Christian way may include something of manliness, for despite Nietzsche (who escaped through the door of insanity) Christianity is *not* a religion for slaves. It may be laid down as axiomatic that the supernatural always builds on the natural; although the natural virtues may be rather feeble, it is such virtue as is already there that God uses.

### MORTIFICATION

For all those who aspire to the spiritual life some sort of mortification is indispensable. About this, the eighteenth-century Protestant mystic, William Law, wrote: "Many people not only lose the benefit, but are even the worse for all their mortifications. It is because they mistake the whole nature and worth of them. They practice them for their own sake, as things good in themselves; they think them to be a real part of holiness, and so rest in them and look no further, and grow full of self-esteem and self-admiration for their progress in them." That is perfectly true, but is not very likely to happen among Catholics, as in the ordinary course of things they would consult a spiritual director, and he would be counted upon to disabuse their minds of any such ideas as William Law rightly condemns. It is worth noting that the Benedictine Rule, which to a large extent was a reaction against the asceticism of the Desert—and even against the Rule of St. Basil, which sought to moderate the extravagances practiced there—specifically forbade the practice of any mortifications (outside the ones prescribed by the Rule itself) except when these were, in every instance and for each individual, sanctioned by the abbot.

One might begin with what is called "the use of creatures." This means that the Christian is warned against preferring any person or place or thing (good though they may be) to the Creator Himself. "Thou hast made us for Thyself," runs the great Augustinian saying, "and our hearts can find no rest until they find rest in Thee." This does not mean of course that our love of God, and our usefulness in His service, may not be increased by our use of creatures, but only that such use (which may include love) should be subordinated to the divine love. Even what is perfectly harmless and innocent in itself may become a hindrance to spiritual progress. "No one," writes St. John of the Cross, "desires to be loved except for his goodness; and when we love in this way our love is pleasing to God and in great liberty; and if there be attachment in it there is greater attachment to God." In other words, there may be considerable help in the spiritual life from creatures if the ultimate object of love is God Himself. A fine poem by Louise Imogen Guiney opens:

> All else for use, One only for desire;
> Thanksgiving for the good, but thirst for Thee:
> Up from the best, whereof no man need tire,
> Impel Thou me.

Such is the basis of mortification, and far from being a peculiarly Catholic (or even a Christian) commodity, every religion demands it. Indeed, it could, I think, be shown that even those who have no real conviction of the existence of God but who have an ethical ideal, are, in the nature of things, obliged to practice some form of asceticism. It is St. Paul who uses the illustration of the way an athlete must train to indicate what he means about buffeting his body and bringing it into subjection. I can have *this* only on condition that I forego *that*.

There are many kinds of mortification. As a rule it is sufficient to accept those that come unsought. It may, for instance, be harder to put up with inconsiderate people or to suffer fools gladly than to wear a hair shirt or sleep on the floor. Blessed Angela of Foligno has said: "No efforts or expense seem too great to purchase our escape from the afflictions which God sends us; and yet they are more beneficial and more meritorious than voluntary penances. For God knows better than we in what regard and by what means our soul has need of being purified and regenerated. Besides, labors and penances which are taken on voluntarily and by choice leave still open, good as they are, a free field for self-love. For these come upon us unexpectedly and undesired, even if we endure them with patience or with joy, seem always impositions, not the growth of our own will and desire; and therefore they exclude self-love and vanity." Similarly St. Francis de Sales wrote in his *Introduction to the Devout Life*, a book which had its origin in the letters he wrote his mother and another highborn lady, Madame de Charmoissy (whom he combined in his book into the character of Philothea—in this passage imagined as a woman of a lowlier station): "Your poverty, Philothea, enjoys two great privileges, by means of which you may considerably enhance its merits. The first is that it came not to you by chance, but by the will of God, who has made you poor without any concurrence of your own will. . . . The second privilege of this kind of poverty is that it is truly poverty. That poverty which is praised, caressed, esteemed, succored and assisted [he is referring to those who might have enjoyed riches but have taken a vow of poverty] is not altogether poverty; but that which is despised, rejected, reproached and abandoned, is poverty indeed . . . for which reason their poverty exceeds that of the religious; although otherwise the poverty of the religious has a very great excellency."

The cross is for all Christians. Christ, the Head of the Mystical Body the Church, has suffered, and if the members are to be worthy of their membership, they must be prepared for their share of renunciation. This is what St. Paul means when he says, "I fill up that which is lacking in the sufferings of Christ." Like Simon of Cyrene, we must help Him to carry His cross; and even such holy souls as have expiated their own sins are drawn by love to try, in so far as this lies within their power, to expiate the sins of others. This was excellently put by Simone Weil, "The supreme greatness of Christianity derives from the fact that it does not seek a supernatural remedy against suffering but a supernatural use of suffering." Christianity is the religion of the cross, and nobody can be a Christian who does not answer Christ's call, "Take up thy cross and follow Me."

I have said that the best mortifications are not those which we choose but those chosen for us by God. However, in addition to these the good Christian will seek out mortifications, the renunciation of this or that permissible pleasure, not because the renunciation is admirable in itself, but because it is a means to a spiritual end. Always the good laid aside should be given up for a greater good. Mortifications of this sort should, whenever possible, be secret, to guard against vainglory. Yet some private penances cannot be concealed, like that black glove that Daniel O'Connell always wore on his right hand when going to Holy Communion, because this hand had killed D'Esterre in a duel.

Mortifications, moreover, should be conditioned by our state in life: thus a man would be distinctly displeasing to God if he announced to his wife that, as a mortification, he intended to forego the marital act. (If this were done by mutual consent, it would be a different matter: St. Paul envisages this, but only that they may be the more free to give themselves to prayer "for a season.") Similarly if a woman became so pious as to neglect her home and husband and children because of the long hours she spent in church, she might come to plume herself on being very devout but actually would be doing a grave wrong to those who had just claims upon her. If she wants to mortify herself, let her get down on her hands and knees and scrub the kitchen floor for the greater glory of God.

The Church is eminently reasonable about all this. It does not itself impose many mortifications, recognizing that God will send some suffering to all, and that most good may be extracted from the way it is accepted. But since many people seem to be able to go through life without having to put up with anything very serious, at any rate with very little compared with what others have to undergo, all are reminded that the exercise of moral discipline is inescapable, and that this too can be a cross—indeed it will be a cross to our ill-regulated dispositions.

The mortifications enjoined by the Church are not very onerous. Once in all conscience they were very severe, in fasting especially. Thus up to the eighth century during Lent there was an unbroken fast all day until the late afternoon after Vespers. Then, as in the monasteries' *collationes* (or spiritual conferences where lives of the saints were read), a meal of eight or ten ounces of food was permitted. Now a fairly decent breakfast is permitted, a good dinner (with meat except on Fridays and a few other days of the season), and a "collation" or light supper (which may be a light lunch instead). Ten years or so ago, a simplification of the law was introduced under which the working man's privileges were withdrawn (since nearly everybody could claim them anyway), so that the fasting regulations were uniform. But they are not binding on those under twenty-one or over fifty-nine. Dispensations are obtainable but are now less necessary than formerly.

As for the Friday abstinence, this does not usually involve a fast as well, and although abstinence merely means giving up meat, people think of it rather loosely as meaning the eating of fish. Unless there is a fast one may eat all the fish (or other meatless foods) one wishes, with due regard to the constitution of one's digestive capacities. Erasmus complained that he did not have a "Catholic stomach." Orestes Brownson, perhaps the most powerful mind Catholic America has produced, was another man who lacked a Catholic stomach—and was bad-tempered on the days when he was unable to consume his customary gargantuan quantities of beef. This does not bother me; on any day in the week I would as soon eat fish as meat. What makes me wonder is how the Christians of the first seven centuries supported their burdens—and whether all of them really observed the ecclesiastical law according to the letter.

Of course, other things are recommended to Catholics during Lent, but not commanded. Many abstain from liquor during that time (probably rather to their general good); others do not go to the theatre; still others do not exercise their marital privileges. (This last was rather general in the days when Lent was strictly kept, but even then it was not ordained.) All are told that during this season they should give themselves more than at other times to prayer and almsgiving, though the interpretation of this is left to the individual. All that is absolutely enjoined is set out clearly in the pastoral letter that each bishop sends out to be read in every church under his jurisdiction. And if there is a diocesan newspaper, the Lenten regulations are published there.

There is no doubt that during Lent and similar periods—the three Ember Days, for example, that fall four times a year, and on the eve of the major feasts—the Church is now very lenient. This does not mean that standards have been relaxed but that the wisdom garnered over the centuries has brought the Church to see that it would be better not to demand more than is likely to be carried out, lest consciences be troubled. Also our standard of living has risen to such a degree that most people take certain comforts—harmless enough in themselves, though maybe rather enervating—for granted. For such people it might be more of a hardship to be deprived of the relaxation of the movies and television than it was for a sixth-century man to subsist on a daily allotment of half a pound of bread. The Catholic Church is really a very sensible institution—inflexible in principle but extremely flexible in the face of special needs.

For this reason the ferocious macerations that ascetics formerly went in for are now definitely discouraged. A mild practicing of the discipline is about as far as anybody goes. And if one wishes to sleep on the floor, no objection is likely to arise, if only because nobody is likely to know about it. In a highly diverting essay Aline Kilmer once described the difficulties a person might encounter in hunting for a hair shirt. In what section of a department store would they be offered for sale? Or would one have to buy an old horse-hair sofa and cut it down to fashion a shirt for one's own wear? Or do like the old lady in the fairy tale who wove her own hair? But her hair always grew again by the morning, and Aline was afraid that her own would *not*. I have heard that hair shirts are still worn by a few people, and that they do not create excruciating pain but give an itch. This may be rather unpleasant but St. Thomas More put up with it for nearly forty years, all of which time he managed to be the most engaging and affable of men. The older type of ascetic (using the word as meaning the exaction from oneself of physical pain) would not now be tolerated in the most austere order. That sort of thing was admittedly practiced by the monks of the Desert; although as Helen Waddell's charming anthology makes clear, their asceticism was usually something sweeter and simpler. Today the kind of asceticism advocated by St. Francis de Sales is taken as the norm, though even during his lifetime there lived in Peru the half-Spanish, half-Indian St. Rose of Lima whose macerations were startling. One would think she was living in a different world; and indeed she was, not only about seven thousand miles away but centuries distant in spiritual climate. She must have been about the last of the ascetics of the old school. Even so, never has the Church approved the sort of macerations that are still practiced by the fakirs of India. The greatest austerities in the history of the Church have never been masochistic, but have been a means to an end and not the end itself.

For a long while the emphasis of Catholic asceticism has been laid on the mortification of the will, and even this is nothing unless it means conformity with the will of God. So there is really nothing very terrifying in the word mortification, if understood in this sense. Who can be a Christian and not wish to conform himself to the will of One who said, "My burden is easy and My cross is light"? There are, it is true, some contemplative orders in which life is lived according to a strict mode—no meat at any time, an almost perpetual silence, a sleep broken for the saying of Office in the small hours, and a bare bed covered with straw. But the Trappists and Carthusians find even physical compensations in their mode of life, as is evident from their serene air and a complexion like a child's. I have heard it said (I do not know with what degree of truth) that cancer never is known among them. And a philosopher as well as a saint might cry, *O solitudo beata! O sola beatitudo!*

Whatever excess there may have been in the mode of asceticism was still due to a striving for sanctity, but a striving at a time when Christian experience had much to learn, so that it sometimes took fantastic forms. Asceticism itself is not *passé;* it is now better understood, better controlled, wiser; it still has the same object in view, a subjection of the will—and through the will the turbulent body—to God's plan for us. It is not something to be practiced according to our own fancies but under a spiritual director who knows the special make-up of his individual penitents.

One form of asceticism is the control of one's thoughts, which also means the control of one's eyes and speech. Especially is this true with regard to the erotic imagination, probably never to be entirely uprooted, and which may even grow stronger with the decline of physical powers, as age advances. La Rochefoucauld said that there comes a time when one does not give up one's vices, but they give one up. It is not true as far as the mind is concerned, and Christ has told us that to look upon a woman with lust is to commit adultery with her.

St. Francis of Assisi, though not among the greatest of ascetics of the physical sort, had been severe enough to make him think in later life that he had been too hard on "Brother Ass," the body. St. Francis Xavier once—only once, as far as we know—attempted a most injudicious form of maceration, from which he might have died; afterwards he left such things and became a whirlwind of work in God's service. And St. Ignatius, who also had some injudicious asceticism of which to repent, wrote to the Duke of

Gandia, now St. Francis Borgia: "With regard to the castigation of the body, I would be for avoiding altogether any form of it that could cause a single drop of blood to appear.... Instead of seeking to shed our blood, it is much better to seek directly the Lord of us all and His holy gifts, such as tears for our sins ... and intensification of our faith, hope and charity, joy in God and spiritual peace." Though Christ said that some things come not except by prayer and fasting, the only time we hear of His fasting was when He spent forty days alone in the desert, when He was tempted of the devil. The fasting of His disciples, He said, would come later; while the Bridegroom was with them they were not to mourn. So it must not be thought that there is even the slightest suggestion being made here that physical austerities have no value, for they have much if wisely and moderately used as a means of taming the clamorous appetites of the unruly body. But there is little if any merit in the infliction of such mortifications for their own sake; it is quite different with regard to interior mortifications: these are a bending of the will in submission to God, and without such submission there can be no spiritual life.

### EXTERNAL DISCIPLINE

It is unnecessary in a book of this sort to touch, even briefly, upon such matters as are expounded in a simple popular way in what Michael Williams wrote, with Julia Kernan's collaboration, in *The Catholic Church in Action*. For while every Catholic is always keenly aware of his obedience to the Pope, he is not often made conscious of the way the Church's organization operates in Rome. He knows, of course, that there is the College of Cardinals, but he does not know as a rule (nor does he usually need to know) in what way they function; still less does he know much (if anything) about the various Roman Congregations and Tribunals and Offices and Commissions, for though his religious life may be more affected by their decisions than he is aware, this does not happen to him directly but through the bishop of the diocese in which he happens to live. Ordinarily he is not even very conscious of his bishop but rather of the bishop's local delegate, his own pastor. His Catholic life runs along very evenly, and only under very exceptional circumstances is there anything in the least out of the way. Yet the smooth working of the machine (if we may call it that) is due to the close synchronization of all its parts.

Much of the external discipline of the Church, in the form in which it has sometimes existed in the past, is now outmoded. For instance we are never again likely to see a pope releasing subjects from their secular allegiance, as happened in the case of Queen Elizabeth I; even St. Pius V, who took this step, afterwards admitted that it had been an error in judgment, as it was certainly something that came too late to be of any use. Similarly the Roman Inquisition (a part of the duties of the Holy Office) has somewhat declined in notoriety, if not in real importance. While it does the same work and passes the same kind of judgments, its penalties are now spiritual and are not implemented by civil enforcement. The Church's disciplinary machinery still exists and formal censures can be, and sometimes are, issued. But diocesan authority normally suffices, and when it is exercised will almost certainly be upheld should an appeal be made to the Holy See. An instance of this may be cited: the flurry in 1928 when a group of French-Canadian extraction in Rhode Island were at odds with their bishop over his alleged conspiracy to assimilate them to American culture in their parochial schools. (They were themselves American citizens but wanted to retain French as their language.) They may, for all I know, have had a good case, but they should have been better advised than to bring action against their bishop in a civil court, for by this they incurred excommunication. Their appeal to Rome failed, as they should have foreseen if they had taken the trouble to look up Canon Law. But in general it must be said that the ecclesiastical machine operates so smoothly that one is hardly aware that it is operating at all. Non-Catholics sometimes picture the laity groveling before a clergy whose boots tread on thoroughly cowed necks. It is not like that. Only once in a very long while is there even the slightest cause for friction. If friction should arise, however, there is a method of dealing with it, according to long-established principles of ecclesiastical law but also with due allowance for natural human susceptibilities. Even non-Catholic bodies have a conception of law, though it is not usually clearly defined, and practically never can be effectually enforced.

In the past, as everybody knows, the Pope was the actual secular ruler of considerable territory. This was not altogether to the advantage of the Church, because the Pope, in his secular capacity, was every now and then involved in war, which usually weakened his spiritual prestige. Yet when Italy took possession of the Papal States, successive popes shut themselves up in the Vatican, as voluntary prisoners, rather than acknowledge themselves as subjects of a civil authority. These popes continued to claim the temporal power, since only as ruling sovereigns could they treat with other states on equal terms. The situation was different from what it had been during the first centuries of the Church, when the Pontiff had merely spiritual jurisdiction. The question was not resolved until 1929 with the signing of the Treaty of the Lateran; then the independent temporal sovereignty of the Pope was acknowledged over the State of Vatican City—a state of not much more than a hundred acres. Its size is of no consequence; what matters is that the Pope is now an independent ruler, and as such is free to deal with the government of any country.

Of course even when the Pope was the "Prisoner of the Vatican" he continued to have diplomatic representatives at his court from many states. And the United States itself had a minister there previously, from 1848 to 1867. Since the spiritual jurisdiction of the Holy Father is world-wide, many questions arise that can only be handled through diplomatic agencies. As for purely ecclesiastical matters, these are so intricate that the business has to be subdivided and given over to this or that Papal department established for the particular purpose. This is not unlike the government of this country, which has to function through a number of different departments, most of them under a member of the Cabinet. When his government is operating well, the average American does not hear much about what is going on; similarly the average lay (or even clerical) Catholic is very content with a machine that functions so justly and so well. Even Canon Law, of which a revised code was issued in 1917, to be effective the following year, does not have in it much that could be of great practical interest to the layman, except perhaps in so far as its regulations bear upon marriage. He knows Catholic discipline to be internal rather than external—a point which it is to be feared many non-Catholics completely miss.

Now and then, however, an attempt is made to establish locally some sort of external discipline for a special purpose. I may be accused of dragging the matter in by the hair, but perhaps the Legion of Decency could be offered as an example.[2] Although it is a national organization, it is rather a plan of boycott, and as such it is not binding on anybody, except to the extent that the taking of a pledge gives further sanction to what all Catholics know is binding upon them without it—the avoidance of objectionable plays and movies. But what *is* objectionable? American Catholics are furnished for their guidance with lists of movies (from various dioceses). These are divided into categories: the unobjectionable, the objectionable in part (which are supposed to be all right for adults—and where are adult minds to be found?) and the wholly objectionable. The last category is very small. Indeed, except for a few notorious cases, it would be hard for most people to know where such movies were being shown. I imagine that one would have to prowl along such places as the Bowery or State Street, Chicago, to discover them should one be resolutely determined to be depraved. But as I have seen such movies, let me give my opinion that they are so stupid and vulgar as to be innocuous to all except adolescents. What are far more dangerous are movies which are artistically on a much higher plane—sometimes they are technically admirable—which leave their audiences with the idea that all that matters in life is what they (but not I) call love, and that adultery and divorce are part of high society. Although those who see them may have come to realize that they cannot aspire to the lavish mode of life depicted in these films, apart from the gadgets which to them

[2] I do not know how accurate it is to style it an "organization." If it is one, I am afraid that it does not operate very efficiently. In the churches of all the dioceses in which I have lived since its establishment, it comes (as far as I can see) into existence on one Sunday a year, when all the members present at Mass are asked to rise and take an oral pledge. It does not seem to me that this is nearly so effective as would be the signing of such a pledge.

seem an indispensable part of the "good life," they may be tempted at least to pattern themselves on Hollywood in its lower aspects.

It must be remembered that the handling of the movie situation is a diocesan matter, and not all diocesan offices take the same line. Thus there was recently a mild uproar over *The Miracle*, when New York State invoked against it the law against blasphemy. In the first place I believe that blasphemy is something very difficult to define, though the New York law has its own definition. But if we leave legal technicalities, I believe it may be said that real blasphemy is possible only to a believer in God. For example, although it may be technically blasphemous to say that Jesus Christ was a mere man, those who say so are, for the most part, at least not culpable; but a Catholic who made this downright assertion would assuredly be blasphemous. Apart from this, I would question whether it is ever advisable for the Church to instigate the state to take action in a question of this sort, for at once great resentment is aroused. Nevertheless, the Church has the right to call the attention of the state to anything that apparently infringes the secular law. I have, myself, no opinion about this movie, as I never saw it; but a number of nationally-known Catholics, headed by Otto L. Spaeth, the President of the American Federation of Arts, who did see it, unanimously gave it their approval as "a profoundly religious film."

I have already mentioned another movie, *God Needs Men*, which, coming right after *The Miracle*, one might suppose would also have been condemned. It passed without any official objection at all. In any event an unfavorable opinion passed in one diocese would not bind Catholics elsewhere.

Nevertheless, the principle behind all this is sound. A bishop is empowered to prohibit for his diocese in much the same way as the famous *Index Librorum Prohibitorum* orders Catholics, unless they have special permission, not to read the works that it lists. This sounds very drastic, and in one sense it is; but to the non-Catholics who accuse the Church of obscurantism, I will ask a simple question: Would they permit their children to read what were, in their estimation, bad books? Surely they would not wish the minds of their children to be soiled by filth. Well, Catholics object not only to pornography but to writings (which are far more dangerous) calculated to undermine faith. Even state laws prosecute lasciviousness, hard though this may be to define.

Let us dispose of this point first: Few, if any, books are totally bad—at least I have read few bad books from which I have not derived some profit. Yet I am in my sixties, and have a large reading experience, so mine is hardly an average case. What the Church does is to list books that most people had better avoid. As a rule these are of a philosophical or theological or historical character, for works that might inflame the passions are governed by the general law. But the latest edition of the *Index* was published in 1938, and few lay Catholics have any very definite idea as to what it contains. (The edition I saw was issued about 1915, and I had time to do no more than glance at its contents.) The additions that are constantly made to the *Index* appear in the *Acta Apostolicae Sedis*, which one would have to go to a monastery or seminary to see.[3]

One might suppose from this that the *Index* cannot be very effective. If so, this removes one of the arguments as to the supposititious tyranny of the Church. As a matter of fact, it would be quite impossible for the Roman authorities to examine more than a small proportion of the books now published annually. At most they examine a few notorious cases. It is the bishops who nowadays have to exercise the practical censorship. If they exercise it at all, it is only by way of protecting those under them. After all, the Church does exist to save souls, and souls may be seriously damaged by reading matter. The position of the Church becomes clear when one thinks of the relation of a father to his children. For the permission to read books known to be on the *Index* a Catholic should approach his ordinary, and if there is any good reason for granting this, it is readily obtainable.

What should be deplored is the way unofficial Catholic groups sometimes take it upon themselves to exercise censorship. They often are not very intelligent in the matter, and even when there

[3] The only book available on the subject in English as far as I know is *What Is the Index?* by Redmond A. Barke, C.S.V., the Director of Libraries of De Paul University.

is validity in their views, the bishop of the diocese is the only person empowered to take action.

## INTELLECTUAL DISCIPLINE

Most people imagine that Catholics can have scarcely any intellectual freedom at all. They might even gather that impression from what has just been said about the reading of forbidden books, though the matter does not loom very large in the consciousness of Catholics. It has been said, and cannot be said too often, that Catholicism reposes upon authority. *Sine auctoritate nulla vita.* The favorite current gibe is that the Church is the perfect instance of totalitarianism, for apparently its steady opposition to Communism is not to be credited to her, as neither are the Papal warnings against Nazism and Fascism. If people would just sit down quietly for five minutes and think, they would surely see that the authoritarianism (which is anything but totalitarian) means that, on the supposition that God exists and that we are His creatures, we owe Him an absolute obedience. The state—or any form of secular authority—has rightfully only such powers as God assigns to it, for such powers come from God, though the community is ordinarily a party to the transaction. (Let our critics look at the American Constitution as a case in point.) These powers may be enlarged or diminished or abrogated; they can never be regarded as absolute. It is the claim to *omnicompetence* on the part of secular authority which is the essence of the evil of totalitarianism. The fallible human instrument of government acts as though infallible, and buttresses itself with the apparatus of secret police, confessions extorted by physical or psychological torture, execution chambers, and labor camps where, at the moment I write, millions of human beings are undergoing a living death. I believe the Catholic lives most at ease in a democracy because it is the form of government most consonant with Catholicism, but even to democracy one cannot accord a divine sanction, except in so far as it is in accord with natural rights, and these operate only in accord with the law of God.

I have already indicated the basis of the Church's authority, which prescinds from purely political questions, and is exercised only where faith or morals are involved. Although it may be admitted that in some places and at some periods it has been injudiciously used, by far the worst instance of this was the Spanish Inquisition, where the emphasis should be laid on the word "Spanish," because the Holy See, far from approving its severity, tried to restrain it. Spain at that time was notorious for political venality, and some of those prosecuted were not heretics at all, but people who had wealth that could be confiscated. Moreover, it was the secular government that carried out the sentences, for the Church sentenced nobody to death, much less executed anybody. The Church might be asked to say whether the accused person was a heretic, just as doctors may be asked whether a person suspected of insanity is really insane or not. It is the state that confines the deranged in an asylum, where many are probably wrongfully detained, just as many probably wrongfully graced an *auto-da-fé*. The Church as such cannot be held responsible for the bad judgment or political subservience of an individual inquisitor; the blame in the matter must be attached to the secular government.

To follow this illustration a moment further—and it is offered only as an illustration—the insane put into asylums are there for the good of society, but also for their own good. So with those accused by the Spanish Inquisition; some were freed as completely innocent (as happened to St. Ignatius Loyola); others who were really tainted were convinced of their errors and recanted; only a small minority ever suffered long imprisonment or death. The fact is that even when the Church appears to be severe, its authority is intended not to oppress but to protect—to protect the rest of Catholics from contamination, and to protect the heretic himself by withdrawing him, if possible, from his heresy. If I might use another illustration it would be that ecclesiastical authority is not a prison but a garden fence, one erected at the edge of a precipice. Or if one may be permitted another illustration, if a ship were built without a rudder, it might have its "freedom" on the wild seas, but would also find its destruction. The passengers depend on properly constructed equipment and expert guidance.

Although the Church would not wish to return to some of the

methods that were in vogue during certain periods of the Middle Ages—which after all represented the general spirit of a time that is long since dead—it still exercises a spiritual authority, but no longer imposes any but spiritual penalties. It should also be added that the Church is only called upon to protect the "deposit of faith," and not the many more or less "pious" beliefs, which are in no sense obligatory, even if their outright rejection might be foolhardy. It would surprise many people if they saw the freedom of speculation that is exercised in one or other of the journals published for the clergy.[4] These are mainly mediums for discussion—very frank and occasionally somewhat acrimonious discussion. When a moral point is involved, the articles are often written in what Edward Gibbon, I believe, described as the "obscure decency of a dead language," and indeed Latin is the textbook and official language of the Church. At any rate such discussion is constant and vigorous. While many issues are closed, even regarding these a good deal of freedom may be allowed in regard to the application of principles. In other fields the discussion is untrammeled.

The very fact that a point is fixed, means that, tethered to it safely, one may roam around it in speculation. If anybody goes too far, the tether at once pulls him up short. Even this much may seem obscurantist to those who like to take it that way, but at least it rules out nebulous thinking and the following of novelties merely because they are novel, though this is not to say that freaks of a mild sort are never to be encountered among Catholics. All that cannot be permitted is freakishness where the fundamentals of doctrine are concerned. Of nothing is the Catholic more grateful than that he lives under intellectual discipline; for he knows how wise it is, and that the Church speaks in the name of God. He also knows how very gently as a rule such discipline is exercised—so gently that only very rarely does he become conscious of it.

If I may be permitted a personal word, my upbringing was in a form of Protestantism that may be described as "orthodox," or

[4] I am assured that a layman's subscription would be accepted should he wish to take one out; at any rate such magazines have often been loaned to me.

"evangelical," or "fundamentalist," if that now somewhat discredited term be allowed to pass. In early manhood I rebelled against much that I had been taught and for a while ran through a number of the theological "isms," only to discover that they led nowhere. I say simply and sincerely that I owe the whole of my intellectual life to my acceptance of Catholicism. I was a smart young man in my early twenties, and, as such young men do, I made a fool of myself before I obtained my Catholic ballast. I do not believe that I attach any great importance to anything that I have done, but whatever it is, my intellectual life did not really begin until I had entered the Church. Then I felt as though I had emerged from a small dark room, full of people talking nonsense—each a different sort of nonsense—and at once I found myself under a clear and open sky, with a bracing wind blowing in my face.

Circumstances, and not any deliberate choice of my own, led me into free-lance journalism in England, and after that—again without any deliberate choice—I found myself publishing books, beginning with my immature early poetry and then a volume of essays, most of them drawn from my contributions to Chesterton's *New Witness*. But before I met this group, many of whom were Catholic, I was already a Catholic. And I must say that among these friends I knew the most stimulating and happy days of my life. Force of circumstances—chiefly the necessity of providing for a growing family—led to my becoming a college professor in this country, and one might suppose that among them I would have encountered a good many people deeply interested in the things of the mind. I did of course encounter *some* people of this sort, but in honesty I am obliged to say that they were the exception rather than the rule.

For this I do not blame the Catholic Church in the slightest degree but rather life as lived in American academic circles. I fancy even that there was something in America itself that was responsible. I remember going on one occasion—I took good care never to go again—to one of the *New Republic's* editorial luncheons, and it was a solemn not to say a dismal experience, so entirely different from the beer and skittles of the *New Witness*, in whose columns we were free to kick up our heels as much as we pleased. I fear that in the United States the intellectual life is often taken with portentous gravity, which may be the reason that Americans have coined the derisive epithet, "low-brow," and perhaps why it is that many people who have excellent brains prefer to pass as low-brows. Particularly is this true of intellectuals in Catholic circles.

Yet I wonder whether that tells the whole story, or whether I would be qualified to tell it, even had I time and space for it here. But at least I may suggest an explanation to account for the inadequacy of some Catholic colleges and universities, or rather a series of interrelated explanations. Most of these institutions are conducted by religious orders or by corporations of secular priests. By the very nature of such administration, certain limitations—as well as certain important advantages—are almost inevitable. Because of their dedication to their calling, such priests often radiate that inner security and spiritual wisdom from which their students will derive the most profit. When they prefer mere textbook teaching, however, they can sometimes seem remote from current ideas which might be stimulating to their students. Then, too, priests in Catholic colleges are not required to produce the scholarly research that is expected of professors in the important secular colleges. Such research is rewarding to both professors and their schools and should, I feel, bring fresh vitality to Catholic teaching. The lay members of Catholic faculties are engaged only when there is an insufficiency of priests. Usually they are poorly paid—a fact which means that few find it possible to enter the field. I am told, however, that the rather unhappy lot of the lay professor has greatly improved during the last fifteen years.

In spite of all this, the ordinary Catholic college is probably at least as efficient, educationally speaking, as all except the larger and more heavily endowed secular universities. Even such inadequacies as may still exist would be more than offset in Catholic eyes by the fact that the student bodies live in a Catholic atmosphere and obtain regular instruction in Catholic doctrine. Although Catholic education at its higher levels (or what should be such) may lack something, at least it provides the inestimable advantages of Catholicism. The worst that can usually be said of it, as it exists in America, is that it is deficient in the kind of intellectual keenness that was found in the Middle Ages (and later), and that still exists to a considerable extent in other countries today.

During the last few years there has been a new outbreak of antagonism against parochial schools, their critics never stopping to consider what would happen if they all decided to go on strike and close their doors. How on earth would the state—*any* state— provide for the sudden influx of several millions of children? The wealthier states have excellent equipment, but in no instance equipment that could be stretched to cope with the situation just indicated. And every state, even those who pay their public schoolteachers best, has a shortage of the teachers needed, ranging from several hundred to several thousand. They may well be glad that the parochial schools shoulder so many of the burdens they would otherwise have to carry themselves, and the taxpayers may be thankful that they have so much less to pay because the parochial schools are not supported out of taxes.

Nevertheless, there are in some quarters bitter murmurings because the higher courts have ruled that parochial school children may be carried in the same buses as are used by the public schools. This, it seems, is an infringement of the principle of the separation of Church and State, about which more will be said later. Similarly there are those who are protesting, on the same grounds, because a brief prayer is sanctioned for the schools of New York State. "Almighty God," this runs, "we acknowledge our dependence upon Thee, and beg Thy blessing upon us, our parents, our teachers and our country." There could hardly be more outcry if the worship of Baal were revived, with a first-grade pupil thrown alive every morning into the furnace! Yet these are the very people who chatter about Catholic intolerance and bigotry. They let the secularist cat out of the bag; the truth is that they want no religion at all, these staunch defenders of the Constitution.

Catholics are supposed to be implacably opposed to public schools. This is not in the least true: their only objection is to the public schools as now secularized. And Catholics of course do not consider it quite fair that the whole burden of supporting parochial schools should be their burden, for this means that after they have paid the school taxes to the township, they then have to tax themselves a second time for the privilege of having their own schools. In several European countries—including England, which has an established Protestant church—some support is given to denominational schools, without anybody's howling "No Popery!" [5]

Catholics would naturally be opposed to the federal control of education, for this is something better reserved to the individual states, subject to certain restrictions. Perhaps this is best expressed in the decision of the Supreme Court delivered on May 30, 1929, regarding the Oregon school law which was aimed at destroying the parochial schools in that state. This is the decisive passage: "The fundamental theory of liberty upon which all governments in this Union repose excludes any general power of the State to standardize its children by forcing them to accept instruction from public teachers only. The child is not the mere creature of the State; those who nurture him and direct his destiny have the right, coupled with the high duty, to recognize and prepare him for additional duties."

On the other hand I must dissent from the more recent Supreme Court decision in the suit recently brought by Vasti McCollum, insofar as it stated as a principle of law the secularist

---

[5] Of course in England Church and State are not separated, even if the nexus between them has grown somewhat tenuous. But to hear some American Protestants talk, one would imagine that the Mayflower Pilgrims came to these shores for the express purpose of supporting this principle. Actually, they came merely to escape the pressure of the Church of England, but they lost no time in establishing Congregationalism, just as Virginia established Anglicanism. It was some time after the Revolution that the last link between Church and State was severed, for all that the first Amendment to the Constitution stipulates is that the *Federal Congress* should make no law disqualifying anybody on the ground of religion. I am not a constitutional lawyer, but theoretically it would seem to be possible for any of the forty-eight states to establish its own church, though I am sure that none would wish to do so. Let it be understood that I am all for the American principle as a *modus vivendi,* but it was not written on the tablets of stone that Moses brought down from Mount Sinai. Of all religious bodies the Catholic Church has benefited most from this principle. But let not other people try to foist upon us their own private interpretations of what that most explicit document, the American Constitution, says in most unequivocal terms.

teaching that God can have no place in the public school system. As a declared atheist, she objected as a parent to the use of the public schools of Illinois for the teaching of religion during school hours and in the public school building. There can be no possible objection to the "released time" under which public school children of various denominations may receive religious instruction elsewhere.[6] Catholics do not regard this as a very satisfactory arrangement; indeed, it is merely better than nothing. But many besides Catholics have been seriously disturbed by the trend to secularize education completely. The alternative may be eight-year-old smokers of marijuana, and thirteen-year-old schoolgirls obtaining extra money for their little pleasures by prostitution. It would be a good thing if Americans would look at the Constitution again. All that it laid down was that no church should enjoy a privileged position—and this was not aimed directly at Catholics, who numbered only about 30,000 souls in the entire country, but mainly at the Congregationalists of New England and the Episcopalians of Virginia. We Catholics are content with the Constitution; we only object when some people try to twist it awry, merely because of their absurd fears about supposititious Catholic machinations. For the sake of better relations with Protestants, I would be prepared to renounce even such trifling bits of support as the provision of bus rides for our children. We have long been accustomed to paying a great deal more than an extra nickel or so a day to give our children a Catholic education.

The Catholic position is contained in the encyclical letter issued on the last day of 1929 by Pius XI on *The Christian Education of Youth.* Although the Pope had European rather than American conditions in mind he enunciates principles which apply everywhere. He lays it down that "there can be no true education which is not wholly directed to man's last end," with which surely no religious person can cavil, just as it is plain reason that "the family and civil society belong to the natural order . . . the Church to the supernatural order." Nor is this likely to be contested: "In the first place comes the family, insti-

[6] Hardly had these words been written when the Supreme Court pronounced in favor of released time.

tuted by God for its peculiar purposes, the generation and formation of offspring; for this reason it has priority of nature and
therefore of rights over civil society. Nevertheless, the family is
an imperfect society, since it has not in itself all the means for
its complete development; whereas civil society is a perfect
society, having in itself all the means for its peculiar ends, which
is the temporal well-being of the community; and so in this respect, that is, in view of the common good, it has pre-eminence
over the family, which finds its own temporal perfection precisely in civil society."

So far what the Pope says would meet with no challenge. But
the deduction he draws, though hardly escapable in logic, would
be sure to arouse many against the Church's position: "First of
all education belongs pre-eminently to the Church." Although I
suppose many Protestants would agree, as long as it were understood that education belonged to *their* church, most non-Catholics would reject the principle *in toto*, either out of fear of the
Catholic Church, which stands almost alone in having an extensive educational organization, or because they believe that education is one of the state's prerogatives. The Pope goes on to say:
"The Church does not say that morality belongs purely, in the
sense of exclusively, to her; but that it belongs wholly to her.
She has never maintained that outside of her fold and apart
from her teaching, men cannot arrive at moral truth; she has on
the contrary more than once condemned this opinion because it
has appeared under more forms than one." But having made this
distinction clear, he asserts: "It is the inalienable right as well
as the indispensable duty of the Church to watch over the entire
education of her children, in all institutions, public or private,
not merely in regard to the religious instruction given there, but
in regard to every other branch of learning and every regulation
in so far as religion and morality are concerned. Nor should the
exercise of this right be considered undue interference, but rather
maternal care on the part of the Church in protecting her children from the grave danger of all kinds of doctrinal and moral
evil."

Even that much many Protestants would accept, however reluctantly, in principle. For Catholics attending a public school

(as vast numbers do) know that, though the teacher theoretically should stick to his subject, some of them wander far afield and find it possible, even while expounding the quantum theory, to insinuate their private agnosticism. Still more often this happens in the case of such subjects as biology, philosophy, history, or even English. Nevertheless, though Church law states that Catholics are not to attend non-Catholic schools, the Bishop is empowered to decide in what circumstances it is permissible: not only are there not enough of such schools but it sometimes happens that a student has special needs that a Catholic school or college is unable to meet. This is especially true of graduate studies, and many priests and Sisters go for their higher degrees to the large secular universities, to obtain training they may put to use in their own establishments. The Pope in his encyclical concedes, "In general it belongs to civil society and the State to provide what might be called civic education, not only for its youth but for all ages and classes." The same would of course apply to graduate and professional schools. This is not an abandonment of principle, for while there may be dangers to Catholic students at a medical or law school, the courses given there may be essential to sound professional equipment.

Due allowance is made by the Church for such requirements. And it is taken for granted in the case of advanced students, who may be presumed to have been well grounded in the faith, that any false doctrine they encounter will be rejected. The Church does not want to treat adult Catholics as though they were children, any more than natural parents would. It is mainly of children and adolescents that Pius XI writes: "Every Christian child or youth has a right to instruction in harmony with the teaching of the Church, the pillar and ground of truth. And whoever disturbs the pupil's faith in any way, does him grave wrong, inasmuch as he abuses the trust which children place in their teachers, and takes unfair advantage of their inexperience and of their natural craving for unrestrained liberty, at once illusory or false."

What other position can the Church take regarding education, since it knows how much depends on the formative years, and must maintain, as did Christ, "What shall it profit a man to gain the whole world and lose his own soul?" Although it might perhaps be granted that to some extent non-Catholic bigotry is fomented by unnecessary Catholic belligerence, a result of the unfortunate situation has been to make Catholics suspicious of public schools because of their increasingly secularist outlook. Those with this outlook flatter themselves that they are the only true Americans. It would not be a bad idea for them to go back to the Founding Fathers who, although many of them were tinged with deism, at least allowed that God, aloof and distant though they supposed Him to be, possessed as creator a claim to the worship and obedience of those whom He had made. It is precisely this that a large part of the people of the society in which we live virtually deny, and in doing so show themselves to be practical, though not perhaps speculative, atheists. It is therefore all the more necessary for the Church today firmly, but let us hope without truculence, to insist that for the human being the matter of paramount importance is the salvation of his immortal soul.

A few concluding words might be offered as to the present condition of Catholic education, and for my data I go to the four and a half columns published on the subject in the *New York Times* for March 30, 1952. There is now a record enrollment in Catholic schools and colleges of 4,000,000 students, though still, and probably for many years to come, Catholics themselves will be unable to undertake the education of all their young people. This, however, represents an increase of about a million during the past ten years, with another million who will have to be provided for within the next ten. For this an expansion program is underway that will cost $250,000,000—a really staggering objective. Already there are nearly 110,000 teachers in our schools, nearly 100,000 of whom are religious. In our nearly 9,000 elementary schools there are over 3,000,000 children, with another 600,000 attending over 2,000 secondary schools (still the weakest spot in our system) and 350,000 attending Catholic colleges. Many of our colleges and high schools have a sprinkling of non-Catholic students. A well-to-do woman explained to me why she sent her daughter to a Catholic academy. It was, so I gathered, that she might learn how to enter a room. "Very nice," I commented. "But perhaps your daughter will learn to do even better than that and find out how to enter heaven." I suspect, though, that this lady's remarks did her less than justice. Surely she could not have been thinking only of manners but also of morals, and felt that her daughter was safer under the charge of nuns than she would have been anywhere else. To this it might be added that our educational institutions, like our hospitals, never attempt proselytism. Of course it is always hoped that the non-Catholic students and patients will at least be brought to appreciate what religion means to a Catholic, and that this will further the amicable accord between Catholics and Protestants. This accord has steadily increased in America, despite the recurring flare-ups of bigotry, one of which we are now passing through, but which I, for one, cannot treat too seriously.

### THE CHIEF DANGERS TO CATHOLICISM

This section will be very brief, a mere footnote to what has already been said in this chapter. Among the dangers I would not include direct attacks on the Church, if only because all these attacks are based upon more or less absurd misunderstandings, and such misunderstandings *can* be removed, with patience on our part, and an appeal to the good will which, at any rate in this country, I am convinced does exist at bottom on both sides. The dangers I have in mind are of another sort.

The chief danger to religion—not merely to Catholicism but to religion of any sort—is the spirit of the world. This sometimes tries to disguise itself, even to the extent of trying to look unworldly. But wherever one finds the soft and the comfortable—even though naked greed is not apparent—there is godlessness.

It may be encountered among Catholics who are regular in the performance of their duties, running side by side with this external performance but gradually encroaching upon it. On the other hand there are people who make no religious profession whatever but who have some concept of the "good life" and who see clearly that attachment to a gadget-strewn way of life rots the intelligence and the character. One does not need to be a Catholic to perceive this; it is only necessary to be a good philosopher or sociologist. But of course the whole problem at once becomes clearer to those who are seeking something more than their own good, but who set first in importance the love of God.

A society such as the one in which most of us have grown up exudes a miasmic atmosphere; and while sometimes this can become a positive stench, usually it is so subtle as to pass quite undetected. I, for one, heartily dislike some of the connotations that there may be in the glibly used expression, "the American way of life." If this means, as it should mean, the democratic process and the upholding of man's dignity and liberty, then I heartily approve. But if it merely means adding to our appliances and luxuries, then I very much deplore the term, especially if it involves a hope of converting Communists from the error of their ways by exhibiting our material resources and our technical "know-how." Radios and T.V. and movies and books and plays and magazines and newspapers can of course further noble ends—ends which need not be specifically Catholic.

It is not necessary (nor even hardly possible) to think of nothing except religion. The broadness of our approach was indicated by St. Paul in his epistle to the Philippians: "Whatsoever things are true, whatsoever things are honest, whatsoever things are just, whatsoever things are pure, whatsoever things are of good report; if there be any virtue, and if there be any praise, think on these things." On the other hand any mind will be eaten by silliness and the soul destroyed by dwelling on things of another sort. While a certain amount of relaxation is essential to good mental balance, the general temper of the modern world is not simply inimical to religion but productive of neuroses. It is not sinful that a child should do his homework with the radio turned on, but it cannot be good for his mind. The same thing applies to a too frequent visitation of movies—even of movies of the most unobjectionable sort. This makes the child depend too greatly upon pleasure and therefore weakens the moral fiber he will need when he encounters definite evil.

This is not always easy to explain to children, as I have found when dealing with my own; and they have even tried to argue that listening to the radio while doing their homework helped them to concentrate! Well, I was able to deal decisively with that one, as I also remained unimpressed by the argument that

Jane and George (of two Catholic families in the same street) were allowed to go to movies three times a week. I was also able absolutely to forbid the bringing into the house of any movie magazine (for even the best of these was chock-full of rubbish), though I suspect that my prohibitions were sometimes circumvented by their reading such stuff in the houses of their friends. If my children are not in every respect all that I could wish, neither am I all that I ought to be. At any rate I did my best for them, and I must confess that, as far as my own family is concerned, I am fairly well satisfied. The four of them who have married have all taken Catholic partners, and in other ways too appear to be falsifying the predictions I sometimes made in my gloomier moments.

But what about Catholic parents who through laziness or ignorance or misguided kindness have neglected their duty? Well, of course their children will, if they practice their religion, arm themselves against the dangers inherent in the world as we find it. However, under the best of circumstances it is all a difficult business, since the tone of society—and it is but natural that the young should be disposed to take its standards for granted— is not conducive to a good Catholic life. It is hard for us not to take our coloring from those around us, and though the normal tendency is for Catholics to associate with other Catholics, these too are in many instances affected by "the contagion of the world's slow stain" and may in their turn help to spread it, in somewhat the same way that flu or polio may be spread, unintentionally, unconsciously. It is gradual corrosion that we have to fear more than any upheaval. And I am not sure that respectability—the distinguishing mark of Protestantism—since it can be so easily confused with virtue, may not be the greatest danger of all.

# PART III
# SOCIAL LIFE

# CHAPTER ONE

## *The Catholic Family*

Some of the aspects of family life have already been dealt with—for instance, the very important question of Catholic education. For marriage, as Catholics view it, is not concerned merely with the procreation of children but their upbringing as good Christians. There should be no serious difficulty about this, because even those who have no religion at all would admit the Catholic principle if they said—as practically everybody would say—that it is the duty of the parents to educate their children to be good members of society, patriotic citizens. Only somebody very depraved would limit the obligations of father and mother to seeing to it that their progeny were fed and clothed and equipped to earn their living.

Furthermore, the dangers, or some of the dangers, that confront a Catholic family in a society such as we live in, have been indicated in the immediately preceding pages. Some of these, it need scarcely be said, would confront even the man and woman who lived alone; but as throughout this book an attempt has been made to treat of what is normal rather than of what is exceptional, the stress has been laid on the family.

The concept of marriage also has been gone into, presenting an aspect of the case that may seem a little startling to some, but which probably most Christian people believe by implication. As Coventry Patmore put it: "The Catholic Church alone teaches as matters of faith those things which the thoroughly sincere person of every sect discovers, more or less obscurely, for himself, but dares not believe, for want of external sanction." If the doctrine presented here may seem a little rarified and "mystical," it is nevertheless the best possible practical guarantee of a well-founded marriage.

193

In discussing marriage, I have stressed the relationship of husband to wife, and touched only incidentally on the relationship of parents to their children. Extremely happy as many childless marriages are, they are incomplete (as none know better than the childless themselves) so long as the nuptial joys do not result in offspring. It is to round out this matter that the family as such is now being dealt with.

First of all I have to relate with sorrow, realizing what I missed, that I had very little home life as a child. I was the eldest of seven children, yet the circumstances of my father and mother, as missionaries in India, were such that when I was about ten I had to be sent to a boarding school in England, India being no good place for adolescents, and therefore did not see my father and mother again until I was sixteen, and then only for a short period. I had, it is true, a home of a kind with my three maiden aunts, with whom my eldest sister was living. With them I spent part of my vacations, but admirable women though my aunts were, they did not understand me very well and always made it clear to me that they wanted me to get out of the house in the morning and stay out until late afternoon. A habit of solitude was therefore forced upon me, which may have done me good in one way, as it certainly fostered my meditative spirit, but otherwise was rather damaging. I therefore had no experience of real family life, except for a brief interval between the time I was sixteen and eighteen, at which time my father and mother went back to India again and I never saw them afterwards except for mere visits to them in my later life. The rest of my brothers and sisters had been born in the interval but grew up beyond my personal orbit. They, like my father and mother themselves, were virtual strangers to me.

This was, of course, an immense loss—one much greater than I understood at the time. I am in no way blaming my parents, because what they were obliged to do was what all army officers and civil servants in India find that they have to accept as their hard lot. I am sure that as much was done for me as was within their power, and I feel a warm love and respect for their memory, as I have affection for my brothers and sisters. But there could be little intimacy, and there is no disguising the fact that a painful lesion was left upon my soul because of my having been thrown so very largely upon my own devices. If I mention the matter at all it is in the hope of explaining the strange position in which I found myself.

At school I had made a few close friends, and the home of one of them offered me later during almost every week end what was almost as near to being a home as anything I ever knew. Perhaps it was in part because of the loneliness engendered that I sought and found during my early twenties a home in the Catholic Church. And if that did not consciously operate as a motive, at least I am sure that the loneliness from which I suffered gave me more time than most young fellows had for thought, and when I had convinced myself of the truth of the Catholic claims, there were no very painful ties for me to sever from a family I hardly knew.

It is not my purpose to harp egotistically upon my personal story, except as it serves to cast some light upon my general theme. But it would seem necessary to carry that story a step further—and that too is a painful one—and to confess that in some important respects I was far from being the best of fathers. I dearly loved the woman I married, as I loved all of our seven children. But as I in my turn was caught in inescapable toils, I could not give them the attention I wished, except intermittently, for the simple reason that I was too preoccupied with earning a living for them.

Had I known just what was going to be involved, I doubt whether I would have had the courage to marry at all, though I am very glad that I did. But I was forced to develop in myself a versatility and resourcefulness I had never imagined I possessed, and similarly and for the same reason I had to tear myself to tatters (and come to a semi-invalidism in my mid forties) merely to keep the pot boiling. Though I had what was probably the best-paid Catholic professorship in America, what I earned was so far from being enough that I had to supplement my income with lecturing far and wide (on one occasion I covered nine states in nine successive days to give nineteen lectures), with summer-school teaching, with private tutoring, and with writing an article over any free week end. On top of which came the books I ground out over the fag end of any vacation. During ten years—no, I think it must have been twelve—I was only once able to stop for a brief period of rest. Even that period I devoted to writing while my wife and children were on the beach.

These details I set down not to excite pity for myself, for I do not feel I need any in view of the enjoyment I found in my work, but to indicate why, whatever my children may think of me, I am not in my own eyes a very satisfactory father. A fairly good "provider," yes; but something more is needed than that. Of all people in the world I should have learned more than I did from my own early history. But as to this I will say no more than that I hope my children will in due time recognize what I did do for them and make allowances for me where I fell short.

One point, already dealt with, that of birth control, obviously did not arise in my case. I mention it only to remark that the Catholic stand in the matter was one of the first things that made me strongly suspect that the Church was the respository of truth. Further, I must say that the widespread belief among non-Catholics that the priests tell the women of their flocks that it is their duty to bear, if possible, a child every year is altogether untrue. The most that the priest will do is to say—he *must* say— that certain methods of contraception are contrary to the law of God. I am almost ashamed to mention the matter at all in this chapter—as what is called birth control seems to me to sully the honor of the whole family and not merely put a sin upon the souls of the parents.

This last bit may be only an instance of purely personal sentiment, for I have not come across it in any of the Catholic arguments against contraception; so I will not press it. But in what follows I think that many who are not Catholics—especially many Christians of all varieties—will be in substantial agreement. Surely none of them will dispute this much, that the nurturing of the children in the fear and love of God imparts a special sweetness to family life. And I should be sorry not to think that great numbers who are not Catholics carry this out, some of them perhaps more conscientiously than most Catholics do.

However, I think it may be said without running any danger of giving offence that in the achievement of this purpose, the

Catholic family has a more clearly marked structure than any others. Parents are not infrequently inadequate and may even give bad examples to their children. But so long as the parents retain enough of the root of religion to wish their children to become better than they are themselves, the parochial school can take over some of the parental obligations, and so can the parish priest. Whether or not the parents do so much as go to Mass, as long as their children do, much may be salvaged, though of course the ideal will be far from being attained. On the other hand, the most devout and zealous of parents will find that the instruction that they should themselves give their children can be powerfully augmented by these auxiliary agencies. The family in that event will be all the more close-knit as a unit, for all the convergent forces will be directed towards a single end.

We may therefore say that the good Catholic family—not the perfect family, which may not exist, but the reasonably good family—is in a very strong position for the fostering of the Christian life. The waif from the stews may become a saint, however deplorable his parents may be, but the child not only has a much greater likelihood of achieving sanctity if it comes from a Catholic family of the type envisaged, but religion will have for him a lovelier charm because of all its endearing natural associations.

In all kinds of small ways this sweetness will manifest itself, as well as in the larger ways which give them their real meaning. But a small child often gets his first impressions from seemingly trivial acts, the significance of which dawns upon him only later, such as making the sign of the cross before he learns that it was on the cross that Christ died for him. Without this religious significance, many customs might be as arbitrary as the Pennsylvania hex marks, or stretch back, as do charms such as the cross in the wooden doors of old New England houses, to witches that have long been forgotten.

Some of these customs may be local and racial rather than Catholic, properly speaking. In Sicily the famous donkey carts are adorned with colored carvings of the saints. They were not imported here, but from Bavaria came the Christmas wreaths on the front door and, before that, the advent wreath with candles one still sees over some family dinner tables. Some Irish people use that most harmless of epithets "Glory be to God!" and will exclaim (not even they could tell you why), "God bless you!" when anybody sneezes. On the other hand, an Irish Catholic mother, who has to leave her children for a short time, knows what she means when she prays, "St. Bridget, keep my babies!" From England come hot cross buns, though in America they are not at all like the English buns and are not restricted to Good Friday. They have dwindled to becoming a tradition almost on a par with that which ordains salmon and fresh green peas on the Fourth of July. Other Catholic customs observed are not realized to be Catholic, for if a hat is raised when a hearse passes, this is usually merely out of respect for the dead and the mourners and not because a prayer is being said for the repose of a soul. Even Santa Claus is not always identified with St. Nicholas of Bari, but about the little Christmas Crib that is to be found in nearly every Catholic home there can be no mistake, for it is a miniature of the larger Crib in the Church. A painting of the Last Supper is often "standard equipment" for a Catholic dining room. Many houses will have a May altar to the Blessed Virgin; in fact some will have an altar to her on which vigil lights will burn all the year. If a child has a little disappointment it will be advised to "offer it up"—its first bit of training in asceticism and submission to the will of God. In all kinds of ways—if only in asking for a fine day for next day's picnic—the child is accustomed to look heavenwards. Quietly, unobtrusively, naturally, it learns to take the divine for granted.

If the children are made more secure in this way, so also are the parents themselves. Whether or not they have children, a Catholic husband and wife will, I believe, except in rare instances that do not enter into the picture, be loyal and faithful and joyous in the bond of love. But even if those who have no religion still retain normally decent standards, the good of their children will in many cases prevent the collapse of a marriage. Obviously this is still more true with regard to those who understand that merely having brought a family into the world is but the preparation for bringing that family, in so far as this lies within their power, to God. It is a truth within the observance of everybody that children give stability to a marriage. If the parents can help mightily in the matter of the salvation of those sent them by God, the children, without even suspecting it in all probability, can do a great deal for their parents in the same way.

Too often, however, what is contributed from either side is measured by a purely material standard, or at least by a standard which may contain some elements of what is called "cultural" value but in which the explicitly spiritual plays little if any part. This is a favorite argument of the birth-controllers: they say they prefer to have few children, thinking it better that they should give them advantages which would be precluded if there were, let us say, six children instead of three. College and a professional school would be possible in the one case; in the other the most that could be looked for would be graduation from high school. It may be granted that there is a good deal of force in this, but the argument overlooks other factors. In the first place, it is questionable whether, even from the material point of view, all the advantage is with those who go to college or who become architects or lawyers. Of these last, there are so many that quite a few of them make a poor living and have to wait years even for that. This is also true of medicine, another overcrowded profession and one which takes longer than any other to equip its practitioners. In any case, far too many young men and women go to college who are not able to make the most of its advantages, and of those who do go, many are spoiled for life by getting it into their heads that society owes them something specially good. As a rough estimate one might say that perhaps half of them have merely been "exposed" to culture, without ever really understanding what it is or discovering what it is they are to do with such scraps as they acquire. In many instances those who aim lower—but whose aim is serious—would do better for themselves as nurses or radio technicians or salesmen or even carpenters or bricklayers.

Nobody is less disposed than I am to undervalue education, but after a rather extensive experience I know that only a minority is capable of being educated beyond a certain point. It is common knowledge that really able young men or women will not be permanently kept out of the specialized training upon which they have set their hearts. The American system has that immense good about it, though one can see also how the idea that everybody should be educated results only too often in a widespread mediocrity. A society whose ideal is that everybody should graduate from college is visibly becoming one of half-educated morons. All of these expect "white collar" jobs, and even on the supposition that all were capable of becoming qualified for such jobs, the numbers of those necessary for the less gaudily gilded but essential occupations would steadily diminish. Somehow or other—God knows how—I have managed to put all my children through good schools and colleges, but had I not been able to do so, I do not believe that they would have been at much of a disadvantage in the business of living, and I believe the same thing could be said of other large families.

Let me be permitted to cite my own case once more. At sixteen my father felt that he had done all he could for me and I started work as an office boy at ten shillings a week and by the time I was eighteen was completely self-supporting. This did not prevent me from greatly improving my education by the tough but rewarding process of self-education, or ending up as a Ph.D., a college professor and a writer. I know that I had more than my fair share of luck, yet mine is by no means a unique case. Others have gone farther with fewer opportunities.

In saying this I trust that I am not obscuring the main point that should be made. Though it is almost impossible for me to picture myself as other than I am, I can believe that I might have been a better, a better-balanced, a happier and even a more prosperous man, had I worked my way upward in the world by means of some trade. Yet I can honestly say that I do not value any success that I may have had as worth a bean compared to my membership in the Catholic Church. There is the yardstick by which to measure everything.

Whatever the current opinion may be, the large family—not merely the Catholic family but *any* large family—has definite advantages. Part of these advantages lie in the economic disadvantages under which they may happen to lie. Setting aside grinding and sordid penury, the frugality that ordinary poverty imposes can be so adjusted as not to be too oppressive. I know, for I have been quite poor and I have been rather well-to-do. Yet in each state, looking back upon them both, I am quite sure that there was no essential difference. When poor, I had to forego many things which were later within my reach, but I did not greatly miss them. The reflection that I later had some luxuries gives me no pleasure, as there was little pleasure obtained even when I was enjoying them. There was a time when the expenditure of a shilling (saved up after several weeks) on a volume of the Everyman's Series was a red-letter day. I have never found such joy subsequently in paying out five or ten dollars for a book, since I always knew that I could lay my hand on that amount. Poverty, except in its extreme form of complete destitution, is no particular hardship; I am thankful that I have known it.

The result for a family that knows it, is discipline, self-sacrifice, co-operation; the reward, the joy of managing to shut the door in the teeth of the prowling wolf, or contriving ways and means to make do on what one has. This is present even in the case of one who has to struggle alone; it is vastly greater when there is a communal effort. A couple of tattered and starving men on a raft in mid-ocean who succeed in capturing a seagull (as Eddie Rickenbacker did) have more delight than the foolish people who spend money upon the inanities of a night club. Similarly a family of the kind that I have in mind discards as something that is an almost impossible dream the idea of having a new suit: Junior's pants are cut down for the brother next to him, and Jane wears Julia's cast-off dresses. The resourcefulness, and even more the courage, that are brought into play are worth more than they could buy in any store—though Jane at the time may doubt it!

In saying this I do not wish to sentimentalize. The hardships are real but they need not destroy joy. I do not wish my children to have to undergo the poverty that I have known, though did that happen to them, I am sure that it would be in some ways for their good and draw out qualities in them which otherwise may remain unexercised. Most of the truisms are true, even if they are trite: it is at least true that riches do not bring happiness, and neither does ordinary poverty sap away joy in life.

If this is true (or may be true) for any large family, so also it is true that a family may be brought all the more closely together because it lacks some of the amenities that are imagined to be necessities. The car may have to be sold—too bad, but the street car and bus are fairly adequate substitutes. The radio may wear out and television be out of the question. There may be no money for so much as a weekly movie. If so, the family may discover even better ways of having fun, because they have to entertain one another. They may not be able to have many outside friends; very well, then they may become in consequence all the firmer in friendships found in the family.

Whatever may be the inconvenience, I do not believe one could easily come upon a member of a large family who is not glad that he was one. Even the privations he and his many brothers and sisters have undergone—managing to do with rather less than others because there were so many of them—so far from leaving bitterness, seem to have in restrospect a charm of their own. They have left a provision of incidents to be lingered over with humor and tenderness. To none do the good old days seem so good as to those who have come through by the skin of their teeth.

By that time their father and mother perhaps are in the grave and are remembered not only with love but pride. The boys will boast of the way they were taken to the woodshed for a good lathering, the girls of the hairbrush wielded by an exasperated mother. Whether they knew it or not when they were children, they know when they have children of their own, how much they owe to those who gave so unstintedly of their care. The shrillness that sometimes came into their mother's voice is forgotten and only her gentleness recalled. That their father now and then had a drop too much is condoned. They all agree that he was wonderful after all.

All except the very youngest often had to act as deputy father and mother to the others. How else could they have been brought up had they not helped to bring one another up? That they sometimes had to adopt a summary style is not resented—it never was. What fun they had together. It may sometimes have been a rough life they shared, but a good one. How different from the families in which there was only one pampered, disconsolate child, or in which the two or three children had been so widely spaced as never to have been much of a community.

It is not being claimed here that all, or even the majority of such families, are those of Catholics. Indeed, it could probably be statistically demonstrated that such is not at all the case. Had Catholic fertility been as far in excess of that of non-Catholics as one might expect, by that factor alone Catholics would be pulling far ahead of all other Americans in numbers. It is not so, though it may be demonstrable that under favorable conditions that is the tendency. It is what has happened in French Canada, where a patriarchal mode prevails, but it does not happen in the United States.

Why is this? Can it be that Catholics are, in spite of their professions, actually practicing birth control? Probably some are, though if so, it is under the rhythm method which, though subject to a recent Papal condemnation if it is deliberately intended to frustrate the ends of marriage, is permitted under certain conditions: too great an economic pressure, or for the better spacing of children, or because the wife is near the end of her tether from frequent child-bearing. The chief reasons are to be found elsewhere. One is that a large number of Catholics are celibate because of having chosen the sacerdotal and religious state. Another is the fact, sometimes deplored by the clergy, that many Catholic men and women who are perfectly free to marry, refrain from doing so, until rather late in life. But undoubtedly the main cause is that life in thickly populated centers—and it is in these that most of the American Catholics are to be found—seems to diminish the reproductive powers. Any of our large cities would be extinct of population within a hundred years were it not replenished from the rural districts. And these are almost all predominantly Protestant. The upshot is that, while the Catholic body does increase, it increases rather slowly. And as Catholics are, upon the average, still rather poorer than other American groups, the economic factor—including the kind of work done, the cramped quarters lived in—operates to slow down their birth rate.

Most of what I have written in this chapter bears rather upon the large family in general, or the large Christian family of whatever sort, than upon the Catholic family. The decent family will have much that is in common with Catholicism, and still more will this be the case of a Protestant family which takes its religion seriously. Although I have said that I was unfortunate in the fact of having known little home life as a boy, and none whatever as a very young man, it would be most ungrateful of me were I not to acknowledge that in the household of my own admirable father and mother, religion permeated all the actions of the day. My only complaint would be, not that there was too much religion, but that it was pressed upon me injudiciously, so that I was constantly being urged to "give my heart to Jesus" and was greatly embarrassed that I was not able until much later to discover just how this was to be managed. But I know that other Protestant households were, perhaps without being less religious than our own, more tactful—or shall I say more respectful of the quirks that might exist in the minds of the young? I say this without any bitterness but rather gratitude, for had I been approached in a different way, it might have happened that my allegiance to the evangelicism of my upbringing would have been so thorough that I would never have thought of Catholicism. The result was that piety was for me always mingled with a powerful ingredient of pain.

It is quite different in many ways with a Catholic family. There prayer is cool and calm and of a liturgical sort without any of that invidious singling out of particular people—and it always seemed that fifty years ago a small boy named Theodore was being made most uncomfortable. The Catholic childhood (something never within my personal experience) is very sweet and often rather playful. From his tenderest years the child is led to the Infant Jesus or the Boy Jesus, and Mary who is His mother, and the benign Joseph who is the guardian of both. Over the Catholic family is the Holy Family, so that it too becomes a kind of holy family, or perhaps it would be better to say that the Holy Family lives on intimate terms with the Catholic family.

So, too, does the Guardian Angel of each child. In the existence of these angels other Christians believe (or should believe), but few except Catholics seem to attach any very definite ideas to the matter, and none except Catholics approach these Guardians with loving intimacy, looking to them in times of danger, or, when unlooked-for danger passes harmlessly, attribute escape to their protection.

Grace before and after meals is a good custom, by no means peculiarly Catholic. What is distinctive is the saying of the Angelus by such as live within the sound of the church bells— and it was the Angelus of the Bow Bells that made those who were that parish Cockneys, a detail that most Cockneys have long ago forgotten. Night prayers are more than "Now I lay me down to sleep," and though that is of Protestant derivation, the rhyme that many Protestants remember is Catholic:

> Matthew, Mark, Luke and John
> Bless the bed which I lie on.

But the Catholic child's prayers are said at his mother's knee, with brothers and sisters kneeling around, and with the nursling of the group doing his best to lisp in his mother's arms. The Our Father, the Hail Mary, an invocation for the repose of the faithful departed and the confiding of the little soul to God— these at least are possible.

I do not want to stress such things too much, for I have known Catholic families who can be as injudicious in the form of their piety as any that are Protestant. Thus one good woman I know, when on Hallow E'en she was accosted by "treat or trick," gravely tried to explain that children in Catholic days were given a cookie or an apple as a reward for saying a prayer for those in purgatory, and sent them marching around the house saying it before they got their "treat." Luckily for her they happened to be Catholic children—otherwise she might still have got her "trick." This seems to me rather like an attempt to reintroduce devotion at the pistol's mouth.

It might require a pistol—or at any rate a good stout cudgel— to assemble a family for the saying of the rosary in the evening. Yet in spite of all the difficulties in the way, some people do manage it. Even better, and more feasible for most, would be the going of the family as a group to Holy Communion. But again there are difficulties, and some of these are created not so much by the social situation as by the customs that have arisen in most American parishes of assembling the children for their own Mass and of steering off the father one Sunday a month with the Holy Name Society and the mother on another Sunday with the women of Our Lady's Sodality. However, one must accept things as they are; the priests of the parish are acting as experience has shown them to be best for their people.

As is notorious, many factors in modern life work for the disruption of the family, so that there are those who look upon it as doomed and a kind of anachronism today. Although this fortunately does not often exist as a positive theory, many act about it virtually on the Q.E.D. principle. The strongest cohesive force for the family is the Catholic Church, though I would be the first to admit that it is not the only force. But as far as the parish unit is concerned, this may be said: the family—and under favorable conditions it is likely to be a large family—is the chief of the parish societies after the parish itself. Those dedicated people who leave the world, as it is called, enter a family of another kind: the very word "abbot" is simply a form of the Syriac *abba*. A monastery is a home. But for those whose lot it is to remain in the ordinary kind of Christian family, and then to found a family of their own, all the beautiful natural virtues and joys point to a supernatural end. Father and mother and children in loving unity are making their way towards their heavenly home.

# CHAPTER TWO

## *The Parish*

B efore coming to a more inward consideration of the significance of the parish, it might be as well to indicate its juridical status. Under the New Code of Canon Law (Canon 216,1)
it is explained that "The territory of each diocese should be
distributed into districts, and to each of these should be assigned
a special church with a determined part of the flock, over which
is to be placed a local pastor, who shall take the necessary care
of souls." However, a few other points might be noted. Missionary
countries, even those which have a hierarchy, do not possess
parishes in the strict sense, for the reason that in such territories,
the ecclesiastical organization cannot be regarded as definitely
fixed. Further a parish will not normally be set up—and never in
a country such as the United States—until a church has been
built.

In such a church the parish priest has a number of clearly
recognized duties and privileges. Incumbent upon him is the
celebration of Mass and the administration of the sacraments.
He is obliged to live close to his church (as a mere chaplain is
not) and it is for him to conduct all marriages, perform all
baptisms and arrange for all funerals, though of course much of
such work is often delegated by him to his assistants or, in special
circumstances, is permitted to be carried out by a priest from
another parish or even another diocese. When a man and a
woman from different parishes get married, the marriage has to
take place in the parish of the bride, unless there is good reason
for excusing from the rule. Similarly, though the parishioners may
attend Mass elsewhere, they are expected but not obliged to
perform at least their Easter Duties in their parish church.

Everybody who is domiciled in the parish, or is residing there
temporarily, is considered a member of the parish; this means of

course that no Catholic, however "homeless," is without a parish. All Catholics are under the obligation of making a financial contribution according to their means to the support of the parish and its priests.

Ordinarily a parish is under the charge of the diocesan, or as they are commonly styled, the secular clergy. When religious are appointed to them they may be removed at the discretion of the bishop or of their own superior, if he finds any cause for withdrawal. The private chapel of a convent of nuns (even if it be a large abbey) cannot be a parish church, though of course Masses are said there. Nor are those externs attending such Masses considered as having fulfilled their Sunday obligation, except in the case of lay people attached to the school, the farm and other offices, unless it is a public or a semipublic oratory.

The obligation of the upkeep of the parish church rests in large part upon the parishioners themselves, for this is their church. In some European countries there may also be a patron or those who draw some part of the revenues according to an arrangement reached with the Ordinary. But while this may be the theory, in the United States, because of the troubles caused by the old trustee system—under which a lay committee could hire and fire their clergy, and often did—in practice the bishop keeps so strict a control that the link between the people and their parish church has tended to become a bit tenuous. A universally satisfactory system has yet to be worked out.

These are the external aspects of a parish—or some of them; it is now desirable that we pass to the parish as it is inwardly. Although actually there were no parishes in the primitive church, they soon appeared, at least in embryo. From one aspect they constitute hardly more than an administrative convenience but from another, and deeper, aspect they are considerably more. If marriage can be regarded as the setting up a church within the Church—and a fruitful union—the parish also must be said to be a microcosm of the Church. As the late Monsignor Martin Hellriegel put it: [1] "This Mystical Body, this divine reality spread

[1] "The Parish in Practice," a paper read at the Liturgical Conference of 1941 and included (pp. 199-200) in the book *The Sacramental Way,* edited by Mary Perkins. Sheed and Ward, 1948.

over the whole world, assumes a very concrete local form in our parish. The parish is for us in all truth the Mystical Body, or, if you will, a 'miniature' mystical body, but the Mystical Body." Yet membership of a parish though normal to Christians, and especially the laity, is not necessary to salvation but is no more than a channel of grace, for, as we have seen, nuns, though they may be living individually and communally a life of the utmost holiness, do not have any parish.

To quote Monsignor Hellriegel again: "The parish is a living organism whose life must grow, unfold itself, and bear fruit. In the organism the pastor, as the word denotes, is shepherd, leader, father. He stands on the shoulders of his forebears—priests and people—and must keep alive what they left behind. But that is not all. He must push forward, augment, perfect the life of this organism. Despite human frailty and limited judgment, he is to his parish in very truth Christ's representative. What he preaches is Christ, what he bestows through the holy sacraments is Christ —Head, Savior and Owner of the Parish." That is the lofty and liturgical view of the parish, and should be remembered no less than the view of it held by Canon Law.

In common experience, as we all know, parishes vary a good deal from one another. This does not mean merely that in some parishes one somehow becomes aware that much may be missing in spiritual life, even though there is (perhaps now and then *because there is*) a feverishly bubbling activity. What is true is that, while all parishes are, at least potentially, storehouses of the best sort of energy, the needs of no two are exactly the same. One of the main duties that rest upon the local priests is to discover precisely what those needs are and then to study how best to meet them. The essence of the matter, the Mass and the sacraments, will be available in even the most negligently run—or conversely, the briskest and most arid—of parishes. And those that are the most efficiently run on the external plane are not always the most satisfactory on that of the spirit. One has sometimes seen a negligently conducted parish suddenly galvanized into new life by the arrival of a new pastor; and this need not be because the new priest is younger and abler or more energetic, but merely because he perceives more clearly what a parish should be, and can become. But it must also be said that not infrequently a new pastor, who starts out with the highest ideals, is gradually broken into routine mediocrity by the dead weight of the lethargy of his parishioners whom nothing seems to arouse. It is a matter which it would be impertinent of a layman, who can only look at such things from the outside, to discuss; and the problems are, one suspects, sometimes so complex that even the most zealous and devoted of priests would find it difficult to find their solution. Although the Curé of Ars (St. John Mary Vianney) is the patron of parish priests, it would be hard to imagine that we shall ever again find a priest who is his match. Yet hundreds of American priests are doing their utmost to achieve sanctity; and great as the obstacles may be in our own bustling country, perhaps some at least may emulate the amazing zeal of the Curé of Ars.

It has been already remarked that the Church is not only a living organism and an organization but a society, however little the individual Catholic may be given to take any active part in its social activities. Yet it is impossible for him to live in isolation, if he is a Catholic at all. We are part of the Communion of Saints, or as St. Paul strikingly put it when speaking of the Mystical Body, "If one member suffer anything, all the members suffer with it. If one member glory, all the members rejoice with it." And if that is true of the Church as a whole, so is it also true of that part of the Church which may be almost the only segment of it within our immediate observation, which is of course the parish.

Primarily this comes out in our joining with the other members to assist at Mass and the receiving of Holy Communion. As the Benedictine Father Paschal Botz has suggested: [2] "The true, dogmatic way of receiving Holy Communion needs to be restored in parish life. It is contrary to the nature of the Mass to commemorate Christ and all His saints, and to forget our neighbor. How different parish life would be, if after Holy Communion we did not bury our faces in our hands so as to shut out the distraction of our neighbor and to see Christ only in our hearts, but rather opened our eyes to Christ in our neighbor and admitted

[2] *Ibid.*, p. 62.

him to our table." It is in the same deeply Catholic spirit that Alice Meynell wrote her fine poem, "The Unknown God," in which she speaks of one of those kneeling near her at Mass going up to receive Holy Communion, and of the way she prayed to Christ in that stranger's life, his unknown heart. That is a profoundly true and beautiful idea; when we ourselves receive Christ at His Table, we can also partake of the banquet with many others, praying to the Christ the other communicants have received, and so entering into a very real communion with them, even if we have never actually met them and perhaps know that we shall never so much as see them again.

There of course is the essence of Catholic social life, though there may be little of this mystical character in Catholic social activities, as we know them in this country. Even our worship may seem at times rather too businesslike, where one congregation is waiting outside to press in for the next Mass as the people present at the previous Mass are elbowing their way out. There is no opportunity to linger and chat, as may happen in a country church. Even so, though we may not come into physical contact with the worshipers, it would greatly enrich our Catholic life to remember that they all share it. Perhaps only a small number of them have been to Holy Communion (if it is one of the late Masses) and we may not have done so ourselves; yet we are all still branched in the Vine, coheirs with Christ of the Kingdom.

In external activities (of which Catholics have many) I think it must be admitted that if these are looked upon as an organized means of bringing people to know one another—and especially young people—Catholics are in many ways behind their Protestant brethren. These activities cannot be regarded of course as being in any sense on an equal importance with the mystical unity that has been touched on, still they serve good purposes that Catholics too often neglect. We are, as a general rule, content to observe the specific practices of our religion—and first things *should* come first—but we somewhat incline to neglect everything else.

There is no reason why we should not have a great deal more of this kind of social life than we do. During the Middle Ages, when life in every department was much less highly organized, there were parish fairs and festivities of many kinds, and while it is true that the guild plays were not normally a parish affair (though they were often staged in a churchyard), these plays, whose actors might be drawn from several local parishes, must be considered a Catholic activity, even if some of their humor would today be considered too broad and boisterous for anything connected with the Church. Those activities cannot be brought back, but recreational facilities can be fostered, and some priests perceive them to be an excellent means of bringing young men and women together, with the consequence of an immense drop in mixed marriages.

We cannot excuse ourselves on the ground that we do not have to operate as Protestant churches upon a competitive basis, and that because of our spiritual solidarity and unassailability we are not called upon to be, among other things, the promoter of societies. It can hardly be brought home to many people that the chief society in any parish is the parish itself, unless steps are also taken by the parish leaders to provide minor units that effectuate this through organized charity, by spiritual organizations, and even by recreational facilities. Nor is any harm done if such groups deflect for their own needs some of the contributions that might otherwise have gone to the general parish funds. As a matter of experience the enthusiasm engendered by such groups for the parish as a center is even in a financial respect (if one must somewhat sordidly consider it) all to the advantage of the central organization. Some of the more obvious schemes for the raising of money may not be especially praiseworthy, but the creation of outlets for activity—so long as it is for a good purpose —never ends quite at that point but goes on to do service to the parish by emphasizing the fact that the people, however diversified their tastes and interests, and in however many units organized, may acquire a centripetal as well as a centrifugal force.

Or so it will be when such efforts are wisely directed and well inspired. Sometimes the most cohesive body on earth seems, in its local manifestation, to be cohesive only in theory, with its members split up into little circles, knowing nobody outside of them and not very interested in anything except their immediate concerns. This, however, is more apparent than real, and when it even appears to be so, it indicates very bad direction. At all events, it is not difficult to recall the members of the parish to what should be their true functions; for the parish is their home as the Catholic Church is their home.

The danger, such as it is, was pointed out in the same paper by the late Monsignor Hellriegel of St. Louis which has been quoted several times in this chapter. "All too often," he writes, "the unity of the parish has to suffer because of societies. Frequently it happens that members of the societies are regarded as first-rate Christians, while those not affiliated are looked upon as less loyal. Innumerable efforts and much time are spent by priests on these societies, efforts that could just as well be made by non-consecrated hands, with the result that little time is left for real priestly-pastoral 'cura' work, particularly on behalf of those who at first had been considered 'second-rate parishioners,' and who finally become so, because the shepherd has so little time for them."

I take it that the Monsignor was speaking of conditions in the Middle West, for I have not observed a disproportionate amount of time being given by the priests in the East to the running of a plethora of small and perhaps not very essential organizations. But I know of course only of what has come under my own notice, and my range of information is limited. If his account of matters is correct he is also correct in believing that most of this work could be done just as effectively by the lay folk of the parish—and usually it is, with only a little general supervision from the clergy. While I thoroughly agree with Monsignor Hellriegel that his spiritual duties should always be a priest's first care, I suggest that the spiritual bonds binding together the members of the Mystical Body may be, so to speak, made all the more palpable by active work. It is within the parish, or some similar Catholic grouping, that the laity may be made more conscious of their privileges, and this should never, and need never, detract from purely spiritual considerations. It is in this fact that one finds the key to what is now being so earnestly recommended to the Catholic laity—and that is Catholic Action.

# CHAPTER THREE

## Catholic Action

This has always existed to some extent and in some form or other but was not given adequate definition, nor its importance fully stressed, until Pius XI in 1934 informed the layman that, because of the very fact of his membership in the Mystical Body of Christ, he should prepare himself to play a larger part than had hitherto been the case in the apostolic work of the Church. "The very sacraments of Baptism and Confirmation," the Pope wrote in his encyclical, "demand the apostolate of Catholic Action . . . since through them we become members of the Church, or of the Mystical Body of Christ, and among the members of this body . . . there must be some solidarity of interests and reciprocal communication of life." In 1937 Cardinal Villeneuve of Quebec, addressing the Catholics of the United States, clarified the matter further by saying: "In our day, when effort is being made to instill a religious spirit in society, it would be a lamentable mistake to give a predominant place, above liturgy, to various organizations and pious works, whose supernatural efficacy depends entirely on how much they are imbued with a liturgical sense. And therefore among the many activities of Catholic Action, the liturgical apostolate should be given first place." This does not of course contradict what was said at the end of the preceding chapter about the importance of an external manifestation of the interior (or liturgical) spirit; it is merely a warning that fussy and feverish little activities, even when seemingly directed to a good end, achieve no lasting good unless they are based upon the spiritual life.

Catholic Action, as defined by Pius XI, was aimed at effecting a wider participation by the laity in the life of the Church. It has two essential aspects; the first is that it must have an apostolic aim, and the second that it be done under the direction of the bishop or his delegate. Thus a personal striving for holiness (though of course not excluded but rather augmented by apostolic work) does not fall within the scope of Catholic Action. Nor does all apostolic work, as for instance efforts to bring the faith to others or to reclaim those who have fallen away, unless these efforts are organizational and authorized by the hierarchy. Thus, to illustrate the matter from my own case, I cannot see how I come under Catholic Action at all. Although I hope that my books may serve an apostolic purpose, none of them was produced in connection with any organization and the only thing the bishop has had to do with them is that, he added his own *Imprimatur* after a *Nihil obstat* set upon them by his *Censor Librorum*. The only way I conceivably may contribute my mite to Catholic Action is that I happen to be the President of the Catholic Poetry Society, which is under the patronage of the Cardinal-Archbishop of New York. But it involves scarcely any work on my part, my function being merely that of a more or less graceful figurehead. In any event the C.P.S. is not professedly apostolic in its aims, so I suppose that it may at best be regarded as coming under the classification of an "auxiliary society." Only that which corresponds to the papal definition can be considered as being, strictly speaking (or really in any sense), Catholic Action. That is nothing else but "the participation of the laity in the apostolate of the hierarchy." The Pope put it, he told us, in these terms only "after due thought, deliberately, indeed one may say not without divine inspiration."

But although a volume of 600 pages was needed to record all of the utterances of Pius XI on the subject, with any number of speeches and official letters from the episcopate, and what is already a rather large library of books, the question is still not very clearly understood—as far as this country is concerned—for a reason that will be mentioned before this chapter is brought to a close. It is intended only to clear the ground for a consideration of some of the principal Catholic lay activities, so that some sort of a touchstone may be provided for them.

The organization may be large (when it is diocesan) or relatively large (when it is parochial), but it also operates to a considerable extent through "cells" suggestive of the Communist organization. However large or however small the group may be, it must have the bishop's authorization and be under the direction of a priest who acts for the bishop. While there is nothing to prevent a band of friends or an individual from operating on personal responsibility,—unless of course they vent ideas at variance with Catholic doctrine—such work, however excellent, is not Catholic Action. Furthermore, as Pius XI explained in a discourse he delivered in 1934 to the International Union of Catholic Women Leagues, "Each situation will have its corresponding apostle: the apostles of the workers will be workers; the apostles of the farmers will be farmers; the apostles of the seamen will be seamen; the apostles of the students will be students." Almost any form of apostolic activity is encouraged, whether or not it comes within Catholic Action, but only such forms as do can be counted upon to fulfill the Pope's design, to derive stability from the backing of the hierarchy, and to draw down upon itself the special blessings reserved for Catholic Action.

All are summoned to this work according to the degree of their capacity. This, however, does not mean that all are in the position of contributing much, if anything, though that is not to be taken as absolving them from the general obligation. But the individual already fully occupied in other ways, or a group (often a society long organized and functioning well) is neither obliged to drop its work in favor of something else, nor to transform its aims so as to make them conform with Catholic Action as it has been defined. They not only may but should continue in the way they have been following; they are auxiliaries. They have the same ends in view; it is merely that they adopt a different mode of procedure from that of Catholic Action. This has been brought into being, not to reorganize from top to bottom what already exists, but to give a pattern and a plan to the many capable of taking their part in the apostolic work of the Church who never knew how to begin and were often distrustful of themselves.

For those already in the field, or who enter it in an individualistic manner, co-ordination with Catholic Action is provided. Thus in 1935 Pius XI wrote to the Brazilian Hierarchy: "We repeatedly urge not only that the associations which are formed should act in perfect harmony, but that they should be suitably conjoined to form one body; that is, that there should be parish associations and diocesan associations, with a directing national council, all congruously united and linked together. As are the ranks of a victorious army, so are the members of one body. What is desired is an integration of forces, not scattered efforts; an ordered conspiring towards the common good, not a fortuitous concurrence of endeavor."

This is explained by way of introducing what will be said later about some of the most important of the many Catholic societies in which the Catholic laity play their part. Seventy pages of small print are given to them in the very informative section about Catholic Action found in the 1951 *National Catholic Almanac*. But although the definition is correctly given there, it is rather loosely applied, apparently because the compilers were anxious not to seem invidious by omitting to make mention of any laudable activity in the service of the Church. For instance, the Almanac lists as a Catholic Action organization the National Catholic Welfare Conference—the peacetime successor of the National Catholic War Council which was formed in 1917 upon America's entry into the First World War, and which so abundantly proved its value that it would have been wasteful to have discarded it when peace arrived. Yet this is really an organization in charge of a committee of bishops, with its various subcommittees all headed by a bishop and under a general secretary who is always a priest.

Moreover nearly all its departments (about which more in a moment) have a priest at their head, all of them very able men, some of national reputations, and although these are assisted by a large staff of laymen and laywomen, these too are specialists and as such receive good salaries. It is hard to see how it falls under the classification of Catholic Action, though there is a close relationship. In spite of its title the organization is not, as one might gather, a legislative body but rather a co-ordinator of information and an executive bureau. As such it furnishes data, among other things, on the modes of Catholic Action most suitable to each diocese, though only upon request, and without any authority to see that its advice is accepted.

Prominent among its departments are the Confraternity of Christian Doctrine—which surely is a mode of Catholic Action—and the one that issues the monthly magazine *Catholic Action.* One may perhaps similarly classify its publications office, its bureau of international affairs, and the Office of United Nations Affairs—a channel of communication rather than a "lobby." [1] All the foregoing are grouped as the several parts of the Executive Department. Other departments are similarly subdivided: those of Education, the Press (which syndicates news to diocesan and other papers), Social Action, the National Council of Catholic Men, the National Council of Catholic Women, Lay Organizations, War Relief Services, National Catholic Community Service, and the Mission Secretariat. If I have overlooked major departments, as I can hardly have failed to overlook important subdivisions, I am sorry; but this gives only the outline and does not pretend to be all-inclusive. In addition there are a number of special committees of the American bishops, formed as occasion for them arises. There is hardly an aspect of American Catholic life that does not come under the scrutiny of the Conference; yet it does no more than inform and advise and integrate.

Among the other forms that Catholic Action takes are the Catholic Youth Apostolate—under which we have, for instance, the Federation of Newman Clubs (the organization that cares for the spiritual interests of Catholics attending non-Catholic colleges), the Knights of Columbus, the Catholic Boy Scouts and the Catholic Girl Scouts, the Catholic Daughters of America, the Daughters of Isabella (with the junior auxiliaries), the Sodality of Our Lady and the Christ Child Society. I shall have more to

[1] Regarding its origin, I printed and edited the letter sent by Cardinal Gibbons to the bishops who formed the first General Committee, in the *National Catholic Historical Review* for January, 1942, where it occupies pages 450-456. I found this letter in the Archdiocesan Archives of Baltimore, but I knew that it was there, because the real author had told me so. There would seem to be no longer any need for concealing his name, as he is dead. He was the learned and utterly charming Sulpician John F. Fenlon. The letter, however, was of course carefully examined by the Cardinal before being issued in his name. As I have let that cat out of the bag, I might as well allow another to escape: the famous article on "The Church and the Republic," first published, I believe, in the *North American Review,* as though written by Cardinal Gibbons, was also by Father Fenlon.

say about some of these later, but the last mentioned, though not a very large group, comprising only about 10,000 members, deserves a special word at this point. It was founded sixty-five years ago by that very remarkable person Mary Merrick who, although bedridden from early womanhood, managed all its activities herself. To continue with a list, which must at best be far from complete, there are such groups as the Young Christian Workers, the Legion of Mary, the Society of St. Vincent de Paul, the six Catholic Greek Letter Societies, the Catholic Laymen's Association of Georgia and the Narberth Movement. The Catholic Laymen's Association was formed to meet attacks made on Catholicism in the press and to counteract this more positively by giving Catholic information; the Narberth Movement, which originated in Narberth, Pennsylvania, in 1929, has distributed millions of very brief leaflets, all written in a cheerful and eminently friendly style. Finally there is the English importation of the Catholic Evidence Guild, which does not seem to have met with the same degree of success here as on the other side of the Atlantic, probably because the English are more accustomed than are Americans to soap-box orators. It was introduced by Frank Sheed and his wife, who constitute the publishing firm of Sheed and Ward.

The listing of these undertakings, great and small but all admirable, is less important that our perceiving exactly what Pius XI meant by Catholic Action. Some confusion exists as to which of these groups are, strictly speaking, Catholic Action, and this may be because an effort has usually been made here to utilize pre-existing groups in large part for the purposes of a wider undertaking in which they are not yet fully or clearly integrated.

# CHAPTER FOUR

## Catholics in Politics

One must declare with all possible emphasis that Catholics, as Catholics, are not in politics at all. It will be observed that none of the branches of Catholic Action mentioned has even a faint political complexion. For that matter even Catholic organizations for economic betterment do not come under Catholic Action, though they have the hearty approval of the Church, declared in the *Rerum Novarum* of Leo XIII and the *Quadragesimo Anno* of Pius XI. They are social rather than apostolic, concerned with the material circumstances of the working classes rather than their salvation, though of course the circumstances of their lives may have a great deal to do with this.

The Church does not pretend to teach economics nor is it allied with any particular political system. It will work with a political movement so long as it does not interfere with the freedom of religion; and it has worked at various times with a number of different governmental concepts. With economics it is unconcerned, so long as justice is not violated. It is implacably opposed to Communism, not so much because this theoretically denies the right to private property, as because it has declared itself atheistic and materialistic. Capitalism is often, even in its modern moderated form, materialistic, and therefore practically even if not theoretically atheistic. But so long as it avoids materialism and seeks to be just to all concerned, the Church will accommodate itself to this, the prevalent economic system of our world. Even so, the two great encyclicals that have been mentioned run counter to much that our world seems quietly to take for granted.

With politics as such the Church is not concerned. Because of a set of historical accidents, which need not be gone into here, the majority of Catholics in the United States belong to the Democratic party, but there is no Catholic party in the slightest degree comparable to the Center party of Germany, and even there it was really a party predominately Catholic rather than a party that every Catholic joined. It must, however, be ruefully conceded that sometimes in the larger American cities Catholic politicians have managed to get control of the municipal government, usually much to the embarrassment of those who have the good of the Church at heart. For such politicians have often been rather venal, and rarely have been what can be described as shining lights of the Faith. Even when they have been admirable Catholics, as was true of Governor Smith, they must be merely regarded as Catholics who, in their private capacity, happen to be in politics. In no sense have they ever been agents of the Church.

This is not to say that there was not an unfortunate time when, because of their being secular rulers of considerable territory, some of the Popes, in that capacity, entered into political alliances and made war with other sovereigns. The policy of the "balance of power" is sometimes imagined to have been a British invention; others have seen its origin in the desperate maneuverings of Richelieu during the Thirty Years' War. It is perfectly true that he was a power politician, as it is also true that the policy of the balance of power has been for a long time the cardinal principle of English statesmen. But it really originated when the Pope, as secular ruler of states less powerful than some of his neighbors, was forced to throw his weight from one side to the other to maintain himself at all. Such a condition has passed away forever. He has incalculable spiritual strength, but as Stalin once asked, "How many divisions has the Pope?"

Unless one is going to consider the signing of a concordat a political act (which technically I suppose it is), the Church stands completely aloof from such concerns. Pius XI signed such a concordat with Mussolini (one that was fairly well observed) and another with Hitler (which can hardly be said to have been observed at all). He would probably be glad to make one with Stalin, if there were any chance of good faith on the part of the Communists, and if it provided an opportunity of helping Catholics in Russia.[1] Yet it has often been imagined by badly informed persons that the concordats with Mussolini and Hitler meant that the Church supported them. Far from that, the concordats soon had to be followed up with the blistering encyclicals *Non Abbiamo Bisogno* (June 27, 1931) and *Mit Brennender Sorge* (March 14, 1937), which made plain the Church's strong dissent from totalitarianism. It is worth noting that in these cases, instead of using the Latin which is usual in such documents, the Pope used the vernacular, so that everybody might read them and nobody be able to say that the translation was not quite accurate.

All that, however, is far away. Here in the United States some of the bishops have now and then made recommendations regarding questions which might appear to have some political coloring. It was so with regard to their stand on a referendum proposed in New England regarding a change in the law to authorize the open dissemination of contraceptive information. There may be some question as to the advisability of this—for it could be made to appear an interference on the part of Catholics with what non-Catholics wished to do—but there can be no question that a moral and not a political issue was involved. My own view, for what it is worth, is that it would be best for the clergy to leave the matter alone, except for the very strong personal control they can exercise upon their own people in the confessional; their right to do that is beyond challenge, and it is doubtful whether a law can ever successfully bar people obtaining knowledge of any sort if they set out to find it. But it is obvious that Catholic voters could not have defeated such a referendum had not a large section of the non-Catholic electorate thought as they did.

Paul Blanshard is prepared to admit that the American Catholic laity are rather decent people—or would be, if not tyrannized over by their hierarchy. In his more genial moments, he even concedes that the American hierarchy would not be bad people, if left alone by the Vatican. But there we have it: the Vatican—presumably the Pope and the College of Cardinals—has concocted

---

[1] In case anybody should not quite understand what a concordat is, it might be explained that it is merely a treaty made between the Pope and some secular ruler regarding the interests of religion.

a plot to subjugate the United States, in which it might permit
non-Catholics to exist on sufferance, but only as "second-class"
citizens. How this is to be brought about by thirty millions of
Catholics, if there are so many, as against four times that number of non-Catholics, he never explains.[2] It would seem that
Catholics have no right to what he calls the "Catholic medical
code" (the word should be "moral" not "medical"), whereas the
Protestant denominations had every right to foist their own moral
code upon the country in the guise of the "noble experiment"
that came to so ignoble an end—doubtless under orders from the
Vatican to the Catholic Irish and German proprietors of speak-
easies.

An interesting and relatively temperate book by William
Warren Sweet, *The American Churches,* similarly charges the
Catholic Church with attempting undue political influence, but
virtually destroys its own thesis by admitting that "it has already
been noted that the authority exercised by the Catholic Church
in America over swarming Catholic immigrants has been a large
factor in their Americanization and control." Nevertheless Dr.
Sweet says: "The anti-Russian propaganda endlessly carried on
in the American Roman Catholic press *and elsewhere* [my italics]
has aroused concern on the part of many thoughtful people because it has undoubtedly increased the difficulty of reaching any
satisfactory international world adjustment which is so necessary
now for the building up of a peaceful world." As far as I can see
this can mean only that the fact of Catholic opposition to Communism cools the opposition to it of men like Dr. Sweet. Rather
than join hands with Rome against Moscow he will join hands
with Moscow against Rome, or at best stand on one side while
Moscow devours everything within sight.

The "gloomy Dean" Inge, of St. Paul's Cathedral in London,
who surely cannot be suspected of sympathy towards Catholicism, remarked as long ago as 1925 in an article in the *Atlantic
Monthly:* "Should Bolshevism threaten world stability, Catholi-

---

[2] In other places Mr. Blanshard, whose strong point is not logic, seeks to
show that the estimates of the Catholic population have been grossly
exaggerated, and that, in fact, there are only about half the number of
active and zealous Catholics that have been supposed.

cism would become the inevitable rallying point of all the forces which oppose Bolshevism." Dr. Sweet, however, thinks that Catholic opposition to Communism does more harm than good. I myself sometimes think that American Catholics—indeed, Americans generally—harp a little too much on this one string. It would be better if we were all somewhat less *anti*-Communist, and instead were more *pro*-Christian, *pro*-American. But it is foolish to blame Catholics for a condition not of their asking.

Bishop Oxnam is an opponent to be treated with respect, for he has a positive interest in religion, whereas Mr. Blanshard (as many Protestants themselves have pointed out) is a thoroughgoing secularist, consumed with hatred for the Catholic Church merely because it will never accept a secularist philosophy. Among the "sinister designs" of the Vatican that Paul Blanshard lists are the Catholic Book Club (which has pitifully few members) and of the Catholic Writers Guild (to which no Catholic writer of any importance belongs). He carries the contentions of his first book, *American Freedom and Catholic Power* into his second, *Communism, Democracy and Catholic Power*. I think the last may be dismissed with the modification of an old joke in *Punch*. It seems that a lady had two dogs named Caesar and Pompey and that, while walking them one day, she encountered a friend who musingly commented, "Caesar and Pompey are very much alike—especially Pompey." So Mr. Blanshard insists that Communism and Catholicism are very much alike—especially Catholicism.

In view of what is now being said about the American principle of the separation of Church and State, let us see what the Catholic position is. The Church, which has a long historical memory, knows that although, under the old monarchical systems of Europe, there was commonly a fairly close collaboration of Church and State, there was also constant friction as to the limits of the authority of each. Yet theoretically—only theoretically, mind, and only in a society in which the ruler of the state and all his subjects are Catholics—the system just indicated is considered best. But the Holy See is well aware that the system has rarely worked well in practice, whereas the American system has always been for the good of the Church, and in no other country in the world have Catholics had such an extraordinary growth as in the United States, in which they are so small a minority. That growth has not been so great that Mr. Blanshard and Dr. Sweet and Bishop Oxnam have the slightest need for worry: even if Catholics should come to power in this country they would never attempt to reduce the rest of Americans to "second-class" citizens. My playful fancy runs ahead of me: I am trying to picture the gentlemen just named (and doubtless there would be others, perhaps one for each of the forty-eight states of the Union) being led out to an *auto-da-fé* in the Yankee Stadium. Bishop Fulton J. Sheen, never more handsome and never more eloquent, would have just finished the sermon by which he consigned them to the flames when, to take formal possession of the new Papal States, the Pope, flying from the Vatican . . . But no, it's no use; I simply cannot picture it. I assure those who may fear that they "smell of the fagot" that they are never actually going to smell it.

Is there then to be no permissible interference with the practice of religion? Strictly interpreted, the First Amendment to the Constitution, which prohibited Congress from making any law that interferes with the free exercise of religion, should have saved polygamy for the Mormons; but it did not. Similarly the state of Virginia decreed, "It shall be unlawful for any person or persons, to display, exhibit, handle, or use any poisonous snake or reptile in such manner as to endanger the life and health of any person." [3] In India the East India Company proceeded to put down the sacred and ancient custom of suttee (as suicide), and also (on the ground that it was murder) the thuggee of a small sect. But to come back to the United States, the police of Pennsylvania could not sit idly by when quite recently a son, two daughters and a son-in-law of a farming family got it into their heads that God had ordered them to offer up an old lady as a human sacrifice. The action was undoubtedly fanatical but people do not go insane in batches. One concludes that common sense has to be invoked in such cases and even that the natural law has to take precedence of the First Amendment.

[3] *Code of Virginia*, 1950. Vol. iv, Sec. 18-73, p. 161. The law proceeded to list the penalties that might be exacted; yet all this definitely interferes with the tenets of a crackpot sect in those parts.

These are extreme instances. But as I have pointed out else-where,[4] Sir Robert Filmer, the defender of the seventeenth-century doctrine of the divine right of kings, argued in his *Patriarcha,* truly enough, that the Puritans opposed to it supported themselves on a Catholic philosophy: "Cardinal Bellarmine and Calvin both look asquint this way." Filmer of course supposed that by producing a Catholic origin for the democratic doctrine he would completely discredit it. But he was an honest controversialist and quoted his Catholic authorities correctly and copiously. His book was read in the United States, in particular by Thomas Jefferson, as we know from the fact that Filmer's book is among those once in the possession of Jefferson and now in the Library of Congress. I am not saying that the Declaration of Independence and the Constitution derive directly from the scholastic philosophers, for I am sure they did not; though Locke, from whom much was directly drawn, himself drew from those philosophers. All I am trying to show is that it is ridiculous to try to pit Catholicism and Americanism against one another.

We have been told a good deal, even by some people (such as John Dewey) who have the reputation of being great scholars, about Mr. Blanshard's ample and exact documentation. That his books do have documentation of a sort may be conceded, but in general it may be said that he does not distinguish between good and bad authorities and has a trick of adroitly slipping in between two statements which have backing, however weak, another statement that has no backing whatever. Professor James M. O'Neill, in his recent *Catholicism and American Freedom* says that perhaps Blanshard's low point as a scholar was reached in what he had to say about the "Americanism" condemned by Leo XIII in 1899 in the apostolic letter *Testem Benevolentiae* addressed to Cardinal Gibbons. Blanshard's confusion of this with what we understand by Americanism is really inexcusable, for though he gives in this instance no reference or footnote of any kind, he does list in his bibliography my *Story of American Catholicism* in which pages 498–521 are devoted to a discussion of the matter. As he nowhere gives the slightest indication of having read my book which, if he had consulted only the twenty-three

[4] *The Story of American Catholicism,* pp. 117, 119.

pages mentioned, would have saved him from an egregious mistake, what can one conclude but that his bibliography is to some extent bogus?

Nobody was more surprised than were the American bishops at the Pope's reproof. "Americanism" in the sense in which Leo XIII used the term did exist as a series of theological errors concocted by a coterie of young French priests, but it did not exist in America. Leo had been specific enough about what he had in mind and had been careful to refer to it as "false Americanism." About all this Mr. Blanshard knows nothing; he has got hold of the fact that the Pope had condemned Americanism, and it never occurs to him to enquire what the Pope meant. That Americanism was condemned is good enough for him; on that basis he proceeds to condemn the Church.

Similarly he and anti-Catholic critics of his stamp stretch the fact that Catholicism is authoritarian into trying to make it appear that Catholicism is totalitarian. The truth is that Catholics, while preferring democracy to any other form of government in secular affairs, cannot think of democracy as a religion but as a political system—no doubt the best that has been devised but one which is susceptible of improvement. Democracy should be regarded as an ideal towards which one works rather than as something perfectly achieved. Nor can it fail to have defects until the society in which it operates removes the more glaring injustices of our economic system. For myself I confess that I am not ready to die for dear old Rutgers but could live quite comfortably under a monarchy, at all events a constitutional monarchy. Majority rule is merely a convenient way of proceeding but, even in purely political matters, is not sacrosanct. This method (with the majority ascertained by free elections) may be counted upon to respect the minority and not to act tyrannously, if only for the reason that as public opinion fluctuates, the minority is sure in due course to become the majority; in which case it might have scores to settle.

I am a very hearty believer in democracy, but as presently constituted it has some defects. One is that a party which has been too long in office, or feels too insecure, is inclined to tolerate a certain amount of venality among those in a position to feather

their own nests. Another defect is that pointed out by Father
V. A. Demant, as quoted by T. S. Eliot in his *Idea of a Christian
Society:* [5] "The fact which renders most of the theories of Church
and State irrelevant is the domination of politics by economics
and finance. The subservience of politics to plutocracy is the
main fact about the State confronting the Church today." In other
words, he who pays the economic piper calls the political tune.
As Mr. Eliot says a little later in his own person: [6] "A certain
tension between Church and State is desirable. When Church
and State fall out completely, it is ill with the commonwealth;
and when Church and State get along too well together, there is
something wrong with the Church."

If in the United States this problem seems, on the governmental
plane, to have been solved, that seems to acerbate all the more
the private critics of the Church. Those who accuse the Catholic
Church in America of seeking political domination really mean,
I am afraid, that they would like to see the Church dominated by
the State. Since under the Constitution, as it stands, this cannot
be, they bitterly assail the Church. They know so little about
history as to be unaware that the American Revolution was in
part caused by the fear that the provisions of the Quebec Act,
which granted religious freedom to the Catholics of Canada,
would be extended to the American colonies. It was even whispered that St. Bartholomew's Day, 1772, had been selected for a
massacre of Protestants by Catholics. George III was accused
of being a Jesuit in disguise and his statue was in several places
adorned with a rosary. [7] Instead the Revolution brought religious
freedom, even to New England. But later there were the nativist
movements which were inspired by fear that the influx of Catholic immigrants would depress the standard of living for other
Americans. It was so violent in some of its manifestations that
cannon were dragged out into the street in Philadelphia to batter
down a church door; the Ursuline convent at Charlestown was

[5] Pp. 68-9.
[6] *Ibid.,* p. 95.
[7] All this may be exaggerated, and no doubt the Revolution would have
occurred in any case. But many of the New England ministers and publicists
made the Quebec Act a talking point, whether or not they really believed
what they were saying.

burned to the ground; and when Archbishop Bedini arrived (with no diplomatic status but commissioned to enquire at once into the possibility of sending an apostolic delegate to this country and to investigate the internal troubles of American Catholics) he came close to being lynched at Cincinnati. That in his case the violence was perpetrated mainly by German radicals and Italian Carbonari does not alter the fact that they were instigated by American Nativists.

Shortly before Bedini's arrival there had appeared the *Awful Disclosures* of Maria Monk, eventually shown to be an impostor and a loose-living woman, but for a time applauded even by the more respectable sort of Protestant controversialist, who took much the same line as does Mr. Blanshard and his friends, that Romanism was seeking to fasten its yoke on freedom-loving Americans. Later the Know-Nothings ran, though unsuccessfully, a presidential candidate, and their movement did not die away until the outbreak of the Civil War. Its successor, the American Protective Association, formed in 1887, was a relatively mild affair. As for the Ku Klux Klan, as reorganized on a different basis after the First World War, though it proclaimed itself to be opposed to Catholics as well as Jews, most of its kind attentions were given to Negroes. It has long been completely discredited in the eyes of all decent Americans, though it still has some members and still perpetrates some outrages. The point is that each of these waves of bigotry was much weaker than the one that preceded it, and though it would be rash to prophesy that there will never again be a really virulent anti-Catholic outburst, history would seem to indicate that this is unlikely. Compared with his foul-mouthed forerunners, Mr. Blanshard is gentlemanly—indeed, one might almost say ladylike.

Recently there has been a furore over President Truman's announced purpose of appointing an ambassador to the Vatican, just as there had been when President Roosevelt circumvented his difficulties by sending a "personal representative" to the Pope. I very much regret Mr. Truman's action, as it can only result in the embroiling of non-Catholics against us. Of course there would be no violation of the principle of the separation of Church and State, any more than there is by the sending of an American ambassador to England, a country in which there is not only an established (Protestant) church but where the ruling monarch is its head. But in order to allay misconceptions I quote from a statement issued in January, 1948, by Archbishop John T. Mc-Nicholas of Cincinnati, who was chairman of the National Catholic Welfare Conference: "We deny absolutely and without any qualification that the Catholic Bishops of the United States are seeking a union of church and state by any endeavors whatsoever, either proximate or remote. If tomorrow Catholics constituted a majority in our country, they would not seek a union of church and state. They would, then as now, uphold the Constitution and all its Amendments, recognizing the moral obligation imposed on all Catholics to defend the Constitution and its Amendments. . . . In complete accord with the Catholic doctrine, we hold firmly that our own constitutional provisions are the best for our country. Even had we authority to do so, we would not change one iota of them." The statement of the American hierarchy issued in November of the same year affirms this stand.

Just what was in Mr. Truman's mind when proposing General Mark Clark as ambassador (an appointment from which General Clark withdrew when he saw the trouble that lay ahead) I am not prepared to say. It could hardly have been an astute move of a politician to placate Catholics, because for every Catholic vote he might have won Mr. Truman would probably have lost three by his ill-advised idea. So presumably he believed that an ambassador at the Vatican would be useful to the country as a whole. That may well be, but the animosity towards Catholics that has been aroused in my opinion weakens rather than strengthens the United States, and offsets even any advantages that American Catholics might have obtained. Good will all round should be our aim. And this might be helped if Mr. Blanshard and his friends stopped trying to thrust their private interpretation of the Constitution down our throats. The Founding Fathers used the plainest and most unequivocal language; may I mildly suggest that it be studied again?

What the Constitution envisaged from the beginning was the introduction of Amendments as necessity for them arose; and the means of obtaining them was indicated. Moreover, decisions of the Supreme Court, which become law as soon as made, can also be overruled by Constitutional amendment. It is not easy to do this, but as the Dred Scott decision and the ruling against the unconstitutionality of an income tax show, it can be done. Therefore Catholics cannot be absolutely sure that the provisions of the Constitution relating to religious liberty, provisions especially prized by them, will not at some time be revoked. For ultimately of course it is the American people themselves who make the law. But we count upon the fair-mindedness of our fellow citizens and the American tradition of religious liberty as well as upon the Constitution itself. After all, even during the most outrageous periods of anti-Catholicism in the past, the majority of Americans, while by no means approving of Catholicism, still more disapproved of violence and injustice. In so far as anything can be certain in this world, we Catholics believe that we are safe in the United States.

# CHAPTER FIVE
## *Catholic Societies*

There are few Catholic societies which can be sharply divided into the two categories of those whose object is spiritual and those whose object is charitable. All the charitable societies aim ultimately at a spiritual good—both to the members who exercise the charity and to those who are its recipients. As for the societies that are spiritual, though some of these rule out of their objectives the performance of corporal works of mercy, this extends only so far as their corporate capacity. Even within that limitation they will, if confronted with an extreme case of material need, do their best to meet it, if no other organization is immediately available; and when the society as such does not act, individual members of the society can be counted upon to do so.

As might be expected, the majority of Catholic societies are spiritual in character, perhaps too much so, as often the members do not know one another very well, rarely meeting except when they assemble to perform their devotions, or when they have business to transact. It is a pity that this should be so, for as has already been remarked, anything that emphasizes Catholic solidarity is much to the good. And a society should be sociable.

The largest and most important of the spiritual societies are, properly speaking, not societies at all. These are the third orders, of which by far the largest is that of the Franciscans. It is, like the others—those connected with the Dominicans, the Carmelites, the Servites—a real part of the religious order, though its members are not canonically religious. Its members share in the merits flowing from all Franciscan good works and have the right to be buried in the Franciscan habit. The rule they follow (drawn up by St. Francis himself but since considerably modified) lays no great hardship on those who adopt it, calling only for the saying of some specified prayers and a monthly meeting when this is possible.

The Benedictines do not have a third order, as St. Benedict wrote only one rule. But their oblates correspond to tertiaries, and like them do their best to live according to the spirit of the rule, though without any of the monastic obligations. Like tertiaries, too, they share in the merits of the order, and after death a certain proportion of the Benedictine Masses are offered for the repose of their souls. The famous foundation made by St. Frances of Rome in the fifteenth century, *Tor di Specchi*, which is hardly distinguishable from other convents, though its canonical status is different, apparently suggested the establishment of the various groups of tertiaries (both men and women) who live much as do the regular members of their orders, though, in the case of women, with a freedom not possible to those who, like the Poor Clares and the Carmelites and the Dominican Nuns of the Second Order, are strictly enclosed and are contemplatives. These one never sees, for even should one visit them in their convents, they are separated from their callers not only by a grille but a thick veil. The many Franciscan and Dominican Sisters one may encounter conducting hospitals, schools and the like are all conventual tertiaries.

The ordinary secular tertiaries are not, strictly speaking, to be regarded as members of a pious society, though for convenience they have been introduced here as such. A true society with purely spiritual aims is that very large group dedicated to the honor of the Holy Name. Indirectly it can trace its origin to a decree of the Council of Lyons (1274) which called for the instruction of the faithful in reverence towards the name of Jesus. Soon afterwards Gregory X ordered John Vercelli, the Master-General of the Dominicans, to make this a special work of his Order. Now, however, it is a parochial society and in the United States has well over three and a half million members, all men. It is now mainly used as a means of getting these men to receive Holy Communion in a body once a month, though many of them "receive" every Sunday and a few of them daily. But the original purpose of reverence to the Holy Name is not forgotten.

Similarly only men belong to the Nocturnal Adoration Society, which, as the name implies, is for praying throughout the night in relays before the Blessed Sacrament on the occasions when it is exposed, as during the Forty Hours Devotion. During the day the same office is normally performed by the Sodality of the Blessed Virgin which, in some ways, is a feminine counterpart of the Holy Name Society, except in the matter of the avoidance of profanity—which, it need hardly be said, no lady would even think of using.

The Society for the Propagation of the Faith is primarily a collecting agency for the foreign missions, though from the start prayers as well as alms have always been solicited in their aid. Its annual membership calls only for the contribution of a dollar a year (though some people give a good deal more, even large amounts) and those who belong are asked to say an Our Father, a Hail Mary and a Glory Be each day for the missions, along with the invocation, "St. Francis Xavier, pray for us." The alms of its members have probably been the greatest single source of mission support since 1920. Like most of the major Catholic societies this has attached to it many spiritual privileges.

Then there are a number of purgatorial societies, in which one may enroll deceased relatives or friends, sure of a stipulated number of Masses being said for them, something much better than the sending of flowers, though one may do that as well, if one wishes. A priest who has accepted a stipend, whether for a single Mass or a series, is obligated under heavy penalties to perform according to his agreement, but is usually free to get another priest to accept the obligation, provided he also passes on with it the offering he may have received. One might add that pastors are required to say a good many Masses for their parishioners, and they and other priests say a number of Masses for which no stipend is offered. Of their own accord, they offer these Masses, for their friends and relatives living and dead, for people whom they merely know of but in whose spiritual good they are especially interested, or for some general intention.

Retreat Leagues might also be mentioned, though retreats themselves do not come under the heading of "societies." Our Lord and His disciples used to withdraw periodically from the pressing crowds to some solitary place for prayer, and these occasions were of course retreats. Religious orders have always had special periods of silence and meditation, and the Jesuits in particular, armed as they are with the *Spiritual Exercises* of their founder, may almost be said to have set the pattern for the modern retreat. They have provided through their patrons a number of very pleasant retreat houses, where usually for a long week end groups of Catholic lawyers or doctors or men from the same parish give themselves to devotion and the "making of the soul." Non-Catholics may attend if they choose, and I understand that Mr. Hore-Belisha, onetime Secretary of War in England, regularly spent periods in a Catholic monastery, though he was a Jew. And I knew a Mormon in Washington who was so enthusiastic about a retreat he had attended that he could talk of nothing else to the little Mormons in the Sunday school of which he was the superintendent. In this instance, I believe, the man became a Catholic, but there is never any attempt at proselytism. The Religious of the Cenacle, founded in France in 1826, provide retreat houses for women not unlike those that the Jesuits provide for men.

Parish retreats sometimes occur. If conducted in the parish church, as they almost always are, they labor under some handicaps, for it is hardly to be expected that those attending can do more than go to Mass in the morning and in the evening to a conference, with a short period of meditation, followed by Benediction. Such a retreat does not greatly differ from the far more common ordinary parish mission, except for placing its emphasis somewhat differently. Where a mission may be said to be a call to repentance—unless it be a mission to non-Catholics, like those in which the Paulist Fathers specialize—a retreat assumes that all those present are good Christians and merely aims at making them still better.

Since with retreats I have wandered somewhat away from spiritual societies in the proper sense of the term, I might as well deal at this point with a most admirable group which is quite unorganized and whose objects are primarily charitable, though by no means exclusively so. By this means I may find a convenient link with Catholic charitable societies as formally constituted.

What I have in mind is the work of Dorothy Day of New York, already touched upon in an earlier section, though there only in connection with her activities in Catholic journalism. How Dorothy Day keeps her enterprises going is something that I have never been able to fathom. She maintains in various American and Canadian cities over thirty of her "houses of hospitality," into which she receives any of the destitute who may apply, if there is room, and sometimes, too, when there is no room, in which case Dorothy or one of her co-workers has to sleep on the floor. She was inspired by a French peasant of genius, now dead, named Peter Maurin, and she inspires in her turn those who go to her, so that of their own accord most of her "guests" become her assistants. She says in her book *House of Hospitality:* "We have no rules, any more than the average family has, and we ask no questions." Disagree though I do with the pacifism of her paper the *Catholic Worker,* I have always been profoundly impressed by her utter selflessness and that of those around her. One might think of them as a kind of religious order, were it not that they are nothing of the kind; and since they do not have so much as a list of members they cannot be called a society. Unpractical though these people may seem to be, the proof of the pudding is in the eating, for they not only conduct their houses of hospitality but several farms, where visitors may do some work (as apparently all do) and where retreats are regularly given.

Dorothy Day is a quite extraordinary person. Born in Brooklyn in 1897, as she tells us in her recently published *The Long Loneliness,* she joined the Socialist Party while at the University of Illinois, before coming to New York to take a position on the *Call,* afterwards going on the staff of the *Masses* and later still becoming a free-lance writer. She came to Christ through her compassion for the poor, and although she says that she was once a Communist, so far from turning informer against them, she continues to regard them with love. Having entered the Church she was obliged to sever a "common law" marriage she had contracted, as the man would not hear of any marriage ceremony, least of all a Catholic marriage. She experienced, she confesses, years of longing for him, but a still larger part of her Long Loneliness was knowing God but knowing Him imperfectly and knowing that she would always suffer until she knew Him completely. She has drawn comfort from the sixteenth-century English nun, Mary Ward, who said: "The pain is great, but very endurable, because He who lays the burden also carries it."

A somewhat similar work was done for the Negroes of Harlem by the Baroness de Hueck. It warms one all over to hear that there are people like this in the modern world.

Passing to what are definitely charitable societies, it might be remembered that, according to Christian ideas, charity is a supernatural virtue, and is not at all the same thing as social service or relief, though it may use—and to be effective is often obliged to use—the technique of the well-trained social worker. Christ told His disciples, "Love one another as I have loved you," and again, "This is My commandment, that you love one another." It is striking that when He described what would happen on the Day of Judgment He said nothing about church attendance, or even sin, in the ordinary sense, but made the criterion of salvation the performance of corporal works of mercy: "Come ye blessed of My Father; possess the kingdom prepared for you from the foundation of the world." About this He was most specific: "I was hungry and you gave Me to eat; I was thirsty and you gave Me to drink; I was a stranger, and you took Me in; I was naked and you covered Me; I was in prison and you came to Me." And when the blessed will cry that they have never seen Christ in such necessities, they will get the answer, "As long as you did it to the least of My brethren you did it to Me." The wicked will be judged by the same principle and will protest in vain that they never saw Christ in need. No, but they had seen Christ's poor in need; therefore the dreadful sentence is: "Depart from Me, ye cursed, into everlasting fire, prepared for the devil and his angels."

The theme runs throughout the New Testament and is often found in the Old Testament as well. Of many passages that might be cited this from the First Epistle of St. John will have to suffice: "Whoso hath this world's goods, and seeth his brother in need, and shutteth up his bowels of compassion from him, how dwelleth the love of God in him?" Charity towards our fellows is thereby taken as a proof of our love of God. Christian charity always springs from that love, and love is a hollow pretence unless there be charity.

There is something else to remember: Christian charity towards our needy fellows augments our own spiritual love. Charity moreover does not end with the giving of an alms or care to the sick; it should begin there but must seek the spiritual good of those assisted more than their material good. This does not mean that the almsgiver is always called upon to preach a little sermon; in most instances he would be very injudicious to attempt anything of the sort and would defeat his own object. It does mean, however, that though bodily necessities should be relieved promptly—and perhaps without any immediate thought of anything else—we should never forget that the salvation of souls is of even greater importance. Yet material needs have to be relieved even when, so far as we can see, it is humanly speaking impossible to touch the heart. Even then, though, we must hope that our corporal works of mercy may prepare the way for spiritual benefits.

One sometimes hears the obnoxious phrase—smelling of the worst kind of sociology—that we should limit our charity to the "deserving" poor. But of course if there is desert, there can be no charity, unless one understands this in the sense that the needy have claims on us, not because they are good men but men. It is nevertheless quite true that, before handing out money (or even pawnable articles) we would do well to make sure that the father of the family we propose to help is not going to squander what he receives in the corner saloon or a crap game. This might be true, even if the man had no wife and family; but their existence makes it all the more incumbent upon us to show another sort of charity—our protection of them. Catholics (like other people) should always try to exhibit a little sense; but they should not forget that it is possible, under the plea of "prudence," to be niggardly. We must be openhearted and openhanded; let us also keep our eyes open.

All this has perhaps been sufficiently well dinned into us by a long line of sociologists and prim ladies bountiful. What has to be borne in mind is the principle as stated by Abbot Marmion in his *Christ, the Life of the Soul:* [1] "There are souls that seek God in Jesus Christ, and accept the Humanity of Christ, but stop there. That is not sufficient: we must accept the Incarnation with all the consequences it involves: we must not let the gift of ourselves stop at Christ's own Humanity but extend it to His mystical Body. That is why—never forget this, for it is one of the most important points of the spiritual life—to abandon the least of our brethren is to abandon Christ Himself, to succor one of them, is to succor Christ in person." Whether the stories told of some of the saints are largely legendary or not, they contain deep spiritual truth. St. Francis of Assisi, still a fashionable young man, conquers his repugnance and embraces a leper; then, mounting his horse again, he looks around—and the leper has vanished into air. St. Elizabeth of Hungary puts a leper in her own bed, and her husband and mother-in-law make their way there indignantly and pull the coverlet down—to find Christ lying in the bed. The same Christ has assured us that we cannot give as little as a cup of cold water in His name and fail to obtain a reward.

The majority of these corporal works of mercy are performed by religious, especially by Sisters, though there are orders of Brothers devoted to hospital work or the care of delinquent boys (out of one of their institutions came Babe Ruth), and probably every order of priests has at least a few of its members in charge of activities of this sort—the majority of its members, precisely because they are priests, are even more usefully employed in purely spiritual duties. There are also a number of charitable organizations made up of either laymen or laywomen or both. Yet when I looked through the list of Catholic Societies in the United States given in the *National Catholic Almanac* I was rather surprised to discover that those engaged in relieving the necessities of the poor were not nearly as many as I had supposed. The list is, however, far from being complete, and my cursory eye notices that even such a beautiful work as that of the Christ Child Society has been overlooked.

This does not mean that charity has grown cold among Catholics—for if so, we would be in a bad way indeed—but rather that

[1] P. 330. Sands.

most of it is private and kept concealed, so that the left hand does not know what the right hand does, which is the best way as far as one's own spiritual good is concerned. But because it is not the most effective way, there are the many diocesan Catholic Charities, modeled on the organization founded by Cardinal Hayes; and within these charities operate the various hospitals and crèches and hostels and young people's clubs of the diocese.

It is on a national rather than a diocesan basis that the many Catholic fraternal orders are organized. The order of the Knights of Columbus, by far the largest of these, is typical in that it makes itself responsible for a good deal of charitable work, which it is well equipped to do, both because of its own organization and because of being in contact with more specialized societies and the parishes through which a considerable—perhaps the main part—of such work is done.

The St. Vincent de Paul Society is the chief of those dedicated to the performance of corporal works of mercy. It was founded in Paris in 1833 by Frederic Ozanam, a brilliant young professor at the Sorbonne. Now it is rather elaborately organized, and the membership is of three kinds—active, subscribing and honorary, the first doing the actual field work, the others assisting by contributions and prayers. The parish branches of the Society are called conferences, and when there are a number of these in a city they are linked together as a "particular council." There are also diocesan councils and for the work as a whole a Superior Council of the United States. During the past twenty-five years the Society has distributed over $50,000,000, not to mention food, clothing, bedding and furniture. And the poor get everything that comes in, for nothing is spent on salaries or administrative expenses. Such a work has, as is ordinarily true of Catholic enterprises of this sort, a vividly apostolic aspect. It therefore falls under Catholic Action and has already been mentioned in the chapter written upon it.

Some of these charities (as is also the case with charity organizations of a non-Catholic sort) are strictly specialized. Thus there is the recently established Guild of Our Lady of Ransom, with headquarters in Boston, that provides legal, social and financial assistance to former inmates of penal institutions. Another of the societies of this type is the Blessed Martin Guild, under the patronage of Martin de Porres, which seeks to overcome prejudice against Negroes and to promote interest in the Colored Apostolate. Finally, since it is possible to instance only a few out of many, there is the St. Paul's Guild of New York City for the aid of convert ministers, who sometimes find themselves in very difficult circumstances on entering the Catholic Church. Those who are unmarried are likely to become priests, and of the rest there are some who are qualified for teaching positions. But now and then a convert minister may need support for a year or two before he is able to equip himself for self-support in a totally new mode of life. Just how much the Guild is able to do for those whom it tries to help I do not know, but it is obvious that the Church cannot in justice welcome souls into their spiritual home and then callously turn them out to shift for themselves in a bleak economic night.

I have said that a very considerable part of Catholic corporal works of mercy are performed by religious orders, especially those of women. There are for instance well over a thousand Catholic hospitals in the United States (a few of them in the charge of nursing Brothers), and they treat over four million patients every year, the majority of whom are non-Catholics. Many people prefer such hospitals to secular institutions—not because the doctors and nurses there are more efficient, for that would be too much to claim—but because they are likely to get greater kindness and consideration while under Catholic care. Other people, for all I know to the contrary, may avoid Catholic hospitals as vaguely sinister; at any moment they might be dragged from bed down to a dungeon of the Inquisition! Yet the furthest that the Sisters will ever go in the case of any non-Catholic who is dying is to suggest the making of an act of contrition; they could hardly do less. Occasionally those known to have been seriously interested in the Catholic Church, if brought in in a state of coma, may be conditionally baptized, on the presumption that their interest would have carried them further.

What arouses Mr. Blanshard's wrath is that Catholic hospitals operate under what he calls "the Catholic medical code," which he does not very clearly understand. With him it simmers down to the kind of case which probably does not happen once in a hundred thousand times, when the doctor has to tell the husband of a woman in labor, "I believe I can save the mother, or I can save the child; which am I to save?" The only thing a Christian can say is, "You must try to save both." It is not permissible for any man to sentence either his wife or child to death, or authorize a doctor to commit murder. Unfortunately there is sometimes reason to believe that an obliging doctor will get rid of a perfectly well-formed infant immediately after birth to save embarrassment to its unmarried mother.

On the other hand, if there were anything whatever in Mr. Blanshard's allegation that Catholic nurses are instructed to put difficulties in the way of non-Catholics' receiving ministers of their own faith during their last moments, one could only say that all those concerned would stand in the gravest danger of the fires of hell.[2] One wonders, however, why Mr. Blanshard should exhibit—I think in this solitary instance—such solicitude for the salvation of souls. Without wishing to be uncharitable in the closing words of a chapter on charity, I must confess that I have been able to find hardly a trace of Christian sentiment in this former Congregationalist minister—a man who, with somewhat shocking jauntiness, says that he believes that he still is one.

Love, whether towards God or man, is most fortunately not a Catholic prerogative; in fact, early in this book I have said that those not professedly of our faith sometimes surpass us in this respect. The most that we are prepared to claim is that though, as St. Paul has said, charity is more than hope, more even than faith, to be a Christian in any real sense calls for the integration of all three theological virtues. We rejoice when we see any signs of that integration elsewhere; may we not ask that others rejoice over any virtues that we may happen to possess, even when they are not in accord with us?

[2] He does cite a passage that bears upon this (on pp. 119–120 of his *American Freedom and Catholic Power*), but it says the exact opposite of what he tries to make out, for its point is how the Catholic nurse, without assisting in the practice of what she believes to be a false religion, may nevertheless bring in a Protestant nurse or a relative or a friend to effect what the patient wishes.

# PART IV
# THE REWARD

# CHAPTER ONE

## *Spiritual Security*

Primarily the reward of being a Catholic is that one is a Catholic. Or rather, the reward is Christ—attained even on earth, in the very real sense that at baptism the Christian becomes a member of the Mystical Body, with the expectation of the Beatific Vision hereafter. As the hymn for Lauds on the Feast of Corpus Christi puts it:

> *Se nascens dedit socium;*
> *Convescens in edulium;*
> *Se moriens in pretium;*
> *Se regnans dat in premium.*[1]

Or as Brother Reginald, the socius of St. Thomas Aquinas during his last days, tells us, one day there came a Voice from the altar, "Thomas, you have written well of me. What reward shall I give you?" Promptly the answer was returned, "Nothing, Lord, but Thyself."

Aldous Huxley says what amounts to much the same thing in one of his commentaries in *Texts and Pretexts*: "Man and the universe," he writes, "are incommensurable. Leviathan and Behemoth—these are the heraldic beasts of God. The universe is vast, beautiful and appalling; by all our human standards monstrous; but precisely because of its monstrousness, divine and to be worshipped. And if the nature of things were not a Behemoth, if it treated the just man according to his merits, where would these merits be? They would be nowhere. Just as 'pleasures are not if they last,' so virtues are not if they are rewarded. In a humanly accepted universe, as Bagehot has pointed out . . . the

---

[1] In youth he gave Himself as our Companion; in maturity as our Food; dying as our Redemption; reigning as our Reward.

245

just man would be nonexistent. For the essence of virtue is disinterestedness. But there would be no disinterestedness in a world which automatically rewarded virtue and punished vice." All that needs to be added is that rewards and punishments—though neither follows automatically—occur sufficiently often to remind us that there is a connection between them and virtue and vice, and if the connection is not always established in this world, it is one of the proofs that there must be another where all will be rectified.

What of the rewards that we feel should be given in this world to virtue? They often seem to be given to vice; it is a matter patent to observation that the wicked all too often prosper, though for certain kinds of wickedness society metes out jail or the hangman's noose, if the wicked should happen to get caught. On the other hand, can we say that what ought to accompany a life of virtue—prosperity, health, position, honor and so forth—are necessarily blessings? Far from it, for good though all these things are in themselves, they are a form—and perhaps the best form—of wealth. Christ Himself has told us that it is easier for a camel to go through the eye of a needle than for a rich man to enter heaven.[2] Position and honor are conducive of pride, and Lord Acton's most famous sentence is, "All power corrupts; absolute power corrupts absolutely." As for health, if it is the least dangerous of all these forms of wealth, this is because those who have it are not conscious of it, until it has been lost, and so derive from it no vainglory. Yet the lustiness of health may foment lust, not in itself evil, though it can lead to evil. On the other hand, ill-health, if meekly accepted from God, may give better health to the soul. We are therefore not always able to say with any confidence that what are taken to be rewards are not rather temptations.

[2] I am of course aware of the all too facile explanation that the "needle's eye" was a postern gate in the city wall through which a man passed with his body at a right angle with his legs, and through which a camel might scramble on its knees—something, in other words, difficult but not impossible. On this principle of exegesis, Our Lord, when He spoke of mountains being cast into the sea, really meant only the tossing of a pebble into a duck pond! It might be a corrective of such nonsense if Biblical critics returned again to the Gospels to study Christ's habitual *a fortiori* style—"Then how much more, O ye of little faith."

It is much easier to be sure about punishments. The lecher is liable to contract a venereal disease, and though he may be able to guard against this and be as lecherous as ever, the drunkard will not escape the misery of a hang-over. Yet even that may be mitigated, for according to Mr. P. G. Wodehouse, who at least twice in his entertaining books provides the recipe, the admirable Jeeves concocts a restorative which works like magic. At any rate the glutton will hardly escape digging his grave with his teeth, even if he has a jolly time doing it. Nor are the spiritual sins always spared, for while the proverb is not always true, that pride goeth before a fall, the avaricious and the envious and the arrogant become so hated of their fellows that they will gleefully be dragged down, should an opportunity ever occur. Yet when our sins are punished we have cause to thank God: it is just possible that we may have sense enough to avoid them in future, and punishment in this life lessens any debt of punishment we have to pay in the life to come.

The other proverb, "Virtue is its own reward," is much too smug. Here what is meant by virtue is rather respectability, which frequently is not really virtuous at all. But the love of God—and this includes the keeping of God's commandments—is rewarded spiritually in this life, though only occasionally, by chance and intermittently, does virtue meet with the reward of material success. Those who think of a reward in other terms find in the love of God the greatest consolation now, and the hope of eternal union with God afterwards.

I do not for a moment suggest that the reward of this nature is limited to Catholics, or even to Christians, and we should all rejoice that it is not so. Indeed, little in this concluding section of my book is restricted to Catholics, unless it be the later chapter entitled "Una Sancta." Yet even the strictly Catholic doctrine set forth there finds acceptance, if only in part, with some non-Catholics. One of the most distinguished Congregationalist preachers of our time, a man to whose church I belonged in my adolescence, and from whom I learned much for which I will never cease to be grateful—I refer to Dr. George Campbell Morgan—of his own accord confided to me fourteen years before his death that he believed in purgatory. He thought it reasonable to suppose that there were many people, not so utterly wicked as to deserve hell, who would nevertheless stand in need of some measure of punishment and purification before they were fit to be admitted to heaven. This was of course eminently sensible of Dr. Morgan. The only cause for the rejection of purgatory by the sixteenth-century reformers was that, since their main purpose was to destroy the power of the priesthood, they refused to admit that Masses or indulgences could do anything towards giving comfort to the faithful departed. As King Henry VIII showed, it was quite possible to make a total denial of the Pope's authority and yet to retain Masses and prayers for the dead. The King's will provided for the saying of Masses in perpetuity for the repose of his own soul.

It is the authority of the Church that imparts serenity and security to the faith that Catholics hold. The Catholic is completely convinced that he possesses the truth. He will not dispute, however, that those belonging to this or that Protestant sect, or even to some non-Christian religion, also possess part of the truth—some a large part, some a small part—but all of it fragments of Catholic truth. It would in fact be impossible to find that even the most degraded form of animism was quite devoid of some element of truth. A system that was completely wrong would be as "miraculous" as one completely right. Whether in religion or philosophy, truth is in widest commonalty spread.

To try to show that Catholics do possess the whole truth was not my purpose, and if it had been, this late point would hardly be the place to argue the matter. All I have done is to show what it is Catholics hold. And I believe that most intelligent and well-informed people have discovered—even when they think Catholics deluded—that Catholics have a deep conviction in their faith. It is in this that a Catholic's happiness reposes, and though—being, after all, only a man with human weakness—his faith may sometimes momentarily falter, or he may lose its altogether, he still knows that it is upon his faith that his happiness depends. To belong to Christ is therefore to be already rewarded by Christ. Though with it will go pain that his union with Christ is not yet perfect, that too is a reward because it is the promise of a further reward.

Yet if faith alone were the criterion, then we are grimly reminded by St. James in his epistle that the devils also believe. He says this to enforce upon our minds that good works are necessary to salvation as well as faith, which is why Luther dismissed this as "an epistle of straw." [3] As for us in this mortal life, "we see through a glass darkly, but then face to face." In heaven there will be no real place for the exercise of faith, as there we shall have a direct and immediate vision of God and inescapably recognize the truth of even the most abstruse Christian doctrines which, as Dante says, have for the Blessed axiomatic force. To some slight extent this is possible even in this life, so that one way of describing a mystic might be to say that he is one for whom mysteries have ceased to exist, as he has penetrated beyond them. This, however, can be only a fashion of speaking, for no man ever lived on earth who plumbed the mysteries to their depth, and even in heaven no saint, nor even the most exalted of angelic intelligences, will ever understand God in His essence completely, though blissfully gazing upon Him.

To leave such considerations, which might involve us in perilous speculations: What the Catholic firmly holds, in a world that is often bewildering, is a trust in Providence. "Yea, though He slay me," cried King David, "yet will I trust Him." The believer does not even begin to pretend to be able to follow all the operations of Providence, though the very fact of his trust may itself from time to time enable him to catch some inkling of God's intricate designs. Yet even when he imagines that he has caught some glimpse of the pattern being woven upon the great tapestry, he cannot be sure that that pattern may not be part of a still larger pattern which may be very different from anything he can so much as guess at. This is why there can be no "philosophy of history," such as many philosophers and some

[3] In spite of this, Luther was the propounder of the Protestant principle that the Bible and not the Church is the final authority—and here he was sitting in judgment on the Bible! Luther of course was one of those men who are more remarkable for their warm blood than their clear head. It might be a little unfair to hold him too closely to all his casual *obiter dicta.* As for the devils' believing, it does not have the virtue of faith; still less are they in the presence of the Beatific Vision, which they forfeited before enjoying it. They *know* rather than believe, but know on the evidence of Christ's acts.

historians have flattered themselves they have discovered. What the Christian does, both with regard to the world scheme and to his personal concerns, is to consign everything to God's hands, in the unshakable assurance that all will be well.

It must be a terrifying, as well as bewildering, experience to those who declare themselves agnostics to live in a world which, as they can find no God in it, can have no meaning. The stoic fortitude of such souls may be admired, just as one must respect an honest inability to reach any kind of faith. However, one suspects that in most cases this profession of agnosticism is merely a convenient excuse for not observing the commandments of God. This seems to have been understood by A. E. Housman (himself an honest agnostic) when he made his Shropshire Lad declare roundly:

> The laws of God, the laws of man,
> They may keep that will and can!

The poor fellow acknowledges himself "A stranger and afraid / In a world I never made"; therefore he befuddles himself with ale, and gets into trouble with young women—and likable though he is upon the whole, as often as not is hanged at eight in the morning in Shrewsbury Jail.

Fortunately few Shropshire Lads end up quite so badly, but all of them—along with a large number of well-educated and respectable people with every social advantage—have to moan:

> I a stranger and afraid
> In a world I never made.

We can be extremely thankful that we did not make the Shropshire Lad's world, except in the limited sense that we have done something to make a mess of a world that could have been better. Apart from this, the world we live in is one in which the lilies of the field grow "richer than Solomon in all his glory," in which all the hairs of our head are numbered, in which no sparrow can fall to the ground without our Father seeing. And though it is no doubt temerarious of me, after having frequently quoted first-rate poetry, to quote a sonnet of my own (and not even one of

my best), I will venture because it expresses, more exactly than
I could hope to do in prose, what it is I want to say:

> Pleading for grace upon a humble knee,
> Or angry that our plans are all undone,
> How should we know what we should seek or shun?
> How plumb the depths of Wisdom's chartless sea?
> More than we dare to ask, or think could be,
> His love prepares. But it would only stun
> To glimpse an arrow of the blinding Sun
> Whose light irradiates eternity.
>
> Beyond the imagination's furthest sweep,
> Beyond the most audacious dream of pride—
> As though with one sole function occupied—
> The Father watches while His children sleep,
> The Spirit broods upon us from the deep,
> The Bridegroom ever yearns towards the Bride.

A trust in Providence will surely seem a very practical thing
even to those people, and they are many, who see little utility
in the formal acceptance of a series of doctrinal propositions.
If only people could have this trust apart from faith, there is
nobody who would not want to have it. But that of course is impossible, for trust springs from faith and is indeed part of it,
not merely a consequence that follows upon it. The last time my
wife and I were in Bermuda, which is a highly respectable
Anglican community, a Protestant one day said wistfully to us:
"I see dozens and dozens of people going in and out of the
Catholic church every time I pass it"—and he did not mean only
when Mass was being said. "Every time I wonder, what is it that
they *find* there? I wish I could find it." My wife answered with
the single word, "Warmth"—which is perhaps as good a way as
any of putting it.

A lot of time would have been needed to explain the whole
matter—for not only do Catholics have faith in God and trust in
God but at least the possibility of moral security. Yet Catholics
would never dream of claiming that they are morally superior to
the many kind, honest, decent, law-abiding people around them,
who often, even at best, seem to have only the very vaguest sort

of religious sense. Some of these people may, it is true, indulge in practices which Catholics hold to be against the natural law, and I find it hard to believe that, even when such people cannot see that these practices are wrong, their moral fiber is not slowly eaten away. Yet otherwise these are, so far as I can judge, very good people. The question that inevitably arises is whether an acceptance of the general framework of the Christian moral tradition—so frequently with them merely a tradition and not something that reposes on definite religious sanctions—is enough or can quite satisfy them. That certain things are "not done," or are "not cricket" provides, at best, a rather flimsy moral support. On that basis there can be no moral security, and one cannot but fear that what support there is will be sapped—a process the reverse of that by which the islands of Bermuda were built by billions of coral insect skeletons.

All that we can do is to leave the moral condition of society as we know it to Providence, thankful for what remains of the Christian tradition. Enough is left upon which to build a better order of society. Most people would at least say that they believe in the Ten Commandments. If they can be brought to integrate these with the Christian revelation, all will yet be well. There are signs that this has already begun to happen; but even should all signs be taken from us, standing amid decay in the darkness, our trust must be in God.

# CHAPTER TWO

## *Intellectual Freedom*

The Catholic Church is constantly under attack on account of the Syllabus of Errors issued by Pope Pius IX at the end of 1864—a document which is commonly misunderstood. In the first place, every one of the eighty propositions condemned was condemned only in the sense in which it was held by those who advanced it, not in some different sense which other people may have attached to it. Thus only a certain brand of "liberalism" was included, and Lacordaire, who had earlier submitted to the Holy See, at the time when his friend, the equally brilliant but more arrogant Félicité de Lamennais, refused to do so, said he intended to die a penitent but an impenitent liberal. Personally I do not like that term at all, as used of Catholics; for you either accept the Catholic faith as a whole and without qualification, or you are not to be considered a Catholic. But usually when people talk about somebody's being a "liberal Catholic," they have in mind merely somebody who did not accept the view of most of their coreligionists about Franco during the Spanish civil war. Catholics about whose orthodoxy there can be no question—ranging from Jacques Maritain and Georges Bernanos to the majority of the English Dominicans—were far from being pro-Franco, and if anybody is interested, I am of their opinion; so on that basis I suppose I would have to be classified as a liberal. But I am certainly not a liberal in the sense of the Syllabus of Errors.

Most of the propositions condemned obviously had to be condemned, and nobody is likely to hurl the Syllabus in the teeth of the present Pope because of what Pius IX said about Pantheism, Naturalism, Absolute Rationalism, Moderate Rationalism, Indifferentism, Latitudinarianism and so forth, even when they do not altogether agree. We find here in advance a condemnation of Communism, or a condemnation implied. It cannot but be recognized that the Church must be true to its doctrines, and the condemnations of the Syllabus have been welcomed by Protestants of the more orthodox variety.

Much the same thing is true about the condemnation of errors about ethics, and even about Christian marriage, though here there were some specific articles that aroused resentment. The Syllabus need not bother us—by which I mean that objections against it are somewhat out of date, in view of the fact that its main points, in so far as religion was directly concerned, were dealt with more fully by the encyclical *Pascendi*, issued by Pius X in 1907 against modernism. This encyclical may be said to have destroyed modernism, wherever it had appeared in Catholic circles, and indeed the Abbé Loisy freely admitted, after he had been excommunicated, that he had long ceased to be a believer.

The question of the Temporal Power, about which various theories were held in 1864 by Catholics, has been settled and so removed from the discussion. We are therefore really left with only two points that may be regarded as rocks of offense. What Pius IX had to say about Socialism, applies not so much to Socialism, as that word is now used, but to Communism; and there the overwhelming majority of Americans of all shades of religious and political belief would agree with the Pope. The other point—regarding errors about the State and its relation to the Church—has already been dealt with in these pages. But it might be as well to say again that the full co-operation of Church and State is postulated only for ideal conditions, such as do not exist in the United States and are likely never to come into existence.

Yet it was supposed in 1864 (and is still supposed in some quarters) that the Pope was making a frontal attack along the whole line against modern progress and civilization. Actually the attack was only on the cast of mind that thought of progress under nothing but its material or technological aspects, and that placed in that kind of progress a superstitious awe that would make it the sole meaning of man's earthly existence. It should by now be obvious to everybody that though atomic energy is capable of being put to beneficent uses, the only use so far made of it—or that is likely to be made of it for a long time to come—has been the wiping out, with a single bomb, of a large city. But even were atomic energy used solely for good, it is still incapable of achieving the whole good of man, and those who place their good here can only obtain incalculable spiritual loss.

So also with the airplane, which has been a terrible engine of destruction, but which, upon the balance, has been useful to man. The radio is, in itself, a very good thing, but it may produce a generation of morons, or may be a means of indoctrinating millions of slaves. Even those who do not think that God matters very much might go and read George Orwell's terrifying *1984* or Aldous Huxley's *Brave New World* if they want to find a picture of the horrors to which scientific advancement is capable of leading us, and how near we already are to them. Although Mr. Huxley will not admit that he is a Christian and Mr. Orwell died affirming his agnosticism, both men said in effect much the same thing that Pius IX did. Scientific discoveries, though they may be and should be used for human betterment, are no substitute for —let us not insist on religion, but for what philosophers of many shades of opinion agree in calling the "good life." This is more likely to be attained by reducing our life to very simple elements than by complicating it, and stifling it, with all the appliances of ingenious but arid minds. Before we talk too much about "progress" it might not be a bad idea to stop and consider to what point we intend to progress—heaven or hell. The word itself indicates no more than movement in a certain direction—one that may turn out to be quite the wrong direction. Accordingly the Syllabus must not be taken to mean opposition to science but only to our attaching too great a value to material things as against spiritual possessions.

Such an attitude is actually the reverse of illiberal, for it secures us against the tyranny of progress for its own sake. Emerson long ago protested that

> Things are in the saddle
> And ride mankind.

So they do, which means that man consents to be their slave. We can be free only by putting "things" in the place that belongs to them, making them serve mankind, always with the understanding that man's destiny is spiritual. Materialism cannot be other than degrading when permitted to be paramount. As we are creatures of flesh and blood, our physical nature has need of the material; being creatures with an immortal soul, we have to guard against our own soulless cleverness, otherwise we shall be crushed by it. Properly regarded, Catholicism, even in what are considered its least liberal and most obscurantist aspects, is a guarantee of human liberty.

Intellectual freedom is not really separable from moral freedom, for they are two aspects of the same whole. In neither case can this freedom be absolute. Nor can it be absolute under any political system, unless it be anarchism, which fortunately cannot work, because it would be chaos. In religion freedom involves our acknowledgment of our dependence upon God. Christ said to those who believed in Him: "If ye continue in My word, then are ye My disciples indeed. And ye shall know the truth, and the truth shall set you free." But any honest man, meaning to do what is right, is *bound* by what he believes to be truth; therefore, so it would seem, he is not set free. Nevertheless the service of God is perfect freedom—freedom because it is service to God. Only by this service is it possible for man to fulfill himself, to realize his true nature. It is a condition far removed from servitude. Only as disciples of Christ and sons of God can we be free.

In the nature of things Catholic doctrine can never change. It can, to be sure, be more clearly defined as occasion demands, and more particularly, that it may be more profoundly understood. New implications may be discovered in it, but these are not, strictly speaking, new but were always there. Cardinal Newman wrote a book on *The Development of Doctrine,* to the scandal of some people of his day who did not understand his drift. He was not offering an adumbration of the later and now defunct modernism, which was really an accommodation of Catholic doctrine to the cast of what is called the modern mind, an interpretation of dogma in a "symbolical" sense, a reduction of the sacraments to "signs" and so forth. Newman was merely trying to trace something of the process of "unfolding," which does not add or alter, any more than one adds or alters by unrolling a bolt of silk. As for the discoveries that some scholars have trumpeted abroad, confident that at the blast the walls of Jericho-Rome would come tumbling down, Karl Adam mildly remarks: "We Catholics acknowledge readily, without any shame, nay with pride, that Catholicism cannot be identified simply and wholly with primitive Christianity, nor even with the Gospel of Christ, in the same way that the great oak cannot be identified with the tiny acorn. There is no mechanical identity, but an organic identity. And we go further and say that thousands of years hence Catholicism will probably be even richer, more luxuriant, more manifold in dogma, morals, law and worship than the Catholicism of the present day. A religious historian of the fifth millennium A.D. will without difficulty discover in Christianity conceptions and forms and practices which derive from India, China and Japan, and he will have to recognize a far more obvious 'complex of opposites'." Yet the Catholic Faith will be the same then as it is now, that which was "once committed to the saints." Well might St. Augustine exclaim in awe and wonder about the "beauty ever ancient and ever new."

There is therefore no hampering of intellectual growth in the Catholic Church—and least of all because its energies are canalized instead of dissipated. The Catholic looks for growth in the Church in somewhat the same way as the father looks for growth in the child. Even after the child has ceased to grow, he may develop, though in his case the time will come when all development ceases. So there have been periods during which the Church reached a point at which it seemed that its development was permanently arrested. The eighteenth century—and running over a little into the century that followed—may be said to have been one of these periods. It looked as though the Church were moribund, incapable of further exertions, and many acute observers confidently prophesied its speedy demise. Such a prophecy nobody would think of making today; instead the critics of the Church are getting desperately afraid of her.

That fear is altogether unnecessary, even on their own premises. And it would not occur if our enemies showed a little com-

mon sense and humor. It will have been noticed that though I
have claimed—doing so of set purpose repeatedly—that the
Church is the custodian of revealed truth, I have always coupled
this claim with wide admissions that elements of truth, which in
some instances are very large elements of truth, are possessed
by those who do not belong to the Church. Similarly, I as readily
grant that many who are not Catholics are, to all appearances,
better people than many of those who are. (On this last point I
am not being "tolerant" but merely conceding what it is impossible to deny.) [1] Nevertheless I think that upon the whole Catholics, though they are not more learned or clever than other people,
possess—and this must be by virtue of their Catholicism—a much
greater degree of common sense. Of course we have our share of
fools; for instance, every once in a while the old chain-letter
nonsense comes up—until the parish priest hears of it and says
some plain words on the subject. But the fact that they have a
definite faith leaves Catholics more or less immune to current
fads.

Odd though this may sound, they are also the least superstitious of people. If you want to find somebody who will go
nowhere and do nothing except when he has his charm in his
pocket, produce—no, not an illiterate Negro but a highly cultivated agnostic. Having no God, he has to substitute some sort
of supernormal power, even if he does not believe in it. But
Catholics, precisely because their faith draws so clear a line
around its content, do not go splurging around in every direction
seeking some new spirituality and always finding some new
charlatan. It is true that I have heard of a small number of so-
called Catholics—among them Lord French's sister, Mrs. Despard,
who forty years ago as an old lady was one of the leaders of the
suffragettes in England—who also dabbled a little in theosophy
and who carried to Mass, so I am told, prayer books specially

---

[1] Catholics have a somewhat grim jest to the effect that those who arrive
in heaven will be greatly surprised at some of the people they find there,
and still more surprised that some of those they quite expected to see fail to
arrive. Similarly a pretty comedy might be written about hell, when the local
sots and gamblers and lechers gather around the primly starched *censor
morum* of their community, shouting, "Look who's here!" But from the first
we have been told, "The first shall be last, and the last first."

compiled for this purpose. Of such people (if they are any longer to be found) one is obliged to say that they were either pretending to be theosophists or pretending to be Catholics; they must have known very well that they were attempting an impossible synthesis of irreconcilable elements. Yet even Mrs. Despard, as far as I know, never attended any of the séances of Krishnamurti when Annie Besant first trotted him out in fashionable London drawing rooms to utter such mystical profundities as "A stitch in time saves nine," or "Too many cooks spoil the broth," or "A rolling stone gathers no moss." The ladies who heard him positively swooned in admiration. It is only due to Krishnamurti to add that some years later he suddenly got tired of playing the role of the incarnation of whatever it was he did incarnate. Yet from New York to Los Angeles one may still find plenty of idle women (and a sprinkling of men) who gawk over yoga and ahimsa and the rest of the rubbish. Catholics, whatever their faults may be, are too clear-headed, too hard-headed, for that.

I may be told that this is a sign of intellectual curiosity; and curiosity maybe it is, but not of the sort that calls for any real use of the brains. It would be better to plump squarely for a frank and honest agnosticism than to equate spirituality with this sort of addled sentimentality. Catholics would not dream of interfering with such people, but we must be pardoned—really we must—if we laugh.

Perhaps the whole point of both intellectual and moral freedom—its wide expanse but also its strictly defined Catholic boundaries—is summed up in the lines of Archibald MacLeish's poem:

> We know the answer, we know all the answers;
> It is the question we do not know.

That is another way of saying that we don't know what it is all about. We do not know the answers but always have a large supply of wisecracks and smart-aleckisms on hand. But Catholics know what the questions should be and can give the answers—at any rate answers which will suffice for practical purposes.

# CHAPTER THREE

## *Moral Freedom*

It was not of course suggested in the previous chapter that Catholics are free to believe whatever their fancy chooses, but rather that their faith protects them against the kind of follies that snare so many other people, that it tends to sharpen the wits of Catholics, and that it provides them with intellectual ballast. Their faith is imposed authoritatively, for it purports to be nothing less than a revelation made by God Himself; but outside the limits of that faith, there is a wide field in which Catholics are free to speculate, and in which many of them do speculate with great avidity, though subject, as they wish to be, to the Church's correction. So far from feeling that their minds are fettered, they know that they are preserved against the vagaries the mind is liable to indulge in when left completely to its own devices.

Similarly there is a wide field in which morals are free—the field of indifferent matters—though, as we have seen in the section on asceticism (even such a moderate amount of asceticism as would be all that might be expected of an ordinary layman), even indifferent matters, if they interfere with the soul's progress to God, should be sacrificed, though good in themselves, for the sake of a greater good. St. Paul tells us that not all the things that are permissible to him are expedient, and while the principle must not be pressed too strictly against the average man and woman—for they incur no sin except by breaking the law of God —it is something that has to be borne in mind by those who wish to go beyond the bare minimum required and to advance in the spiritual life. No claim is being made here that Catholics are more free in this respect than other people; all that is being pointed out is that in moral issues they have the same freedom, no more and no less.

Nevertheless there is a sense in which they are more free than others—more free because they have a moral guide in the Church. For instance, many American non-Catholics whose upbringing was in one of the stricter sects (and this is also true of many English non-Catholics) are never quite able to shake off the idea that this or that quite harmless thing—card-playing, dancing, theatre-going, drinking or even smoking—is more or less reprehensible.[1] The children of many such people went into revolt, at any rate many did during the years of the "lost generation" that followed 1918. But a large number of them remained uneasy, and though the generation that succeeded them was not so oppressed with the irrational Protestant taboos, even some of these are not quite comfortable in mind. When they rolled up their sleeves or hitched up their socks (so to speak) one might catch sight of the gyves of the chain they had snapped. This, I fancy, largely accounts for the emergence of a number of very queer cults, and also for the popularity of psychoanalysis in this country, in some ways the queerest cult of all.

It is rather amusing to note the history of prohibition in this connection. There are those who imagine (quite erroneously) that it was an integral part of puritanism. The early Puritans in this country would have been very much astonished had they

---

[1] My parents never allowed me to attend a theatre. I vividly recall that my mother, when I was about seventeen, at which time I had one of my brief experiences of home life, was seriously troubled in conscience when a friend who was staying with us (a missionary, like herself, with the Plymouth Brethren in India) proposed sending me with her son, a youth of about my own age, to a conjuring performance in Queen's Hall. In the end she let me go, but with a divided mind. Similarly when I bought my first pipe (which I thought I had carefully hidden) she came upon it by accident and asked in a shocked voice, "And when did you start smoking?" She did not forbid this, however, especially after I had scored the debating point that Charles Hadden Spurgeon, the great Baptist preacher of the Victorian era, and a man whom she greatly admired, constantly puffed cigars. He cheerfully retorted to somebody who reproved him, "Better to smoke now than smoke in hell!" No logical answer of course, but it served. I hope I am not giving the impression that my parents were grim, but they were undoubtedly stricter even than most people of their own strict persuasion. I am glad of this, as it placed many things in sharp relief.

been told so, for though like all sensible people and even drunkards (theoretically) they disapproved of excess, most of them drank heartily without the slightest qualms of conscience. In fact, a gathering of ministers in New England was a privileged occasion for the consuming of rather more than the usual amount of sound strong rum. It was only when good people could not fail to notice that the prevalence of drunkenness had become a grave problem—this was largely due to the American climate and its effect upon the American character—that the Protestant denominations (with the exception of the Episcopalians, who for the most part remained aloof) banded together on the dogma that the taking of a glass of wine or beer was a sin that would not be forgiven in this world or the world to come.

The Eighteenth Amendment and the Volstead Act had of course the backing of many beside the Protestant leaders. Some industrialists believed that they should support the enactment of laws designed forcibly to prevent their workmen getting drunk over the week end, not because their moral sense was outraged but because they thought that their hands would be more reliable if they were deprived of liquor. However, I am not concerned with these industrialists, or even with the giving of a thumb-nail sketch of prohibition: all that needs to be noted is that, in so far as it reposed upon a moral concept, that concept was false. It was the surviving part of a complete system that had made a long list of things which Christians were not supposed to do. As against this, the Catholic Church had a rational moral system, and this disapproved, in the case of such things, only of what was done to excess. St. Francis de Sales even wrote that the placing of bets on the result of any game or contest was excellent, as it furthered relaxation, and relaxation he saw to be necessary to the psychic health of most people.

The Catholic position is that enough unquestionable sins exist for us to avoid calling things sinful which are, when moderately practiced, entirely innocent. If only in that respect it gives men a very important kind of moral freedom. As for the real sins into which Catholics, like other people, are liable to fall on account of human frailty, they do not have to drag around with them a load of secret guilt which grows heavier and heavier, festering all the time, but are able promptly to rid themselves in the confessional and have a clean heart and a mind at peace. In addition to which it should be said that the moral discipline of Catholicism and the supervision that the Church is in a position to exercise goes a long way towards the prevention of sin. There can be very few non-Catholics who have never—if only during some special crisis—wished that some such means of moral release were available for themselves.

One might make another comparison of moral with intellectual freedom. Whatever may be urged against the Church's doctrinal authority, it is a wholly specious argument that control in moral matters destroys freedom. It is the moral discipline of Catholicism that serves to enable people to live according to their true nature as human beings. Sin prevents this, deforming men and thus appearing as a monstrous anomaly. The unbridled following of one's appetites—lust, drink, even ambition—is something that, at times of special stress, may be overwhelming when the aid of grace is lacking, and so may be partially extenuated. Even so, it is surrender to one's appetites that constitutes bondage. Quite apart from religious sanctions, everybody knows that some principle of restraint should be accepted, otherwise the orderly life of society would be impossible. A moral law of some sort has to operate; the only difficulty is to make this law effective without religious sanctions. Otherwise there will always be the argument that morals are in a perpetual state of flux, and then the amoralist can claim that he is only a day or two ahead of his time. Moreover, there is always a megalomaniac around who will say that, however advisable restraints are for other people, he is in a class by himself. But the superman and the irresponsible artist are just the ones who should be restrained most decisively—in a padded cell if civil law cannot deal with them.

Without bringing a general charge against psychoanalysts and psychiatrists (for what I am about to say is not at all true of the best of them), there are some members of this sacred college who virtually take the line that if their patients are oppressed with a sense of guilt, they should get rid of their temptations by yielding to them. This only means that large parts of the moral law are jettisoned, by which it may be true that some people are saved from having a nervous breakdown, but which may also put them (as it will almost certainly put the "psychologist" who gives such advice) in the danger of hell-fire. Even for the restoration of mental balance there are ways that are a good deal more efficacious than this.

How seriously moral standards have decayed in some quarters is shown by the fact that Walter Mehring in his *Lost Library* can nonchalantly toss over his shoulder the remark that the German dramatist Ernst Toller found a hero's death "the only one open to a writer in our times: suicide in a New York hotel." On this ground the American poet Harry Crosby must presumably be pronounced to be at least twice as heroic, as he committed suicide with his ladylove in a New York hotel. On a somewhat similar basis "mercy killers" are often condoned, though in nine cases out of ten it is to himself that the killer shows mercy; he is tired of looking after a bedridden mother or wife or child who is so inconsiderate as to go on living a little too long.

I am aware of course that these are extreme instances, but they are indicative of an alarming trend. The vast majority of people, even those who profess no religion, still hold, with however loose a hand, to traditional Christian morals. Common experience has shown conclusively that moral restraints enlarge moral freedom by indicating a line beyond which one must not pass, and so preserve us from chaos. Here all sensible people are agreed. But the Catholic thinks that the Church knows best how to put these moral restraints into operation. It has a clear code, a definite discipline, and a long experience of dealing with the complicated and deceitful human heart. Other religions are still older than Catholicism, and these also have garnered a considerable store of wisdom, but no other religion has given its priesthood so intimate and powerful a moral technique as the Catholic Church possesses. It is therefore Catholicism which stands virtually alone in being able to *apply* morals.

Here I summon two Catholic witnesses—both of them women as it happens—Sigrid Undset and Alice Meynell. In her essay, "Reply to a Parish Priest" in her *Stages on the Road*,[2] Fru Undset records that a friend of hers who had been deceived by his wife,

[2] P. 241. Knopf.

in seeking her sympathy and advice, said: "Tell me, Sigrid, do you believe at all that a woman *can* be true to a man?" To this came the decided answer, "No, I don't. I not only believe but I know that a woman can be true till death, if she has an ideal which demands her fidelity. But true to a man—no, I don't believe any woman can be that." The opinion may take what some will consider a pessimistic view of human nature, but I am inclined to agree. Love, however romantic, however intense, is no guarantee, for even though it would be saying far too much to declare that it will eventually die, it is sure to find itself under a partial eclipse now and then—and at such times only an ideal can support it.

Sigrid Undset goes on to make the observation: "We have no right to assume that any part of European tradition, cultural values, moral ideas, emotional wealth, which had its origin in the dogmatically defined Christianity of the Catholic Church, will continue to live a 'natural' life, if the people of Europe reject Christianity and refuse to accept God's supernatural grace. One might just as well believe that a tree whose roots were severed should continue to bear leaves and blossoms and fruit. A sentimental clinging to this or that particular section of Christian tradition is no use. Break off a few sprigs of a felled tree and put them in vases for indoor decoration—and see how long they will keep fresh!" With this I agree without any hesitation. All the same we may be thankful that large parts of the Christian tradition still survive, and I think that this tradition is not completely severed from the parent trunk but has more vigor than we may sometimes imagine. Therefore there is always hope that the process of deliquescence may be arrested, though only by a return to our origins.

The passage from Alice Meynell that I wish to quote occurs in a letter she wrote to her daughter Olivia: [3] "I saw, when I was very young, that a guide in morals was even more necessary than a guide in faith. It was for this that I joined the Catholic Church. Other Christian societies may legislate, but the Church *administers* legislation. Thus she is practically indispensable. I may say that I hold the administration of morals to be of such vital im-

[3] Viola Meynell's *Alice Meynell: a Memoir,* p. 332. Scribners.

portance that for its sake I accepted, and now accept, dogma in matters of faith—to the last letter." That has a special interest because with most converts it is the other way around: they first reach a purely intellectual conviction of the truth of Catholic dogma, or perhaps even more frequently first convince themselves of the authority of the Church and then accept its doctrines. From this they proceed to accept its authority in the realm of morals. My guess is that there would be twice as many converts as there actually are except for the moral difficulty. Many who would cheerfully gulp down the Pope and the sacramental system and even indulgences, find that birth control sticks like a fishbone in their gullet. Alice Meynell did not become a Catholic in the way of most masculine theorists (though she had a mind as good as any man's—"the finest mind of our time" Chesterton called it in the memoir he wrote of her in the *Dublin Review*) but because she had feminine practicality. There is, however, no conflict between the two processes: faith and morals in the Catholic Church always go together.

The point that certain sins (those of the flesh, for instance) are not sinful *because* of the incidental pleasure they impart—for that remains God's will even in the sin—is constantly misunderstood by many of the critics of the Catholic Church. This is probably because they are attributing to her the Manicheean strain that lingers in the Protestantism they themselves have discarded. The average non-Catholic is, I am afraid, a religious illiterate.

To this I might add a further observation, and with it end this chapter. There are some sins which, far from imparting pleasure, are only a torment—envy, for instance. But since a consideration of spiritual sins would carry me further afield than I have time to go at present, I ask: Does the thief have more pleasure in his stolen goods than a man who possesses goods of the same sort legitimately? Well, perhaps he may have a perverted sort of exultation; even so, he cannot have security, for he never knows when the police will catch up with him. For much the same reason, I simply cannot believe that there can be anything like the same degree of sexual pleasure to be obtained from an "affair" as there is in marriage. A casual encounter may give a "collector" of women occasion to boast of another trophy, but the pleasure is mostly that of pride. Such an encounter cannot possibly provide the period of adjustment necessary for the maximum of pleasure. Well, I may be told that a man who has a mistress for a long while can obtain all that a husband may obtain from his wife. But can he? Will not he and his mistress lack the quiet trust and security of marriage? After all, I am certain that nearly everybody will agree with me that the greatest part of sexual pleasure is psychological and that the physical element comes second. In this I am taking the most obvious of cases, the one that is within most people's personal experience. Similar conclusions would have to be reached with regard to other sins. The man of pleasure winds up, even in this world, in desolation.

The devil is the enemy of man, his enemy because man is most like to God of all His creatures. Sin is of all things the greatest of imaginable frauds, if only because sin does not have any real existence, being merely the deprivation of good. When Satan first showed himself in the Garden of Eden it was to lure Eve to destruction with a lie; he is still a liar and the father of lies. The very least appropriate thing that can be said of the devil is that he is a gentleman.

# CHAPTER FOUR

## *Spiritual Solidarity*

The essential fact about the Catholic Church is not that it is universal—important though that fact is—the same everywhere in faith and its obedience to the Holy See (though not always in discipline and liturgy); the essential fact is that the Church is an organism, a living thing, not merely a system. The doctrine of the Mystical Body of Christ, so often referred to in these pages, runs throughout St. Paul's epistles, whether explicitly stated or only implied. Writing to the Romans he says: "As one body we have many members, but all the members have not the same office; so we being many are one body in Christ, and everyone members of another." Writing his first Epistle to the Corinthians he uses almost the same words: "For as the body is one, and hath many members, and all the members of that one body, being many, are one body; so also is Christ." It was a concept burned into his mind in the light that blinded him on the road to Damascus where he was going to arrest Christians and drag them to Jerusalem for trial. The Voice that spoke to him that day said, "Saul, Saul, why persecuteth thou Me?" From that moment he understood that he was not merely persecuting Christians but Christ Himself. Indeed, Monsignor Kolbe in his *Four Mysteries of the Faith,* a book from which I have drawn more than one quotation already, suggests that when St. Paul wished to individualize Christ he refers to Him as Jesus, otherwise the universalized and Mystical Body is referred to as Christ. Our Lord had established this identity between Himself and His followers when He said that on the Day of Judgment, the blessed would be those who had performed works of mercy to their fellows, and therefore to Him, and that those who had failed to do such works would be told, "Depart from Me, ye cursed."

Whatever divergences of discipline and rite (never of doctrine or obedience) there may be among Catholics, they are all one. Against this the many Protestant denominations are nowadays much of a muchness in the order of their services, but for all that remain sects, and often have been warring sects. The original plan of the reformers of the sixteenth century was to set up a state church which should be the only church in the state, though even then they could not agree on doctrine. Therefore in Germany the principle was announced of *Cujus regio, ejus religio,* and although this could not work in that welter of principalities —some Catholic and some Protestant—in England at least Henry VIII's assertion that he, as king, was the head of the Church, came close to working for a while, as those opposed to him had their heads lopped off or were hanged, drawn and quartered. Some of his bishops, who at heart disagreed with him but were trying to save their skins, blandly explained that the primary Christian duty was to the monarch, and that if he commanded more than was justified, he and not those who obeyed would be answerable to God.

Yet even the English compromise broke down under the Stuarts and Protestantism tended towards what Edmund Burke called "the dissidence of dissent and the Protestantism of the Protestant religion." Though he was speaking of religious conditions in the colonies just before the American Revolution, present-day American Protestants are no doubt correct in contending that religious establishments wither in the American air, in spite of the fact that the first colonists lost no time in setting up an established church, and proscribing all those who disagreed with them. Even in England, where the king is still head of the Church of England (it is now the young Queen) nonconformists in the aggregate outnumber the adherents of the establishment. All the same, *Cujus regio, ejus religio* is the classic Protestant formula. It is one abhorrent to Catholicism.

All the major religions of the world—Hinduism, Buddhism, Israel and Islam—have split into sects.[1] And so has Christianity, with one exception—the Church founded by Christ. It has been rent by schism from time to time, and sects—all more or less

[1] Confucianism is not a religion but rather a philosophy.

heretical—have appeared. But the Catholic Church remains unchanging because it is built upon the Rock. It is this Church that has preserved stability and, because of stability, solidarity among its members.

All men desire solidarity, with perhaps the exception of a few eccentrics who like to go their own way. But organic unity is so obviously desirable that Protestantism—or its more intelligent sections—has for a generation or two been trying to find some formula for unity, even if the formula is no more than a shibboleth. It is natural for men to want this, and all Catholics would be very glad to see Protestants form themselves into a single body comparable to the Catholic Church, if this were possible, however artificial and contrived such a unity had to be. The cohesion of the Catholic Church is based on the connection of all its parts with the Papacy, but where is the Catholic Protestant Church to find its Pope, or who will yield him obedience should he be found? However, this is only to ask a question *ad hominem*, for Protestantism is not going to prop itself upon a pope whose authority would have to be conferred by men, when it began by casting off the authority of the Pope appointed by Christ. Confronted with such an impasse the most they can hope for is amalgamation for convenience in administration and a certain amount of liturgical uniformity. Uniformity of doctrine, since this can be brought about and preserved only by authority, is beyond its reach, unless its doctrines are stated in such very broad and general terms as to have little or no meaning. It is conceivable that eventually Protestants will return *en masse* to the fold their ancestors left, as it is also conceivable that they will eventually dwindle to nothing; but I believe that all Protestants would agree with me that they are obliged to cling to their principle of private judgment to be Protestants at all. There is no indication that, except for individuals, they intend ever to renounce it.

There is, however, a rival Catholic Church already in existence —Communism. To this extent Mr. Blanshard has some slight foothold in his latest book, *American Freedom and Catholic Power*, otherwise based upon a fabricated basis. Where he sees the Vatican as the great enemy, some of the others protesting against the President's bull-headed determination to submit to the Senate the name of an ambassador to the Vatican have hit upon "Spellmanism" as their favorite term of abuse. Yet Mr. Truman, whatever other motives he may have had, was clearly actuated mainly by fear (and well he might have it!) of Communism. What we have to remember is that Communism has become for millions a religion or a surrogate for religion. Having tried to get rid of what Karl Marx called the "opium of the people," since nature abhors a vacuum, the Russians have put Communism in its place.

First let it be remembered that though the Catholic Church would be always opposed to the economic doctrine that there must be no private property, it raises no objection to the kind of socialism that existed in England. But for that matter the Church is equally opposed to industrialist capitalism, unless the workers are assured of a reasonable wage, liberty of action, and a decent status. Communism declares its adhesion to a materialist dialectic, but many of the supporters of capitalism are also materialistic in their philosophy and are therefore (to that extent) subject to condemnation. In the eyes of the Church the choice does not narrow down to one between capitalism and communism.

Having said this, I may be permitted to remark that a thoroughgoing form of communism prevails in the religious orders of the Catholic Church. In all of them property is communally held, and in some orders there is even the practice of speaking of *our* cell and *our* book, enforced by having the members of the community change cells every year, so that they never come to think that what is provided *for their use* actually *belongs* to them. But that outside of such a system a radical communism is not really workable has been shown by the many modifications introduced into Bolshevism since its revolution of 1917. At the outset no doubt many idealists believed that the most absolute sort of communism was attainable, if it was not already attained; by degrees it has become only state capitalism, enforced by wholesale executions and vast prison camps for the recalcitrant, or even for political rivals.

What may be questioned is whether Communism need have come to this, even if it could never have worked as the idealists envisaged. It might have succeeded fairly well as a method of economic organization, had it been content to be nothing else, though it still would have been unable to supply the deeper human needs. As such the Church might not have approved all the details of its policy; on the other hand it might have found no reason for outright condemnation. But Communism has decided to substitute Godless Russia for the Holy Russia of the Czars. And it has set out to conquer the world politically, just as the Catholic Church has always had a declared intention of converting the world.

Communism has its Pope and hierarchy (any member of which is liable to arrest, to make a confession of enormous crimes against his "orthodoxy" under torture and to end up with a bullet through the back of his head in the cellar of his prison); it has also its dogmas—or what is called the "party line"—never irrefragable as with Catholicism, and a discipline so complex and terrifying that it can follow and execute people of whom it disapproves, even when they are living in foreign countries, as with Trotsky in Mexico and Krivitsky under the shadow of the Capitol in Washington. This is the Catholic Church of Atheism.

Human beings because of their nature need some sort of a spiritual shelter, and if they do not find it in Christianity, there are minds so strangely constituted as to run instead towards a materialistic shelter which, by some process incomprehensible to me, they manage to invest with a kind of spiritual light, what Milton called "darkness visible." There is (or was) an ideal in Communism, and for those unable to become Christians this sometimes serves. I suppose that few of them approve the cruelties of Moscow but overlook them as being merely temporary. What must be noted is their discipline and devotion and loyalty. In this respect many Catholics might learn a good deal from them. As for Russia, its conversion, unrealistic though most people would consider such an idea, has been the Catholic aim for thirty-five years. Russia was once a profoundly religious nation, and may be so again.

# CHAPTER FIVE

## *Una Sancta*

As I have indicated earlier in this book, the Mystical Body does not comprise merely the Christians upon earth; the One Holy Catholic Church is made up of them together with those who are triumphant in heaven, and those who are in process of reaching heaven through the purifying pains of purgatory. Of those in heaven we only know the names of a very small number, relatively speaking. As for those in purgatory, we do not know who they are; for though we pray for the repose of the souls of our deceased relatives and friends, there is rarely any sure means of ascertaining that they have not gone straight to heaven—or straight to hell. We pray for them, hoping for the best and the best may be a good deal better than we would dare to imagine.

Some few of the canonized saints are among the most famous people who ever lived; of others we have little information; of the overwhelming majority we know nothing whatever: they are not in the Martyrology, nor are the names of the "multitude that no man can number" written anywhere but in the Lamb's Book of Life. Our ignorance of their glory can be of small consequence to them, and though we may have some loss, even that need not be a great deal if we have a general devotion to the Blessed.

First of all of course is the Queen of angels and saints, Mary the Mother of God. It may at first sight seem a little strange that she should be set above the angels, pure spirits, pure intelligences. But as King David sang, "Thou madest man a little lower than the angels," and in certain respects man is, or may be, even higher than the angels, precisely because he is not merely an intelligence but will eventually be reunited to his body in heaven, to be filled with an even more ineffable beatitude. But Mary already has her body, and her mind was never clouded either with

actual sin or the propensities of original sin. She is, as Words-
worth put it in a celebrated sonnet, "Our tainted nature's solitary
boast."

The Blessed Virgin is our Mother as well as Christ's Mother.
She is the Queen of Heaven but also the Refuge of Sinners. As
St. Bernard said in his *Memorare*, "Never was it known that anyone sought thy intercession and was left forsaken." The same
saint, in one of his many sermons on her, says that great as is the
luster of her virginity, still greater is that of the humility that
could say to the archangel, "Be it done unto me according to thy
word." Oliver Wendell Holmes, the New England Unitarian, in
one of his Autocrat books (I forget which) spoke for many non-
Catholics when he remarked that Protestantism has been im-
poverished by not having a Mother as well as a Heavenly Father
whom they could invoke. Indeed, there is no obvious reason why
they should not honor all the saints. Some of them, such as the
Anglicans, would declare that they do honor the Blessed Virgin,
if not to the same extent as Catholics. But it is usually a rather
frosty and distant kind of respect that they accord. Mostly the
asking of the help of the saints is looked upon as a piece of
Popish superstition.

The Church began with Mary. It had long been foretold by
psalmist and prophet but its visible presence on earth began with
her. Though she owes all her glorious prerogatives to her Son,
we owe part of our redemption to her for her co-operation in the
Incarnation. Christ might have appeared on earth in the flesh,
miraculously mature in His manhood from the first instant, in
much the same way that Adam was created. But He did not;
instead He passed through all the stages of human development,
and was God-Man from the moment of His conception by the
Holy Ghost, thus sanctifying all the stages of human gestation.
But if He willed to be born of a woman, it was because Mary
willed to bear Him. A tender devotion towards the Blessed
Virgin is one of the surest marks of Catholic piety. One does well
to invoke one's favorite saints; one would not do well at all without invoking Mary.

Before I come to the saints, it might be well to offer a few
observations on the angels. Actually we do not know a great deal

about them, but we know that there are an immense number of them grouped in various grades, the nine "choirs," the idea that Milton conveys by his massive line:

Thrones, dominations, virtues, princedoms, powers.

St. Thomas Aquinas adds that each angel is the sole specimen of his species, but this grouping is only of a general sort, and the speculations about the angels made by the pseudo-Dionysius the Areopagite and St. Thomas himself, while they may be logical inferences, are not as a rule matters of faith.

It is somewhat different with regard to the guardian angels, though here too faith rather than philosophy is the basis of Catholic thought and sentiment. That guardian angels do exist we know from what Christ Himself told us, and it is the common teaching of theologians that at birth—that is, even before baptism—every human being is entrusted to the care of an angel who watches over him. For the most part we shall never know while on earth what it is that our guardian angel has done for us, for his work is largely that of defending us from spiritual evils and physical dangers of which we may be quite unaware. It is harmless to picture them as human beings with wings, though that is merely something taken over from Greek and Roman art, of which a magnificent example is the Winged Victory in the Louvre. Actually, being pure spirits, they have no bodily form.[1] However, they appeared in bodily form to some of the saints—St. Rose of Lima, for instance, even while a child, used to consort with her guardian angel in the garden of her father's house, but she left no description of him. What matters is that we should not be sentimental on the subject and treat it as a pretty theme about which to talk to children. Adults, even more than children, need the protection of their guardian angel and

---

[1] They must, however, assume such a form when appearing to men. In fact they *must* do so, if they are to be seen at all. This was so in the case of the theophanies of the Old Testament, and it was so in the case of Joan of Arc, for instance. Often her angels were merely voices, but she was quite positive that at other times they showed themselves to her. As described by Ezechiel and in the Apocalypse, the angels have six wings; so had the unified seraph seen by Francis of Assisi when he received the stigmata.

should pray to him every day. As Gerard Manley Hopkins put it in one of the stanzas of "The Bugler's First Communion":

> Frowning and forefending angel-warder
> Squander the hell-rook ranks sally to molest him:
> March, kind comrade, abreast him;
> Dress his days to a dexterous and starlight order.

It is a very good thing to make a comrade of our guardian angel. Although his guardianship will remain even should we neglect him, it becomes much more effective with our co-operation.

It is worth noting that when Christ referred to the angels—and usually He did so in a somewhat offhand way, knowing that they were taken for granted by everybody—although those who heard Him speak about other matters were often perplexed and on several occasions scandalized, saying so bluntly, nobody ever found it difficult to accept the idea of the existence of angels. This was because the idea was not at all new to them; they knew about angels from the frequent reference to them in the Old Testament. On the other hand most Protestants, even those who believe in angels because of the scriptural warrant, dismiss them from their thoughts. It is a great (and unfortunately deliberate) impoverishment.

> The angels keep their ancient places;—
> Turn but a stone, and start a wing!
> 'Tis ye, 'tis your estrangèd faces,
> That miss the many-splendoured thing.

The saints are our guardians too, and there are few points more often misunderstood about Catholicism than the invocation of saints. It is imagined somehow to detract from the glory due to God, but of course would be nothing without God. A clear distinction has to be drawn between the adoration given to God, which is called *latria*, and the reverence and honor given to the saints, which is known as *dulia*. That given to the Blessed Virgin is *hyperdulia*, something more than *dulia* but still infinitely below what is offered the Godhead. No Catholic can possibly be unaware of these distinctions, though he may not know the terms just mentioned. He is also aware that every benefit he receives comes from God, and that the saints we invoke (including the Blessed Virgin) can do no more than pray to God for us.

It might be reasonable to ask: Why bother with the saints at all? Since everything comes from God, would it not be more expeditious to go to Him direct? One may do so of course, but because Christians on earth are part of the Mystical Body, of which the saints form another part, God wishes us to pray as members of that Body. Solitary prayer is good, but the prayer to which a special promise was given by Christ was that offered when two or three are gathered in His name. We are not intended to live our spiritual lives off in a corner by ourselves but in the company of other Christians. And if Protestants sometimes ask good people to pray for them, on what grounds can they possibly think that the saints, those united to God in heaven, should not also be asked to pray?

About the Church Militant I need not say anything at this point, as this forms the subject of my book. But I cannot pass by a fine passage from Monsignor Kolbe. It runs: "If I am a member of His, and I suffer with Him and He with me, His life is my life, His merits my merits, His thoughts my thoughts, and the Father pardons me and sanctifies and glorifies me because by infinite mercy I have in His Son satisfied equally infinite justice."

Before coming to a brief consideration of the Church Suffering, or the souls in purgatory, it should be made clear that the expression the "communion of saints" does not refer merely to the saints in heaven, or even such communion as may exist between Christians still on earth and those enjoying the Beatific Vision. It refers just as much to those in purgatory, sometimes referred to as the "poor souls" and sometimes as the "holy souls." All parts of the Church act and counteract upon one another.

I am not very fond of the term "poor souls," for they have, after all, the inexpressible joy of knowing that their salvation is certain. No doubt they suffer, but this is because they neglected to take advantage of the opportunities they had of purifying themselves in this life. Dante saw them dwelling "contented in the flame" and John Henry Newman has a similar idea in his hymn "For the Dead":

For daily falls, for pardon'd crime,
They joy to undergo
The shadow of Thy cross sublime,
The remnant of Thy woe.

The teaching of the Church is that the souls in purgatory can do nothing to shorten their sojourn, while on the other hand those on earth can do a good deal for them. The best means of help is by Masses, and as every Mass has satisfactory value for the remission of temporal punishment due to sin, it can be of immeasurable help and alleviation to the souls in purgatory, especially to those for whom this satisfactory value is applied. The souls in purgatory have no bad or mediocre dispositions to prevent the application of this satisfaction to themselves, although how far our prayers and good works actually avail them depends upon the wisdom and mercy of God. Yet every prayer, for this or any other purpose, does avail—of this we can be sure.

If we can help the souls in purgatory, they in turn can help us. To illustrate the point I will tell a perfectly true story about the poet Edwin Arlington Robinson, who was a close friend of mine and who spent every summer (as I spent a few) at the MacDowell colony at Peterborough, New Hampshire. One summer he was affected by insomnia and mentioned it at the breakfast table, saying that he thought it was because of the coffee he had drunk at dinner the previous evening. Upon this William Thomas Walsh, the biographer of Isabella the Catholic, Philip II and St. Teresa, said, "Oh, I'll see to it that you sleep tonight; so drink all the coffee you like." What he did was to walk down that morning to the Catholic church and arrange that a Mass be said for the holy souls, and sure enough Robinson's insomnia left him. I was not at Peterborough that year and the story first came to me from Father James M. Gillis, the editor of the *Catholic World*. A month or so later I saw Robinson and asked him about it, and he said, "Yes, I don't know what the poor souls had to do with it, but that's just what happened." Finally I saw Walsh, and he said the same thing. The remarkable fact is that, as between the three of them, there was not the slightest discrepancy. Years later one of the colonists, in telling the story, substituted my name for that of Walsh's; but she was familiar with the rest of the details. All I need add is that Walsh had a great faith in this devotion and told me that through it he had received extraordinary answers to prayer—once the obtaining of $3,000 which he needed in a hurry and could see no chance of getting. After all, as the holy souls must be presumed to be grateful to those who pray for them, $3,000 is not a very large sum for getting from purgatory to heaven.

What purgatory is like we do not know. Popularly it is supposed to be a mild form of hell, but one that comes to an end. Probably it is not very like that at all, for where hell is punitive, with a fire that does not cleanse, purgatory (whether or not there is any of the fire that Dante saw, though in only one of its circles) is primarily purifying, the making apt of the soul for heaven. I suggest that the pain those in purgatory suffer is principally their not yet having the union with God for which they yearn. If this is (as for many it is) a pain even on earth, the pain in the future life may be reduced in proportion to the purgatorial pains they may willingly have borne in this life for their sins.

The doctrine of purgatory is one of great consolation. Though violently repudiated by the early Protestants (as was the sacrament of penance, to which it is closely related), it is constantly being smuggled back in one form or another. Even the most "liberal" Protestants do not often in their hearts indulge in the vulgarism of thinking that no differentiation can be made in the hereafter between the good and the bad, but postulate some degree of punishment for those who deserve it, even though they may flinch from the notion that it is eternal. But on the supposition of the existence of hell—the reality of which was once affirmed by all Protestants and is still affirmed by some of them— not many of us would be confident that we are among the few who should escape it and pass immediately to God's glory. The Catholic doctrine is very much milder than that maintained by uncompromising Protestants of the old school, under which it would seem that only a very small select minority would have any chance of salvation, whereas the rest (there being no intermediary state) could expect nothing but the bottomless pit and the worm that dieth not. Indeed, without some such hope as the Catholic doctrine offers, many of us might yield to despair and give up the struggle as useless. The fact that they might reasonably count upon purgatory may have saved millions of people from hell.

One sometimes hears a Catholic say, "Well, I shall be perfectly satisfied if I can just scrape into purgatory by the skin of my teeth. I'd be willing to stay there hundreds of years." A remark of that kind is usually not intended to be taken with solemn literalness, and I may occasionally have talked along those lines myself. Of course anybody who aims merely at "getting under the wire" would be foolish; he would be in serious danger of "not making it," just as the college student the height of whose ambition was a grade of 70 might find himself conditioned or even marked F. And if he was really clever enough to estimate precisely the amount of work it took to obtain a passing mark, he might spend his brains more profitably (and with less effort) in getting something a good deal better. Finally, though we can only picture purgatory in terms of longer or shorter periods, is it not outside of time? All that one can say is that it does not last forever, as do hell and heaven; but it may well be that although we are obliged to use a time measurement to make it intelligible to us, another completely different quality enters in—perhaps varying degrees of intensity. What matters is not how long we stay in purgatory but how effectually its purifying work is done; for all we know, it may be accomplished instantly.

Eternal life, too, is not simply a life that never ends—that is, it is not simply a lot of time. Endlessness is one of its properties, but another of its properties is qualitative rather than quantitative. Lovers have some inkling of this when they talk of an "eternal instant." Heaven is the eternal "now." Those in purgatory are absolutely assured of partaking such an eternity with the saints in heaven, as we on earth may hope for it. The Church Militant, the Church Suffering, and the Church Triumphant are the three constituent parts of the One Holy Catholic Church.

# CHAPTER SIX

## *Happiness on Earth*

There used to be an advertisement that said of a certain brand of chocolates that there was "happiness in every box." That is certainly to make happiness a tawdry thing; indeed, it is not happiness at all, unless perhaps in the sense that a girl may get some happiness out of the fact that her beau is willing to show his love for her by bringing her a box of chocolates. Even that is pleasure rather than happiness, and surely the eating of the candies can be only pleasure—and not a very lofty one at that. All this is not worth mentioning in the same breath with earth's best joys, and these in turn are faint compared with the inexpressible joys of paradise.

The Christian religion is one of joy rather than happiness. It was so also with the religion of the Old Testament, the words of the psalm, "The King shall rejoice in God," being paralleled by those in the Epistle to the Philippians, "Rejoice in Jesus Christ." And it is interesting to note that it is this epistle, written when St. Paul was in prison in Rome, that is most full of this note. The religion of the cross is also the religion of joy, in fact one might say gaiety. But although even the more sedate state of happiness cannot be perfect on earth, perhaps that will be a better term to use than joy. I take the one to be normally attainable from day to day in a quiet fashion, whereas joy to many people comes only at relatively infrequent moments.

Both happiness and joy are attainable without much of what the world considers pleasure. Yet I do not think that Thomas Merton—admirable though his books are—can be said without qualification to be right when in his *Seeds of Contemplation* [1] he declares that man was not created for pleasure. In the sense in

[1] P. 172.

which I suppose he means this—that man was created for something besides pleasure—he would be right; but of course all pleasure has been given by God, though we may renounce some pleasures, even the pleasure normally taken in our food, as was done by St. Francis of Assisi when he sometimes sprinkled ashes over what he was about to eat. Pleasure is a secondary and not a primary end of life; the primary end is joy. Even if there were no hereafter, the Catholic belief would bless this life. This is why Pascal's argument of the wages strikes one as unfortunate, for it seems to be his assumption that present misery is worth paying even if there is only a remote chance of future blessedness. Logical perhaps—but certainly chilling.

This life, nevertheless, is what the Church calls a vale of tears. We can all expect some pain, and not a few people have to endure a good deal, while none quite escape—unless they are very fortunate (or perhaps very unfortunate). As Dr. Johnson writes grimly in his *Vanity of Human Wishes:*

> Yet hope not life from grief or danger free,
> Nor think the doom of man revers'd for thee.

But Johnson was of course so good a Christian (in spite of his dour or at least melancholy cast of mind) that he was well aware that grief, danger and pain are not merely man's "doom"; they are a means of reminding us that we have no abiding city here and that our eyes should be always raised to the hills whence cometh our salvation.

For some unaccountable reason the idea has often got abroad that paganism was a jolly sort of religion, in contrast with the gloom of Christianity. It was expressed by Swinburne in his paraphrase of Julian the Apostate:

> Thou hast conquered, O pale Galilean; the world has grown grey
> with Thy breath.

But the poem in which the line occurs makes up a fancy picture which a man as learned as Swinburne should have known better than to present. Paganism at its best—I am thinking of the paganism of the Mediterranean basin and more particularly the paganism we know through our reading of the classical Greek and Latin authors—was rather stern and austere and even puritanical. The element of despair is often present in the noblest specimens of Greek drama, a sense that man had reached a dead end. And the virtues of the early Roman republic were strict but hardly merry. At its worst period later, there was also a great amount of junketing, as one may see by reading Catullus, Petronius or *The Golden Ass*, but there was also immense corruption. And it all concludes with what Catullus expressed:

> *Nobis, quum semel occidit brevis lux*
> *Nox est perpetua una dormienda*

which Swinburne filched and paraphrased in his "Hymn to Proserpine" as:

> Only a sleep eternal
> In an eternal night.[2]

Even love is largely torment, summed up by Catullus in the two famous and untranslatable lines:

> *Odi et amo. quare id faciam, fortasse requiris.*
> *nescio, sed fieri sentio et excrucior.*[3]

Perhaps it was under the influence of Swinburne that the youthful Chesterton began his literary career with much the same idea. Christians—and especially priests—were in the eyes of the creator of the rubicund Father Brown (drawn from an actual priest, who died only recently) somber people, necessarily so because of the religion they professed. This runs through poem after poem of *The Wild Knight* and was not completely unsaid until *The Ballad of the White Horse* was published in 1911. Then his hero, Alfred the Great, sang:

> It is only Christian men
> Guard even heathen things.

[2] I will attempt a more literal translation with:
> When once has died our day's brief light
> We sleep in an unending night.

[3] They are of course easy to translate, if it is simply a question of giving the bald meaning; but to translate would be to ruin, especially the final terrible word of the distich.

By this he meant that though heathens, being human beings, got some fun out of life, it is only Christianity that saves this fun from festering into disillusionment and despair.

Chesterton, by the way, made a number of discoveries while he was on the road to this conclusion. The most important of these was that our capacity to enjoy can be best kept alive by wonder. This was the opposite of Horace's frigid advice, *Nil admirari*, which might be rendered as "Never be astonished by anything; never allow yourself to be carried away." Chesterton, trying to find out how to keep the nerve of wonder at its keenest, hit upon the truth that this can be done only on condition that we remain humble and preserve the freshness of a child's vision.

But let us leave the poets and go back to the Catechism. In the old *Baltimore Catechism* the question and answer run: "Why did God make you?" "God made me to know Him, to love Him, and to serve Him in this world and to be happy forever with Him in Heaven." The revised edition of the same work makes the answer: "God made us to show forth His goodness and to share with us His everlasting happiness in heaven. To gain the happiness of heaven we must know, love and serve God in this world." With that moderation characteristic of the Church the word is "happiness," but even "joy," as applied to heaven, would be inadequate. "Eye hath not seen, nor ear hath heard, nor hath it entered into the heart of man what things God hath prepared for those who love Him."

There used to be a notion (and perhaps there still is) entertained by those with little religion, that religion might be useful to keep the "lower orders" in their place. While they were told that they might hope to get to heaven if they behaved themselves and touched their forelock to the Squire, I am afraid that the Squire (and the Parson, too, who was in many cases his younger brother) took it for granted that the lower orders would rank as footmen to St. Peter or chambermaids to the cherubim. On a somewhat higher level, the liberal makes the mistake of thinking of religion, not as sublime truth, but as a decorative appendage to what he calls the good life. There is just a grain of justification for both ideas, but both miss the essential point. If religion merely results in a staid respectability, it is not good for much. A really religious man like King David could dance before the ark with such disregard for his position as to be reproved by his prim wife Michal. But as Patmore exclaimed in one of his poems:

> Shall I the mote that dances in Thy ray
> Dare to be reverent?

I might as well quote Patmore again, this time one of his prose sentences: "Life is not only joyful, it is joy itself." To this I add a short passage from the Meditations of the late seventeenth-century ecstatic Thomas Traherne: "Your enjoyment of the world is never right till every morning you awake in Heaven; see yourself in your Father's palace; and look upon the skies, the earth and the air as celestial joys; having such a reverend esteem of all, as if you were among the Angels. The bride of a monarch, in her husband's chamber, hath no such causes of delight as you. You never enjoy the world aright till the sea itself floweth in your veins, till you are clothed with the heavens and crowned with the stars; and perceive yourself to be the sole heir of the whole world, and more than so, because men are in it who are every one sole heirs as well as you. Till you can sing and rejoice and delight in God, as misers do in gold, and kings in sceptres, you can never enjoy the world."

At the risk of boring dull and commonplace people who are in need of being constantly amused (if any such have read this book), I will venture to go back to Traherne once more: "The corn was orient and immortal wheat, which never should be reaped, nor was ever sown. I thought it had stood from everlasting to everlasting. The dust and stones of the street were as precious as gold. The gates were at first the end of the world. The green trees, when I saw them first through one of the gates, transported and ravished me; their sweetness and unusual beauty made my heart to leap, and almost mad with ecstasy, they were such strange and wonderful things. The Men! O what venerable and reverend creatures did the aged seem! Immortal Cherubims! And young men glittering and sparkling angels, and maids strange seraphic pieces of life and beauty! Boys and girls tumbling in the street, and playing, were moving jewels. I knew not that they were born or should die. But all things abided eternally as they were in their proper places. Eternity was manifest in the light of day, and something infinite behind everything appeared. . . . The city seemed to stand in Eden, or to be built in Heaven. The streets were mine, the temple was mine, the people were mine, their clothes and gold and silver were mine, as much as their sparkling eyes, fair skins and ruddy faces. The skies were mine, and so were the sun and moon and stars, and all the world was mine; and I the only spectator and enjoyer of it."

Such feelings could only be expressed by a Christian poet, and Traherne was always a better poet in prose than in verse. But not even a poet can be expected *always* to feel like that. Poetic feelings come and go like the tides of the sea, only their movements cannot be calculated; even Traherne had ups and downs of feeling.

> Could we but live at will upon this perfect height,
> Could we but always keep the passion of this peace!

cried Lionel Johnson. Alas, we cannot. It has to be enough that we would like to do it, that we ought to be able to do it, that joy should be our normal climate, as it is always the climate to which the Christian can return.

This would indeed be a desolate world were it not for God, and there are few unbelievers who do not envy those able to believe, even while thinking them happily self-deluded and that it is nobler to bear their own loneliness than to drug themselves with an anodyne. As to this, I will freely grant that if religion were no more than an anodyne, an "escape" such as some try to find in alcohol, it could not be regarded as religion at all. Only that is religion which a man—even if he is negligent about its practice—will admit to be incomparably the most important fact in life. Although I am not quite convinced by the thesis of Alastair Cooke's brilliant book on the Hiss trials, there is something in it. It was more or less inevitable that the "lost generation" should be succeeded by a generation of false idealists. The real solution, the only solution, even though it is so generally overlooked, is God. As Carl Jung has said: "Among all my patients in the second half of my life . . . there has not been one whose problem in the last resort was not that of finding a religious outlook on life." [4]

It would be quite false to say that all joy has its root in religion; the most that is being suggested here is that religion is the surest source of joy. Though artists are often unhappy men, they have a very genuine joy while they are engaged in artistic creation. This may be succeeded by quiet satisfaction—but sometimes by dissatisfaction, even when what has been achieved is what the world considers great. Thus Virgil on his deathbed tried to arrange that all copies of the *Aeneid* should be destroyed, so conscious was he of its imperfections, and St. Thomas Aquinas delivered as his final judgment of the *Summa*, "What a lot of straw it is!" Yet of course they had intense joy while at work, Virgil in the beauty of his hexameters and Thomas in the concise symmetry of his thinking. The joy that flows from religion, however, is another matter. Although many Christians do not seem to have much of it, their plight was pithily put by St. Francis de Sales, "A sad saint is a sorry saint." Even so, I would prefer the saddest of saints to one whose bonhomie was artificially manufactured, Dale Carnegie style.

Happiness is founded on gratitude. It is impossible for the ungrateful man to be happy, even when he does not labor under a sense of wrong, real or (as often as not) imaginary. The Mass is essentially thanksgiving, from the opening psalm when the priest goes to the altar of God, to "God who giveth joy to my youth." One of those horrible Moody and Sankey hymns warbles a little too glibly:

> Count your blessings, count them one by one,
> And it will surprise you what the Lord has done.

The sentiment, however, is sound, even if somewhat vulgarly expressed. I prefer what St. Paul writes in his Epistle to the Colossians: "Let the peace of God rule in your hearts, to the which also you are called in one body; and be ye thankful."

Since I have been writing about joy and happiness in terms that are perhaps too generalized, it may be in order to speak now

[4] *Modern Man in Search of a Soul*, p. 264. Harcourt, Brace.

of the virtues that go with Christian joy, and without which that joy is not very securely based.

Let us start with poverty, though I suppose the suggestion that it has any connection with joy may seem startling and paradoxical. The farthest that the Old Testament seems to go in this direction is to ask: "Give me neither poverty nor riches; feed me with food convenient for me"—a moderate standard which, if people only observed it, might accomplish a good deal. I am aware that there is a sordid poverty that is hard to endure because of the injustice it inflicts on those dependent upon us. But setting this on one side, poverty can give freedom and lightness to the spirit. I know, because during certain periods of my youth I was very poor (but fortunately had, at that time, nobody else to look after), so I was happy—I thought then in spite of my poverty, but now I am inclined to think because of it. Christ demands from all of us—not actual poverty in every case, for that is usually what is called a "counsel of perfection," but always poverty of spirit. Yet in one instance He seems to have demanded more than this. It was from the rich young man, who kept the law, but was too attached to his wealth. He was told to sell all that he had and give to the poor, and went away sorrowful. He would have liked to follow Christ, but not on those conditions. When Christ remarked to His disciples that it was easier for a camel to go through the eye of a needle than for a rich man to be saved, He greatly perplexed them. One would gather from their question, "Who then can be saved?" that, though all of them were of lowly origin, they had a vague notion that in some way the rich must be morally better than the poor. Obviously Christ did not think so; His answer was a characteristically sardonic "With God all things are possible." Yes, a rich man conceivably might be saved, but they were not to forget that the publicans and whores might be in a better spiritual state than the impeccably respectable (and usually well-to-do) Pharisees.

If all this strikes people as a "hard doctrine," let them reflect that the pagan philosophers of antiquity were unanimous in holding that man's felicity does not consist in increasing his needs but in reducing them. We are all liable to be clogged and encumbered by our comforts. It is no sin to be rich, but it is a very real spiritual danger, for the rich are all too likely to sink into their wealth as into quicksands. St. Paul warns his readers to "use this world, as if they used it not," by which he means that they must not become attached to riches. This may be extended to include position and honor and fame as well as stocks and bonds, but so as not to confuse a clear issue, let riches be understood simply as material riches, money—what is rightly called filthy lucre, though most people are only too glad to get their hands on it.

This does not mean that the father of a family should be parsimonious towards his children; on the contrary he should do the very best he can for them according to his state in life. But he would do his children a great wrong if he inculcated in their minds that wealth was of more worth than it is, if he did not try to instill in them poverty of spirit. As an instance of what I mean a man—not a very rich man but one who was rather well off— once told how ashamed he was when one day he drove his second car (a Ford) into the filling station he used, instead of his Cadillac. The attendants, noticing the make of car but not who was in it, left it waiting while they gave obsequious attention to a Packard. It hurt him to discover that he himself had hitherto been looked after so well merely because of his financial rating. That man had poverty of spirit, and it is undoubtedly possessed by many others who have more than their average share of this world's goods. On the other hand, a large proportion of the poor derive no merit from their condition because they are unduly preoccupied with trying to get on in the world and are bitterly envious of those who have more than themselves. They no less than the rich should be poor in spirit. This interior attitude is incumbent upon all who aim at something more than avoidance of positive sin.

Too often Christians who happen to be rich—Catholics among them—are treated with special deference by the ministers of their denominations. This is understandable enough—all too understandable—but is detestable. Those who flatter them do so in the hope of getting sizable donations, which are of course to be used for a good purpose, but which should never be angled for. In this connection it might be as well to remember the fierce denunciation in the Epistle of St. James: "Go to now, ye rich men; weep and howl in your miseries which shall come upon you. Your riches are corrupted, and your garments are moth-eaten; your gold and silver is cankered. . . . You have stored up to yourselves wrath against the last days." And Pius XI in his encyclical against atheistic Communism points out that there may also be what is, in effect, an atheistic capitalism, all the more dangerous because it can go with a punctilious observance of the externals of religion. Mildly but devastatingly the Pope remarks: "Is it not deplorable that the right of private property defended by the Church should so often have been used as a weapon to defraud the workingman of his just salary and his social rights?" Those guilty of this may well "howl" in anticipation of the wrath of God.

There was in the eighteenth century a Squire Lambton, who is now remembered only for a single remark of his. This was that a man might "jog along" on £40,000 a year. It is quoted so often because it is considered funny, which it is. But from another point of view it is horrifying. Unless Mr. Lambton was being facetious, he had a philosophy which, as far as one can see, would be pretty sure to land him in hell.

Chastity nowadays is a virtue which is often less respected even than the poverty that has been touched upon. An emperor's granddaughter (at least she claimed to be one, though of illegitimate descent) once calmly told me that in her opinion virginity was a commodity that should be got rid of as soon as possible. Apparently this strikingly beautiful young woman had lost no time in getting rid of hers. I was too flabbergasted by the flippancy of the confession to suggest that she might read Francis Thompson's poem, *"Ad Castitatem":*

> Teach Love the way to be
> A new Virginity.

> Do thou with thy protecting hand
> Shelter the flame thy breath has fanned;
> Let my heart's reddest glow
> Be but as sun-flushed snow.

And if they say that snow is cold,
O Chastity, must they be told
    The hand that's chafed with snow
    Takes a redoubled glow.

Chastity is obligatory on all; virginity of course is not, nor is celibacy. But chastity does not take the same form in all cases. A husband and wife, living a normal married life, should not be less chaste than a monk and a nun, but obviously their chastity will be of a different kind. If celibacy is placed by the Church as higher than matrimony, it is matrimony which, after all, is a "great sacrament," whereas celibacy is not, but a condition that derives its merit from ascetic renunciation. Those who marry do not make this renunciation (though they make renunciations of another sort, beginning with "forsaking all others") and it is not expected or desired that more than a relatively few will be celibate. All the same the married are strictly enjoined to be chaste according to the state of life they have entered.

No obedience in the monastic sense can rest upon the ordinary Christian, and while it will probably be admitted that what has been said about poverty and chastity has universal application, it may also be thought to be forcing things a bit to bring in obedience at all. Yet this is not really so. Everybody owes obedience to somebody—to his duly authorized ecclesiastical superiors, to the Pope, to the secular government. It is a question in my mind whether if a man were genuinely "drafted" for the presidency, he would have a right to refuse to submit to the clearly expressed wishes of the people. Superiors themselves are not free from obedience in some form; the Pope is the Servant of the servants of God, the king is the father of his people and not a tyrant, for if he is, he may look for assassination when opportunity occurs. And all men, even the most exalted, ultimately owe obedience to God.

I have had members of religious orders confide to me that of all their vows they find obedience hardest to observe faithfully. Ordinarily poverty is not much of a burden, and may even be a relief, as all economic responsibility is passed on to somebody else. Celibacy is, so I am assured, not very difficult to maintain, especially when one belongs to a class set apart. But obedience, being the surrender of the will in matters where it need not be surrendered, cuts deeply at the core of personality. Yet it should be borne in mind that the obedience exacted, even in an order like that of the Jesuits, whose tone and temper are military, is not quite what may be imagined. If the colonel gives a soldier an order, that order is carried out at once, without any discussion, almost automatically; but if a religious superior gives an order, his subject is perfectly free to make representations, and is finally obligated to obedience only if the superior still insists that his order be carried out, and if the order does not contravene the rule. Such representations are probably rarely made, for a good superior is always a reasonable man and not a martinet.

In obedience there is great sweetness, such as a child finds in obeying his parents, or a wife finds in obeying her husband—and that obedience is yielded more frequently than is sometimes supposed. Always there is more joy and peace in obeying than in commanding. Though the average lay person—he to whom this book is primarily addressed—will have fewer opportunities to exercise this virtue, he cannot altogether escape the obligation of obedience and would be a poor Christian if he tried, as for that matter he would make an unsatisfactory member of civil society.

This chapter has been mainly built around those virtues to which those in a religious order bind themselves by vow, but with the intention of showing how they rest, at least to some extent, upon all Christians. But as a kind of postscript to what has been said early in this book about the theological virtues of faith, hope and charity, incumbent upon all Christians, it might not be out of place to conclude with a glance at some other virtues, which if not always specifically Christian, may yet be said to have a strong Christian coloring.

Of these the first is undoubtedly humility, which is the establishing of a right relationship between the creature and his Creator. The opposing element of pride was recognized by Dante to be the main ingredient in every sin, for in his *Purgatorio*, as he went up the mountain towards the Earthly Paradise, upon his emerging from each of the circles where sins are expiated and cleansed, he finds that another "P" (*peccatum*) cut by the angel upon his forehead has gone. One went the instant they had passed the first circle of the Proud, and all the remaining six representing the seven deadly sins simultaneously greatly diminished.

Many natural graces spring from this virtue. Along with kindness, to which it is kin, it is the basis of good manners. One sees in St. Francis of Assisi a courtesy exercised towards all of God's creatures, even towards those that are inanimate, to Sister Water and Brother Fire. While few people would be capable of this, except in a self-conscious and rather forced imitation of Francis that would destroy all its merit, all must have the humility which perceives an absolute dependence upon God. We forever teeter on the brink of nothingness and, brought into existence by God, are sustained only by His will. As Emily Brontë has it in the best of her poems:

> Though earth and man were gone,
> And sun and universes cease to be,
> And Thou wert left alone,
> Every existence would exist in Thee.

God is the only subsistent Being, having what man lacks, the perfection of existence in Himself.

Dante put it in a single line:

> *e la voluntade è nostra pace—*

His will is our peace. To which might be appended the amusing emendation that Chesterton made of Tennyson:

> Self-knowledge, self-control and self-esteem,
> These three alone will make a man a prig.

Closely related to humility is patience, that St. Catherine of Siena seems to have looked upon as a primary virtue, which means that, with her, patience was another term for humility. Dr. Johnson said that though courage was not the whole of virtue, no man's virtue was secure unless he possessed courage. Courage can be lifted to a supernatural plane, when those naturally faint of heart put their trust in God, and say with the valiant St. Paul, "I can do all things through Him who strengtheneth me."

Similarly we are told to possess our souls in patience; how else *could* we possess our souls?

When I think of simplicity I immediately remember a story told of Alice Meynell—whose poetry I have quoted often here, though I admire her prose still more, and who is to me personally beloved. It seems that she was visiting her nephew Father Butler, who was a monk at Downside Abbey, and greatly amused the community by the way she exclaimed, "How *difficult* it is to be simple!" I can picture her long, thin hands clasped and the look in her face and the tone in her voice—but simplicity *is* difficult, and not only in the writing that Mrs. Meynell may have had in mind. Of course the monks of Downside knew that. Yet Christ has told us that unless we become like little children we cannot enter the kingdom of heaven. This means that we must be child-like not childish, for as St. Paul remarked, "When I became a man I put away childish things." Catholics do not have a monopoly on simplicity; other Christians exhibit this charming virtue, as do some who are not Christians at all. But I think that it may be claimed that the practice of the Catholic religion is calculated to make one humble and patient and simple and childlike. I think it was Ross Hoffman who said: "Catholicism is at once the most complex and the simplest of things; one cannot live long enough to learn it all, yet it can be taught to a child—in a very real sense, of course, *only* to a child."

With this should go a keener insight, a deeper apprehension into reality. Of course in this life nothing is seized by the intellect, so St. Thomas Aquinas declared, which is not first in the senses, yet we do not get much farther than understanding anything only as a congeries of external phenomena. It was the theme of Tennyson's "Flower in the Crannied Wall," the poem in which he was, for once, a good philosopher. Much the same concept is expressed better (though perhaps not as poetry) in Alice Meynell's sonnet "To a Daisy":

> Slight as thou art, thou art enough to hide
>      Like all created things, secrets from me,
>      And stand a barrier to eternity.
> And I, how can I praise thee well and wide
> From where I dwell—upon the hither side?

Thou little veil for so great mystery,
When shall I penetrate all things and thee,
And then look back? For this I must abide.
Till thou shalt grow and fold and be unfurled
Literally between me and the world.
When I shall drink from in beneath a spring,
And from a poet's side shall read his book.
O daisy mine, what will it be to look
From God's side even of such a simple thing.

What does this all boil down to? To nothing less than conformity to the will of God, accepting it gladly and not grimly. How can one possibly be happy when one is at odds with one's Creator and one's Heavenly Father? As St. Paul has it, our standard is, "The will of God, your sanctification." The whole essence of Christianity is there; indeed, it is the essence of all religion, whatever form it may take. But in the case of Christianity it means taking up one's cross, knowing that Christ Himself is bearing the greater part of the burden, and rejoicing in that knowledge because through the carrying of the cross, the acceptance of the will of God, one is united to our Redeemer.

# CHAPTER SEVEN

## *Hope of Heaven*

There is a wonderful phrase in French, *nostalgie de la boue*. If we are not homesick for the stars it is likely that we shall get homesick for the gutter. As I have already said, those go to hell who choose to go there, who would be out of place elsewhere. And though philosophy insists that evil is always presented to the mind in the guise of a specious good, there is no doubt that there are people who take a kind of perverse pleasure and pride in their degradation.

The hope of heaven is not of course the certainty of heaven; if it were, the whole virtue of hope, in its supernatural sense, would be obliterated. This is a point that is missed by those Protestant sects that lay a great—an unwarranted—stress upon what they call "assurance"; their members talk about the people around them as being "saved" or still of the "unsaved," meaning those who have experienced "conversion" and those who have not. That this is (or may be) a very genuine experience need not be denied, but it does not guarantee salvation, though it may provide some ground for hope that those who have passed through it will be among the saved.

The danger of this attitude is that it can lead to antinomianism. According to the extreme "evangelical" theory anybody who is what they called saved, is saved for ever. This being so, as one of the elect he is under a temptation to have a merry time in disregard of the moral law. Few fortunately take this position, though it would seem logically to flow from their premise. More often they say that those who, after professing to have been converted, or "saved," lapse into evil courses, could not really have been converted at all. That is to say in effect that nobody can ever be quite sure whether a conversion is genuine or not,

or whether those who claim to be among the saved belong to
that group. And this brings us back again to hope, which is all
that Catholics dare to profess. It may be a rather faint hope, or
even a desperate hope, or a strong hope inducing a serene confidence; but it is hope—I will not say "only" hope, for hope is,
with faith and charity, one of the evangelical virtues.[1] As such it
is necessary for salvation.

Sometimes non-Catholics, especially in America, think that
Catholicism with its constant reminders of death must be a very
gloomy religion. There is no denying that Catholics do think a
good deal about death; the prayer most frequently said among
them, the "Hail Mary," asks the prayers of the Mother of God
"now and at the hour of our death." But those who believe in
eternity would be foolish not to keep life's end before them.
For my part I would like to see more representations of the
Dance of Death, such as are found in many medieval drawings
and in the famous frescoes in old St. Paul's Cathedral in London.
I daresay it would be considered macabre to thrust this on our
queasy generation, but it would be a great deal better than the
ostrich attitude towards unpleasant facts that so many people
assume. As dirged the Scottish poet of the late fifteenth century,
William Dunbar:

> Unto the Death gois all Estatis
> Princes, Prelatis, and Potestates;
> Baith rich and poor of all degree.—
> *Timor mortis conturbat me.*

Hell is of course a most unpleasant subject. As the colored man
remarked after hearing his minister's lurid sermon, "Ah just don't
think ah could stand it." Well, it is no use being sensitive about
the matter or to consider (rather patronizingly) that God would
never consign anybody to eternal loss. As a matter of fact, it is
not God who consigns the wicked to hell, but they themselves.
Those who go to hell go there only because that is what they wish.

---

[1] Here of course the word "evangelical" is used in the Catholic sense;
on the previous page it was used in the sense attached to it by such Protestant
sects as claim to be evangelical, because of the emphasis they lay on conversion.

They will be eternally separated from God because they have deliberately separated themselves from Him in this life. They have destined themselves to hell, just as it may be taken as the predestination of heaven when anybody hungers for union with God. As William Law wrote: "Covetousness, envy, pride and wrath are the four elements of self, or nature, or hell, all of them inseparable from it. And the reason why it must be thus, and cannot be otherwise, is because the natural life of the creature is brought forth for the participation of some high supernatural good in the Creator. But it could have no fitness, no possible capacity to receive such good, unless it was in itself both an extremity of want and an extremity of desire for some high good. . . . Its whole life can be nothing else but a plague and torment of covetousness, envy, pride and wrath, all which is precisely nature, self, or hell. . . . These four properties generate their own torment." Only in analogy can one speak of the "wrath" of God, since God has no passions. Hell is a necessary exclusion springing from the very nature of evil.

For all, whether they go to heaven or hell, as the Preface for the Mass for All Souls' Day puts it, "Life is changed but not taken away." But though all will have life, for some life will be a living death. Dante, passing through the wood of the suicides in his *Inferno,* is told by Virgil that on the day of resurrection the souls of the suicides tormented as twisted trees shall drag their bodies from their graves—but only to have them eternally dangling, each from his own bough. While these wretched bodies will only add to their pain, the blessed now in heaven will receive their glorified bodies, all in inconceivable beauty and health, all—from the extremely aged to the newborn—at the time of life when the body is at the apex of its perfection, but forever endowed with a perfection they have never known on earth.

It is a false spirituality which supposes that only the soul is immortal; we are, as St. Paul says, waiting for "the redemption of the body." And the glorified bodies we shall have will, we may be sure, in no way diminish our power of recognizing our loved ones in Paradise or our communion with them. It is impossible that there should be deprivation in heaven; rather our mortal good, often forgotten or not fully valued, will be, not merely restored to us, but in a very real sense made completely ours for the first time. Those who imagine that Christianity depreciates the body obviously cannot have reflected upon the points that have just been presented. It is Christianity that promises not only redemption of the soul to those who believe but also the redemption of the body.

Beyond this we know little of what awaits us, and for this we shall have to wait. Dante in the concluding canto of his *Divine Comedy*, though he declares that it has been given him to have had one glimpse of the Beatific Vision, and though he shows himself capable as a poet of dealing with everything else, prescinds from describing this. Chesterton translates the passage (*Paradiso*, XXX, 49–72):

> Then Bernard smiled at me, that I should gaze
> But I had gazed already; caught the view,
> Faced the unfathomable ray of rays
> Which to itself and by itself is true.

> Then was my vision mightier than man's speech;
> Speech snapped before it like a flying spell;
> And memory and all that time can teach
> Before that splendid outrage failed and fell.

> As when one dreameth and remembereth not
> Waking, what were his pleasures or his pains,
> With every feature of the dream forgot,
> The printed passion of the dream remains:—

> Even such am I; within whose thoughts resides
> No picture of that sight nor any part
> Nor any memory; in whom abides
> Only a happiness within the heart,

> A secret happiness that soaks the heart
> As hills are soaked by slow unsealing snow,
> Or secret as that wind without a chart
> Whereon did the wild leaves of the Sibyl go.

O light uplifted from all mortal knowing,
    Send back a little of that glimpse of thee,
That of its glory I may kindle glowing
    One tiny spark for all men yet to be.

That same St. Bernard, Dante's final guide, who in the *Divine Comedy* typifies mystical theology, wrote in his own person: "Who is God? I can think of no better answer than, He who is. Nothing is more appropriate to the eternity which God is; if you call God good, or great, or blessed, or wise, or anything else of this sort, it is included in these words, namely, He is." To which perhaps might be added this from Rabi'a, a woman saint of the Sufi sect of Islam: "God, if I worship Thee in fear of hell, burn me in hell. And if I worship Thee in hope of Paradise, exclude me from Paradise; but if I worship Thee for Thine own sake, withhold not Thine everlasting beauty." Allowing for some touches of extravagance of statement, the heart of the matter is there.

Catholicism is a definitely unworldly religion, however worldly may be some of those who profess it. This, however, does not mean that the world is not good or that a yearning for God means a desire to escape from earth. But while using the world (that is, the many good things provided by God in the world for His children), and while seeking to serve God in the world, we cannot but be conscious that our destiny is not fulfilled here. What the Christian should do is not to deny but seek to transfigure the world in which he finds himself, using whatever God meant us to use, but without allowing himself to become too attached to it, and always seeing in it a symbol of something greater. To suggest that there is evil in matter is rank Manicheeism, an abominable heresy that, in one form or another, is always liable to infect the mind with spurious spirituality. Only this much may we hold: that life is transitory; that we lodge at an inn, having no abiding place, and we may enjoy any comforts we can find there, a warm hearth, good food and wine, happy song and sound sleep; but we are traveling elsewhere: we are looking for a city whose builder and maker is God.

Francis Bacon pronounced prosperity to be the ideal of the

Old Testament, and adversity of the New. It took that very Victorian Victorian, Lord Macaulay, to popularize the apologetic argument that Protestantism must be presumed true because Protestant countries are more prosperous than Catholic countries. Actually this meant nothing more than that England had become the richest of European countries because the rest had been so ravaged by the Napoleonic wars, and that the United States, another predominantly Protestant country, was also prosperous because it had enjoyed a long peace, and had almost inexhaustible natural resources to exploit. But the argument, even if Macaulay's facts must be conceded, is detestable. T. S. Eliot states the issue better.[2] He writes: "The more highly industrialized the country, the more easily a materialistic philosophy will flourish in it, and the more deadly that philosophy will be. Britain has been more highly industrialized longer than any other country. And the tendency of unlimited industrialism is to create bodies of men and women—of all classes—detached from tradition, alienated from religion, and susceptible to mass suggestion: in other words a mob. And the mob will be no less a mob if it be well clothed, well housed and well disciplined."

Surely only the smuggest kind of Victorian could take much satisfaction in society as it was during the Victorian age. Now the very term has become one of derision, often very unjustly, for the period was notable not only for its appalling complacency but for the protests made against such a spirit. What has been suggested here is a middle ground—the acceptance of the world, in so far as it may be safely accepted, always with the conviction that the ideal is a kingdom not of this world, to which, however, the world may be seen to point. If one must have artificial criteria, such as those advanced by Macaulay, one has only to remember the joy and jollity of the peasants of Catholic countries of his time, illiterate perhaps but dancing to fiddles on the village green, and often more prosperous than the strait-laced English traveler imagined.

All such criteria—those that I have suggested as a corrective hardly less than those which I think they should correct—are ultimately beside the point. Man has come into this world—a

[2] *The Idea of a Christian Society,* p. 19.

good world, except to the extent that man himself has spoiled it—to prepare for heaven. Never has God left him to his own foolish devices but has given him, first, reasoning faculties by which he might deduce the existence of a Creator, and then a steadily broadening revelation which was completed by the Incarnation of the Son of God and the redemption He effected of sinful man. By baptism man has been made a coheir with Christ of the kingdom, and becomes a member of the Mystical Body of Christ, the Catholic Church, the greater part of which is already enjoying the bliss of Paradise. In this Church we may find our home on earth and our home in the life to come.

Finally we might ponder the Preface of the Mass for Trinity Sunday, which reads in part: "O holy Lord, Father almighty and everlasting God. Who with Thine only-begotten Son and the Holy Ghost art one God, one Lord; not in oneness of a single person but in the Trinity of one substance. For that which we believe from Thy revelation concerning Thy glory, the same we believe also of Thy Son, and of the Holy Ghost, without difference of separation. So that in confessing the true and everlasting Godhead, we shall adore distinction in persons, oneness in being, and equality in majesty. Which the angels and archangels, the cherubim also and the seraphim do praise, nor cease to cry out with one voice: *Sanctus, Sanctus, Sanctus, Dominus Deus Sabaoth, Pleni sunt caeli et terra gloria tua, Hosanna in excelsis.*"

(1)

J
912
Nat

C  OCEAN

EUROPE
*pages 32 – 37*

ASIA
*pages 44 – 49*

PACIFIC

OCEAN

AFRICA
*pages 38 – 43*

EQUATOR

INDIAN

OCEAN

AUSTRALIA
*pages 50 – 55*

ANTARCTICA
*pages 56 – 59*

**NATIONAL GEOGRAPHIC**

# BEGINNER'S World Atlas

NATIONAL GEOGRAPHIC
WASHINGTON, D.C.

*Photographs from Getty Images*

NATIONAL GEOGRAPHIC

# BEGINNER'S World Atlas

## Table of Contents

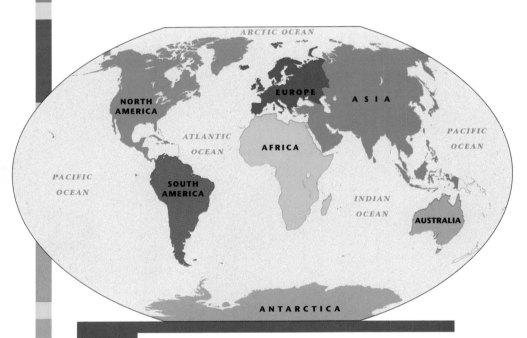

# What Is a Map?

**A** map is a drawing of a place as it looks from above. It is flat, and it is smaller than the place it shows. A map can help you find where you are and where you want to go.

## Mapping Your Backyard...

### ...from the ground
From your backyard you see everything in front of you straight on. You have to look up to see your roof and the tops of trees. You can't see what's in front of your house.

### ...from higher up
From higher up you look down on things. You can see the tops of trees and things in your yard and in the yards of other houses in your neighborhood.

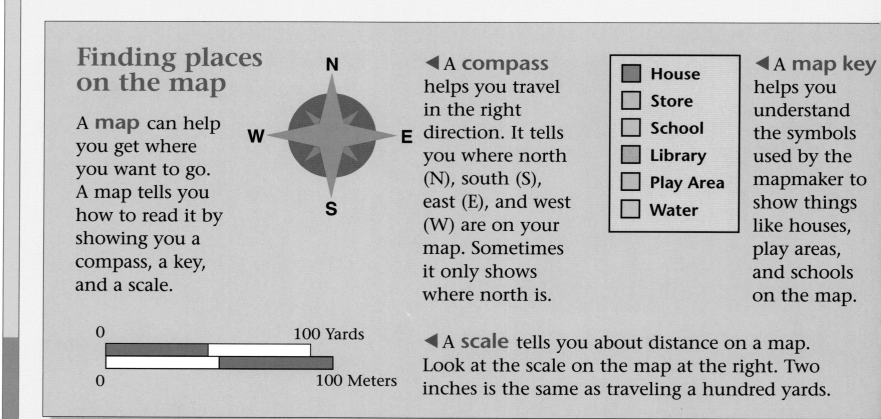

## Finding places on the map

A **map** can help you get where you want to go. A map tells you how to read it by showing you a compass, a key, and a scale.

◀ A **compass** helps you travel in the right direction. It tells you where north (N), south (S), east (E), and west (W) are on your map. Sometimes it only shows where north is.

**House**
**Store**
**School**
**Library**
**Play Area**
**Water**

◀ A **map key** helps you understand the symbols used by the mapmaker to show things like houses, play areas, and schools on the map.

◀ A **scale** tells you about distance on a map. Look at the scale on the map at the right. Two inches is the same as traveling a hundred yards.

0          100 Yards

0          100 Meters

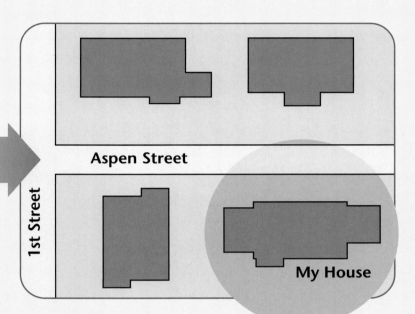

## ...from a bird's-eye view

If you were a bird flying directly overhead, you would see only the tops of things. You wouldn't see walls, tree trunks, tires, or feet.

## ...on a map

A map looks at places from a bird's-eye view. But it uses drawings called symbols to show things that don't move, such as houses.

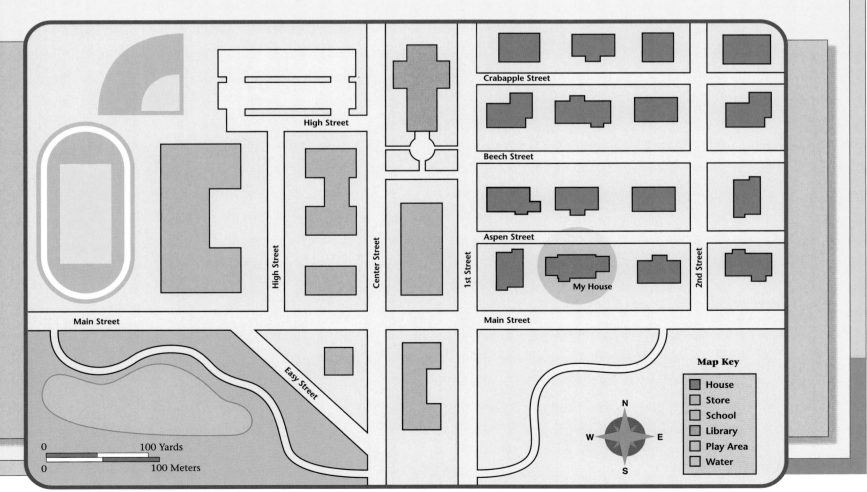

**Map Key**

- House
- Store
- School
- Library
- Play Area
- Water

# Making the Round Earth Flat

**F**rom your backyard Earth probably looks flat. If you could travel into space like an astronaut, you would see that Earth is a giant ball with blue oceans, greenish-brown land, and white clouds. Even in space you can only see the part of Earth facing you. To see the whole Earth at one time you need a map. Maps take the round Earth and make it flat so you can see all of it at one time.

## ▼ Earth in Space

From space you can see that Earth is round with oceans, land, and clouds. But you can see only half of Earth at one time.

NORTH AMERICA

EQUATOR

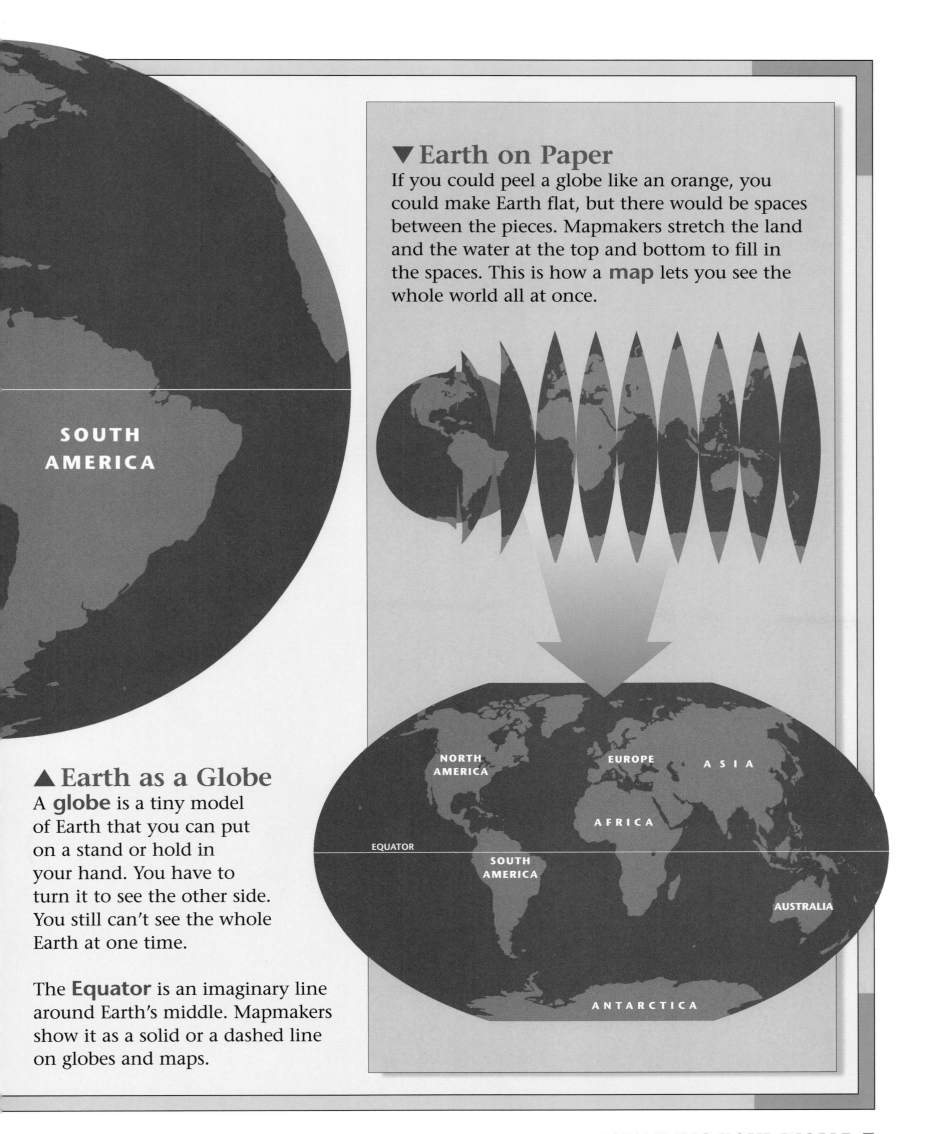

## ▼ Earth on Paper

If you could peel a globe like an orange, you could make Earth flat, but there would be spaces between the pieces. Mapmakers stretch the land and the water at the top and bottom to fill in the spaces. This is how a **map** lets you see the whole world all at once.

NORTH AMERICA

EUROPE

ASIA

AFRICA

EQUATOR

SOUTH AMERICA

AUSTRALIA

ANTARCTICA

SOUTH AMERICA

## ▲ Earth as a Globe

A **globe** is a tiny model of Earth that you can put on a stand or hold in your hand. You have to turn it to see the other side. You still can't see the whole Earth at one time.

The **Equator** is an imaginary line around Earth's middle. Mapmakers show it as a solid or a dashed line on globes and maps.

# The Physical World

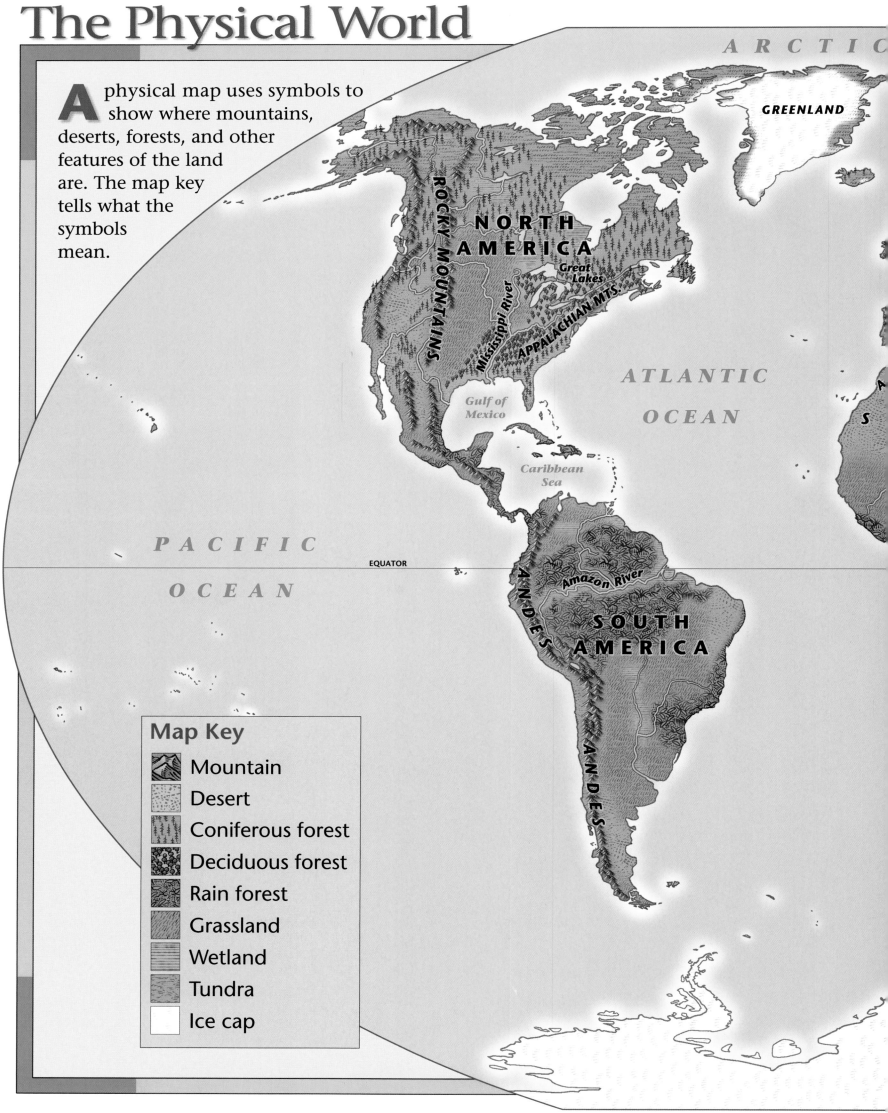

**A** physical map uses symbols to show where mountains, deserts, forests, and other features of the land are. The map key tells what the symbols mean.

ARCTIC

GREENLAND

NORTH AMERICA

ROCKY MOUNTAINS

Great Lakes

Mississippi River

APPALACHIAN MTS.

ATLANTIC OCEAN

Gulf of Mexico

Caribbean Sea

PACIFIC OCEAN

EQUATOR

ANDES

Amazon River

SOUTH AMERICA

ANDES

**Map Key**

- Mountain
- Desert
- Coniferous forest
- Deciduous forest
- Rain forest
- Grassland
- Wetland
- Tundra
- Ice cap

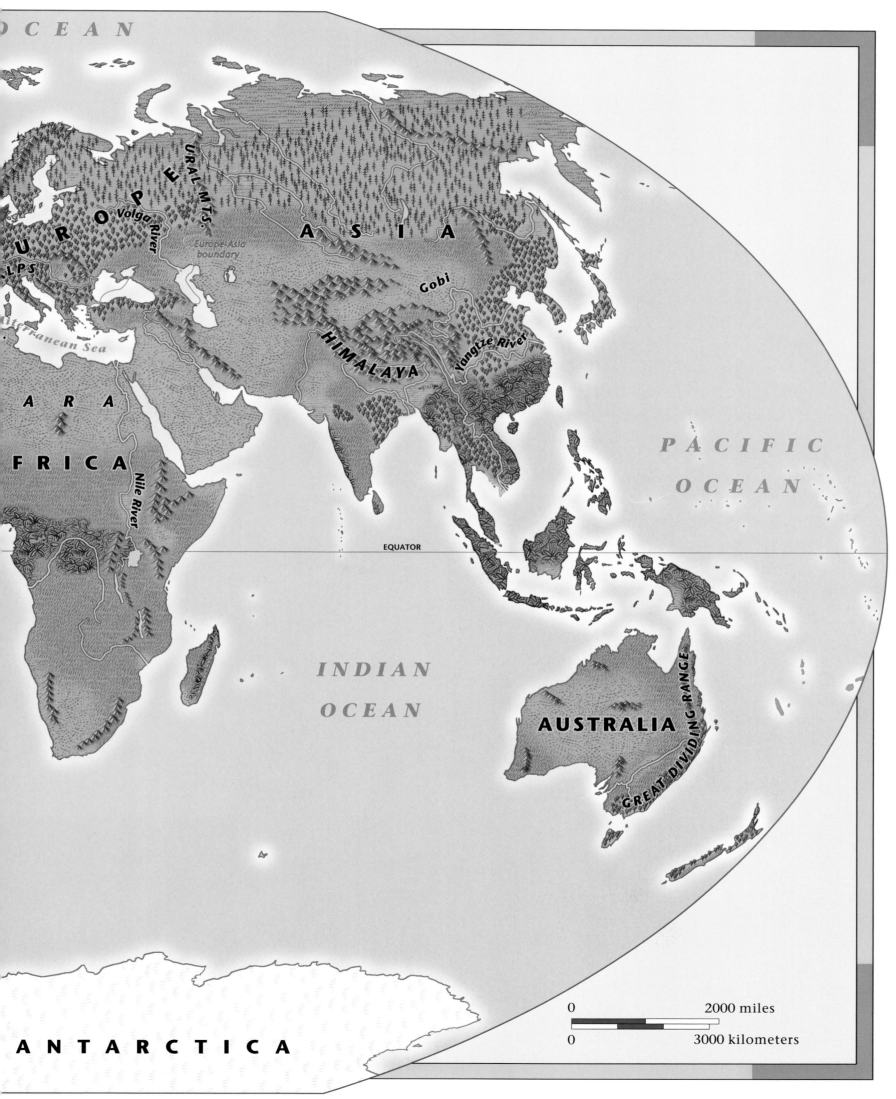

# The Physical World Close Up

The Earth's surface is made up of land and water. The biggest landmasses are called **continents**. All seven of them are named on this map. **Islands** are smaller pieces of land that are surrounded by water. Greenland is the largest island. Land that is almost entirely surrounded by water is called a **peninsula**. Europe has lots of them.

**Oceans** are the largest bodies of water. Can you find all four oceans? **Lakes** are bodies of water surrounded by land—like the Great Lakes, in North America. A large stream of water that flows into a lake or an ocean is called a **river**. The Nile is Earth's longest river.

These are Earth's main physical features. But continents also have mountains, deserts, forests, and many other kinds of physical features. The **map symbols** below show the features that will appear on the physical maps in this atlas. Each symbol is followed by a brief description that explains its meaning. There is also a photograph so you can see what each feature looks like in the real world.

Each continent has different kinds of features, so each physical map will have its own map key.

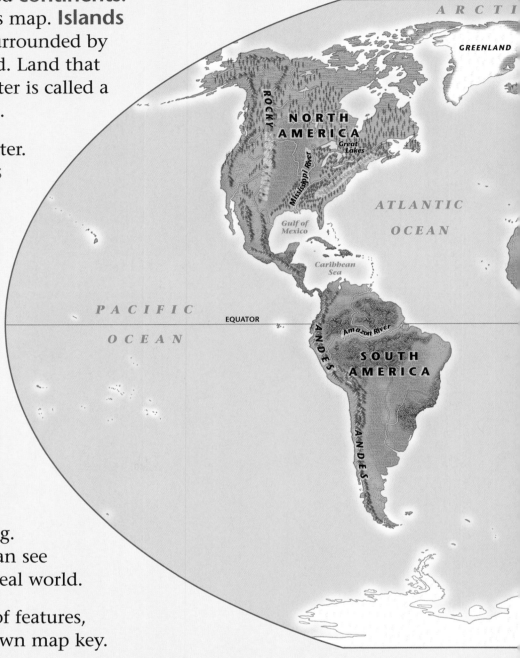

 **Mountain**
Land that rises at least 1,000 feet above the surrounding land

 **Desert**
Very dry land that can be hot or cold and sandy or rocky

 **Coniferous forest**
Forest with trees that have seed cones and often needlelike leaves

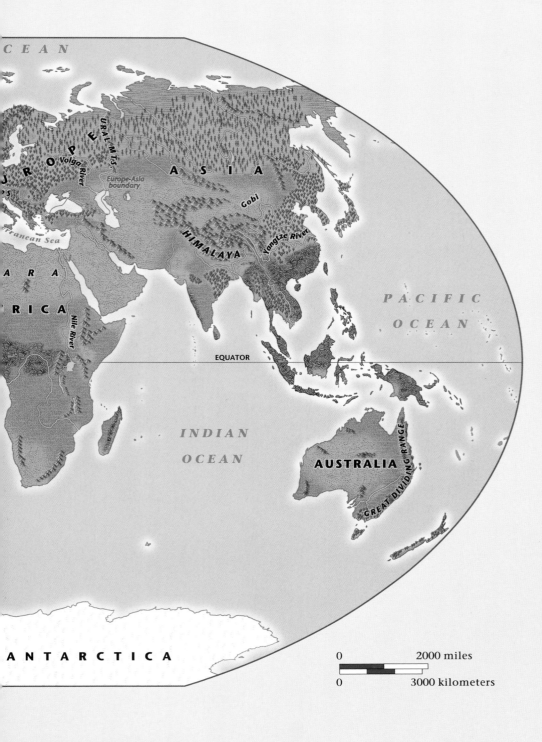

OCEAN

EUROPE

URAL MTS.

Volga River

Europe-Asia boundary

ASIA

Gobi

HIMALAYA

Yangtze River

Mediterranean Sea

SAHARA

AFRICA

Nile River

PACIFIC OCEAN

EQUATOR

INDIAN OCEAN

AUSTRALIA

GREAT DIVIDING RANGE

ANTARCTICA

0          2000 miles

0          3000 kilometers

**Ice cap**
A permanent sheet of thick ice that covers the land, as in Antarctica

**Tundra**
A cold region with low plants that grow only during warm months

**Wetland**
Land, such as a marsh or swamp, that is mostly covered with water

**Deciduous forest**
Forest with trees that loose leaves in fall and grow new ones in spring

**Rain forest**
Forest with trees that keep their leaves all year and need lots of rain

**Grassland**
A grass-covered area with too little rain for many trees to grow

# The Political World

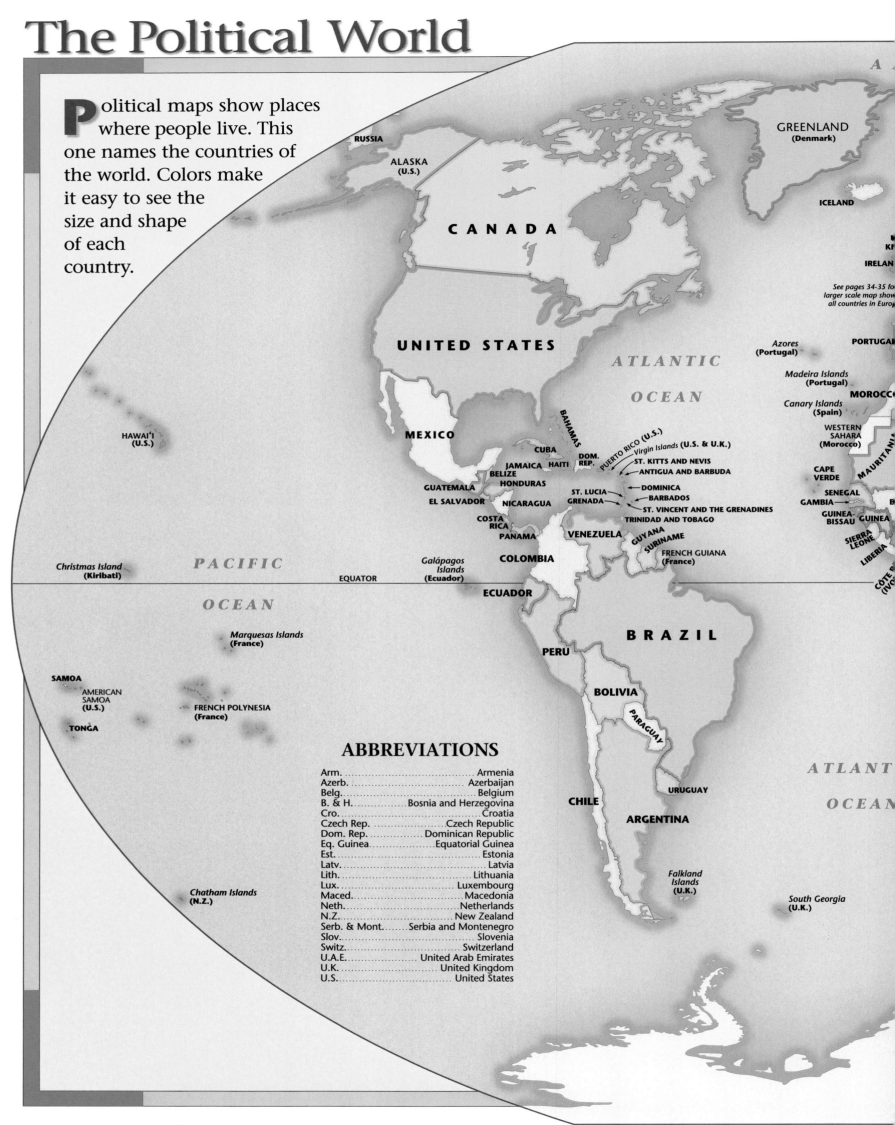

Political maps show places where people live. This one names the countries of the world. Colors make it easy to see the size and shape of each country.

See pages 34-35 for larger scale map show all countries in Europ

RUSSIA

ALASKA (U.S.)

CANADA

UNITED STATES

HAWAI'I (U.S.)

MEXICO

GUATEMALA
BELIZE
EL SALVADOR
HONDURAS
NICARAGUA
COSTA RICA
PANAMA

BAHAMAS
CUBA
JAMAICA  HAITI  DOM. REP.
PUERTO RICO (U.S.)
Virgin Islands (U.S. & U.K.)
ST. KITTS AND NEVIS
ANTIGUA AND BARBUDA
DOMINICA
ST. LUCIA  BARBADOS
GRENADA
ST. VINCENT AND THE GRENADINES
TRINIDAD AND TOBAGO

VENEZUELA
GUYANA
SURINAME
FRENCH GUIANA (France)
COLOMBIA

GREENLAND (Denmark)

ICELAND

IRELAN

KI

PORTUGA
Azores (Portugal)
Madeira Islands (Portugal)
MOROCC
Canary Islands (Spain)
WESTERN SAHARA (Morocco)
MAURITANI
CAPE VERDE
SENEGAL
GAMBIA
GUINEA-BISSAU  GUINEA
SIERRA LEONE
LIBERIA
CÔTE (IVO

ATLANTIC OCEAN

Christmas Island (Kiribati)

PACIFIC OCEAN

EQUATOR

Galápagos Islands (Ecuador)

ECUADOR

Marquesas Islands (France)

SAMOA
AMERICAN SAMOA (U.S.)

FRENCH POLYNESIA (France)

TONGA

PERU

BRAZIL

BOLIVIA

PARAGUAY

Chatham Islands (N.Z.)

CHILE

URUGUAY

ARGENTINA

Falkland Islands (U.K.)

South Georgia (U.K.)

ATLANT

OCEAN

## ABBREVIATIONS

Arm. .................................... Armenia
Azerb. ................................. Azerbaijan
Belg. ...................................... Belgium
B. & H. .............. Bosnia and Herzegovina
Cro. .......................................... Croatia
Czech Rep. .................... Czech Republic
Dom. Rep. ............... Dominican Republic
Eq. Guinea ................. Equatorial Guinea
Est. ............................................ Estonia
Latv. .......................................... Latvia
Lith. ...................................... Lithuania
Lux. .................................... Luxembourg
Maced. ................................. Macedonia
Neth. ................................. Netherlands
N.Z. .................................. New Zealand
Serb. & Mont. ....... Serbia and Montenegro
Slov. ....................................... Slovenia
Switz. .................................. Switzerland
U.A.E. ................. United Arab Emirates
U.K. ............................ United Kingdom
U.S. ............................... United States

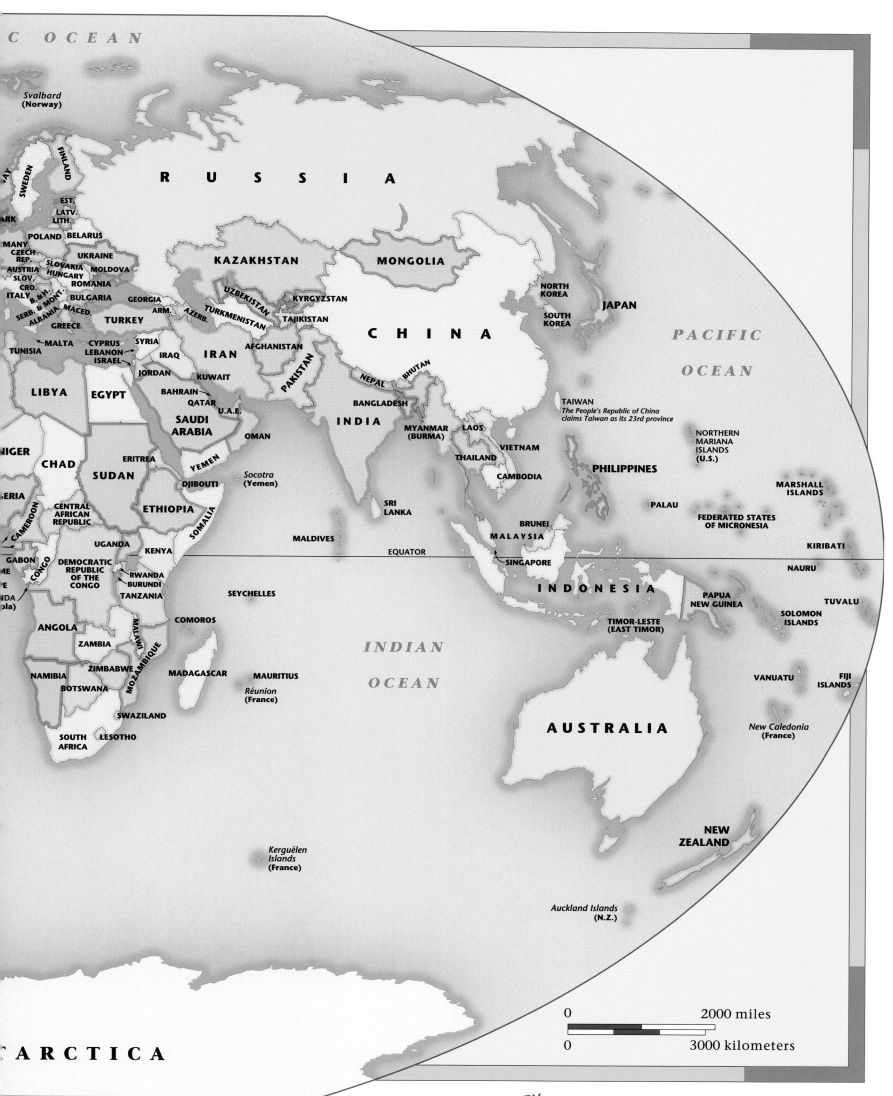

C OCEAN

Svalbard
(Norway)

SWEDEN
FINLAND

EST.
LATV.
LITH.

MANY
POLAND
BELARUS

CZECH
REP.
SLOVAKIA
UKRAINE

AUSTRIA
HUNGARY
MOLDOVA

SLOV.
ROMANIA

ITALY
CRO.
BULGARIA
GEORGIA

B.&H.
SERB. & MONT.
ARM.

ALBANIA
MACED.
AZERB.

GREECE

MALTA
CYPRUS
SYRIA

TUNISIA
LEBANON
IRAQ
IRAN

ISRAEL

JORDAN
KUWAIT

LIBYA
EGYPT
BAHRAIN
QATAR

U.A.E.

SAUDI
ARABIA
OMAN

NIGER
ERITREA
YEMEN

CHAD
SUDAN
DJIBOUTI

ERIA
CENTRAL
AFRICAN
REPUBLIC
ETHIOPIA
SOMALIA

CAMEROON
UGANDA
KENYA

GABON
CONGO
RWANDA
BURUNDI

ME
DEMOCRATIC
REPUBLIC
OF THE
CONGO

NDA
TANZANIA

ola)

ANGOLA

NAMIBIA
ZAMBIA
MALAWI

ZIMBABWE

BOTSWANA
MOZAMBIQUE

SWAZILAND

SOUTH
AFRICA
LESOTHO

RUSSIA

KAZAKHSTAN
MONGOLIA

UZBEKISTAN
KYRGYZSTAN

TURKMENISTAN
TAJIKISTAN

AFGHANISTAN
CHINA

PAKISTAN
NEPAL
BHUTAN

BANGLADESH

INDIA
MYANMAR
(BURMA)
LAOS

THAILAND

NORTH
KOREA
JAPAN

SOUTH
KOREA

PACIFIC

OCEAN

TAIWAN
The People's Republic of China
claims Taiwan as its 23rd province

NORTHERN
MARIANA
ISLANDS
(U.S.)

VIETNAM
PHILIPPINES

CAMBODIA

Socotra
(Yemen)

SRI
LANKA

MALDIVES
EQUATOR

BRUNEI
MALAYSIA

SINGAPORE

MARSHALL
ISLANDS

PALAU

FEDERATED STATES
OF MICRONESIA

KIRIBATI

NAURU

SEYCHELLES
INDONESIA

PAPUA
NEW GUINEA

TUVALU

SOLOMON
ISLANDS

COMOROS

TIMOR-LESTE
(EAST TIMOR)

INDIAN
MADAGASCAR
MAURITIUS

OCEAN

Réunion
(France)

VANUATU
FIJI
ISLANDS

AUSTRALIA
New Caledonia
(France)

Kerguélen
Islands
(France)

NEW
ZEALAND

Auckland Islands
(N.Z.)

ARCTICA

0                2000 miles

0                3000 kilometers

# What This Atlas Will Teach You

Yo hold the world in your hands as you look through the pages of this atlas. You will find a physical and a political map of each continent. Here is what you will learn about each one.

**Mountains, Asia**

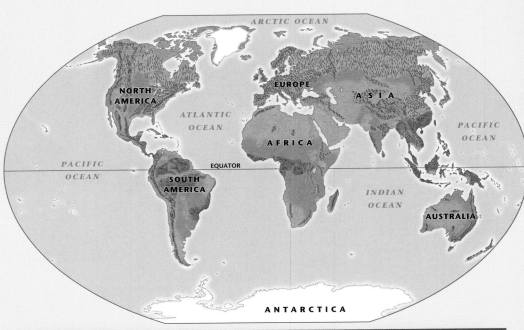

**Coral reef, Pacific Ocean**

**THE PHYSICAL WORLD**

 **Land regions** You will find out what kinds of land cover a continent. Does it have mountains and deserts? If so, where are they?

 **Water** You will learn about a continent's chief lakes, rivers, and waterfalls. You'll see that some continents have more water than others.

 **Climate** Climate is the weather of a place over many years. Some continents are colder and wetter or hotter and drier than others.

 **Plants** You'll discover what kinds of plants grow on a particular continent.

**Camels, Ind**

 **Animals** Continents each have certain kinds of animals. Did you know that tigers live in the wild only in Asia?

**Desert, North America**

Vancouver, Canada

Grapes, Mediterranean region

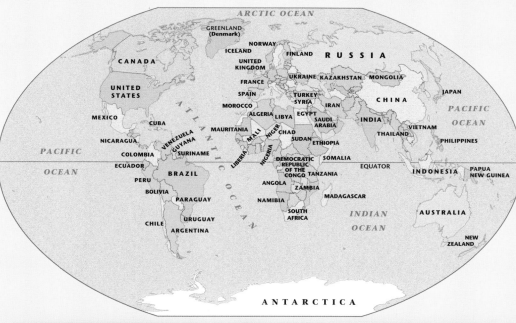

Eurostar train, Europe

## THE POLITICAL WORLD

**Countries** You will learn about the countries that make up a continent. Maps show country names in type like this: **UNITED STATES**

**Cities** You will find out which are the most important cities on a continent. The map key will tell you which cities are country capitals.

**People** You will learn where groups of people on a continent come from, where they live, what they do, how they have fun, and more.

**Languages** Many languages are spoken on most continents. Here you will find out which languages most people speak.

**Products** This section will tell you which goods produced on a continent are most important to the people living there.

Eiffel Tower, France

Schoolgirls, Vietnam

# North America

**N**orth America is shaped like a triangle ▼. It is wide in the north. In the south it becomes a strip of land so narrow that a Marathon runner could cross it in two hours. Ships make the trip on the Panama Canal. The warm islands in the Caribbean Sea are part of North America. So is icy Greenland in the far north. The seven countries between Mexico and South America make up a region commonly called Central America. It connects the rest of North America and South America.

Kha-hay! I'm from the Crow tribe in Montana. This beautiful valley is in Yosemite National Park, in California. It's in the Sierra Nevada mountains. Look for it on the map when you turn the page.

# North America

*Mt. McKinley (Denali)*
*Highest elevation in North America*

## The Land

**Land regions** The Rocky Mountains run along the west side of North America through Mexico. There, the mountains are called the Sierra Madre Oriental. Lower mountains called the Appalachians are in the east. Grassy plains lie between the two mountain chains.

**Water** Together the Mississippi and the Missouri make up the longest river. The Great Lakes are the world's largest group of freshwater lakes.

**Climate** The far north is icy cold. Temperatures get warmer as you move south. Much of Central America is hot and wet.

**Plants** North America has large forests where there is plenty of rain. Grasslands cover drier areas.

**Animals** There is a big variety of animals—everything from bears, moose, and wolves to monkeys and colorful parrots.

▲ North America is famous for its **deciduous forests.** Leaves turn fiery colors each fall!

▲ A white-tailed deer nuzzles her babies in a meadow near the **Great Lakes.** Deer live in almost every country on the continent.

◀ Palm trees grow along sandy beaches on islands in the **Caribbean Sea.** In this part of North America the weather is warm year-round.

▼ **Deserts** are found in the southwestern part of North America. The large rock formation on the right is called The Mitten. Can you guess why?

◀ Dragonlike iguanas live in the **rain forests** of Mexico and Central America. This harmless lizard can grow as long as a man's leg.

A

ARCTIC
OCEAN

GREENLAND

Brooks Range

n River

Mackenzie River

Great
Bear Lake

Great
Slave Lake

Hudson
Bay

Columbia River

R O C K Y   M O U N T A I N S

Lake
Winnipeg

Missouri River

G R E A T   P L A I N S

Great Lakes

Sierra Nevada

Colorado River

Death Valley
west elevation in
North America

Mississippi River

Ohio River

Appalachian Mountains

ATLANTIC
OCEAN

SIERRA MADRE OCCIDENTAL

Rio Grande

SIERRA MADRE ORIENTAL

Gulf of Mexico

W E S T   I N D I E S

PACIFIC
OCEAN

CENTRAL AMERICA

Caribbean Sea

0        600 miles

0        900 kilometers

SOUTH AMERICA

▲ This view from
a plane shows that
**Greenland** has high
mountains and lots
of snow and ice.

## Map Key

Mountain

Desert

Coniferous forest

Deciduous forest

Rain forest

Grassland

Wetland

Tundra

Ice cap

# North America

## The People

**Countries** Canada, the United States, Mexico, and the countries of Central America and the West Indies make up North America.

**Cities** Mexico City is the biggest city in North America. Next in size are New York City and Los Angeles. Havana, in Cuba, is the largest city in the West Indies.

**People** Ancestors of most people in North America came from Europe. Many other people trace their roots to Africa and Asia. Native Americans live throughout the continent.

**Languages** English and Spanish are the main languages. large number of people in Canada and Haiti speak French. There are also many Native American languages.

**Products** North America's chief products include cars, machinery, petroleum, natural gas, silver, wheat, corn, beef, and forest products.

▲ Skiing and ski jumping are popular sports in the **Rocky Mountains.**

▲ This farmer is harvesting wheat on a big farm in **Canada.** Canada and the United States grow much of the world's wheat.

▲ This pyramid at **Chichén Itzá** was built long ago by the Maya people.

▲ This is **Mexico City.** More people live here than in any other city in North America.

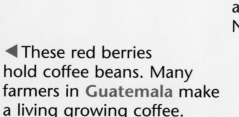

◄ These red berries hold coffee beans. Many farmers in **Guatemala** make a living growing coffee.

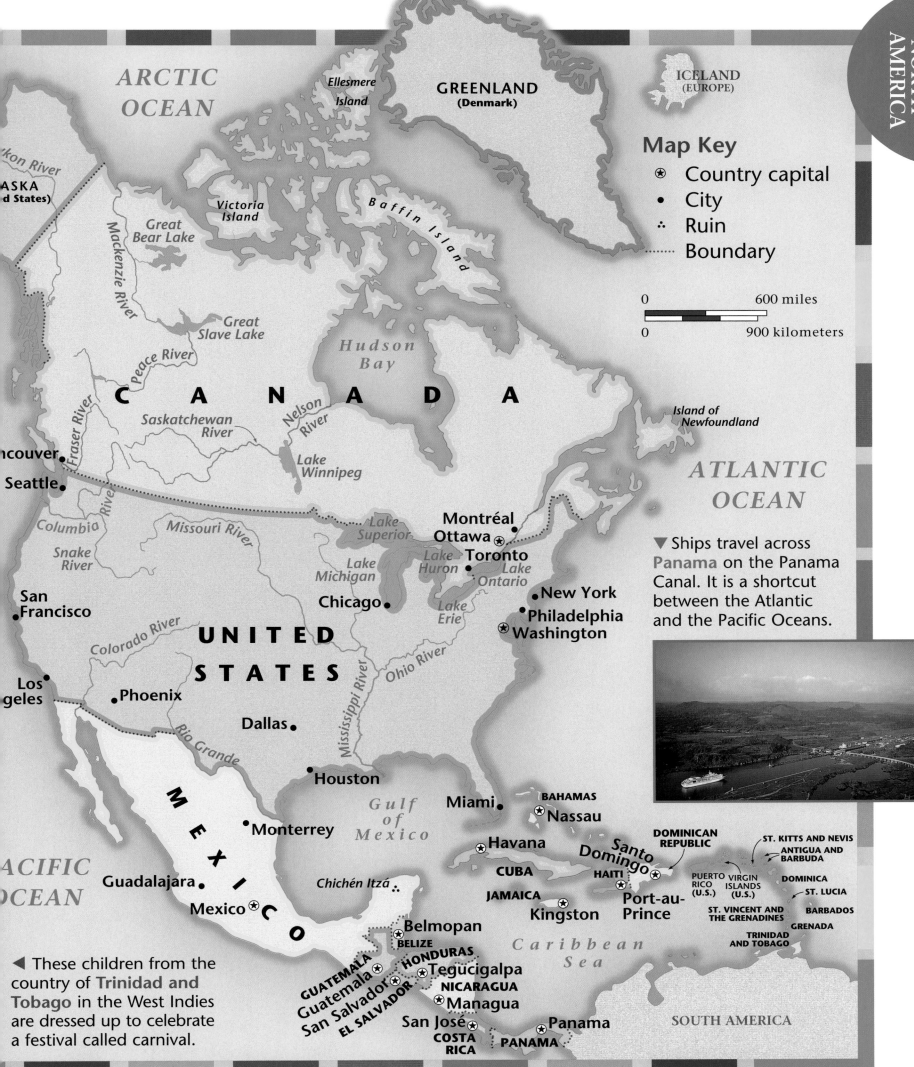

ARCTIC
OCEAN

Ellesmere
Island

GREENLAND
(Denmark)

ICELAND
(EUROPE)

ALASKA
(United States)

Yukon River

Victoria
Island

Baffin Island

Great
Bear Lake

Mackenzie River

Great
Slave Lake

Peace River

Hudson
Bay

C A N A D A

**Map Key**

⊛ Country capital
• City
∴ Ruin
⋯⋯ Boundary

| 0 | 600 miles |
| 0 | 900 kilometers |

Saskatchewan
River

Nelson
River

Island of
Newfoundland

Fraser River

Vancouver

Lake
Winnipeg

ATLANTIC
OCEAN

Seattle

Columbia River

Missouri River

Lake
Superior

Montréal
Ottawa ⊛
Toronto

▼ Ships travel across
**Panama** on the Panama
Canal. It is a shortcut
between the Atlantic
and the Pacific Oceans.

Snake
River

Lake
Michigan

Lake
Huron

Lake
Ontario

San
Francisco

Chicago

Lake
Erie

New York
Philadelphia
Washington ⊛

U N I T E D
S T A T E S

Ohio River

Los
Angeles

Phoenix

Colorado River

Dallas

Mississippi River

M E X I C O

Rio Grande

Houston

Gulf
of
Mexico

Miami

BAHAMAS
⊛ Nassau

PACIFIC
OCEAN

Monterrey

DOMINICAN
REPUBLIC

ST. KITTS AND NEVIS
ANTIGUA AND
BARBUDA

Guadalajara

Chichén Itzá ∴

Havana ⊛

Santo
Domingo

Mexico ⊛

CUBA

HAITI

⊛

PUERTO
RICO
(U.S.)

VIRGIN
ISLANDS
(U.S.)

DOMINICA

ST. LUCIA

JAMAICA

Port-au-
Prince

ST. VINCENT AND
THE GRENADINES

BARBADOS

Kingston ⊛

GRENADA

Belmopan ⊛

BELIZE

Caribbean
Sea

TRINIDAD
AND TOBAGO

◀ These children from the
country of **Trinidad and
Tobago** in the West Indies
are dressed up to celebrate
a festival called carnival.

GUATEMALA

HONDURAS
Tegucigalpa ⊛

Guatemala ⊛
San Salvador ⊛

NICARAGUA

EL SALVADOR

Managua ⊛

San José ⊛
COSTA
RICA

Panama ⊛

SOUTH AMERICA

PANAMA

# United States

## The People

▲ Chinese New Year is a big celebration in **San Francisco**. Lots of Chinese live there.

**States** The United States is made up of 50 states. Alaska and Hawai'i are separated from the rest of the country. So you can see them close up, they are shown near the bottom of the map. Use the small globe to see their real locations.

**Cities** Washington, D.C., is the national capital. Each state also has a capital city. New York City has the most people.

▲ Sandy beaches, like this one in **Delaware**, are popular places to visit in the summer.

**People** People from almost every country in the world live in the United States. Most live and work in and around cities.

**Languages** English is the chief language, followed by Spanish.

**Products** The chief products include cars, machinery, petroleum, natural gas, coal, beef, wheat, and forest products.

▶ Baseball is a popular sport in the United States along with soccer, basketball, and football. This girl lives in **California**.

Seattle
Olympia
**WASHINGTON**
Portland
Salem
**OREGON**
Columbia River
IDA
Boise
**C A L I F O R N I A**
Sacramento
San Francisco
San Jose
**N E V A D A**
Carson City
Sal
Las Vegas
Los Angeles
San Diego
A
Pho
Tuc

**PACIFIC OCEAN**

**ALASKA**
Juneau

0       400 miles
0       600 kilometers

Honolulu
**HAWAI'I**

0       150 miles
0       200 kilometers

CANADA

**Missouri River**

MONTANA
Helena

NORTH DAKOTA
Bismarck

SOUTH DAKOTA
Pierre

WYOMING

MINNESOTA

Minneapolis
St. Paul
WISCONSIN
Milwaukee
Madison

Lake Superior

MICHIGAN

L. Huron

Lake Ontario

MAINE
Augusta

Montpelier
VT.
N.H.
Concord

NEW YORK
Rochester
Albany
Buffalo
MASS.
Boston
Providence
Hartford
RHODE ISLAND
CONN.

Cheyenne

NEBRASKA
Omaha
Lincoln

IOWA
Des Moines

River

Denver
COLORADO

Topeka
Jefferson City
Kansas City

KANSAS

Wichita

Santa Fe
Albuquerque

NEW MEXICO

El Paso

Tulsa
OKLAHOMA
Oklahoma City

Forth Worth
Dallas

TEXAS

Austin

Houston
San Antonio

Rio Grande

MEXICO

Lansing
Detroit

L. Michigan

Chicago

ILLINOIS
Springfield

INDIANA
Indianapolis

Cincinnati

St. Louis

MISSOURI

ARKANSAS

Little Rock

Memphis

Mississippi River

Cleveland
Pittsburgh

OHIO
Columbus

Frankfort

KENTUCKY

Nashville

TENNESSEE

L. Erie

PENNSYLVANIA
Harrisburg
Trenton
NEW JERSEY
Baltimore
Philadelphia
MARYLAND
Dover
DELAWARE
Annapolis
Washington, D.C.
WEST VIRGINIA
Charleston
Richmond

VIRGINIA

Raleigh

NORTH CAROLINA
Charlotte

SOUTH CAROLINA
Columbia

▲ This bridge is in **New York City**. The Empire State Building stands tall against the sky.

Atlanta
Birmingham

ALABAMA
Montgomery

MISSISSIPPI

Jackson

LOUISIANA

Baton Rouge
New Orleans

GEORGIA

Savannah

Jacksonville

Tallahassee

FLORIDA

Orlando

Tampa

Miami

**Gulf of Mexico**

## Map Key

⊛ Country capital
⊙ State capital
• City
⋯ Boundary

0 —— 400 miles

0 —— 600 kilometers

◀ A scarecrow stands guard over a field of sunflowers in **Kansas**.

▶ Spicy boiled crawfish are a favorite dish in **Mississippi** and other states that border the Gulf of Mexico.

ATLANTIC OCEAN

New York

# Canada

## The People

▲ Royal Canadian Mounted Police often perform their famous Musical Ride in Ottawa.

 **Provinces** Canada is divided into ten provinces and three territories. Nunavut is a brand-new homeland for Eskimos. The largest number of people live in Ontario and Quebec.

 **Cities** Ottawa is Canada's capital. Toronto, Montreal, and Vancouver are among its largest cities and ports.

 **People** Canada has fewer people than the state of California. Most Canadians live within a hundred miles of the country's southern border. The territories have a lot of land but very few people.

▲ Banff, in Alberta, is one of several national parks in the Rocky Mountains of western Canada.

 **Languages** Canada's street signs are often in two languages. That's because English and French are the chief languages. Most French-speaking Canadians live in Quebec.

▼ During Canada's long, cold winters, ice hockey is a popular sport. The Hockey Hall of Fame is in Toronto, Ontario.

 **Products** Canada's chief products include cars, forest products, petroleum, natural gas, aluminum, nickel, iron ore, beef, and wheat.

ARCTIC O

Beaufort
Sea

ALASKA
(U.S.)

YUKON
TERRITORY

Mackenzie River

Grea
Bear L

Yukon River

●Whitehorse

N O R T H
T E R R I T O
Yellowkn

BRITISH

COLUMBIA

Peace River

A L B E R

Edmonton●

Fraser River

Vancouver
Island

●Vancouver

Calg

Victoria◉

PACIFIC

OCEAN

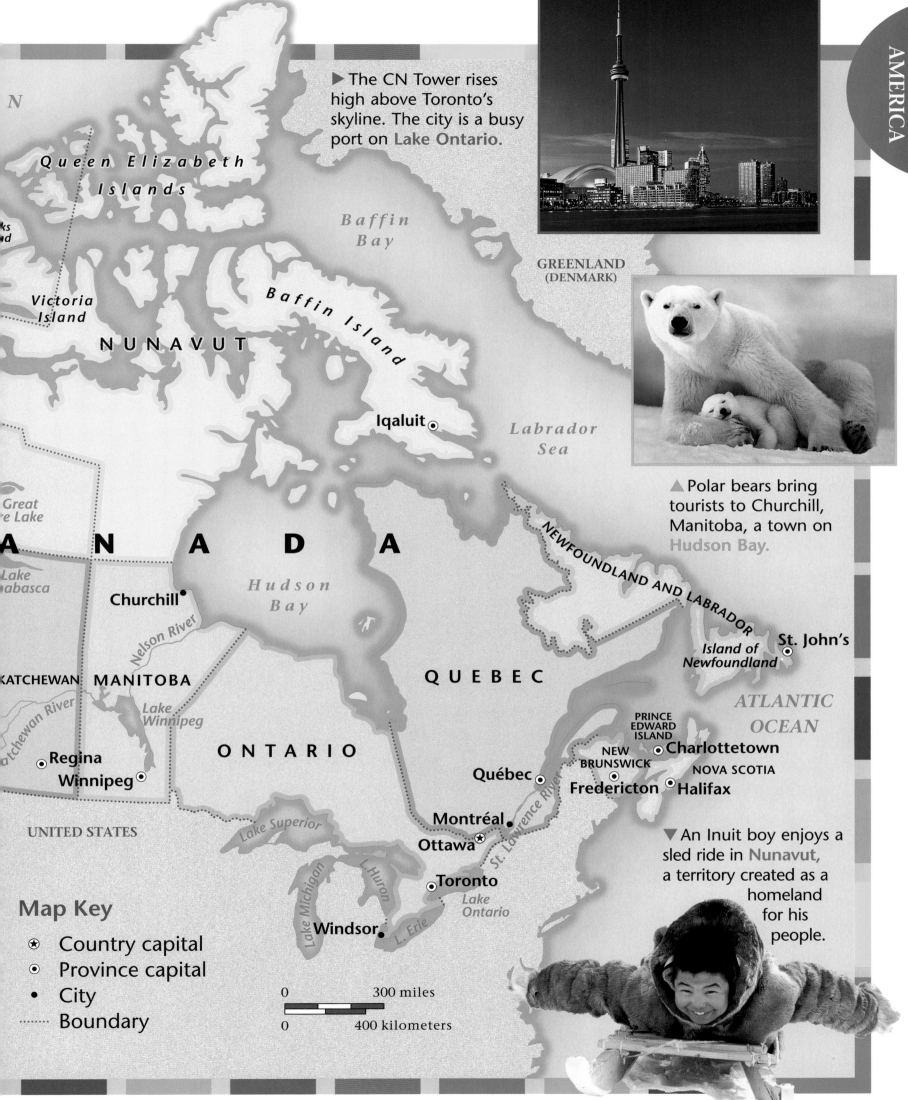

*N*

Queen Elizabeth Islands

Baffin
Bay

*rks
d*

Victoria
Island

NUNAVUT

Baffin Island

GREENLAND
(DENMARK)

▶ The CN Tower rises high above Toronto's skyline. The city is a busy port on **Lake Ontario.**

Iqaluit ⊙

Labrador
Sea

▲ Polar bears bring tourists to Churchill, Manitoba, a town on **Hudson Bay.**

*Great
re Lake*

**C A N A D A**

Hudson
Bay

NEWFOUNDLAND AND LABRADOR

*Lake
abasca*

**Churchill** •

Nelson River

St. John's ⊙

Island of
Newfoundland

KATCHEWAN   **MANITOBA**

atchewan River

**QUEBEC**

ATLANTIC
OCEAN

*Lake
Winnipeg*

PRINCE
EDWARD
ISLAND

⊙ **Regina**

**ONTARIO**

NEW
BRUNSWICK

⊙ **Charlottetown**

NOVA SCOTIA

**Winnipeg** ⊙

**Québec** ⊙

**Fredericton** ⊙ **Halifax**

UNITED STATES

*Lake Superior*

**Montréal** •

St. Lawrence River

▼ An Inuit boy enjoys a sled ride in **Nunavut,** a territory created as a homeland for his people.

**Ottawa** ✪

## Map Key

*L. Huron*

**Toronto** ⊙

*Lake Michigan*

*Lake
Ontario*

✪  Country capital

**Windsor** •

*L. Erie*

⊙  Province capital

•  City

⋯⋯  Boundary

| 0 | | 300 miles |
| 0 | | 400 kilometers |

# South America

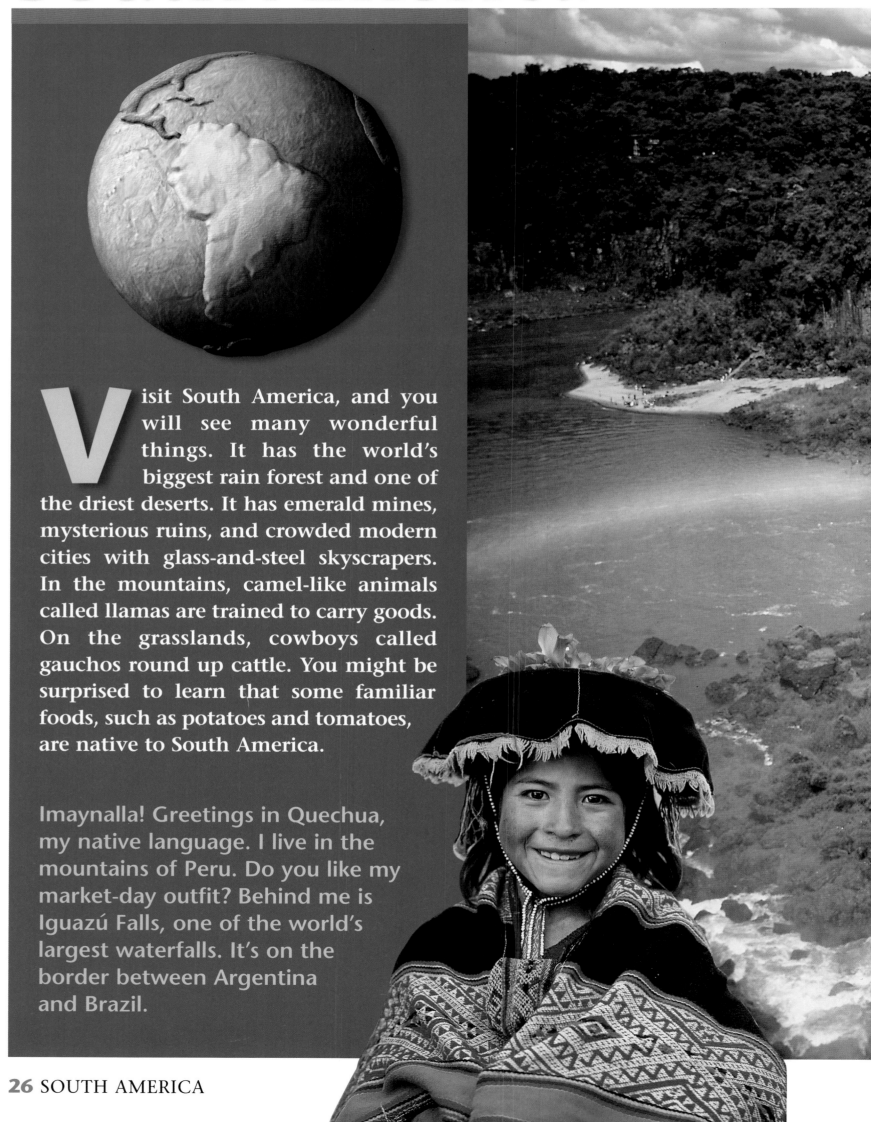

Visit South America, and you will see many wonderful things. It has the world's biggest rain forest and one of the driest deserts. It has emerald mines, mysterious ruins, and crowded modern cities with glass-and-steel skyscrapers. In the mountains, camel-like animals called llamas are trained to carry goods. On the grasslands, cowboys called gauchos round up cattle. You might be surprised to learn that some familiar foods, such as potatoes and tomatoes, are native to South America.

Imaynalla! Greetings in Quechua, my native language. I live in the mountains of Peru. Do you like my market-day outfit? Behind me is Iguazú Falls, one of the world's largest waterfalls. It's on the border between Argentina and Brazil.

# South America

## The Land

**Land regions** Snowcapped mountains called the Andes run along the whole west coast. Rain forests and grasslands cover much of the rest of the continent. The continent's driest desert lies between the Andes and the Pacific Ocean.

▲ Cold outside and hot inside, snow-covered **volcanoes** are scattered throughout the Andes.

► The world's largest water lilies grow in the **Amazon River**. They are big enough to hold a child.

**Water** The Amazon River carries more water than any other river in the world. More than 1,000 streams and rivers flow into it. Lake Titicaca, in the Andes, is the continent's largest lake.

**Climate** Much of South America is warm all year. The coldest places are in the Andes and at the continent's southern tip. Each year about 80 inches of rain falls in the rain forests.

**Plants** The Amazon rain forest has more kinds of plants than any other place in the world. Grasslands feed large herds of cattle and sheep.

▲ The **Atacama**, in northern Chile, is one of the world's driest deserts.

**Animals** Colorful macaws, noisy howler monkeys, and giant snakes live in the rain forest. Sure-footed llamas, huge birds called condors, and guinea pigs live in the Andes. The flightless rhea, which looks like an ostrich, roams the wide southern grasslands.

▼ Imagine living in a place where birds are as big and as colorful as these macaws. They live in the **rain forest**.

Lake Maracaibo

Orinoco River

A M A Z O N

Negro River

Amazon River

Amazon River

B A S I N

A N D E S

Lake Titicaca

Atacama Desert

Paraguay River

Paraná River

Iguazú Falls

Paraná River

Mt. Aconcagua
*Highest elevation in South America*

Río de la Plata

ATLANTIC

OCEAN

PACIFIC

OCEAN

Valdés Peninsula
*Lowest elevation in South America*

Falkland Islands

Strait of Magellan

EQUATOR

▲ Llamas are camel-like animals that live in the **Andes**.

## Map Key

Mountain

Desert

Rain forest

Grassland

Wetland

0      600 miles

0      900 kilometers

# South America

◄ Many bananas sold in the United States and other countries come from **Ecuador**. Check the label the next time you go to the store!

## The People

**Countries** South America has just 12 countries—French Guiana is not really a country because it belongs to France. All but two of these countries border an ocean. Can you find these two countries on the map?

**Cities** Most of the largest cities are near the oceans. São Paulo, in Brazil, is South America's biggest city. Bolivia has two capital cities: La Paz and Sucre.

▲ Long ago, the Inca people built the city of **Machu Picchu** high in the Andes of Peru.

**People** The native people came from the north long ago. Colonists came from Europe, especially from Spain and Portugal. They brought African slaves to work in the fields. Most people in South America are descendants of these three groups.

► Soccer is the most popular sport in South America. This famous player, known as Pelé, is from **Brazil**.

**Languages** Spanish and Portuguese are the continent's chief languages. Indians speak Quechua and other native languages.

**Products** South America's chief products include bananas, cattle, coffee, copper, emeralds, oranges, and sugar.

◄ This man plays his guitar to entertain people on the streets of **Buenos Aires**, in Argentina. Guitar music is popular in South America.

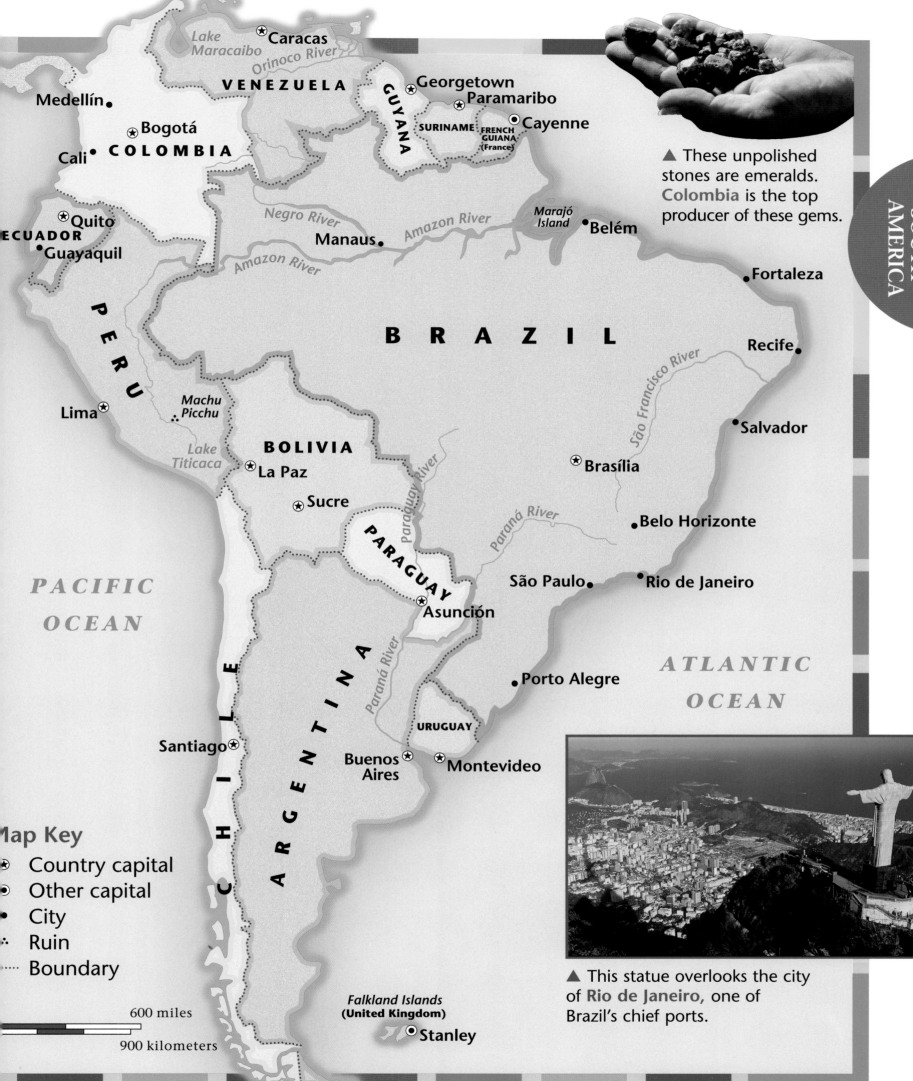

Medellín

Caracas

*Lake Maracaibo*
*Orinoco River*

**V E N E Z U E L A**

Georgetown
Paramaribo

**GUYANA**

SURINAME

FRENCH
GUIANA
(France)

Cayenne

⭐ Bogotá

**C O L O M B I A**

Cali

Quito

**ECUADOR**

Guayaquil

*Negro River*

Manaus

*Amazon River*

*Marajó Island*

Belém

▲ These unpolished
stones are emeralds.
**Colombia** is the top
producer of these gems.

*Amazon River*

Fortaleza

**B R A Z I L**

Recife

**P E R U**

*Machu Picchu*

*São Francisco River*

Lima

*Lake Titicaca*

**B O L I V I A**

⭐ La Paz

Salvador

⭐ Brasília

⭐ Sucre

Belo Horizonte

**P A R A G U A Y**

*Paraná River*

São Paulo

Rio de Janeiro

⭐ Asunción

**PACIFIC
OCEAN**

*Paraná River*

Porto Alegre

**ATLANTIC
OCEAN**

**A R G E N T I N A**

**URUGUAY**

Santiago

Buenos Aires

Montevideo

**C H I L E**

**Map Key**

⭐ Country capital

⊙ Other capital

• City

∴ Ruin

···· Boundary

600 miles

900 kilometers

*Falkland Islands*
(United Kingdom)

Stanley

▲ This statue overlooks the city
of **Rio de Janeiro,** one of
Brazil's chief ports.

# Europe

**T**ravel through the countryside in Europe and you might think you have wandered into the pages of a storybook. You'll see castles, cuckoo clocks, and cobblestone streets. But Europe is also one of the most modern continents. You can ride one of the world's fastest trains through a tunnel beneath the English Channel, watch sports cars being made in Italy, and visit famous museums in Paris. On a map Europe may look like it is part of Asia, but it is considered to be a separate continent.

Sveiks! I'm from Latvia, a country on the Baltic Sea. I am wearing a costume for a dance. Wouldn't you like to visit this town in Austria? It's on a lake high in the Alps, Europe's highest mountains.

# Europe

*Iceland*

**ATLANTIC OCEAN**

 **Land regions** Europe's most obvious feature is its coastline, cut with bays and peninsulas of every size. The Alps are high mountains that form a chain across much of southern Europe.

▲ People often try to climb the Matterhorn. It is one of the highest peaks in the Alps.

 **Water** Several large rivers flow across Europe. Some of the most important include the Danube, Rhine, Volga, and Rhône.

**Climate** Warm winds from the Atlantic Ocean help give most of Europe a mild climate. This climate plus plenty of rain makes much of Europe good for farming.

▲ Much of Europe is farmland. Fields of lavender grow in the mild climate east of the Rhône. Perfume is made from these flowers.

*Ireland*

*Grea Brita*

**Plants** Europe's largest forests are in the north. Cork and olive trees grow along the Mediterranean Sea.

**PYRENEES**

**IBERIAN PENINSULA**

M

 **Animals** Reindeer are common in the far north. Many kinds of goatlike animals live in the Alps. Robins, nightingales, and sparrows are among Europe's native birds.

0          600 miles

0          900 kilome

**AFRICA**

► This is a kind of wild goat called an ibex. It is one of many kinds of hooved animals that live in the Alps and other mountainous parts of the continent.

► Europe has many sandy beaches on the Mediterranean Sea. The most famous are along the coast, in Italy and France.

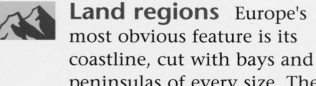

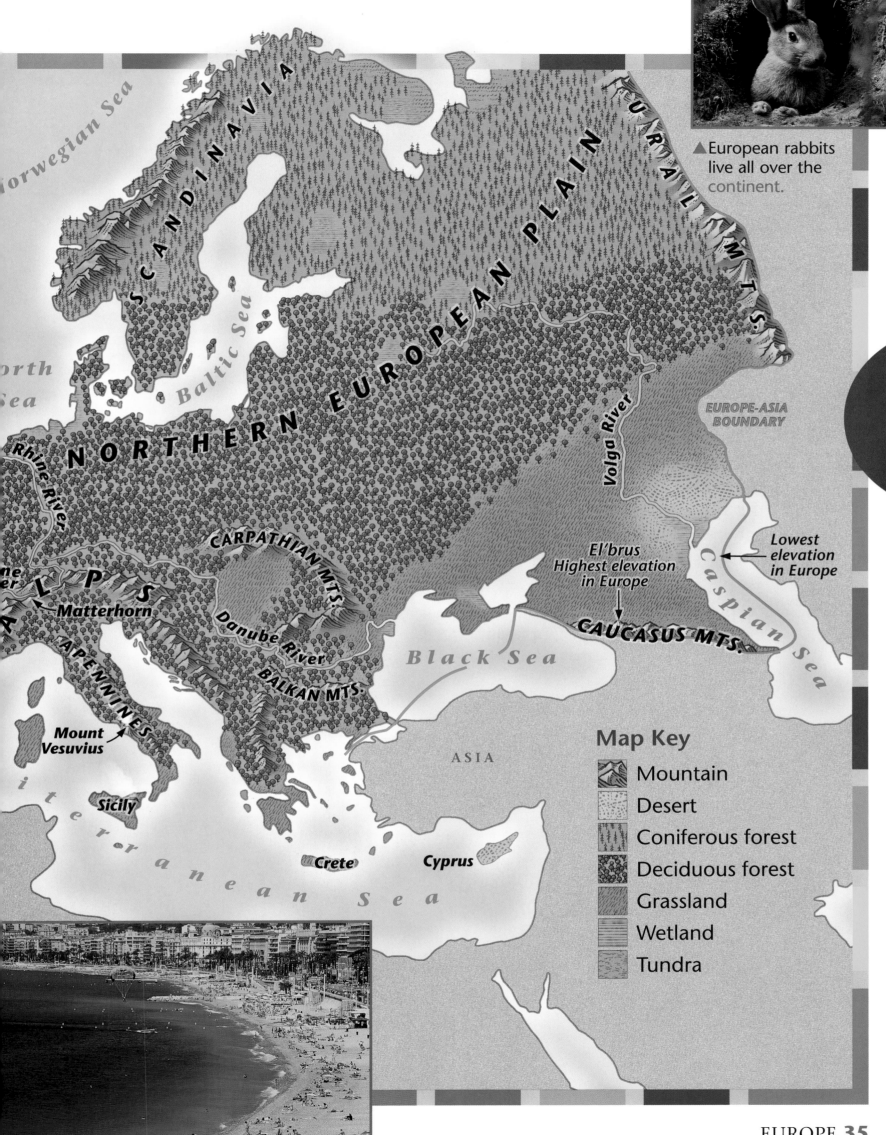

Norwegian Sea

North Sea

SCANDINAVIA

Baltic Sea

NORTHERN EUROPEAN PLAIN

URAL MTS.

Volga River

EUROPE-ASIA
BOUNDARY

Rhine River

*Seine River*

ALPS

Matterhorn

CARPATHIAN MTS.

Danube River

BALKAN MTS.

APENNINES

Mount
Vesuvius

Sicily

*Mediterranean Sea*

Crete

Cyprus

Black Sea

ASIA

El'brus
Highest elevation
in Europe

CAUCASUS MTS.

Caspian Sea

Lowest
elevation
in Europe

▲ European rabbits
live all over the
continent.

## Map Key

- Mountain
- Desert
- Coniferous forest
- Deciduous forest
- Grassland
- Wetland
- Tundra

# Europe

▲ St. Basil's is a famous Russian orthodox church. It is in **Moscow**, Russia's capital city.

## The People

**Countries** There are 44 countries in Europe. Even though most of Russia is in Asia *(see pages 48–49)*, the country is usually counted as being part of Europe. There are five island countries: Iceland, United Kingdom, Ireland, Malta, and Cyprus.

**Cities** Most cities in Europe are within a few hundred miles of the sea. London, in the United Kingdom, is Europe's largest city.

▲ Bagpipe music is popular in Scotland, which was once an independent country. Today, Scotland is part of the **United Kingdom**.

**People** There are many different ethnic groups in Europe—usually one main group for each country. More people live in cities than on farms.

**Languages** About 50 languages are spoken in Europe, including English, French, German, and Russian. Many Europeans speak more than one language.

**Products** Europe's chief products include iron, coal, petroleum, cars, machinery, wheat, fruit, and olives.

▼ People gather to hear the pope speak in **Vatican City**, the world's smallest country. It is surrounded by the city of Rome.

◀ The euro is currently the official money in **Italy** and 11 other members of the European Union *(see page 61)*.

Reykjavík ⊛ **ICELAND**

*ATLANTIC OCEAN*

*Faroe Islands (Denmark)*

Or Isl

Edinburgh

**IRELAND**
Dublin ⊛

**UNIT**

**KINGD**

London

*English Chan*

**FR**

Borde

*PORTUGAL*

Lisbon ⊛

⊛ Madrid

**ANDORRA**

**SPAIN**

Seville

*Balearic (Spai*

**GIBRALTAR** (U.K)

A F

## Map Key

- ✷ Country capital
- • City
- ⋯⋯ Boundary

*Norwegian Sea*

EUROPE-ASIA BOUNDARY

0 _____ 600 miles
0 _____ 900 kilometers

**N O R W A Y**
**S W E D E N**
**F I N L A N D**

tland nds

Oslo ✷
Stockholm ✷
Helsinki ✷
• St. Petersburg

✷ Tallinn
**ESTONIA**

**R U S S I A**

orth Sea

Riga ✷
**LATVIA**

✷ Moscow

**DENMARK**
Copenhagen ✷

Baltic Sea

**LITHUANIA**

KALININGRAD (Russia)
✷ Vilnius

THERLANDS
• Hamburg
✷ Amsterdam
ssels

✷ Minsk

**BELARUS**

**KAZAKHSTAN**

Volga River

Berlin •
Warsaw ✷

GIUM

**GERMANY**
**POLAND**

Rhine River

• Kraków

✷ Kiev

Volgograd •

MBOURG

Prague ✷
**CZECH REPUBLIC**

**U K R A I N E**

Danube River

**SLOVAKIA**

Vienna ✷ ✷ Bratislava

**MOLDOVA**

ern
**SWITZERLAND**
LIECHTENSTEIN
**AUSTRIA**

✷ Budapest
**HUNGARY**

Chişinău ✷

Caspian Sea

**SLOVENIA**
Ljubljana ✷
**CROATIA**
✷ Zagreb

**ROMANIA**

**GEORGIA**
T'bilisi ✷
Baku •

SAN MARINO
**BOSNIA AND HERZEGOVINA**
✷ Belgrade

Danube River

✷ Bucharest

**AZERBAIJAN**

MONACO

Sarajevo ✷
**SERBIA AND MONTENEGRO**

*Black Sea*

**ITALY**

orsica ance)

Podgorica ✷
**BULGARIA**
✷ Sofia

VATICAN CITY
✷ Rome
• Naples

Tirana •
✷ Skopje
**MACEDONIA**

Istanbul •
✷ Ankara

*Sardinia (Italy)*

**ALBANIA**

**G R E E C E**
**T U R K E Y**

ASIA

Sicily

✷ Athens

**MALTA**
✷ Valletta

*Crete*

CYPRUS
✷ Nicosia

d i t e r r a n e a n   S e a

◀ Inspectors examine cheese at a market in the **Netherlands**. Europe is famous for its cheeses.

▲ These girls are dressed for a festival in **Spain**. Such celebrations keep folk traditions alive.

# Africa

Elephants lumber across the grasslands. Gorillas groom each other in a mountain forest. Hippopotamuses swim in a river. Amazing animals are just part of what Africa has to offer. You can also visit a busy, modern city such as Nairobi, in Kenya; see how diamonds are mined in South Africa; shop in colorful, outdoor markets; take a sailboat ride past temples on the Nile; and climb some of the world's highest sand dunes in Earth's biggest hot desert. It's called the Sahara.

Jambo! Beautiful beadwork is part of a Masai girl's traditional dress. I live in Kenya where elephants like these roam free. In the distance stands Kilimanjaro, the highest peak in Africa. You can find it on the map on the next page.

# Africa

## The Land

**Land regions** Most of Africa is a high, flat plateau. There are few mountains. The Sahara and the Kalahari are among its largest deserts. Rain forests grow along the Equator. Grasslands cover most of the rest of the continent.

**Water** The Nile and the Congo are Africa's longest rivers. Most of Africa's largest lakes are in the Great Rift Valley.

◄ Zebras live on grasslands called savannas near the Equator. No two zebras have exactly the same pattern of stripes.

**Climate** The Equator crosses Africa's middle, so many places on the continent are hot. It is always wet in the rain forest. Much of the rest of Africa has wet and dry seasons.

**Plants** Thorny trees called acacias provide food and shade for grassland animals. Date palms grow around desert water holes. Mahogany is one of many kinds of rain forest trees.

▲ Giant sand dunes in the Sahara tower high above this jeep. This huge desert covers most of northern Africa.

**Animals** Some of Africa's most familiar animals are shown here. There are also lions and many kinds of antelopes. Lemurs live on Madagascar, Africa's largest island.

◄ Hot springs boil on the shores of a lake in the Great Rift Valley. This is actually a series of valleys that run through the eastern part of the continent.

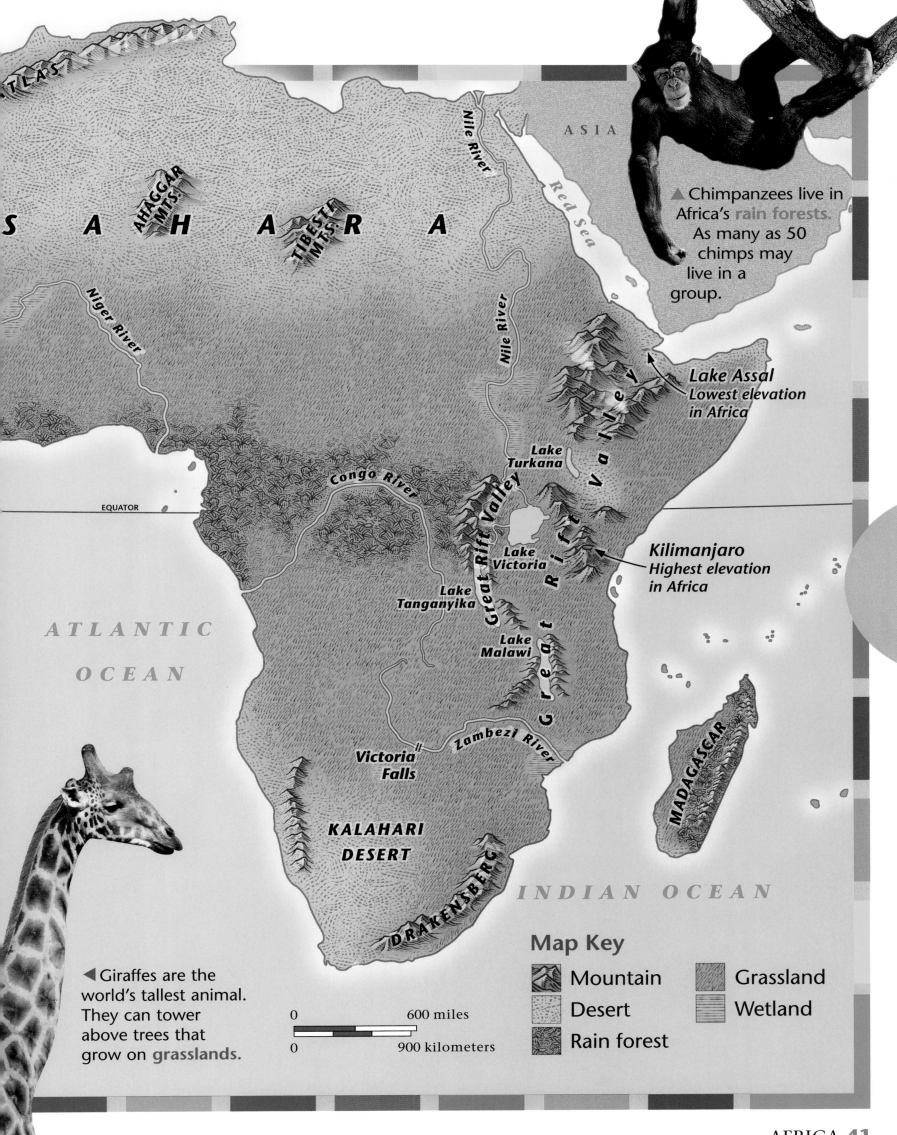

ATLAS

S A H A R A

AHAGGAR MTS.

TIBESTI MTS.

Niger River

Nile River

Nile River

ASIA

Red Sea

▲ Chimpanzees live in Africa's **rain forests**. As many as 50 chimps may live in a group.

Lake Assal
*Lowest elevation in Africa*

Congo River

EQUATOR

Lake Turkana

Great Rift Valley

Lake Victoria

Lake Tanganyika

Kilimanjaro
*Highest elevation in Africa*

Great Rift Valley

Lake Malawi

ATLANTIC OCEAN

Zambezi River

Victoria Falls

KALAHARI DESERT

DRAKENSBERG

MADAGASCAR

INDIAN OCEAN

◄ Giraffes are the world's tallest animal. They can tower above trees that grow on **grasslands**.

0    600 miles
0    900 kilometers

**Map Key**

Mountain      Grassland

Desert        Wetland

Rain forest

AFRICA

AFRICA **41**

# Africa

◀ These boys are picking dates. **Algeria** is a leading producer of this fruit.

*Canary Islands (Spain)*

**WESTERN SAHARA (Morocco)**

**Countries**   Most of Africa's 53 countries were ruled by European countries from the late 1800s to the 1960s. Sudan has the most land. Nigeria has the most people.

**Cities**   Cairo and Kinshasa are Africa's biggest cities. Both are on large rivers near the coast. More people live in villages and on farms than in cities.

▲ **Harare** is Zimbabwe's capital. It is one of the many modern cities in Africa.

MAURITA

Nouakchott
**CAPE VERDE**
Praia    Dakar    **SENEGAL**
Banjul
**GAMBIA**    Bama
Bissau
**GUINEA-BISSAU**    **GUINE**
Conakry
Freetown
**SIERRA LEONE**    **LIB**
Monrovia

**People**   People in northern Africa's largest countries are mostly Arabs. Most black Africans live south of the Sahara in hundreds of different ethnic groups. Most Europeans live in South Africa.

**Languages**   Arabic is spoken in the north. Native languages are spoken south of the Sahara. English, French, and Portuguese are the main European languages.

▲ Small sailboats called feluccas carry goods to trade along the **Nile**. This river is the longest in Africa.

**Products**   Africa is a leading producer of cocoa beans, gold, diamonds, and petroleum.

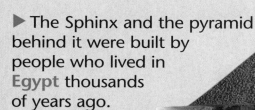

▶ The Sphinx and the pyramid behind it were built by people who lived in **Egypt** thousands of years ago.

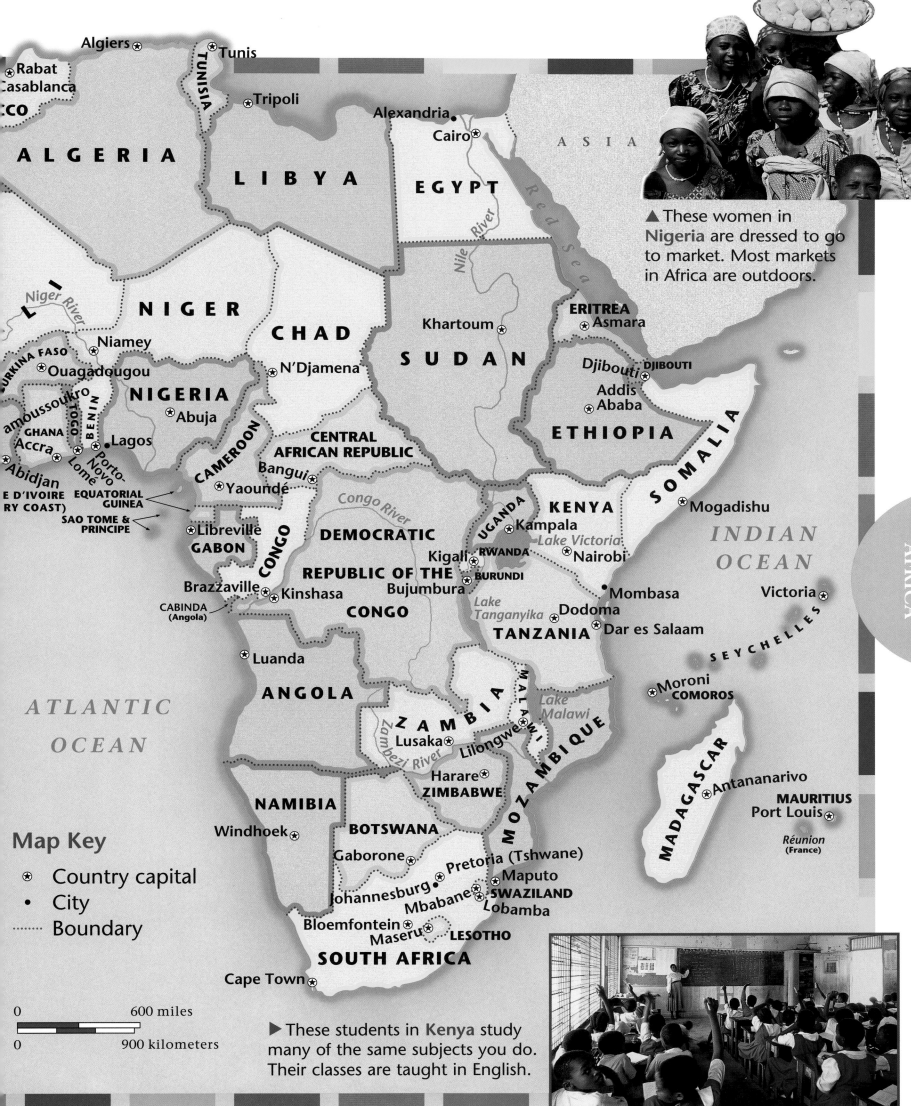

Algiers ⊛

Tunis ⊛
TUNISIA

⊛ Rabat
Casablanca
CO

⊛ Tripoli

Alexandria •
Cairo ⊛

ASIA

ALGERIA

LIBYA

EGYPT

Red Sea

▲ These women in **Nigeria** are dressed to go to market. Most markets in Africa are outdoors.

Niger River

NIGER

CHAD

Khartoum ⊛

ERITREA
⊛ Asmara

BURKINA FASO
⊛ Ouagadougou

⊛ Niamey

N'Djamena ⊛

SUDAN

Djibouti ⊛ DJIBOUTI

amoussoukro
TOGO
BENIN
GHANA
Accra ⊛

NIGERIA
⊛ Abuja

Addis
Ababa ⊛

⊛ Abidjan
E D'IVOIRE
RY COAST)
Lome
Porto-
Novo
• Lagos

ETHIOPIA

EQUATORIAL
GUINEA

CAMEROON

CENTRAL
AFRICAN REPUBLIC

SAO TOME &
PRINCIPE

Bangui ⊛

⊛ Yaoundé

Congo River

UGANDA
⊛ Kampala

KENYA

SOMALIA

⊛ Mogadishu

⊛ Libreville
GABON

CONGO

DEMOCRATIC

Kigali ⊛
RWANDA
BURUNDI

Lake Victoria
⊛ Nairobi

INDIAN
OCEAN

Brazzaville ⊛
CABINDA
(Angola)

REPUBLIC OF THE
⊛ Kinshasa
CONGO

Bujumbura ⊛

Lake
Tanganyika

Dodoma ⊛

• Mombasa

⊛ Victoria

TANZANIA
• Dar es Salaam

SEYCHELLES

⊛ Luanda

ANGOLA

ATLANTIC
OCEAN

ZAMBIA
Lusaka ⊛

Zambezi River

MALAWI

Lake
Malawi

⊛ Moroni
COMOROS

Lilongwe ⊛

MADAGASCAR

NAMIBIA

Harare ⊛
ZIMBABWE

MOZAMBIQUE

⊛ Antananarivo

MAURITIUS
Port Louis ⊛

BOTSWANA

Réunion
(France)

**Map Key**

⊛  Country capital

•  City

······  Boundary

Windhoek ⊛

Gaborone ⊛

Pretoria (Tshwane) ⊛
Johannesburg •
Maputo ⊛
Mbabane ⊛ SWAZILAND
Lobamba

Bloemfontein •
Maseru ⊛ LESOTHO

0 ———— 600 miles
0 ———— 900 kilometers

SOUTH AFRICA

Cape Town ⊛

▶ These students in **Kenya** study many of the same subjects you do. Their classes are taught in English.

# Asia

**A**sia is Earth's largest continent. Mount Everest, the world's highest mountain, is here. Asia also has some of the world's longest rivers, biggest deserts, and thickest forests. The Dead Sea is the lowest place on the continent. It is called "dead" because its water is too salty for fish and other animals to live in. More people live in Asia than anywhere else. The world's very first cities were built along river valleys in Asia long, long ago.

Namasté! I'm from Nepal. In mountainous countries like mine, farmers cut wide steps called terraces into hillsides to make flat land to grow crops on. Rice grows on these terraces in Indonesia.

# Asia

## The Land

**Land regions** Much of Asia is a rolling plain covered by grasslands, forests, and tundra. The Himalaya and other high mountains stretch across the south. Deserts cover much of southwestern and central Asia.

**Water** Asia has huge rivers and lakes. The Yangtze is the longest river. The Caspian Sea (partly in Europe) is the world's largest saltwater lake. Lake Baikal is the world's deepest lake.

**Climate** Northern Asia has long, icy winters and short cool summers. Most of southern Asia is warm year-round with heavy summer rains.

**Plants** Areas of coniferous forest called taiga stretch across the north. The central grasslands are known as the Steppes. Rain forests grow in the southeast.

**Animals** Tigers, giant pandas, and cobras live in the wild only in Asia.

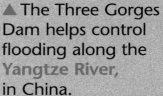

▲ A climber stands at the top of a peak in the **Himalaya**. Mount Everest rises in front of him.

▲ The Three Gorges Dam helps control flooding along the **Yangtze River**, in China.

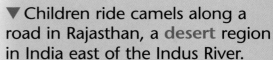

*Mediterranean Sea*
*Black Sea*
*CAUCASUS MTS.*
*Caspian Sea*

Dead Sea
*Lowest elevation in Asia*

*Persian Gulf*

**ARABIAN PENINSULA**

*Arabi Sea*

| 0 | 600 miles |
|---|---|
| 0 | 900 kilometer |

A F R I C A

▼ Children ride camels along a road in Rajasthan, a **desert** region in India east of the Indus River.

ARCTIC OCEAN

Bering Sea

EUROPE

EUROPE-ASIA BOUNDARY

URAL MOUNTAINS

THE STEPPES

Aral Sea

Ob River

Irtysh River

Yenisey River

Lena River

Amur River

Lake Baikal

TIAN SHAN

GOBI

Yellow River

Indus River

HIMALAYA

Brahmaputra

Ganges River

Mt. Everest
Highest elevation
in Asia

Yangtze River

Mekong River

Bay
of
Bengal

PACIFIC
OCEAN

South China Sea

New
Guinea

EQUATOR

Borneo

Sumatra

INDIAN
OCEAN

AUSTRALIA

▲ Boys play in a
**rain forest** in Indonesia.
These forests grow
throughout Southeast
Asia, where winds
called monsoons

## Map Key

Mountain

Desert

Coniferous forest

Deciduous forest

Rain forest

Grassland

Wetland

Tundra

▼ A herder leads his reindeer
past taiga, a kind of
**coniferous forest.** Forests
like this are found throughout
northern Asia.

▶ Giant pandas live only in
leafy bamboo forests that
grow on **mountains** in
southwestern China.

ASIA

ASIA **47**

# Asia

## The People

**Countries** Asia has 46 countries. China is the largest country with boundaries entirely in Asia. Russia takes up the most area, but it is counted as part of Europe *(see pages 36–37)*. Indonesia is Asia's largest island country.

**Cities** Much of Asia is too high, too dry, or too cold for people to live in. Most cities are near the coast or along busy rivers. Tokyo, in Japan, is the largest city.

**People** Asia has more people than any other continent. Each ethnic group has its own language, customs, and appearance. Most people work as farmers or fishermen.

**Languages** So many languages are spoken in Asia that even neighbors can have trouble understanding each other. India, for example, has 16 official languages!

**Products** Asia's chief products include rice, wheat, petroleum, cotton, rubber, tea, motor vehicles, and computers.

▲ **Hong Kong** is one of Asia's busiest trading centers. It is a special province of China.

◄ This boy in **Shanghai** draws symbols used in writing the Chinese language. Each symbol stands for a word or an idea.

▼ This young boy works in a spice market. In **India** people mix lots of spices together to make a strong flavor called curry.

► This masked dancer is from Bali. Bali is one of more than 3,000 islands that make up the country of **Indonesia**.

EUROPE

Istanbul
Ankara
T'bilisi
ARMENIA
Yerevan
LEBANON
Beirut SYRIA
Jerusalem Damascus
ISRAEL Amman
JORDAN
Baghdad Tehra
IRAQ
KUWAIT
Kuwa
SAUDI
BAHRAIN
Riyadh QATAR
Doha
ARABIA
UNITED A
EMIRA
Mu
Sanaa
YEMEN O M

TURKEY
GEORGIA
Mediterranean Sea
Black Sea
Red Sea
AFRICA

0        600 miles
0        900 kilomete

ARCTIC OCEAN

Bering
Sea

Novaya
Zemlya

North
Land

New Siberian
Islands

Sakhalin

PACIFIC
OCEAN

► Water buffaloes, like
this one in Vietnam,
are used for pulling
plows in rice fields.
Rice is Asia's most
important food crop.

EUROPE-ASIA
BOUNDARY

scow

R U S S I A

Ob' River

Irtysh River

Yenisey River

Lena River

Amur River

Lake
Baikal

KAZAKHSTAN

Astana ⊛

Aral
Sea

UZBEKISTAN

MENISTAN

bat

Tashkent

Bishkek ⊛

KYRGYZSTAN

Dushanbe

TAJIKISTAN

AFGHANISTAN

Kabul ⊛

Islamabad ⊛

PAKISTAN

rachi

Ulaanbaatar ⊛

M O N G O L I A

Harbin •

Shenyang •

Beijing ⊛

Yellow River

C H I N A

Xi'an •

Chengdu •

Yangtze River

Chongqing •

Wuhan •

Shanghai •

NORTH
KOREA

Pyongyang ⊛

⊛ Seoul

SOUTH
KOREA

JAPAN

⊛ Tokyo
• Yokohama

Map Key

⊛ Country capital

• City

........ Boundary

Delhi •

New Delhi ⊛

N E P A L

Thimphu ⊛

⊛ BHUTAN

Brahmaputra River

Kathmandu •

Ganges River

Mekong River

BANGLADESH

Kolkata
(Calcutta) •

⊛ Dhaka

I N D I A

Mumbai •
(Bombay)

Bay
of
Bengal

MYANMAR
(BURMA)

Yangon •
(Rangoon)

Bangkok ⊛

THAILAND

LAOS

⊛ Vientiane

• Hanoi

Hainan

VIETNAM

Taipei •

TAIWAN
The People's Republic of China
claims Taiwan as its 23rd province.

• Hong Kong

Philippine Sea

⊛ Manila

PHILIPPINES

South China Sea

Chennai •
(Madras)

SRI LANKA

MALDIVES

Male ⊛

• Colombo

CAMBODIA

Phnom ⊛
Penh

• Ho Chi
Minh City

Bandar Seri Begawan

BRUNEI ⊛

MALAYSIA

New
Guinea

MALAYSIA

Kuala Lumpur ⊛

SINGAPORE

Sumatra

Borneo

Sulawesi
(Celebes)

I N D O N E S I A

INDIAN
OCEAN

⊛ Jakarta
Java

Bali

Dili •

TIMOR-LESTE
(EAST TIMOR)

AUSTRALIA

► This pipeline carries
oil from Saudi Arabia
to tanker ships in
the Persian Gulf.

# Australia

**A**ustralia is a most unusual place. It is Earth's smallest and flattest continent and one of the driest, too. It has many large deserts. "Aussies," as Australians like to call themselves, nicknamed their continent "the land down under." That's because the entire continent lies south of, or "under," the Equator. Most Australians live in cities along the coast. But Australia also has huge cattle and sheep ranches. Many ranch children live far from school. They get their lessons by mail or from the Internet or the radio. Their doctors even visit by airplane!

Awa! I'm an Aborigine, one of Australia's native people. My face is painted for a special ceremony. The giant rock behind me is sacred to my people. We call it Uluru. You might know it as Ayers Rock.

# Australia

## The Land

▲ Limestone towers rise above a **desert** in Western Australia. Desert covers much of the continent.

**Land regions** The Great Dividing Range stretches along the east coast and into Tasmania. Most of the rest of Australia is a plateau covered by grasslands and deserts.

**Water** The Darling, Australia's longest river, is dry during part of the year. So is Lake Eyre, the continent's largest lake. Water lies underground in the Great Artesian Basin.

**Climate** Most of the continent is very dry. Winds called monsoons bring heavy seasonal rains to the northern coast. Southern Australia can be cold in winter, but much of the continent is warm year-round.

▲ A school of fish swims past the **Great Barrier Reef.** It is the world's largest coral reef.

**Plants** Eucalyptuses, or gum trees, and acacias are the most common kinds of plants. They grow throughout Australia.

**Animals** Australia has many unusual mammals. Koalas and kangaroos raise their young in pouches on their bellies. The platypus is a mammal that has a bill like a duck's. Its babies hatch from eggs.

▶ Koalas live only in **eucalyptus forests.** At one time koalas almost became extinct. Now they are protected by strict laws.

▲ Moss covers trees and logs in a forest in **Tasmania.** This island has a much wetter climate than most of mainland Australia.

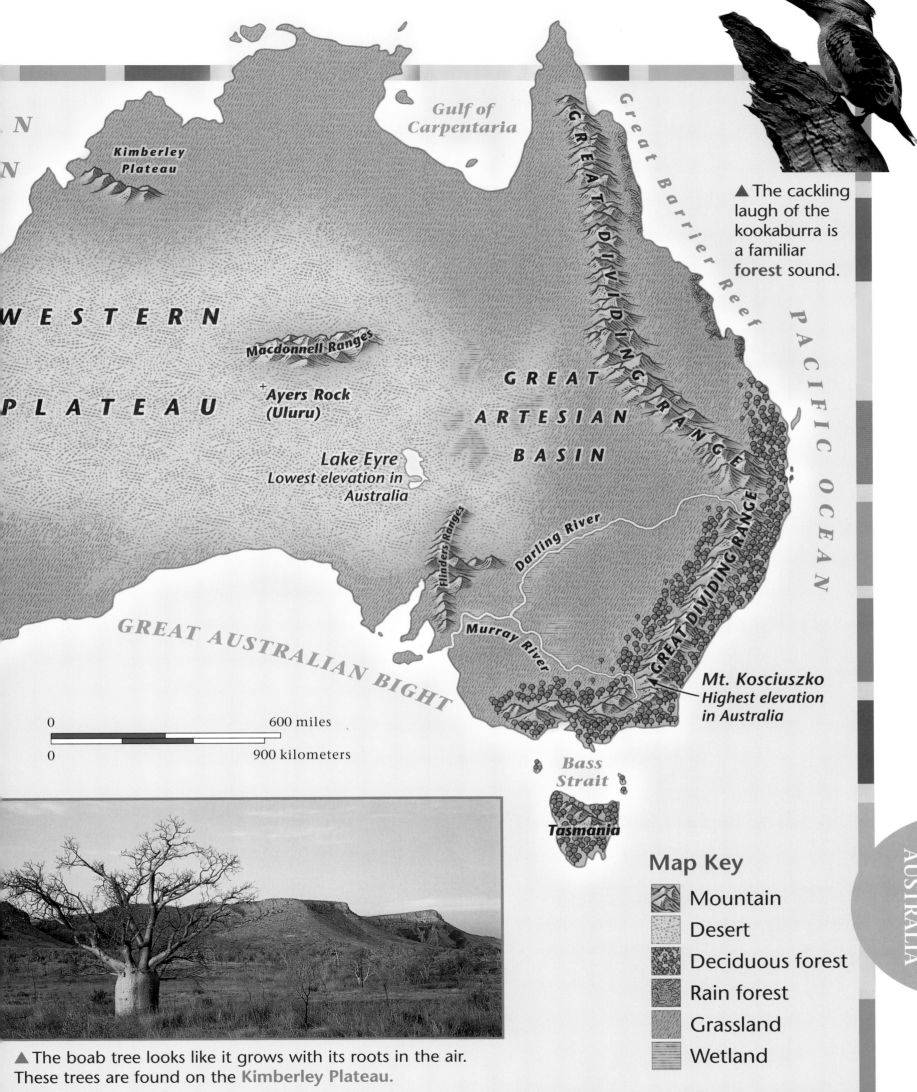

Gulf of
Carpentaria

Kimberley
Plateau

WESTERN

PLATEAU

Macdonnell Ranges

+Ayers Rock
(Uluru)

Lake Eyre
*Lowest elevation in
Australia*

Flinders Ranges

GREAT
ARTESIAN
BASIN

GREAT DIVIDING RANGE

Great Barrier Reef

PACIFIC OCEAN

Darling River

Murray River

GREAT DIVIDING RANGE

GREAT AUSTRALIAN BIGHT

Mt. Kosciuszko
*Highest elevation
in Australia*

▲ The cackling
laugh of the
kookaburra is
a familiar
forest sound.

0                    600 miles

0                    900 kilometers

Bass
Strait

Tasmania

**Map Key**

Mountain

Desert

Deciduous forest

Rain forest

Grassland

Wetland

▲ The boab tree looks like it grows with its roots in the air.
These trees are found on the **Kimberley Plateau**.

AUSTRALIA

# Australia

## The People

**Countries** Australia is the only continent that is also a country. It is divided into six states—including Tasmania—and two territories.

▲ Surfing is a popular sport in Australia. There is a city near **Brisbane** named Surfers Paradise.

**Cities** All the chief cities are near the coast—even the capital, Canberra. Sydney has the most people, followed by Melbourne, Brisbane, and Perth.

◀ A monorail zips people around **Sydney.** The city is a busy port and the capital of the state of New South Wales.

**People** Most Australians are descendants of settlers from the United Kingdom and Ireland. Aborigines came to Australia from Asia some 40,000 years ago.

▼ Cafés, like this one, can be hundreds of miles apart in the **outback.** Few people live in this dry, central region.

**Languages** English is the main language of Australia. Aborigines speak some 250 different languages.

**Products** Australia's chief products include wool, beef, wheat, fruits, bauxite, coal, uranium, and diamonds. Most manufactured goods are imported.

◀ The world's largest cultured pearls are grown in oyster beds along Australia's **northern coast.**

IN
OC

Po
Hedla

Perth●

Darwin

*Gulf of Carpentaria*

NORTHERN TERRITORY

Cairns

▲ This family lives on a farm in **Queensland**, where wheat is an important product.

Townsville

Mount Isa

*PACIFIC OCEAN*

Mackay

Alice Springs

QUEENSLAND

Rockhampton

A U S T R A L I A

WESTERN AUSTRALIA

SOUTH AUSTRALIA

*Lake Eyre*

Brisbane

Gold Coast

*Darling River*

NEW SOUTH WALES

GREAT AUSTRALIAN BIGHT

Adelaide

*KANGAROO I.*

*Murray River*

Sydney

Canberra

AUSTRALIAN CAPITAL TERRITORY

VICTORIA

Melbourne

*PACIFIC OCEAN*

Map Key
◎ Country capital
○ State or territory capital
• City
···· State boundary

0                    600 miles
0                    900 kilometers

TASMANIA

Hobart

▼ Australia has huge cattle farms called stations. Some of the largest are in **Western Australia**.

◀ This Aborigine is playing a wooden pipe called a didgeridoo. Many of Australia's native people live in the **Northern Territory**.

# Antarctica

**B**rrrr! Antarctica takes first place as the coldest continent. It is the land around the South Pole. An ice cap two miles thick in places covers most of the land. Temperatures rarely get above freezing. It is also the only continent that has no countries. It has research stations but no cities. The only people are scientists, explorers, and tourists. Everyone stays for awhile, then goes home. The largest land animals that live here year-round are a few kinds of insects!

Chances are you'll see more penguins than people if you visit Antarctica. Like the whale behind them, Penguins depend on the ocean for food. They come ashore to have their babies.

# Antarctica

## The Land

**Land regions** The Transantarctic Mountains divide the continent into two parts. East Antarctica, where the South Pole is located, is mostly a high, flat, icy area. West Antarctica is mountainous. Vinson Massif is the highest peak.

**Water** Most of Earth's fresh water is frozen in Antarctica's ice cap. The ice breaks off when it meets the sea. These huge floating chunks of ice in the ocean are called icebergs.

**Climate** Antarctica is windy and dry. It gets very little snow. Most of the snow that falls turns to ice. The thick ice cap has built up over millions of years.

**Plants** Billions of tiny plants live in the surrounding oceans. Mosses and lichens grow on the land.

**Animals** Penguins and other seabirds nest on the coast. Whales, seals, and tiny shrimplike animals called krill live in the oceans.

◄ Jellyfish grow very large under the **sea ice** around the continent. Here they have few enemies so they live a long time.

▲ This strong-sided ship is an icebreaker. It cuts a path through ice in the **Ross Sea**.

*ATLANTIC OCEAN*

▲ Few people have ever climbed Antarctica's mountains. This one is called "the Razor." It is near the coast in **Queen Maud Land**.

▼ Elephant seals come ashore along the rocky **Antarctic Peninsula** during the summer.

## Inset map

ATLANTIC
OCEAN

AFRICA

UTH
RICA

INDIAN
OCEAN

ANTARCTICA

ACIFIC
OCEAN

AUSTRALIA

## Main map

INDIAN OCEAN

QUEEN MAUD LAND

ENDERBY LAND

Weddell Sea

RONNE ICE SHELF

Berkner Island

INSULA

ELLSWORTH LAND

Vinson Massif
Highest elevation
in Antarctica

WEST ANTARCTICA

ANTARCTICA

+ South Pole

EAST ANTARCTICA

Lowest elevation
in Antarctica

TRANSANTARCTIC MOUNTAINS

MARIE BYRD LAND

SHACKLETON ICE SHELF

WILKES LAND

ROSS ICE SHELF

Roosevelt Island

Dry Valleys

Ross Island

Mount Erebus

ndsen

PACIFIC OCEAN

Ross Sea

INDIAN OCEAN

▼ The **Dry Valleys** are bare, rocky places with ice-covered lakes. The tents belong to scientists who say this region looks like Mars.

## Map Key

Mountain

Research station

Ice cap

Glacier

0   400 miles

0   600 kilometers

ANTARCTICA **59**

# World at a Glance

## Land
### The Continents, Largest to Smallest

1. **Asia:** 17,213,300 sq mi *(44,579,000 sq km)*
2. **Africa:** 11,609,000 sq mi *(30,065,000 sq km)*
3. **North America:** 9,449,500 sq mi *(24,474,000 sq km)*
4. **South America:** 6,880,500 sq mi *(17,819,000 sq km)*
5. **Antarctica:** 5,100,400 sq mi *(13,209,000 sq km)*
6. **Europe:** 3,837,400 sq mi *(9,938,000 sq km)*
7. **Australia:** 2,969,906 sq mi *(7,692,024 sq km)*

## Water
### The Oceans, Largest to Smallest

1. **Pacific Ocean:** 65,436,246 sq mi *(169,479,100 sq km)*
2. **Atlantic Ocean:** 35,338,040 sq mi *(91,526,400 sq km)*
3. **Indian Ocean:** 29,829,823 sq mi *(74,694,800 sq km)*
4. **Arctic Ocean:** 5,390,024 sq mi *(13,960,100 sq km)*

### Highest, Longest, Largest
The numbers below show locations on the map.

❶ **Highest Mountain on a Continent**
   Mt. Everest, in Asia: 29,035 ft *(8,850 m)*
❷ **Largest Island**
   Greenland, in the Atlantic Ocean:
   840,065 sq mi *(2,175,600 sq km)*
❸ **Largest Ocean**
   Pacific Ocean: 65,436,246 sq mi
   *(169,479,100 sq km)*
❹ **Longest River**
   Nile River, in Africa: 4,241 mi
   *(6,825 km)*
❺ **Largest Freshwater Lake**
   Lake Superior, in North America:
   31,701 sq mi *(82,100 sq km)*
❻ **Largest Saltwater Lake**
   Caspian Sea, in Europe-Asia:
   143,254 sq mi *(371,000 sq km)*
❼ **Largest Hot Desert**
   Sahara, in Africa: 3,475,000 sq mi
   *(9,000,000 sq km)*
❽ **Largest Cold Desert**
   Antarctica: 5,100,400 sq mi *(13,209,000 sq km)*

## People

*More than 6 billion people live on the Earth—enough to fill a string of school buses that would circle the Equator almost 24 times! More than half the world's people live in Asia.*

### Five Largest Countries by Number of People

1. **China, Asia:** 1,300,060,000 people
2. **India, Asia:** 1,086,640,000 people
3. **United States, North America:** 293,633,000 people
4. **Indonesia, Asia:** 218,746,000 people
5. **Brazil, South America:** 179,091,000 people

### Five Largest Cities* by Number of People

1. **Tokyo, Japan (Asia):** 12,360,000 people
2. **Mumbai, India (Asia):** 11,914,400 people
3. **São Paulo, Brazil (South America):** 10,434,300 people
4. **Moscow, Russia (Europe):** 10,101,500 people
5. **Delhi, India (Asia):** 9,817,400 people

*Figures are for city proper, not metropolitan area

# Glossary

**bauxite** a substance mined from the Earth that is the chief source of aluminum

**capital city** a place where a country's government is located

**city** a settled place where people work in jobs other than farming

**coral reef** a stony formation in warm, shallow ocean water that is made up of the skeletons of tiny sea animals called corals

**country** a place that has boundaries, a name, a flag, and a government that is the highest worldly authority over the land and the people who live there

**environment** the world around you, including people, cities, beliefs, plants and animals, air, water—everything

**ethnic group** people who share a common ancestry, language, beliefs, and traditions

**European Union** an organization of 25 European countries (Austria,* Belgium,* Cyprus, Czech Republic, Denmark, Estonia, Finland,* France,* Germany,* Greece,* Hungary, Ireland,* Italy,* Latvia, Lithuania, Luxembourg,* Malta, Netherlands,* Poland, Portugal,* Slovakia, Slovenia, Spain,* Sweden, and the United Kingdom)

**glacier** a large, slow-moving mass of ice; glaciers that cover huge areas are called ice caps

**lemur** an animal related to monkeys that is active at night and lives mostly in forests on Madagascar, in Africa

**lichen** a plantlike organism that is part alga and part fungus and that usually lives where few plants can survive

*The euro is the country's official currency.

**mosses** nonflowering, low-growing green plants that grow on rocks and trees throughout the world

**outback** the name Australians use for the dry interior region of their country where few people live

**plains** large areas of mainly flat land often covered with grasses

**province** a unit of government similar to a state

**state** a unit of government that takes up a specific area within a country, as in one of the 50 large political units in the United States

**Steppes** a Russian name for the grasslands that stretch from eastern Europe into Asia

**taiga** a Russian word for the scattered, coniferous forests that grow in cold, northern regions

## Pronunciations

*Note: Syllables printed in all capital letters should be accented.*

**Aborigine** ah buh RIJ uh nee

**Ayers** ARZ

**Baikal** by KALL

**bauxite** BAWK site

**boab** BO ab

**Buenos Aires** bway nus AR eez

**didgeridoo** DIH juh ree doo

**eucalyptus** you kuh LIP tus

**Eyre** AR

**felucca** fuh LOO kuh

**Harare** hah RAH ray

**Himalaya** him AHL yah

**Kalahari** ka luh HAR ee

**Kilimanjaro** kih luh mun JAR o

**Kinshasa** kin SHAH suh

**koala** kuh WAH luh

**Latvia** LAT vee uh

**lichen** LIE kun

**Liechtenstein** LIKT un shtine

**Maasai** MAH sigh

**Monaco** MAH nuh ko

**Nigeria** nigh JIR ee uh

**Quechua** KEH chuh wuh

**Rio de Janeiro** REE oo dee zha NAY roo

**San Marino** san muh REE no

**Sudan** soo DAN

**Sumatra** suh MAH truh

**taiga** TIE guh

**Tasmania** taz MAY nee uh

**Uluru** oo LOO roo

**Yangtze** yang SEE

**Zambezi** zam BEE zee

**Zimbabwe** zim BAH bway

## Greetings in Native Languages

**awa** AH wuh
*an Australian Aborigine word for a friendly "hello"*

**imaynalla** ee my NAH yuh
*"greetings" in Quechua, a Native American language of South America*

**kha hay** kaw HAY
*"greetings" in Crow, a Native American language of the United States*

**namasté** no mo STAY
*"I salute you" in Nepalese, the language of Nepal, in Asia*

**sveiks** SVAYKS
*"hello" in Latvian, the language of Latvia, a country in eastern Europe*

**jambo** JAM bo
*"hello" in Swahili, a language spoken throughout East Africa*

# Index

Pictures and the text that describes them have their page numbers printed in **bold** type.

## National Geographic Society

John M. Fahey, Jr.
*President and Chief Executive Officer*

Gilbert M. Grosvenor
*Chairman of the Board*

Nina D. Hoffman
*Executive Vice President, President of Books and
Education Publishing Group*

Ericka Markman
*Senior Vice President, President of Children's Books
and Education Publishing Group*

Stephen Mico
*Senior Vice President and Publisher,
Children's Books and Education Publishing Group*

### Staff for this book

Nancy Laties Feresten
*Vice President, Editor-in Chief
of Children's Books*

Suzanne Patrick Fonda
*Project Editor*

Marianne R. Koszorus
Bea Jackson
*Art Directors*

Carl Mehler
*Director of Maps*

Sharon Davis Thorpe
David M. Seager
*Designers*

Susan McGrath
*Writer*

Marilyn Mofford Gibbons
Margaret Sidlosky
*Illustrations Editors*

Jennifer Emmett
*Associate Editor*

Jo Tunstall
Priyanka Lamichhane
*Editorial Assistants*

Thomas L. Gray
Joseph F. Ochlak
Nicholas P. Rosenbach
*Map Editors/Researchers*

Stuart Armstrong
Tibor G. Tóth
*Map Illustration*

Michelle H. Picard
*Map Production Manager*

Stuart Armstrong
John S. Ballay
Tibor G. Tóth
Greg Ugiansky
Martin S. Walz
*Map Production*

Ann Ince-McKillop
Marcia Pires-Harwood
*Text Research*

Janet Dustin
Jean Cantu
Aaron Hubbard
*Illustrations Assistants*

Connie D. Binder
*Indexer*

Rebecca E. Hinds
*Managing Editor*

Jeff Reynolds
*Marketing Director
Children's Books*

Laurie J. Hembree
*Marketing Manager
Children's Books*

R. Gary Colbert
*Production Director*

Lewis R. Bassford
*Production Manager*

Vincent P. Ryan
Maryclare Tracy
*Manufacturing Managers*

### Consultants

Osa Brand
*Educational Affairs Director
Association of American Geographers*

Peggy Steele Clay
*Teacher-in-Residence
National Geographic Society*

Jacki Vawter
*Specialist in Early
Childhood Education
Alexandria, Virginia*

### Acknowledgements

We are grateful for the assistance
of John Agnone, Peggy Candore,
Alexander L. Cohn, Anne Marie
Houppert, Sandra Leonard, and
Lyle Rosbotham of the National
Geographic Book Division.

One of the world's
largest nonprofit
scientific and
educational
organizations, the
National Geographic Society was
founded in 1888 "for the increase
and diffusion of geographic
knowledge." Fulfilling this mission,
the Society educates and inspires
millions every day through its
magazine, books, television
programs, videos, maps and atlases,
research grants, the National
Geographic Bee, teacher
workshops, and innovative
classroom materials.

The Society is supported through
membership dues, charitable gifts,
and income from the sale of its
educational products. This support
is vital to National Geographic's
mission to increase global
understanding and promote
conservation through exploration,
research, and education.

For more information please call
1-800-NGS-LINE (647-5463) or
write to the following address:

NATIONAL GEOGRAPHIC SOCIETY
1145 17th Street N.W.
Washington, D.C. 20036-4688
U.S.A.

Visit the Society's Web site:
***www.nationalgeographic.com***

## Illustrations Credits

Photographs are from Getty Images except where indicated by an asterisk (*)

All illustrated physical maps and accompanying icons by Stuart Armstrong

Cover globe and all locator globes digitally created by Tibor G. Tóth

**Front Matter:**
Ed Simpson 2 (top); Michael Scott 2 (bottom); Connie Coleman 3 (top left); Paul Chesley 3 (top right); James Martin 3 (center left); Art Wolfe 3 (center right); Nicholas DeVore III 3 (bottom)

**Understanding Your World:**
*Sally J. Bensusen/Visual Science Studio 4 (top art) and 5 (top left art); *Theophilus Britt Griswold 4–5 (bottom art) and 5 (top right art); *Hal Pierce: NASA Goddard Laboratory for Atmospheres, data from NOAA 6 (left); *Tibor G. Tóth 6–7 (art); John Warden 10 (left); Hugh Sitton 10 (center); Steven Weinberg 10 (left); Andrea Booher 11 (top); Greg Probst 11 (top center); *Stephen and Michele Vaughan Photography 11 (bottom center); Cosmo Condina 11 (bottom left); *Michael Nichols 11 (bottom center); Tom Bean 11 (bottom right); John Noble 14 (top left); A. Witte/C. Mahaney 14 (top right); Jack Dykinga 14 (center left); Bruno DeHogues 14 (center right); *Arvind Garg/Corbis 14 (bottom); Stuart McCall 15 (top left); Chad Ehlers 15 (top right); Martine Mouchy 15 (center); Mark Harris 15 (bottom)

**North America:**
Ed Simpson 16; Rosemary Calvert 16–17; Charles Krebs 18 (top); Stephen Krasemann 18 (top center); Mark Lewis 18 (bottom center); Bruce Wilson 18 (bottom left); James Randklev 18–19; Charles Krebs 19; Gary Brettnacher 20 (top); George Hunter 20 (top center); Mark Lewis 20 (bottom center left); Cosmo Condina 20 (bottom center right); Nick Gunderson 20 (bottom left); *Alison Wright/Corbis 20 (bottom right); Will & Deni McIntyre 21; Billy Hustace 22 (top); Jake Rais 22 (center); * © David Young-Wolff/PhotoEdit 22 (bottom); Pete Seaward 23 (top); Philip H. Coblentz 23 (bottom left); Royalty-Free/Corbis 23 (bottom right); Tim Thompson 24 (top); Cosmo Condina 24 (center); *Mike Cassese/Reuters/Corbis 24 (bottom); Chris Thomaidis 25 (top); T. Davis/W. Bilenduke 25 (center); Wayne R. Bilenduke 25 (bottom)

**South America:**
Michael Scott 26; Tony Dawson 26–27; Nicholas DeVore III 28 (top); *James Holland 28 (top center); Bryan Parsley 28 (bottom center); Frans Lanting 28 (bottom); William J. Hebert 29; *Stuart Franklin 30 (top); Robert Frerck 30 (top center); *Heinz Kluetmeier/*SPORTS ILLUSTRATED* 30 (bottom center); Robert Frerck 30 (bottom); *Don Kincaid 31 (top); Ary Diesendruck 31 (bottom)

**Europe:**
Connie Coleman 32; John Lawrence 32–33; James Balog 34 (top); Michael Busselle 34 (center); Art Wolfe 34 (bottom); Richard Passmore 34–5; *Bruce Coleman Ltd. 35; Jerry Alexander 36 (top); Yann Layma 36 (center); coins: *Fotosearch, paper money: *Medio IMages/Index Stock 36 (bottom left); Louis Grandadam 36 (bottom right); Maarten Udema 36–7; Anthony Cassidy 37

**Africa:**
James Martin 38; Renee Lynn 38–39; Chad Ehlers 40 (top); Kevin Schafer 40 (top center); Hugh Sitton 40 (bottom center); Michael Busselle 40 (bottom); Michael Busselle 40–41; Tim Davis 41; Will & Deni McIntyre 42 (top); Daniel May 42 (top center); Hugh Sitton 42 (bottom center); Sylvain Grandadam 42 (bottom); Sally Mayman 43 (top); Paul Kenward 43 (bottom)

**Asia:**
Nicholas DeVore III 44; *Gilbert M. Grosvenor/NGS Image Sales 44–45; Chris Noble 46 (top); *China Photos/Reuters/Corbis 46 (center); *Arvind Garg/Corbis 46 (bottom); James Nelson 47 (top); Paul Harris 47 (bottom left); Keren Su 47 (bottom right); *Walter Hodges/Corbis 48 (top); Michael Ventura 48 (center); Nicholas DeVore III 48 (bottom); *Kenneth Love 48–49; Keren Su 49 (top); Wayne Eastep 49 (bottom)

**Australia:**
Paul Chesley 50; Ed Collacott 50–51; Fred Bavendam 52 (top); Stuart Westmoreland 52 (top center); Grilly Bernard 52 (bottom center); Penny Tweedie (bottom left); Sam Abell 53 (top); Oliver Strewe 53 (bottom); *Photo Index 54 (top); Matthew Lambert 54 (top center); Oliver Strewe 54 (bottom center); *David Doubilet 54 (bottom); David Austen 55 (top); Paul Souders 55 (bottom left); Robert Frerck 55 (bottom right)

**Antarctica**
Art Wolfe 56; Tim Davis 56–57; Kim Westerskov 58 (top); *Gordon Wiltsie 58 (center); *Norbert Wu 58 (bottom left); David Madison 58 (bottom right); *Maria Stenzel 59

**Back cover:**
Kevin Schafer (top left); Art Wolfe (top right); Masa Vemusi (bottom left); David Muench (bottom right)

The Library of Congress has cataloged the 1999 edition as follows:

National Geographic beginner's world atlas / photographs from Tony Stone Images
   p.   cm.
   Includes index.
   Summary: Maps, photographs, illustrations, and text
present information about the continents of the world.

   1. Children's atlases.   [1. Atlases. 2. Geography. ] I. Title.
II. Title: Beginner's world atlas
G1021 .N39  1999  <G&M>
912—dc21
                 CIP
                 MAPS

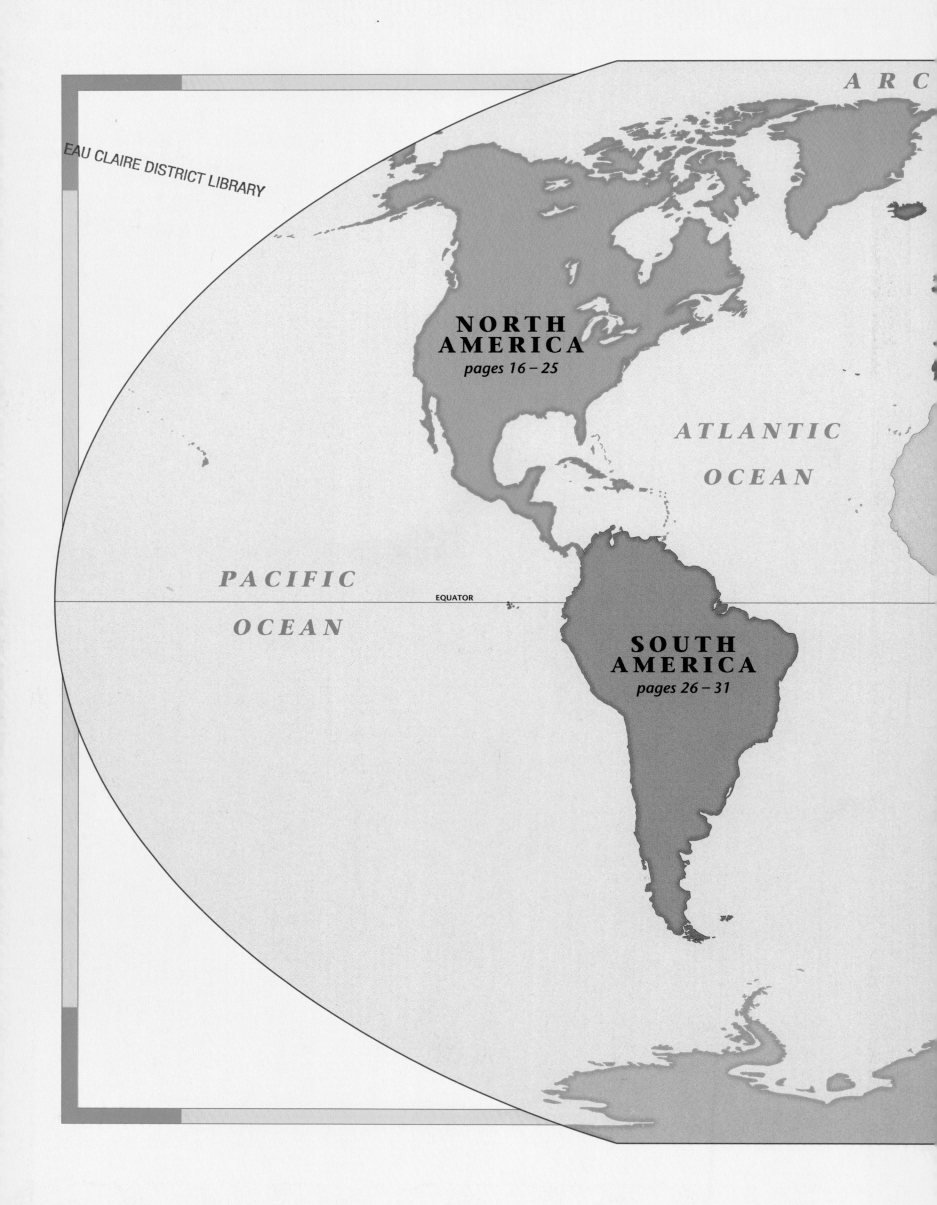

A R C

**NORTH AMERICA**
*pages 16 – 25*

ATLANTIC

OCEAN

PACIFIC

EQUATOR

OCEAN

**SOUTH AMERICA**
*pages 26 – 31*